HEALTH SERVICES RESEARCH

DONALD MAINLAND

Editor

A SERIES OF PAPERS
COMMISSIONED BY
THE HEALTH SERVICES RESEARCH STUDY SECTION
OF THE
UNITED STATES PUBLIC HEALTH SERVICE

CONTENTS

Page

CONTENTS

CONTENTS

SUBCOMMITTEE IN CHARGE OF RESEARCH PAPERS PROJECT

Philip D. Bonnet

Duncan W. Clark

Eliot Freidson
Chairman of the Subcommittee

Herbert E. Klarman

Thomas McCarthy
Executive Secretary of the Study Section

Donald Mainland
Project Coordinator

Paul J. Sanazaro

Kerr L. White
Chairman of the Study Section and Project Director

HEALTH SERVICES RESEARCH I

FOREWORD

During the past few decades the problems involved in the provision of health services have become increasingly complex, for various reasons—the increase of medical knowledge and techniques, leading to more complex and more expensive types of care; the increased diversity of interrelationships in society; the increase of urbanization; the changes in the age composition of populations; and, perhaps most importantly, the growing belief that everyone has the right to the "best" health care. Clearly the only approach to such problems is through research. But research in this area is very difficult and, although it has increased in amount and quality during recent years, it falls far short of what is needed.

In a particularly advantageous position to assess this need, and to consider ways of meeting it, is the Health Services Research Study Section of the United States Public Health Service, one of the committees of specialists, outside the Public Health Service itself, assembled primarily to review research grant applications, but encouraged by the Health Service to survey their respective fields of research and make proposals for improvement. The Health Services Study Section is composed of persons from many disciplines, including hospital administration, health department administration, clinical practice and research, medical education, psychology, sociology, epidemiology, operations research and biostatistics. In 1963, the Study Section decided to select topics that required exploration and to commission selected persons to write papers. It was believed that by looking at the current state of knowledge, at the merits and defects of previous

7

research, at needs and possible methods of future research, such papers would tend to increase the quantity, and improve the quality, of investigation.

Some of the selected authors had not previously worked in the health care field. By soliciting papers from these authors the Study Section hoped to obtain fresh views of familiar problems and also to capture the interest of experienced investigators who, even if they did not themselves come into this field, might tempt their colleagues or graduate students to do so.

In September, 1964, most of the authors who had agreed to write papers assembled for a two-day "briefing conference" with the Study Section, some staff members of the Public Health Service and a few other workers in the health care field, to discuss not only organizational plans but the topics of each paper. The Study Section emphasized, however, that it had no intention of dictating to the authors, and the only guideline that it offered was a question that an author could apply to his paper: "Is this paper likely to promote research—good research—in this field?"

The papers were arranged in two series, not by topic but to suit the authors' schedules of other commitments. The first series was presented at a "prepublication conference" in Chicago, October 15 and 16, 1965,[1,2] the other series at a similar conference in New York City, May 6 and 7, 1966. The participants in the conferences[3] were the authors, persons who had been commissioned to prepare written reviews of the papers, Study Section members and certain guests from the Public Health Service and other organizations.

Each paper had been assigned to two reviewers who would approach the topic from different points of view. For example, a paper on a sociological aspect would be assigned to a sociologist and to someone who was familiar with the administration of health services. In nearly every instance each participant received copies of the papers and reviews prior to the conferences. Therefore the authors' and reviewers' oral presentations could be limited to discussion of selected items, and discussion of each paper by the audience could extend to half an hour or longer.

After each conference the authors submitted final manuscripts revised, as far as they chose, in the light of the written reviews and conference discussion. The following pages contain seven of the 1965 series of papers which, in the opinion of the Research Papers Subcommittee of the Study Section and with the concurrence of the Milbank Memorial Fund Editorial Board, met the requirements of the project. The contents of the written reviews have been utilized, along with the oral comments of conference participants, in the short summaries of Discussions that follow each paper. For these summaries the Study Section is greatly indebted to Miss Ilona Melstrads.

The project has been supported by PHS grants CH-00108 and CH-00159 from the Division of Community Health Services. In addition several officials of the Public Health Service provided extensive informal assistance and encouragement throughout the project.

DONALD MAINLAND
Professor of Medical Statistics
New York University Medical Center

REFERENCES

[1] United States Department of Health, Education, and Welfare, Public Health Service Division of Community Health Services, THE RESEARCH BASIS OF COMMUNITY HEALTH SERVICES, Washington, United States Government Printing Office, 1965.

[2] Rosenblum, Marcus, Research in Health Services, *Public Health Reports,* 81, 351–362, 1966.

[3] The participants in the 1965 conference are listed at the end of this volume. Papers presented at the 1966 conference are scheduled to appear as Part 2 of the *Milbank Memorial Fund Quarterly* October 1966.

INFLUENCE OF SOCIAL AND ECONOMIC RESEARCH ON PUBLIC POLICY IN THE HEALTH FIELD
A REVIEW

ODIN W. ANDERSON

INTRODUCTION

The findings of social and economic research are being increasingly utilized to support (or criticize) policies affecting the operation and development of the health services system. Indeed, the health field shares this aura of research findings with other social problems for which solutions are sought. Persons who wish to influence public policy[1] in the health field in the United States have not always had systematic data on the economy of the country and the health and welfare activities directly dependent on this economy.

My thesis is that systematic data gathering and research do not appear until a public policy consensus emerges providing the framework for social and economic research bearing on policy. Such a framework quite unconsciously establishes the guidelines for the selection of data and research problems within the feasibilities of time, resources and research methods. Social research relating to public policy is then largely instrumental, serving to analyze the context in which public policy decisions are made to implement such decisions and to evaluate alternatives and their consequences in terms of the objectives sought.

In the United States systematic research in the social and economic aspects of the health field began at a comparatively early date in the development of its health services system, i.e., in the 1920's. With the possible and recent exception of Canada, the United States has more systematic information on the operation of its health services

11

system than any other country, particularly as to use and expenditure patterns of the general public and the flow of funds from source to objectives. The effect of this research on the development of the health services system is not easy to trace. Official proceedings, policy statements, speeches and papers bearing on public policy in the health field are studded with facts to support one or another view. The United States is a fact-loving nation, but in matters of public policy is not prone to assemble data solely to comprehend the operation and dynamics of the health services system. The preference is rather to use facts as brickbats to throw at a policy adversary or as armor— fragile at best—to defend one's position from the brickbats thrown from another policy position. However, when a certain stage of policy consensus of social objectives is reached, along with some agreement on methods, social and economic research may be useful to narrow the range of controversy. In the 1961 annual report of the Brookings Institution, its president, Robert D. Calkins, wrote: "In many areas, policy and action continue to be improvised on the basis of prevailing beliefs more than on an informed appraisal of issues and alternatives."

If this is true for public policy in general, as Calkins implies, it is certainly true for health services in particular. The health field has such an aura of life saving, altruism and alleviation of pain and suffering that realistic thinking about money, resources and implementation is inhibited.

Policy decisions seem to pass through three overlapping stages as to the sources and kinds of information. When a new enterprise or activity starts for which little previous experience is available and for which data on which to base decisions is lacking, the policy makers intuitively draw from their experiences in life activities and the social environments of which they are products and apply such experiences and backgrounds to the new activity. The new enterprise or activity evolves from previous forms and traditions with such reciprocal adaptations as seem necessary. The generation which participates in decision making during this stage absorbs intuitive knowledge because those without experience are hard put to criticize such decisions, and those with experience do not systematize their experience for the future generation who will eventually take their place. Consequently, new recruits are inducted into the decision making structure for which a systematic body of knowledge has not yet been developed.

In the next stage a great many isolated and disparate "facts" become a part of the decision making folklore, as decision makers compare notes in similar enterprises and acquire a feeling for ranges, distributions, repetitions and so on. Decision making is allowed a rather large margin of error because few if any specific criteria are available to guide it.

Finally, in the third stage, systematic data gathering and organizing define the total system of the enterprise, along with its component parts and sub-parts. Experience as such diminishes in importance and the assimilation of the growing body of data and knowledge in formal training periods reduces the necessity for the apprentice period. The presumption is that generalizable knowledge can be applied to operating situations in a fairly short time. Coincidentally, the growing body of knowledge increases the possibility of operational specifications and reduces the permissable margin of error condoned in earlier stages.

PUBLIC POLICY WITHOUT RESEARCH, 1875–1920

Several decades passed before need was felt for systematic research on the social and economic aspects of the health services system for public policy purposes.[2] The last quarter of the nineteenth century was the starting point of the development and growth of the health services system in this country. The discovery of the bacteriological causes of postoperative infections and the gradual perfection of ether anesthesia made surgery both relatively safe and painless thus directly affecting the development of the modern hospital.

The physical resources of the health services system expanded tremendously from 1875 to 1920. In 1873, the United States had only 178 hospitals. Undoubtedly most of these were mental hospitals which had undergone a period of expansion during previous decades. By 1910, this number had increased to almost 4400 general hospitals.[3] The great majority of these hospitals were financed by the private fortunes resulting from the rapid industrial expansion after the Civil War.

During the last quarter of the nineteenth century apparently as many physicians were in practice in relation to population as are currently practicing. Medical discoveries, increasing general wealth and the rise of a substantial middle class directly affected the health services system. All the states passed licensure laws governing medical practitioners, pharmacists and nurses. Surgeons, and later those physi-

13

cians engaged in general medicine, were able to make mutually satisfactory arrangements with the expanding hospitals to admit private
patients and in return provided free care for charity patients. The
medical profession then, and in substance since, maintained private
offices separate from the hospitals.

The health services system was given an infusion of new medical and
scientific knowledge which transformed American medical education
and medical practice in less than a generation. Shortly after 1900,
the Council on Medical Education of the American Medical Association and the Association of American Medical Colleges were struggling
to upgrade medical education. They were successful in persuading
state legislatures to enact licensure laws, but the *coup de grace*
against substandard medical schools was delivered by the revelations
of the famed Flexner report in 1910, which was financed by the
Carnegie Foundation and instigated by the American Medical Association.[4] The key point for upgrading standards was that states would
henceforth license only physicians who were graduates of medical
schools approved by the American Medical Association. Abraham
Flexner, a layman and educator, single-handedly visited more than
150 medical schools in the United States and Canada and wrote
a profile on each one outlining laboratory facilities, range of specialties
taught, access to teaching beds, affiliation with a university and so on.
Even in terms of standards in force at that time, conditions found
were by and large deplorable. Within ten years—1910 to 1920—
almost one-half of the original 160 or so medical schools vanished,
leaving the schools that met basic standards. Flexner's report was
by no means a model of good research, but was an informal survey
which was, judging by its impact, completely adequate and well
timed.

From the present perspective the health services system appeared to be developing at a rather dizzy pace. Not only was the basic
structure established as it is today, but by 1916, a great deal of activity
in 16 states urged the establishment of some form of state government sponsored health insurance for the general population. The
American Association for Labor Legislation, an association of economists, social workers and political scientists, flushed by their recent
victories in workmen's compensation, began agitating for health
insurance. A committee of the American Medical Association was also
interested in studying the need for some form of health insurance.
The short period from 1916 to 1919 was rife with study commissions

14

of one kind or another in 16 states pondering the cost of medical care and making recommendations. The commissions accumulated general compilations of disparate social and economic facts. Systematic data were, as yet, not available. Common sense notions, of course, recognized that groups with an income below a certain level were not receiving adequate medical care because of costs. Judging from German and British experience, health insurance presumably had to be government sponsored to cover the bulk of the population. The agitation for government-sponsored health insurance collapsed very suddenly at the end of the decade because the general support was inadequate in the face of rather vehement opposition from insurance companies and from the American Medical Association, as expressed in its official policy statement at its annual meeting in 1920.[5]

The period before 1920, however, did witness the beginnings of some systematic social and economic research in the health field. As early as 1908, the *Journal of the American Medical Association* reported the results of a birth record survey of midwifery in Chicago sponsored by a joint committee of the Chicago Medical Society and Hull House, the well-known settlement house. Among other things, the report declared—amusing by hindsight: "At the outset the members of this committee were fully convinced that midwives now and probably for years to come are socially inevitable. . . ."[6] Five years later the prediction of this committee was still accurate since the records of the county clerk revealed that one-half of the almost 40,000 births in 1913 were registered by midwives and the other half by physicians.[7] In due time this problem apparently solved itself.

The United States Public Health Service, reorganized in 1912, and the United States Children's Bureau (then in the Department of Labor) began some significant research in various types of morbidity, such as pellagra, and causes of infant mortality. Likewise, Lee K. Frankel and Louis I. Dublin, of the Metropolitan Life Insurance Company, pioneered in surveying morbidity patterns in a population insured by that company.[8]

Therefore, the period from 1875 to 1920 is characterized by decision making to develop the health services system by people in appropriate positions drawing on their experiences in the American culture, adapting here, innovating there, with very little systematic data to go on. The concrete and pivotal research results were coming from the physical, biological and medical sciences and the health services system was absorbing the results of such research more or less spontaneously.[9]

Contemporary medical practice and hospitals were adapting themselves to the new medical developments. The margin of tolerable error was great in those days if for no other reason than that specifications for operating criteria were lacking. Belief in inevitable progress was unbounded even though then, as now, it was permeated by a great deal of worry about rising cost.[10]

In the face of rising cost one hospital administrator anticipated the financial backbone of the American health services system. At the annual meeting of the American Hospital Association in 1909, Frederick R. Brush said:[11]

> The hospitals were for the poor. They are largely now for the rich. In time they may be for all.
> Consciously or not, all concerned in hospital management are daily working out the beginning of this great extension—hospital provision for the Third Estate.

Later, the intrepid health insurance pioneer and sociologist, Michael M. Davis, began his steady flow of perceptive and needling writing starting with the dispensary movement in 1918,[12] now less descriptively known as the outpatient department. The book by Davis and his co-author, Andrew R. Warner, provided some fascinating passages, from present-day perspectives, on the rosy future of the dispensary movement. Complaints, however, were noted of the seemingly inexplicable unwillingness of physicians to flock into group practice salaried arrangements. Note this passage:[13]

> The general public and a number of physicians do not as yet understand the nature and advantage of this new type of medical work. They still think of the hospital as the medical hotel, and look down upon the Dispensary as a medical soupkitchen.

Apparently the desirability of the industrial model for medical practice has been ever pervasive. By the early 1920's the outpatient department movement stabilized for the indigent only. It has never been popular with the self-pay segment of the population. The physicians and hospitals regarded the outpatient departments as a holding action for the growing and visible voluntary and private sector of the health services system—financially largely a self-liquidating system— while charity was dispensed as a by-product of this system.

By 1920, however, the basic structure of the health services system achieved the main characteristics it has today. Obviously, this system did not need systematic research to come into being. After the basic structure was created other questions posed by younger men came to to the fore.

THE BEGINNING OF SYSTEMATIC RESEARCH ON PUBLIC POLICY, 1920–1935

After the agitation for some form of government-sponsored health insurance suddenly abated the country did not face this particular policy problem for another 15 years or so. After 1920, the United States Public Health Service began to move into research on the morbidity of the general population in addition to the concern with the usual reportable and communicable diseases. Hagerstown, Maryland, became famous as a "laboratory" for testing research methodology on morbidity in the general population and use of health services. The growth in county public health departments contributed to this interest on a local level. But researchers like Edgar Sydenstricker on the staff of the Public Health Service visualized the possibility of utilizing data on morbidity to measure the need for personal health services.[14] In fact, Sydenstricker did make an early attempt to relate morbidity to use of services.[15] The Children's Bureau also sponsored a series of pioneering studies on the relationship between economic factors and infant mortality in a number of urban areas and in the early 1920's published a monograph.[16] These studies fed directly into testimonies supporting the Sheppard-Towner Act in 1921, which provided the first federal grants-in-aid to states for infant and maternity care. After a two-year extension in 1927, this legislation continued in effect until Congress quietly let it die for lack of appropriations in 1929.

In the meantime, in 1925 and 1926, a number of people were continuing discussion of the economic and social aspects of the health field. These were leaders in the country—physicians, members of the public health profession and economists.[17] In April, 1926, an informal conference was held in Washington attended by a number of persons in these fields. At this meeting a committee of five was appointed to formulate a series of studies on the economic and social aspects of the health services and develop plans for a committee to conduct them.[18] The result was a conference held in Washington in 1927, simultaneously with the annual meeting of the American Medical Association. The conference was attended by 60 people, a seemingly large group for so specialized and technical a subject, but indicative of strong support for the studies. The Committee on the Cost of Medical

Care was created consisting of 42 persons—14 private practitioners of medicine, six from public health, eight from institutions and organizations involved with medicine, such as hospitals, the American Medical Association and insurance companies, five economists, and nine persons at large representing the public. The chairman of the committee was Ray Lyman Wilbur, President of Stanford University. The committee membership read like a who's who in health services and public policy.

This committee delineated several areas for intensive study: 1. incidence of disease and disability in the population, 2. existing facilities, 3. family expenditures for services, 4. incomes of providers of services, 5. organized facilities for medical care serving particular groups of the population. Other agencies conducted studies along the same lines, but in cooperation with the committee.[18]

The committee was completely a non-governmental undertaking, and was privately financed by six foundations: Carnegie Corporation, Josiah Macy, Jr. Foundation, Milbank Memorial Fund, Russell Sage Foundation, Twentieth Century Fund, and the Julius Rosenwald Fund. Philanthropy had played an important role in the development of the health field up to this time. Now the effort with the Committee on the Cost of Medical Care represented a high point in philanthropic foundation activity, first, because of the joint financing, second, because of the interest in making the consumers' problems explicit. The health services edifice had been raised and revealed a desire to learn what needs it would serve, how much it was costing and how it was to be paid for on a day-to-day basis. Capital expenditures were apparently not considered a problem yet. The foundations contributed around one million dollars, a very large sum in those days for research in the economic and social aspects of health services, a new area of research. Virtually all people of note in the health field and social sciences were participating. The Committee was truly an endeavor mustering the research resources of a nation. A full-time research staff of 75 technical experts in research and statistics, not to mention those employed on a temporary basis, were engaged to work under the general direction of Harry H. Moore, an economist from the University of Chicago and the director of research enterprise.

The period from 1928–1932, when the studies were being conducted, was one of watchful waiting by the many parties who had a direct interest in the findings. The American Medical Association editorialized:[19]

18

> Most physicians and most economists and most social workers are willing to wait until the Committee on the Cost of Medical Care, a group with which the medical profession is cooperating wholeheartedly, has brought into the situation data on which to base reasonable action for the future.

Twenty-eight reports were published, 27 of which were field studies. The last report, in 1932, contained the sweeping recommendations which were supposed to flow directly from the research results. In essence the studies, particularly number 26, showed that illness and expenditures for health services fall unevenly onto families over a year so that a small minority experience severe illnesses and large medical expenditures. A few case studies were made of medical care organizations which employed physicians in group practice units attached to an industry or were independent plans.

This extremely brief allusion does a disservice to the scope and detail of the studies. Never before in this or any other country was such an ambitious attempt made to establish a benchmark of factual information for the consideration of public policy in the health field.

The effect of the reports was immediate. Problems can be studied in a calm atmosphere and findings published, but recommendations based on the research split the committee in factions. Majority and minority reports were prepared. The main burden of the recommendations of the majority was a virtual reorganization of fee-for-service and solo medical practice to group practice, plus group payment for services, or application of the insurance principle. This plan could be financed from either or both private and government sources.[20] Drawing on experience abroad the signers of the majority report felt that physicians could better guard their professional prerogatives in groups when negotiating with insurance agencies of various kinds. The solo practitioners were too vulnerable as individuals and could be picked off one at a time, as it were.

The supporters of the majority report may not really have believed that both of these major recommendations could be carried out on any large scale. The insurance principle was a novel enough innovation, not to mention the reorganization of medical practice. Combining the two recommendations vitiated the possibility of accepting health insurance as a principle. The signers of the majority report, however, apparently believed that to attach a pooling of funds mechanism to the prevailing structure of practice was impossible. They surely felt that a fee-for-service method of payment was undesirable and to be eliminated as soon as possible because it discouraged the formation of group practice units.

The response of the signers of the minority report was anything but vague; it was as clear and unequivocal as it was vigorous. The minority report attacked the recommendation for group practice units based in or adjacent to hospitals. Insurance itself was accepted in principle cautiously, providing that certain safeguards would be set up, mainly, medical society control, free choice of physicians and fee-for-service method of payment.

In 1932, the organization of services became the primary issue in the eyes of the medical profession, and the insurance method of pooling funds was a subsidiary although important issue. The profession's counter-response was to attach the insurance mechanism to the contemporary structure of practice and under the control of the medical societies. The reaffirmation by the minority of the proper role of government—traditional public health program, public responsibility for the indigent and special groups—plus the role of insurance now made the medical professions policy quite explicit.

In the meantime, the American Hospital Association was moving ahead with concrete plans to endorse voluntary hospital insurance. In 1933, the association officially endorsed hospital insurance and the "adoption of some plans which would distribute the costs of sickness and benefit the sick individual" and "would be one of the most effective ways to offset the increasing demand for more radical and potentially dangerous forms of national or state medicine. . . ."[21] Thus was the American Hospital Association joined with the American Medical Association in opposing some form of government-sponsored health insurance, but taking quicker and more aggressive action to implement voluntary health insurance by covering hospital care.

By 1933, the issues were clear, and both the American Hospital Association and the American Medical Association had declared their positions and intentions. The beginning of the voluntary health insurance movement, i.e., hospital care, which the majority report of the Committee on the Cost of Medical Care had suggested only in passing, proved to be the opening wedge. In due course health insurance became a pooling and payment mechanism for the existing structure of health services.

As a governmentally sponsored sequel to the extensive findings of the committee reports, in the winter of 1935–36, the United States Public Health Service launched a large-scale survey of the incidence

20

of illness and attendant social and economic factors. This study was in part inspired as a white-collar Works Progress Administration project. The survey, known as the National Health Survey, gathered data by means of a house-to-house interview of more than 700,000 households in urban communities in 18 states and 37,000 households in rural areas in three states.[22] The combined results of the committee studies and the National Health Survey provided the basic data on health and medical care in the United States until the early 1950's.[23] By the mid-1930's this country seemingly had a systematic body of knowledge regarding the patterns of morbidity, use and expenditures for health services in the general population. The type of research personnel engaged in these studies were by and large biostatisticians, economists and public health workers. The work was financed by private philanthropists and the federal government. The research was conducted outside of university auspices and wholly action and public policy oriented. The economic bias regarding reasons for differences in use of services by income groups was quite heavy.

THE EMERGENCE OF THIRD PARTY PAYMENT, 1935–1952

The establishment and growth of health insurance from 1933 to 1952, and the debates regarding the primary vehicle—voluntary or government health insurance—conditioned all the thinking on public policy problems. All other considerations such as level of costs, volume, quality and method of organization were subsidiary until the early 1950's. This was a free-wheeling period for voluntary health insurance, no doubt stimulated by the constant possibility of Congress seriously entertaining some form of government-sponsored health insurance in every Congress from 1938 to the end of the Truman administration. In any fundamental sense—and with few but interesting exceptions presaging the direction of future research—little systematic research yielded new data during this period. Large-scale research efforts were apparently being held in abeyance until the health field would arrive at some consensus equilibrium regarding the role of voluntary health insurance. Previously collected data, and those from official sources relating to facilities, personnel, income levels and so on, were worked and reworked to justify government-sponsored health insurance in two major conferences sponsored by the federal government in 1938, and again in 1948.[24] Contributing greatly to the accumulation of factual knowledge was the Division of Research and Statistics created by the Social Security Act and headed by I. S. Falk. This division was and is an important governmental source of data and information, and is now headed by Ida C. Merriam. The result of assembling the existing data is contained in the well-organized and exhaustive statistical volumes of the President's Commission for the Health Needs of the Nation published early in 1953.[25] While these conferences and the President's Commission represent the global assembling of information for direct national policy-making purposes, many books were written and a few original studies made.

Although the publications of the Committee on the Cost of Medical Care and the National Health Survey overlap chronologically with the books to be mentioned that were published in the early 1930's, these books can be regarded as representive of a trend of writing concerned with the operation of the health services system itself rather than primarily directed to the problems of the general population. Two books deserve this designation: one by A. M. Simons and Nathan Sinai, THE WAY OF HEALTH INSURANCE, and another by Michael M. Davis and C. Rufus Rorem with the justifiably alarming title, THE CRISIS IN HOSPITAL FINANCE, both published in 1932.[26] Nathan Sinai was then on the technical staff of the Committee on the Cost of Medical Care and on leave from the University of Michigan.

The book by Simons and Sinai was seemingly the stimulus for a series of books on health insurance abroad and its application in this country. The book by Davis and Rorem began probing into the internal operation of the health system. The authors ventured the opinion that ". . . these papers in book form . . . may perhaps stimulate thought and action upon the difficult and pressing issues which confront the trustees, administrators, physicians, public officials and others concerned with hospitals and clinics" during the worsening economic crisis.[27]

In the course of the decade of the 1930's after the passage of the Social Security Act and absence in it of a provision for health insurance, other books on this subject appeared. They were usually in a vein favorable to the concept of government-sponsored health insurance, although the one by Millis, a University of Chicago economist, pleaded caution,[28] and another, by the Secretary of the Wisconsin State Medical Society, left no doubt as to his opposition.[29]

As evidence of a continuing and rising tide of interest not only in health insurance, but also in the full range of programs and problems in the health services system, as distinguished a medical body as the New York Academy of Medicine saw fit to sponsor a group with the portentous title of Committee on Medicine and the Changing Order, with Malcolm Goodridge as Chairman. A series of books was commissioned dealing with medical education, medical services provided by government, medical research, voluntary health insurance, nursing and nursing education, medicine in industry and preventive medicine. The Academy, through this committee, apparently wished to establish a benchmark for general public policy discussion. Perhaps the book sponsored by the committee of most direct concern to this monograph is the one which for the first time described and evaluated the status of voluntary health insurance of that time. Blue Cross and Blue Shield plans were now beyond the infancy stage and some kind of stock taking was warranted.[30]

Concurrently with the activities of the New York Academy of Medicine other books were being published in profusion on the general problems in medical care organization and financing. A professor of finance at Northwestern University wrote a monograph on the issue of government-sponsored health insurance.[31] His appraisal was largely negative. During the same decade Franz Goldmann, then in the School of Public Health at Yale University, wrote two books scrutinizing voluntary health insurance and public welfare medical care.[32] As sort of a climax to the decade the Brookings Institution, under the authorships of George W. Bachman and Lewis Meriam for Senator Smith of New Jersey, then interested in the issue of government health insurance, published a quite critical review of the social insurance and government health insurance concept.[33]

While this general and "global" writing was going on, other studies of significance in the development of an enterprise were beginning to appear directed to operating problems in the implementation of the health insurance mechanism. Two studies are of particular interest because they were premature in that the health field did not apply the findings. Consequently, they appear to have been "lost" and almost 20 years later the problems of so-called abuse and overuse of services, which these studies anticipated, are now being discussed and implemented by utilization committees of various kinds.

One of these studies was conducted by Nathan Sinai and Marguerite F. Hall of the School of Public Health, University of Michigan, in the medical care plan in Windsor, Ontario, set up for relief recipients in that city in the 1930's The Province of Ontario delegated the Essex County Medical Society the responsibility of providing medical

23

care on a per capita cost basis to the population which was receiving relief assistance, a sizable group during the depression period. The medical society wished to use the fee-for-service method of paying the participating doctors, but was fearful of rising use and cost which was assumed to be inherent in such a method. Sinai and Hall together with a local physician, Roy E. Holmes, devised a statistical control technique to monitor the volume of services provided by individual physicians and thus establish a distribution of low to high prescribers. The physicians above certain magnitudes would be brought to the attention of the physicians' own medical review board.[34] This statistical technique was applied and is still used in modified form in the Windsor Medical Services, which developed out of the medical relief program. A continuation of this interest in an impersonal statistical control was the result of a study of the Windsor plan conducted in the late 1950's by members of Sinai's staff. This study showed that, whatever the standards, the so-called abuse of physicians' services in the plan was minimal.[35]

Another study conducted during the same period in Albany, New York, at the behest of a legislative commission, concerned the use of hospital care anticipating concern with utilization 20 years later. The current director of the state hospital planning and construction agency, John Bourke, was associated with this project. It was an early attempt to study patterns of hospital use. The study was based on hospital and welfare records of almost 3000 patients discharged from the wards of 11 "representative" hospitals in New York state. Further, personal visits were made to 771 of these patients.[36]

By the beginning of the decade of the 1940's, research in the economic and social aspects of the health field began to get a foothold in universities, for the most part in departments of rural sociology and in the School of Public Health at the University of Michigan. Nathan Sinai established the first research unit in medical care and related problems in a university when he created the Bureau of Public Health Economics in 1945. Concurrently the Agricultural Extension Service of the United States Department of Agriculture stimulated a large number of local studies through the extension departments of land grant universities staffed by sociologists with an interest in problems of rural life. Under the auspices of the Social Science Research Council, a group of rural sociologists met in Birmingham, Alabama, to discuss appropriate social research projects. A report was published which became the first report on health services prepared exclusively by sociol-

24

ogists, social anthropologists and social psychologists.[37] Because of the work of the Farm Security Administration during the depression, plus the activities described by the Agricultural Extension Service, the rural population appeared to get special consideration. The ultimate expression of this interest was a detailed compendium prepared by two former medical officers in the Farm Security Administration, Frederick D. Mott and Milton I. Roemer.[38]

One study by rural sociologists in Michigan deserves special mention because of the significant and largely successful attempt to develop a method measuring need for personal health services in a population. Some preliminary work had been done by Roemer, and his work fed directly into that of the rural sociologists. The research team from Michigan State University (then Michigan State College) devised a list of symptoms which should be brought to a physician's attention if a person is suffering from any one of them. The symptoms approach has been used in various studies since then, probably because of the pioneering efforts of the Michigan group.[39]

The Bureau of Public Health Economics in the School of Public Health at the University of Michigan began early to direct its research to public policy problems. The first publication was an analysis of the emerging legislation to exempt Blue Cross and Blue Shield plans from the usual state insurance laws governing private insurance companies. The legislation applying to these non-profit and vendor sponsored plans was an expression of a public policy quite peculiar to American conditions.[40] Other studies followed, one directed to the comprehensive medical care program for the recipients of old-age assistance in the state of Washington, anticipating the later frantic interest in the problem of medical care for the aged.[41] Another was a study of the operation of the Emergency Maternity and Infant Care Program for the wives and dependents of servicemen during World War II and while the program was still in operation. This program had all the elements of a national health program and the administrative problems inherent in any medical care program regardless of sponsorship. With national health insurance legislation pending, this study was felt to be both pertinent and timely.[42]

The foregoing studies had little direct influence on public policy formulation although a body of knowledge was presumably evolving which would form a base for teaching and further research. A compendium that did emerge during the 1940's, in characteristic American fashion was the one produced by the Commission on Hospital Care.[43]

25

The commission was financed by the Commonwealth Fund, the W. K. Kellogg Foundation and the National Foundation for Infantile Paralysis. A review of the roster of the membership of the commission reveals representation from the whole range of major interest groups in America. The Study Director was Arthur Bachmeyer of the University of Chicago. The problem area of concern was the American hospital system and, more specifically, the maintenance of and the planning for this system. The commission was set up in relation to the pending legislation in Congress to provide grants-in-aid for hospital construction and improvement in the United States. The Hospital Survey and Construction Act (Hill-Burton) became law in 1946. The commission was to examine the hospital system in the United States and to use the state of Michigan as a model for other states to emulate in hospital planning when the Hill-Burton funds became available. No new data were collected but a formula to measure need for hospitals was devised called the bed-death ratio which was the first attempt at some systematic method to establish bed-population ratios.

The 1940's, then, was one of a great deal of activity in research and data gathering which culminated in the five-volume report of the President's Commission for the Health Needs of the Nation. The country was at a new threshold of policy discussion and social and economic research relating to it. Several universities besides Michigan were attempting to establish teaching and research units after World War II. Among these were North Carolina, Yale, Harvard, University of California at Berkeley and Johns Hopkins. But the bitterness and rancor which attended research in the controversial area of health care inhibited their development to a viable degree. In the early 1950's, as the immediate possibility of the enactment of some form of government-sponsored health insurance subsided, a new framework of policy discussion emerged. Social research in this type of framework was possible on an accelerating basis.

THE HEALTH SERVICES SYSTEM AND RESEARCH, 1952–1965

The Truman commission, and the election of Eisenhower as the first Republican president in 20 years, ushered in a new period of consensus. This consensus was not necessarily reached harmoniously and by due deliberation. The Eisenhower administration characteristically preferred to go slowly and to stabilize trends in social legislation that had taken place since the enactment of the Social Security Act.

Voluntary health insurance at this time covered almost 60 per cent of the population and paid one-half of the general hospital bill, with employers paying an increasingly large proportion of the premium through collective bargaining. Voluntary health insurance was permitted to work out its destiny without the seeming harassment—albeit salutary—from needling, liberal politicians in the Congress. The types of research, compilations of data and books which had characterized the period from 1932 to 1952, had now spent its force. The kind of research that was now needed was an evaluation of the health services system along two major lines: 1. research to evaluate the benefit structure of voluntary health insurance, and, 2. research in the operational and organizational problems of the system. The system had gone through a phenomenally free-wheeling period of expansion with little open concern for the costs, level of use and quality. The primary endeavor was to exploit the prevailing system to its fullest, and increased use and expenditures attest to this implicit policy, although other forms of organizing physicians' services had emerged.

Retrospectively, the fact that the social research resources of the country rose to this challenge quite well is little short of amazing. A new generation of social researchers necessarily emerged to build on the magnificant pioneer work. But in the new era other social science disciplines had to become involved and new or more refined methodologies employed. Hence the entrance of sociologists, social anthropologists and social psychologists and the widespread employment of social survey, interviewing and sampling technology.

Early in the decade of the 1950's, another commission type of study agency was established to investigate the costs of general hospital care and voluntary health insurance. Regarded as a natural sequel to the Commission on Hospital Care, which issued a report in 1947, described previously, the Commission on Financing of Hospital Care was established late in 1951 as an independent agency financed by private funds.[44] The commission was made up of 34 persons from the usual interest groups in the United States concerned with health services and public policy. The objective was "to study the costs of providing adequate hospital services and to determine the best systems of payment for such services." Research was apparently moving into methods of financing the day-to-day operation of the hospital system in view of steadily rising per diem rates. The previous commission had been primarily concerned with supply and distribution. The commission established in 1951 was limiting itself to "voluntary" methods of financing hospital care in its range of possible alternatives. In due course three volumes of new data and information were amassed on the financial problems of American general hospital system providing some more insight into its operation.[45]

No other general compendium of information and recommendations relating to public policy was to be compiled until shortly after 1960, when a large conference was held in Washington, on the problems of the aged, with the controversial aspect of providing health services for this age group.

The 1950's reveal a broadening of the base of research problems under investigation, the induction of the behavioral scientists in increasing numbers and the stabilization of research in the social and economic aspects of health services in universities. Further, toward the latter part of the decade, several states were requesting systematic investigation of the rising use and costs of hospital and physicians' services reflected in the intermittent requests on the part of health insurance agencies for higher rates.

Two broad categories of problems were being investigated; 1. those dealing with the problems of the general population relating to their expenditures for and use of health services, and the effectiveness of contemporary health insurance benefits; and, 2. relating to the operational aspects of the insuring agencies and the health services personnel and organization. Not to be overlooked, however, in two categories is the resumption of the nationwide morbidity studies of 1935–36, on a permanent basis in 1956, by an act of Congress. Since this time a steady stream of excellent morbidity and physical handicap studies has been produced expanding into use of health services as well.[46] More recently a National Center for Health Statistics has been created. Further evidence of interest in data gathering under government sponsorship was the creation of a Subcommittee on Health Economics by the U. S. Committee for Vital and Health Statistics. In due course an excellent report was published summing up the nature and sources of health economic data in this country.[47] In 1961, another agency was created in the Department of Health, Education and Welfare, the Health Economics Branch in the Division of Community Health Services with Agnes Brewster as chief. She was previously secretary to the above-mentioned Subcommittee on Health Economics. The central concern unifying research efforts of the 1950's was the attempt to comprehend the operation of this very complex system on which society was placing a high

28

value. The relatively straightforward research in patterns of expenditures and use of services in the general population, and the distribution of morbidity was now being continued, but was directly related to the operational problems of the health insurance agencies and the health services system. With regard to morbidity chronic and long-term illness was now viewed with sufficient concern as a problem in itself to warrant special attention. Accordingly a Commission on Chronic Illness was established to investigate this problem and was in operation from 1949 to 1956. This commission had the sponsorship of the American Medical Association, the American Hospital Association, the American Public Health Association and the American Public Welfare Association. Research studies were made between 1950 and 1956. The commission was financed by many private sources and the United States Public Health Service.[48] A great range of skills and interests composed the membership of the commission. A rather impressive technical staff was assembled under the direction of Morton L. Levin, 1950–51, and Dean W. Roberts, from 1952–1956. Four volumes were published, two of which attempted to set forth and define chronic illness as to prevention and management, and the other two of which contained very detailed results of extensive field studies in Hunterdon County, New Jersey, and Baltimore, Maryland. These studies reached a new and high level of sophistication in research methodology. Quite successful attempts were made to measure morbidity, unmet need and so on. In this respect the fourth volume, by Ray E. Trussell and Jack Elinson, a sociologist and social survey specialist, is of special interest.[49] The research findings revealed, as expected, rather staggering disease problems to cope with in terms of current knowledge and resources.[50]

As stated earlier, by 1952, voluntary health insurance had become enough of a force to be regarded as the chief vehicle for financing personal health services, particularly for general hospital care, and increasingly for physicians' services such as surgery and obstetrics. Still, no systematic evaluation had been done of the impact of voluntary health insurance on families with relatively high expenditures, and no nationwide family surveys had been conducted to update the data on use and expenditure patterns in the general population since the days of the Committee on the Cost of Medical Care. Only relatively crude evaluations were possible by national aggregates from the Department of Commerce and the Social Security Administration. The latter agency published annual summaries beginning in 1948, on the total national expenditures by components of service in the private sector of the health services economy. Also, and very important at this time, estimates were made of the total expenditures for personal health services paid for by voluntary health insurance. In December, 1952, the Social Security Administration reported that, after 15 or more years of growth, voluntary health insurance was paying 15.3 per cent of the total private expenditures for all types of services.[51] This was a crude figure involving services which were in effect not covered by insurance at that time. This figure was attacked by the Secretary and General Manager of the American Medical Association, George Lull, as a "perversion of statistical information" in that insurance was not intended to cover 100 per cent of expenditure anyway.[52] The interest aroused by this seemingly innocuous figure of 15.3 per cent does indicate that research findings are not necessarily inherently dull. What this figure revealed, however, was a lack of sophistication in the interpretation and evaluation of health insurance benefits, which was to evolve later in the decade as more detailed data became available. Also, supporters of voluntary health insurance were shocked that the figure was this low and doubted its authenticity. A year later, however (showing that in social science research corroboration of a previous finding is possible), the Social Security Administration figure was confirmed by a nationwide survey of households conducted by Health Information Foundation and the National Opinion Research Center, University of Chicago, but with a detailed analysis of its significance.[53]

The chartering of the Health Information Foundation in 1950, is of interest because this research and data dissemination agency is in the American tradition of private philanthropic funds being supplied for studies, commissions and so on going back many years. The source of funds for HIF was mainly from the pharmaceutical manufacturers at a time when this industry was growing rapidly as a result of the breakthroughs in research on antibiotics. Annual contributions from the industry enabled the financing of a research agency chartered as a nonprofit and tax-exempt corporation to develop a research program directed to social and economic problems in the health field during the 1950's and into the 1960's. In 1962, the agency and staff were moved to the University of Chicago and became an operating unit in the Graduate School of Business.[54] Concurrently, other units in addition to the Bureau of Public Economics, University of Michigan and Health Information Foundation were established. These included the Research Department of Health Insurance Plan of Greater New York (HIP), the Bureau of Hospital Administration, School of Business Administration, University of Michigan, and the School of Public Health and Administrative Medicine, Columbia University. Later, research units directed to medical care and related problems were established in the Jewish Hospital of St. Louis in association with the Social Science Institute, Washington University, and the Programs in Hospital Administration, Graduate School of Public Health, University of Pittsburgh, School of Public Health, University of Minnesota, School of Business Administration, Cornell University and the School of Hygiene, Johns Hopkins University. Other individuals and sites conducted research, but the ones mentioned established formal structures with continuing personnel and projects.

The great amount of research into the social and economic aspects of the health services that was done in the 1950's and 1960's now appears to fall into patterns not quite apparent at that time. All of it was action oriented, or certainly the main rationale for the research itself was to relate to some public policy and health administrative problem. Some of the research was more immediately action-oriented than others, and the degree of immediacy rose in different contexts with interesting implications for the strategy of social research touching public policy. The agencies of the federal government, for example, were primarily to compile data and publish them in such form as to be readily available. The research objectives of Health Information Foundation were to develop a research program and projects within it to comprehend the structure and operation of the existing health services system and its impact on the general population. If this could be accomplished, even in part, it would then serve as a base to push out the peripheries as accomplishments and deficiencies were revealed. The research strategy was chiefly one of accepting the prevailing health services and health insurance structure as a given, examine generic problems within it and push out to examine the deviations from or innovations in the system.

When the foundation embarked on its large scale field studies in 1953, the words "comprehensive medical care," "subsidy," and, to some extent, "service benefits," "experience rating," "means test" and others were dirty words depending on the viewpoint. In this context, in the 1950's, the Health Information Foundation became a reference point for research in the social and economic aspects of the health services for other researchers and agencies that were getting started later in the decade. Health Information Foundation conducted and sponsored a series of studies directed to some comprehension of the operation of the health services system from the standpoint of the general public, the providers of service and the health insurance agencies. The first one with this objective was an overview of the field from already existing data,[55] and the nationwide survey of families alluded to earlier.[56] The nationwide survey enabled the health insurance agencies to evaluate their benefit patterns in relation to the expenditure patterns of the American households. By common-sense standards existing health insurance benefits were quite adequate for some services such as hospital care and surgery, but inadequate for the other services. Evaluation surveys of Blue Cross-Blue Shield health insurance plans were made in Birmingham, Alabama, and Boston, Massachusetts, and of a private insurance company in Boston as to the benefit levels among its subscribers.[57]

In somewhat overlapping succession Health Information conducted or sponsored a series of studies to examine various types of medical prepayment plans offering the complete range of physicians' services either in a fee-for-service type of arrangement or in a group practice structure. The nationwide survey had indicated the need for some broadening of health insurance beyond hospital based services. The intent was to show the feasibility of insuring home and office calls in the prevailing structure of medical practice as well as in the group practice type and to show the results of various alternatives.[58]

In the meantime, because of the rapid changes in the health services system and the continued growth of voluntary health insurance, Health Information Foundation and National Opinion Research Center felt justified in conducting another nationwide survey of family expenditures, use of services and health insurance in 1958, five years after the survey described previously.[59] Here, results showed, among other things, that although aggregate expenditures had increased by 42 per cent, one-half of this increase could be attributed to increased use and the other half to increased price. Further, the proportion of total expenditures for health services had increased to 19 per cent (from 15) although families with high magnitude expenditures had a larger proportion of their costs covered than was true five years earlier.

Continuing with the problems of the general population, but this time focussing on the aged, because of the specific public policy concern with this group, Health Information Foundation sponsored a nationwide survey of the aged. This was conducted by Ethel Shanas, a sociologist, engaged by National Opinion Research Center for the purpose. Although a public policy consensus had emerged regarding the place of voluntary health insurance as the primary mechanism for financing personal health services, no such consensus existed regarding those who are 65 years of age and over. The apparent abeyance of the issue of government-sponsored health insurance re-emerged in debates regarding health services for the aged as a special problem group. A great deal of census and income data were available on this group, plus data from old-age assistance programs, public medical care programs, mental hospitals, general hospitals and so on. That serious social and medical problems existed among the aged was not doubted, but systematic, nationwide data were lacking on the social situation of the aged, their illnesses and their use of and expenditures for health services to give a perspective on this growing segment of the population. If one were to believe some of the allegations, the aged were seemingly wholly sick, impoverished, neglected and lonely. In the survey by Shanas, people 60 years of age and over were interviewed in their homes and some perceptions of their conditions were obtained. This systematic survey revealed, as expected, that those 65 years of age and over had lower incomes than those in younger age groups, were likely to have more illnesses and were high users of health services, and consequently their expenditures were also relatively high. Shanas' study did provide a perspective, however, in that, by an illness index constructed for the purpose, 14 per cent (including those in institutions) were found to be unable to care for themselves physically. If priorities were needed in meeting hard-core problems, obviously this 14 per cent would be them.[60] Because this survey was to examine the total situation of the aged, as were the surveys of the general population by Anderson and associates, proponents of various public policy viewpoints could find support by judicious selection of data that were presented.

The culmination of interest in the aged as far as fact finding and research were concerned is found in the White House Conference on Aging held in Washington, January 9–12, 1961. This conference originated by an act of Congress in January, 1958. A budget was appropriated to be used by states in statewide studies on the entire range of social, economic and health problems of the aged and for state conferences. A nationwide advisory committee was established as well. State after state made surveys of a more or less fact-finding nature, the results of which were fed into state conferences and ultimately into the White House Conference. About 2500 delegates attended the conference and a rather elaborate structure of workshop groups, committees and subcommittees was outlined, the deliberations of which would flow into recommendations for action. As far as health services for the aged were concerned, majority and minority recommendations split along the familiar dichotomy of financing through the Old Age and Survivors' Disability Insurance section of the Social Security Act or through the Public Assistance Section. Certainly, the interest of the conference was to crystalize a climate of opinion to deal on a broad scale with the problems of a segment of the population which was increasing both relatively and absolutely.[61] The Medicare bill was passed in August, 1965, embodying the administration proposals.

Later in the decade two other university based research centers emerged in direct response to the expressed desires of politicians and policy makers in two states for data and information by which to guide public policy and legislation. This is not to say that other people and agencies were not conducting research as well, but the Health Information Foundation, and the two centers that were developed later: the unit in the School of Public Health and Administrative Medicine, Columbia University (under Ray E. Trussell), and the unit in the Bureau of Hospital Administration, School of Business Administration, University of Michigan (under Walter McNerney) are the most remarkable. The research directions and general styles are largely a reflection of the personality characteristics and career interests of the people who set research policy in the three centers.

Trussell responded to the interest of the Superintendent of Insurance and the Commissioner of Public Health in the burgeoning problems of costs of personal health services, shortly after Trussell became Professor and Dean of the School of Public Health and Administrative Medicine. Walter McNerney responded to the request of a commission created by the Governor of Michigan after Michigan Blue Cross had petitioned the state insurance commissioner for a substantial rate increase. In a few states, particularly in New York and Michigan, costs of health services and voluntary health insurance became public issues, and inevitably entered the political arena.

A description of Trussell's research situation, main sources of funds, and apparent research policy is in order. The Departments of Insurance and Public Health engaged Trussell as a university based consultant by commissioning the School of Public Health and Administrative Medicine, Columbia University to conduct a series of studies on use, costs, quality and so on of personal health services in New York. Trussell quickly assembled a staff of sociologists, statisticians, physicians and health administrators. They engaged in quite massive record studies

34

in hospitals, prepayment plans and so on and published voluminous reports with recommendations presumably flowing from the findings published in the reports.[62] Trussell's operating style is a good example of a close relationship between fact-finding projects feeding data directly to a policy-making body to be used in its wisdom for its own ends. Indeed, Trussell himself embodied the fusion of facts gatherer and policy maker, a role seldom played by researchers in the social sciences. The state executive departments had earlier access to research findings than other groups, although eventually all information was in the public domain. Trussell's reports produced exceedingly good newspaper copy, a means of sparking public interest. This was particularly true in the study made of the quality of care received by a sample of Teamster Union families in New York City. An examination of the hospital and medical case records by board certified internists of surgical procedures in New York hospitals revealed a high proportion of what the examiners felt were unnecessary procedures, particularly hysterectomies.[63] By all standards this was not sophisticated research, but it served the purpose of showing up undesirable practices, and demonstrated the power of facts.

While the critics of the prevailing health services system were finding a great deal of ammunition in most of Trussell's reports, another study by him and his staff did not give the same degree of comfort. Financed by the joint management-labor Foundation on Employee Health, Trussell and his staff, with the cooperation of the National Opinion Research Center, conducted a complicated survey of machinists' union members in three types of plans in which they were enrolled from coast to coast: those enrolled in a major medical type plan in Utica, New York, Blue Cross-Blue Shield in New Jersey, and Kaiser Permanente in the San Francisco Bay Area. Contrary to a few previous studies, results showed that the use of hospital care hardly varied among the three types of plans.[64]

The research unit that developed at the University of Michigan in the Bureau of Hospital Administration operated in a different context and with a different style. Shortly after Walter McNerney became the director of the bureau, the State Commissioner of Insurance was faced with a request for substantial rate increase by Michigan Blue Cross. The Governor was sufficiently disturbed by rising costs of hospital care to turn this now public issue over to a citizens' committee appointed by him. The idea was to examine all facets of the cost problem in a nonpartisan atmosphere, with the public, the providers of service and the health insurance agencies being involved through inclusion in the commission that was created. As in New York state, a body independent of the state governmental apparatus was needed to carry out studies. Unlike New York, however, the commission was not a creature of a legislative committee. Instead it was nonpartisan or bipartisan. In turn the commission requested the University of Michigan to carry out the investigation although no state funds were available. Within the university, the Bureau of Hospital Administration was interested in assembling the staff and conducting the studies. Financing came from the W. K. Kellogg Foundation. The operating context was one in which McNerney would conduct research and publish reports directed to problems as he saw them with the consultation and advice of an advisory committee. Further, the commission was not to be privy to findings and reports before anyone else. The findings would immediately be made public. The commission would, of course, have access to counsel and discussion on the part of the study staff.

The Michigan project, published in two large volumes, embodied a series of studies on the entire health services system of the state of Michigan in various degrees of depth.[65] Not intended to be light or entertaining reading, the study is rewarding to the student of the health services system who cares to try. It includes a population survey more or less similar to the ones done by Health Information Foundation and National Opinion Research Center, plus some inquiry into unmet need as defined by those interviewed. Additional subjects are cost studies of a sample of hospitals, reviews of state expenditures from tax sources and an attempt to review the legal and informal controls in the health services system. Since the series of studies was precipitated by Blue Cross applying for a rate increase, the most important study was the one attempting to establish criteria for the "effectiveness of hospital use." This was the first systematic attempt to apply professional criteria to hospital use, whereby medical specialists in practice and in medical schools formed the criteria for 18 diagnoses comprising 46 per cent of the annual hospital admissions in Michigan. Applying these criteria to a sample of 5000 hospital discharges showed that less than three per cent of the admissions were inappropriate.[66]

Research sites and research personnel have increased in the past few years. The preceding three sites are mentioned because they were pace setters during the 1950's and early 1960's and were receiving attention. Concurrently, research reports bearing on the health services system were being published dealing with matters of quality of services, regulations governing the Blue Cross and Blue Shield plans and differences in use of hospitals in various organizational contexts. The group practice plans were claiming to show lower and purportedly more efficient use of hospital services than plans using the fee-for-service method of payment. Some allusion has already been made to the studies conducted by Anderson and Sheatsley in New York City and Trussell's group at Columbia University.[67] The report which probably received the most attention in this regard was prepared by I. S. Falk in which he compared hospital utilization rates in various contexts in several parts of the country, showing relatively low use of hospitals in association with group practice.[68] Two studies conducted by the Research Department of Health Insurance Plan of Greater New York seemed to cancel each other out regarding lower hospital use in a group practice context.[69] A review paper by Herbert E. Klarman left the net conclusion regarding hospital use in different organizational contexts somewhat in doubt.[70] A later study of the Federal Civil Service Employees, however, indicated that hospital use is lower in group practice plans.[71]

Some worthwhile research has been done to measure the quality of physicians' services. The studies of rural general practitioners in North Carolina by Peterson and the evaluation of prematurity in HIP by its research staff deserve special mention.[72] Other studies on the human relations aspects of hospital and medical organization began to emerge, indicating that the surface had hardly been scratched regarding knowledge of the internal dynamics of the health services system. These studies stifle casual generalizations about the physician-patient relationship, human relationships within hospitals and other organizational matters which are not the frontiers of research in the health field.[73] Similarly, increasing interest is being shown in the cultural and other behavioral aspects of the general population relating to use of and attitudes to health services.[74] Professional economists are also showing increasing interest in the health field as indicated by selected publications[75] and a meeting of economists held in Ann Arbor, Michigan, in 1962, to discuss the application of economics to the health field.[76] One gratifying development, in view of generally chronic neglect of this problem area, was the creation of the Joint Commission on Mental Illness and Health in 1955, financed by grants from the National Institute of Mental Health and from a great variety of private sources. The director was Jack R. Ewalt. The Joint Commission was a nongovernmental organization representing a variety of national agencies concerned with mental health. Several books were sponsored dealing with these problems.[77]

Two books in this period stand out as symbols of deepening concern with rather fundamental policy issues in voluntary health insurance. The first issue, the question of community vs. experience rating of health insurance plans, has always been discussed and debated in a curious atmosphere of unreality by the proponents of the community rating approach. The Blue Cross and Blue Shield plans had more or less stumbled into the concept of a flat rate for any group enrolled regardless of the composition of the group, and insurance companies had been using the experience rating principle and carried over to health insurance as part of their competitive and cost control mechanism. Duncan M. MacIntyre wrote a brilliant analysis of the community rate compared to experience rate principles as applied to voluntary health insurance. Although sympathetic in principle to the community rate concept, his conclusion was that the community rate was not tenable unless Blue Cross–Blue Shield were granted a monopoly in an area, an unlikely possibility.[78] Further, he reasoned that the utility of the community rate in enabling these plans to cover low-income and high-risk segments of the population and hence keep them off tax-supported medical care programs was quite exaggerated.

The other book is a Ph.D. dissertation by Robert Eilers.[79] He made a useful analysis of the laws and regulations governing the Blue Cross and Blue Shield plans which had not been done since the rather brief study by Anderson in 1944.

Evidence indicates the present time to be a period of resynthesis somewhat similar to the one which occurred in the late 1930's. In this regard an industrial relations economist, Joseph Garbarino, wrote an interesting account of the nature of the medical market in a relatively limited geographic, economic and medical area, the San Francisco Bay Area.[80] As a refreshing change of treatment of this field, Garbarino described the bargaining, negotiating, wheeling-and-dealing context of the health services system, and revealed in good sociological and political style the juxtaposition of forces in buying and selling health services.

In a similar vein, but with less attention to the wheeling-and-dealing atmosphere, the husband and wife team, Herman and Anne Somers, political scientist and economist, respectively, wrote a lively and pertinent book on the problems and issues in financing and organizing the health services system.[81] Unlike books on this subject in the 1930's, the

Somers were sympathetic to some form of government-sponsored health insurance and would accept voluntary health insurance as the main vehicle for financing personal health services given certain conditions. Another useful overview which devotes a great deal of detailed attention to the patterns of health insurance all over the world, is the one by Joseph F. Follman.[82]

Recently, Seymour E. Harris published a compendium on the health field in the United States which was an overview of masses of data, problems, issues and personal observations. Harris had been interested in the health field for 30 years and this book was an expression of his cogitations.[83] An interesting aspect of this book, revealing the changing social and political environment, was his observation that, while he supported government-sponsored health insurance in the 1930's, he now felt that, in the United States, some sort of partnership between private and public financing was clearly indicated. This outlook, and with a view to assessing the past developments and future directions that the health field will take in this country, is leading to investigations in comparative health services systems.[84]

CONCLUSION

Fundamental values in society are evolved from the life experiences of people and not from scientific research by dispassionate scholars. In the United States, the Judeo-Christian tradition and the liberal-democratic, political-economic system set the framework for the consideration of social policy relating to health services. In this context, a fundamental value subscribed to by all groups within the liberal-conservative spectrum is that all people should have relatively equal access to health services regardless of financial status. This value defines the nature of the arena in which public policy relating to health is debated and implemented. If this value had never been accepted, the research development described in the foregoing would not have come about. If personal health services had been regarded as simply another commodity which could be sold in the open market as any other commodity, research would have been mainly of a market and price trend nature. The research that has been conducted was motivated in the spirit of promoting relatively equal accessibility by some means or other, and from one source of funds or other. Factual information on the characteristics and operation of the health services system has been presented in such

39

manner that the solutions are presumed to be self-evident. Research reports have been pervaded with a certain naïvete that an optimum health service may be attained if doctors become more altruistic, patients wise, and health insurance agencies would reduce cost of administration, and so on. No sophistication is discernible in the assessment of possibilities, of the tolerances of providers of services, the recipients of services and the health insurance agencies as to what is a workable equilibrium between them. Those who favor the bureaucratization of medicine also want to personalize care; those who believe that personalized care can only be provided in a free-choice and fee-for-service context are apt to underplay the impact of catastrophic costs of disease episodes which are quite avoidable in a group practice and insurance arrangement. The field is positively rife with incompatible objectives which research can elucidate and expose. But the results of research are not applied rationally in public policy because of the overlapping needs and inherent frictions between the parties mentioned. Sometimes research is expected to answer questions which at the moment, at least, are unanswerable.

Researchers need to be exceedingly careful to differentiate between conclusions flowing from data and conclusions flowing from "best judgment," professional opinion, conventional wisdom and so on. Research data bearing on public policy are regarded as objective and reasonable when they are in accord with an already accepted policy consensus, and are regarded as biased if such consensus is not supported. In this connection Freidson carefully expressed his impression that in group practice physicians are more likely to be peer directed than patient directed and in a solo practice fee-for-service type of arrangement the physicians are more likely to be patient oriented than peer oriented.[85] If these orientations are inherent in the respective structures, profound questions are raised regarding incompatible objectives which have not been faced with candor in debates and discussions.

In view of this seemingly pessimistic outlook regarding the influence of research on public policy, what is then the value of social and economic research in the health field? According to Paul Lazarsfeld in his presidential address to the American Sociological Association in 1962:

> The greatest difficulty in providing concrete examples (of the utility of social research) comes at the two extremes of the utilization spectrum: the exponents of basic social change and the people who want guidance for immediate policy and action are most often disappointed.[86]

40

This observation by Lazarsfeld would then indicate that those who wish to attain some comprehension of the operation and dynamics of the health services system would not belong among either of the extremes described. Those who subscribe to this objective for research are probably regarded as "conservative" in that they push research along certain directions with no intent of answering specific questions, except incidentally, but intend to provide a factual universe in which to think about policy. During the last 20 years, a body of knowledge regarding the characteristics and operation of the health services system has emerged. Further, operating agencies have seen fit to expand or establish research divisions to gather "intelligence" for their own interests and also for the field in general.[87] If the information and data accumulated during the last 20 years were to vanish suddenly, many of us would flounder around in the health services universe in even worse confusion than now. To be limited to the findings of the Committee on the Costs of Medical Care and the National Health Survey of 1935–36, in the context of today's problems, would be most unfortunate. Within this perspective, a body of knowledge is developing.

Return to the preamble and the three stages of decision making and the appearance of and need for data. The operational problems of health services—measurement of costs, evaluation of quality, development of administrative controls—are in the third phase. How to select problems for research, how to develop adequate methodology, and how to interpret and translate findings to application should assist in assessing the net results of possible alternatives, assuming this degree of rationality is possible. This third phase is the entrance to a broad area of alternatives where can be demonstrated the instrumental value of research in the consensus of both objectives and alternatives now present. Accordingly, and to repeat deliberately, the choice of research problems relevant to current and future needs will be research in measurement of costs, evaluation of quality and development of administrative controls—the supply side of the equation. Clearly, the full range of the social and economic sciences need to be involved in this endeavor. If this degree of rationality is not possible, the relative effects of countervailing powers applied by the providers of services, the recipients of service and the sources and control of funds on the dynamics of the health services system may be measured on the assumption that a resolution acceptable to all parties simultaneously is unattainable. Resolutions acceptable to only one at a time are available and these are relatively temporary.

REFERENCES

[1] Public policy may be defined as any set of values, opinions and actions which moves decision making in the political, social and economic system in certain directions, regardless of source in a pluralistic society.

[2] The pioneer studies of Griscom and Harris in New York City, and especially of Shattuck in Massachusetts, may be argued to be the forerunners of survey research in public health policy. But these studies were directed to the sanitary environmental conditions affecting populations before the bacteriological revolution and were never part of the mainstream of medical care organization for personal health services. *See:* Griscom, J. H., THE SANITARY CONDITION OF THE LABORING POPULATION OF NEW YORK WITH SUGGESTIONS FOR IMPROVEMENT, New York, Harper & Row, Publishers, 1845; Harris, Elisha (Editor), Report of the Council of Hygiene and Public Health of the Citizens' Association of New York Upon the Sanitary Condition of the City, 1865, reported in Rosen, George, A HISTORY OF PUBLIC HEALTH, New York, MD Publications, 1958, p. 234; Shattuck, Lemuel, REPORT OF A GENERAL PLAN FOR THE PROMOTION OF PUBLIC AND PERSONAL HEALTH . . . RELATING TO A SANITARY SURVEY OF THE STATE, Boston, 1850, reprinted by Harvard University Press, 1948.

[3] The first nationwide survey of hospitals in the United States was conducted by the United States Bureau of Education in 1872–73, and was reported in Transactions of the American Medical Association, 24, 314–333, 1873. The next survey was conducted by the American Medical Association in 1909.

[4] Flexner, Abraham, MEDICAL EDUCATION IN THE UNITED STATES AND CANADA: A REPORT TO THE CARNEGIE FOUNDATION FOR THE ADVANCEMENT OF TEACHING, New York, Carnegie Foundation, 1910.

[5] Anderson, Odin W., Health Insurance in the United States, 1910–1920, *Journal of the History of Medicine*, 5, 363–396, Autumn, 1950.

[6] Midwives of Chicago, *Journal of the American Medical Association*, 50, 1346–1350, April 25, 1908.

[7] Abbott, Grace, The Midwife in Chicago, *American Journal of Sociology*, 20, 684–699, March, 1915.

[8] Frankel, Lee K. and Dublin, Louis I., *Community Sickness Survey, Rochester, New York, September, 1915*, Washington, D.C., United States Government Printing Office, 1916.

[9] These medical research developments are graphically expressed by Dr. Herman Biggs, when he was Commissioner of Health of New York City in 1911, who coined the motto, "Public health is purchasable. Within natural limitations a community can determine its own death rate." Quoted in Winslow, C. E. A., THE LIFE OF HERMAN BIGGS, Philadelphia, Lea & Febiger, 1929, p. 230. Dr. Lawrence J. Henderson of Harvard University is quoted, "I think it was about the year 1910 or 1912 when it became possible to say of the United States that

42

a random patient with a random disease consulting a doctor chosen at random stood better than a fifty-fifty chance of benefiting from the encounter." Quoted in Gregg, Alan, CHALLENGE TO CONTEMPORARY MEDICINE, New York, Columbia University Press, 1956, p. 13.

10 In his presidential address at the fifth annual conference of the Association of Hospital Superintendents of the United States and Canada, George Ludlum said, "It is, I think, an acknowledged fact that the per diem cost of patients per capita is constantly increasing. [This increase] is due in large measure to the advance and development of medical and surgical science . . ." *National Hospital Record*, 7, 52, December, 1903.

11 Brush, Frederick R., *Transaction of the American Hospital Association*, Eleventh Annual Conference, 11, 182, 1909.

12 Davis, Michael M. and Warner, Andrew R., DISPENSARIES: THEIR MANAGEMENT AND DEVELOPMENT, New York, The Macmillan Company, 1918.

13 *Ibid.*, p. 353.

14 Sydenstricker, Edgar, The Incidence of Illness in a General Population Group, *Public Health Reports*, 40, 279–291, February 13, 1925.

15 ———, The Extent of Medical and Hospital Service in a Typical Small City, Hagerstown Morbidity Studies Number 3, *Public Health Reports*, 42, 121–131, January 14, 1927. Sufficient studies were being conducted from various sources on the relationship of mortality, morbidity and economic states to justify a summary monograph: Collins, Selwyn D., ECONOMIC STATUS AND HEALTH: A REVIEW AND STUDY OF THE RELEVANT MORBIDITY AND MORTALITY DATA, Washington, United States Government Printing Office, 1927, Public Health Bulletin number 165.

16 Woodbury, Robert M., CAUSAL FACTORS IN INFANT MORTALITY: A STATISTICAL STUDY BASED ON INVESTIGATIONS IN EIGHT CITIES, United States Children's Bureau, Publication number 142, Washington, United States Government Printing Office, 1925.

17 *The Five-Year Program of the Committee on the Cost of Medical Care*, Washington, The Committee on the Costs of Medical Care, 1928.

18 They were the American Dental Association, American Medical Association, Metropolitan Life Insurance Company, National Bureau of Economic Research, National Tuberculosis Association, Milbank Memorial Fund, the Julius Rosenwald Fund, and the Rockefeller Foundation.

19 Editorial, *Journal of the American Medical Association*, 93, 459, August 10, 1929.

20 *The Final Report of the Committee on the Costs of Medical Care*, Washington, The Committee on the Costs of Medical Care, 1928.

21 Transactions of the 35th Annual Convention of the American Hospital Association, Milwaukee, September 11–15, 1933, p. 737.

22 Perrott, George St. J. and Tibitts, Clark, The National Health Survey, *Public Health Reports*, 54, 1663, September 15, 1939.

23 Two basic volumes established the basis for subsequent research in medical care and disease and social factors. The first was the report number 26 of the Committee on the Costs of Medical Care, alluded to above. The second was Sydenstricker, Edgar, HEALTH AND ENVIRONMENT, New York, McGraw-Hill Book Company, 1933.

[24] These were the National Health Conference, Washington, D. C., July, 1938, and the National Health Assembly, Washington, D. C., May, 1948.

[25] The President's Commission on the Health Needs of the Nation, BUILDING AMERICA'S HEALTH, Washington, United States Government Printing Office, 1953.

[26] Simons, A. M. and Sinai, Nathan, THE WAY OF HEALTH INSURANCE, University of Chicago Press, 1932; Davis, Michael M. and Rorem, C. Rufus, THE CRISIS IN HOSPITAL FINANCE AND OTHER STUDIES IN HOSPITAL ECONOMICS, Chicago, University of Chicago Press, 1932.

[27] Davis, Michael M. and Rorem, C. Rufus, *Ibid.*, p. vii.

[28] Millis, Harry A., SICKNESS AND INSURANCE: A STUDY OF THE SICKNESS PROBLEM AND HEALTH INSURANCE, Chicago, University of Chicago Press, 1937.

[29] Crownhart, J. G., SICKNESS INSURANCE IN EUROPE, Madison, Wisconsin, the author, 1938. Other books were: Falk, Isadore S., SECURITY AGAINST SICKNESS: A STUDY OF HEALTH INSURANCE, New York, Doubleday, Doran & Co., 1936. Falk was the study director for the Committee on the Costs of Medical Care Report number 16, and later became Research Director of the Division of Research, Social Security Administration. Reed, Louis S., HEALTH INSURANCE: THE NEXT STEP IN SOCIAL SECURITY, New York, Harper & Row, Publishers, 1937. Reed had been on the staff of the Committee on the Costs of Medical Care. Armstrong, Barbara, THE HEALTH INSURANCE DOCTOR: HIS ROLE IN GREAT BRITAIN, DENMARK, AND FRANCE, Princeton, N.J., Princeton University Press, 1939; Orr, Douglas W. and Orr, Jean Walker, HEALTH INSURANCE WITH MEDICAL CARE: THE BRITISH EXPERIENCE, New York, The Macmillan Company, 1938.

[30] Sinai, Nathan, Anderson, Odin W. and Dollar, Melvin L., HEALTH INSURANCE IN THE UNITED STATES, New York, The Commonwealth Fund, 1946.

[31] Simpson, Herbert D., COMPULSORY HEALTH INSURANCE IN THE UNITED STATES: AN ANALYSIS AND APPRAISAL OF THE PRESENT MOVEMENT, Evanston, Illinois, Northwestern University Press, 1943.

[32] Goldmann, Franz, PUBLIC MEDICAL CARE: PRINCIPLES AND PROBLEMS, New York, Columbia University Press, 1945; and VOLUNTARY MEDICAL CARE INSURANCE IN THE UNITED STATES, New York, Columbia University Press, 1948.

[33] Bachman, George W. and Meriam, Lewis, THE ISSUES OF COMPULSORY HEALTH INSURANCE, Washington, The Brookings Institution, 1948.

[34] Sinai, Nathan, Hall, Marguerite and Holmes, Ray E., MEDICAL RELIEF ADMINISTRATION: FINAL REPORT OF THE EXPERIENCE IN ESSEX COUNTY, ONTARIO, Windsor, Ontario, Essex County Medical Economic Research, 1939.

[35] Axelrod, S. J. and Patton, R. E., The Use and Abuse of Prepaid Comprehensive Physicians' Services, *American Journal of Public Health*, 42, 566–674, May, 1952.

[36] *Medical Care in New York State*, New York State Legislative Document number 91, Report of the Temporary Legislative Commission to Formulate a Long Range State Health Program, Albany, 1940, Chapter 3.

[37] Duncan, Otis D., SOCIAL RESEARCH IN HEALTH, New York, Social Science Research Council, 1946.

[38] Mott, Frederick D. and Roemer, Milton I., RURAL HEALTH AND MEDICAL CARE, New York, McGraw-Hill Book Company, 1948.

[39] Hoffer, Charles R. and Schuler, Edgar A., Measurement of Health Needs and Health Care, *American Sociological Review*, 13, 719–724, December, 1948; and Hoffer, Charles R., *et al.*, HEALTH NEEDS AND HEALTH CARE IN MICHIGAN, East Lansing, Michigan, Michigan State College, 1950.

[40] Anderson, Odin W., STATE ENABLING LEGISLATION FOR NON-PROFIT HOSPITAL AND MEDICAL PLANS, 1944, Ann Arbor, University of Michigan Press, School of Public Health, 1944.

[41] ——, ADMINISTRATION OF MEDICAL CARE: PROBLEMS AND ISSUES, Ann Arbor, The University of Michigan Press, School of Public Health, 1947. Based on an analysis of the Medical Dental Care Program for the Recipients of Old-Age Assistance in the State of Washington, 1941–45.

[42] Sinai, Nathan and Anderson, Odin W., EMIC: A STUDY OF ADMINISTRATIVE EXPERIENCE, Ann Arbor, Michigan, School of Public Health Economics.

[43] Commission on Hospital Care, HOSPITAL CARE IN THE UNITED STATES, New York, The Commonwealth Fund, 1947.

[44] Blue Cross Commission of the American Hospital Association, Health Information Foundation, John Hancock Mutual Life Insurance Company, W. K. Kellogg Foundation, Michigan Medical Service (Blue Shield), Milbank Memorial Fund, National Foundation for Infantile Paralysis, and the Rockefeller Foundation.

[45] Commission on Financing of Hospital Care, FINANCING HOSPITAL CARE IN THE UNITED STATES, New York, Blakiston, 1954–55, Volume 1, Factors Affecting the Costs of Hospital Care; Volume 2, Prepayment and the Community; Volume 3, Financing Hospital Care for Nonwage and Low-Income Groups.

[46] United States National Health Survey, ORIGIN AND PROGRAM, May, 1958.

[47] United States Committee on Vital and Health Statistics, United States Statistics on Medical Economics, PRESENT STATUS AND RECOMMENDATIONS FOR ADDITIONAL DATA, Washington, United States Government Printing Office, 1964.

[48] American Cancer Society, American Dental Association, American Heart Association, American Hospital Association, American Medical Association, American Psychiatric Association, American Public Health Association, American Public Welfare Association, Arthritis and Rheumatism Foundation, Commonwealth Fund, Equitable Life Assurance Society, Johns Hopkins University, Liberty Mutual Insurance Company, Muscular Dystrophy Associations of America, National Foundation for Infantile Paralysis, National Health Council, National Multiple Sclerosis Society, National Society for Crippled Children and Adults, National Tuberculosis Association, New York Foundation, New York Life Insurance Company, Public Health Service, Rockefeller Foundation, Eli Lilly and Company and the Metropolitan Life Insurance Company.

[49] Commission on Chronic Illness, CHRONIC ILLNESS IN THE UNITED STATES, Cambridge, Massachusetts, Harvard University Press (for the Commonwealth Fund), 1959, Volume III, Chronic Illness in a Rural Area, the Hunterdon Study.

[50] *Ibid.*, four volumes.

[51] Voluntary Insurance Against Sickness: 1948–51 Estimates, *Social Security Bulletin*, 15, 3–6, December, 1952.

45

[52] *The New York Times,* 102, 512, January 4, 1953.

[53] Anderson, Odin W. and Feldman, Jacob J., FAMILY MEDICAL CARE COSTS AND VOLUNTARY HEALTH INSURANCE: A NATIONWIDE SURVEY, New York, McGraw-Hill Book Company, 1956, p. 24.

[54] In 1964, the University of Chicago created the Center for Health Administration Studies with Health Information and the Program in Hospital Administration as components.

[55] Serbein, Oscar N., PAYING FOR MEDICAL CARE IN THE UNITED STATES, New York, Columbia University Press, 1953.

[56] Anderson, Odin W. and Feldman, Jacob J., *op. cit.*

[57] The dates of publication bear no necessary relationship to the sequence in which the studies were started. The chronology is the starting and completion dates of the projects. Anderson, Odin W. and Staff of the National Opinion Research Center, VOLUNTARY HEALTH INSURANCE IN TWO CITIES: A SURVEY OF SUBSCRIBER-HOUSEHOLDS, Cambridge, Massachusetts, Harvard University Press, 1957.

[58] Darsky, Benjamin J., Sinai, Nathan and Axelrod, Solomon J., COMPREHENSIVE MEDICAL SERVICES UNDER VOLUNTARY HEALTH INSURANCE: A STUDY OF WINDSOR MEDICAL SERVICES, Cambridge, Massachusetts, Harvard University Press, 1958; Shipman, George A. Lampman, Robert J. and Miyamoto, S. Frank, MEDICAL SERVICE CORPORATIONS IN THE STATE OF WASHINGTON, Cambridge, Massachusetts, Harvard University Press, 1962; Anderson, Odin W. and Sheatsley, Paul B., COMPREHENSIVE MEDICAL INSURANCE—A STUDY OF COSTS, USE AND ATTITUDES UNDER TWO PLANS, New York, Health Information Foundation, 1959.

[59] Anderson, Odin, W., Collette, Patricia and Feldman, Jacob J., CHANGES IN FAMILY MEDICAL CARE EXPENDITURES AND VOLUNTARY HEALTH INSURANCE: A FIVE-YEAR RESURVEY, Cambridge, Massachusetts, Harvard University Press, 1963. In 1963, a similar survey was conducted with the National Opinion Research Center as the field agency and Ronald M. Anderson as the project director in collaboration with Odin W. Anderson. Preliminary data are to be found in *Progress in Health Services,* November–December, 1965, January–February, 1966, and March–April, 1967. A book is in preparation.

[60] Shanas, Ethel, THE HEALTH OF OLDER PEOPLE: A SOCIAL SURVEY, Cambridge, Massachusetts, Harvard University Press, 1962.

[61] United States Department of Health, Education and Welfare, THE NATION AND ITS OLDER PEOPLE; REPORT OF THE WHITE HOUSE CONFERENCE ON AGING, January 9–12, 1961, Washington, United States Government Printing Office, 1961.

[62] Columbia University School of Public Health and Administrative Medicine, PREPAYMENT FOR HOSPITAL CARE IN NEW YORK STATE; A REPORT ON THE EIGHT BLUE CROSS PLANS SERVING NEW YORK RESIDENTS, New York, Columbia University Press, 1961; and PREPAYMENT FOR MEDICAL AND DENTAL CARE IN NEW YORK STATE: A REPORT ON THE SEVEN BLUE SHIELD PLANS AND HEALTH INSURANCE PLAN OF GREATER NEW YORK, GROUP HEALTH INSURANCE, INC., AND GROUP DENTAL INSURANCE INC., SERVING NEW YORK RESIDENTS, New York, Columbia University Press, 1962.

[63] Trussell, Ray E., Ehrlich, J. and Morehead, Mildred A., THE QUANTITY, QUALITY AND COSTS OF MEDICAL CARE SECURED BY A SAMPLE OF TEAMSTER FAMILIES IN THE NEW YORK AREA, New York, Columbia University Press, 1962.

[64] Columbia University School of Public Health and Administrative Medicine with the Cooperation of the National Opinion Research Center, FAMILY MEDICAL CARE UNDER THREE TYPES OF HEALTH INSURANCE, New York, Foundation on Employee Health, 1962.

[65] McNerney, Walter J. and Study Staff, HOSPITAL AND MEDICAL ECONOMICS: A STUDY OF POPULATION, SERVICES, COSTS, METHODS OF PAYMENTS AND CONTROLS, Chicago, Hospital Research and Educational Trust, 1962.

[66] Fitzpatrick, Thomas B., Riedel, Donald C. and Payne, Beverly C., Character and Effectiveness of Hospital Use, *Hospital and Medical Economics*, 1, 361–588, 1962.

[67] Anderson and Sheatsley, *op. cit.*; Trussell, *op. cit.*

[68] United States Steel Workers of America, SPECIAL STUDY ON THE MEDICAL CARE PROGRAM FOR STEEL WORKERS AND THEIR FAMILIES. INSURANCE, PENSION AND UNEMPLOYMENT BENEFITS DEPARTMENT—A REPORT, Pittsburgh, United Steel Workers, 1960.

[69] Densen, Paul M., *et al.*, Prepaid Medical Care and Hospitalization in a dual Choice Situation, *American Journal of Public Health*, 50, 1710, 1960; and Densen, Paul M., *et al.*, Prepaid Medical Care and Hospitalization; Comparison of a Group Practice and Self-Insurance Situation, *Hospitals*, 36, 65, November 16, 1962.

[70] Klarman, Herbert E., Controlling Hospital Use Through Organization of Medical Services, *Proceedings of the Fifth Annual Symposium on Hospital Affairs*, University of Chicago, December 14–15, 1962.

[71] Perrott, George St. J. and Maher, Nancy E., The Federal Employees Health Benefits Program: Third Term Coverage and Hospital Utilization, *Group Health and Welfare News*, Special Supplement, February–March, 1965.

[72] Peterson, Osler L., *et al.*, An Analytical Study of North Carolina General Practice, 1953–54, *Journal of Medical Education*, 31, 1–165, December, 1956, Part 2; Shapiro, Sam, Weiner, Louis and Densen, Paul M., Comparisons of Prematurity and Prenatal Mortality in a General Population and in a Population of a Prepaid Group Practice, *American Journal of Public Health*, 48, 170–187, February, 1958. A very early forerunner to medical quality studies was the one sponsored by the Committee on the Costs of Medical Care: Lee, Roger I. and Jones, Lewis W., THE FUNDAMENTALS OF GOOD MEDICAL CARE: AN OUTLINE OF THE FUNDAMENTALS OF GOOD MEDICAL CARE AND AN ESTIMATE OF THE SERVICE REQUIRED TO SUPPLY THE MEDICAL NEEDS OF THE UNITED STATES, Chicago, University of Chicago Press, 1933.

[73] Selected examples are: Hughes, Everett C., Hughes, Helen M. and Deutscher, Irwin, TWENTY THOUSAND NURSES TELL THEIR STORY, Philadelpha, J. B. Lippincott Co., 1958; Field, Mark G., DOCTOR AND PATIENT IN SOVIET RUSSIA, Cambridge, Massachusetts, Harvard University Press, 1957; Freidson, Eliot, PATIENTS' VIEWS OF MEDICAL PRACTICE—A STUDY OF SUBSCRIBERS TO A PREPAID MEDICAL CARE PLAN IN THE BRONX, New York, Russell Sage Foundation, 1961; Burling, Temple E., HOSPITALS: A STUDY IN HUMAN ORGANIZATION, New York, G. P. Putnam's Sons, 1956; Goss, Mary E. W., Influence and Authority Among Physicians in an Out-Patient Clinic, *American Sociological Review*, 26, 39–50, February, 1961; Georgopoulos, Basil S. and Mann, Floyd C., THE COMMUNITY GENERAL HOSPITAL, New York, The Macmillan Company, 1961.

[74] Paul, Benjamin D. (Editor), HEALTH, CULTURE AND COMMUNITY, New York, Russell Sage Foundation, 1955; Saunders, Lyle, CULTURAL DIFFERENCES

47

AND MEDICAL CARE; THE CASE OF THE SPANISH-SPEAKING PEOPLE OF THE SOUTHWEST, New York, Russell Sage Foundation, 1954; Koos, Earl L., THE HEALTH OF REGIONVILLE; WHAT THE PEOPLE THOUGHT AND DID ABOUT IT, New York, Columbia University Press, 1954; Feldman, Jacob J., THE DISSEMINATION OF HEALTH INFORMATION: A CASE STUDY IN ADULT LEARNING, Ph.D. Dissertation, University of Chicago, March, 1965.

[75] *See*, for example, Fein, Rashi, ECONOMICS OF MENTAL ILLNESS, New York, Basic Books, Inc., Publishers, 1958; Weisbrod, Burton A., ECONOMICS OF PUBLIC HEALTH; MEASURING THE ECONOMIC IMPACT OF DISEASES, Philadelphia, University of Pennsylvania Press, 1961; Mushkin, Selma J. and Collings, Francis d'A., Economic Costs of Disease and Injury, *Public Health Reports,* 74, 795–809, September, 1959; Klarman, Herbert E., THE ECONOMICS OF HEALTH, New York, Columbia University Press, 1965.

[76] This meeting was sponsored by the Bureau of Public Health Economics and Department of Economics, University of Michigan and supported in part by the Public Health Service. Proceedings of the Conference, May 10–12, 1962, were published as THE ECONOMICS OF HEALTH AND MEDICAL CARE, Ann Arbor, Michigan, University of Michigan Press, 1964.

[77] Among these were, Jahoda, Marie, CURRENT CONCEPTS OF POSITIVE MENTAL HEALTH, New York, Basic Books, Inc., Publishers, 1958; Albee, George W., MENTAL HEALTH MANPOWER TRENDS, New York, Basic Books, Inc., Publishers, 1959; Gurin, Gerald, Veroff, Joseph and Feld, Sheila, AMERICANS VIEW THEIR MENTAL HEALTH, New York, Basic Books, Inc., Publishers, 1960.

[78] MacIntyre, Duncan M., VOLUNTARY HEALTH INSURANCE AND RATE MAKING, Ithaca, New York, Cornell University Press, 1962.

[79] Eilers, Robert, REGULATION OF BLUE CROSS AND BLUE SHIELD PLANS, Homewood, Illinois, Richard D. Irwin, Inc., 1963.

[80] Garbarino, Joseph W., HEALTH PLANS AND COLLECTIVE BARGAINING, Berkeley, California, University of California Press, 1960.

[81] Somers, Herman M. and Somers, Anne R., DOCTORS, PATIENTS AND HEALTH INSURANCE; THE ORGANIZATION AND FINANCING OF MEDICAL CARE, Washington, The Brookings Institution, 1961.

[82] Follman, Joseph F. Jr., MEDICAL CARE AND HEALTH INSURANCE; A STUDY IN SOCIAL PROGRESS, Homewood, Illinois, Richard D. Irwin, Inc., 1963.

[83] Harris, Seymour E., THE ECONOMICS OF AMERICAN MEDICINE, New York, The Macmillan Company, 1964.

[84] Anderson, Odin W., Health Services Systems in the United States and Other Countries: Critical Comparisons, *New England Journal of Medicine,* 319, October 17 and October 24, 1963.

[85] Freidson, Eliot, PATIENTS' VIEWS OF MEDICAL PRACTICE; A STUDY OF SUBSCRIBERS TO A PREPAID MEDICAL CARE PLAN IN THE BRONX, New York, Russell Sage Foundation, 1961.

[86] Lazarsfeld, Paul, The Sociology of Empirical Social Research, *American Sociological Review,* 27, 757–767, December, 1962.

[87] American Medical Association, American Hospital Association, Blue Cross Association, Social Security Administration, Public Health Service, American Dental Association, Health Insurance Association of America.

DISCUSSION

Discussants generally agreed with Dr. Anderson that health care policy, and the methods of implementing it, had in the past seldom been based on the results of research. The suggestion was made, however, that a historical review could be supplemented by a forward-looking survey, to indicate further what might be some of the more profitable lines of research which have a bearing on public policy today, as exemplified by Dr. Anderson's own work on the means test.

Agreement was also voiced with Dr. Anderson's optimism that the present consensus in the health area (as demonstrated by medicare and the regional centers program) would provide greatly expanded opportunities to apply social and behavioral science methods to the health field. This broad consensus on policy would also, in his view, permit research to fully develop its instrumental function and to aim at the objective discovery of the best ways of fulfilling the consensus in goals. In the future, the influence of research may expand its scope and go beyond its instrumental function. Although goals (such as the recognition of everyone's right to medical care regardless of income) stem from, or are entwined with, social and political ideology, and hence are difficult to study, the facts unearthed today by research workers might influence the next generation of policy makers.

The discussion centered largely on the reasons why research had, in the past, exerted limited influence on policy making. These reasons included the academic attitude toward practical and policy-related research, the inadequacy of research tools in the behavioral and social sciences and the lack of communication between researchers and policy makers. In all these areas, attention was called to new developments that promised a closer relationship between research and public policy in health in the future.

The academic attitude. Many problems call for immediate action, and many policy decisions would have been sounder if a more informed study had been made of what was happening in the area concerned. Such information is often lacking because of an aura of second-class citizenship around persons why try to investigate problems

49

that do not lend themselves to very refined tools of analysis. The fact was pointed out, however, that now increasingly many Ph.D. research projects concern practical problems, but that the results, although apparently reasonable, may not be relevant under the complex conditions of the practical world. The basic defect, therefore, seems to lie in the lack of adequate feedback from that world and in the fact that preliminary findings never get the necessary second look from those involved in their implementation.

In view of the rapidly changing social situation and the need to encourage more research on policy issues, operational research should be accorded more respectability. Such research is a uniquely powerful tool for testing the actual effects of theories in the concrete world. Measures and criteria for policy-related and applied research also need to be developed so that policy makers may determine whether a particular piece of research is acceptable. While these criteria will undoubtedly differ from those used in evaluating other types of research, a clearer definition can be obtained of what is tolerable in this difficult situation. Students in the field could then be better inculcated with methods of assessing problems to study and how to weigh evidence.

Inadequacy of tools. In the early part of the century the tools of the social and behavioral sciences were insufficiently developed to deal adequately with policy-related problems, but great improvement appears to be taking place. Health economists in particular are developing tools useful for decision making. They have shifted their emphasis from financing health services to such problems as the following: the allocation of resources for health care; the effect of investment in health care on the general economy; the means by which health services reach the consumer; the effect of a health-program choice on resources available for other programs, such as education; and cost-benefit analysis, which can improve decision-making by quantifying factors that enter into decision but that have not previously been examined systematically.

Lack of communications. A major problem that was identified is the failure of communication between scientists who should contribute to policy decisions and those persons who make the decisions. The problem has lessened somewhat recently, especially for economists in relation to the Federal Government; but other disciplines must also find ways of reliable communication.

A particular difficulty was emphasized. In research one always begins with assumptions and abstractions. Often the nature of the data introduces limitations, forcing the researcher to use techniques which, although the best available under the circumstances, are not ideal. Results may be unreliable and statistical flaws may not be detected. At a certain stage the results are not even ready for an attempt at application. Yet decision-makers may seize upon them eagerly and accept them as the solution to their problems. In communicating his findings the researcher should communicate also their qualifications and limitations.

One discussant suggested that if research is to become effective in public policy, the role of the researcher may have to change—he may have to work on the principle that information is power, which can be used with political astuteness to influence for better the course of public policy in health. Other speakers disagreed, and emphasized the danger of a researcher's forgetting his true purpose, which is to try to understand and predict. Only someone who knows about policy can recommend, and this ability requires certain characteristics, such as maturity of judgment, whereas the researcher as such excells in the care he exercised in his procedures and in the originality of his ideas. The institutionalization of feedback between the academic and practical worlds, which would alleviate many of the difficulties mentioned, is considered a priority item.

RESEARCH INTO THE ORGANIZATION
OF COMMUNITY HEALTH SERVICE AGENCIES
AN ADMINISTRATOR'S REVIEW

HENRIK L. BLUM

INTRODUCTION

The relevance of research in facilitating the delivery of health services can hardly be questioned at this time when health investments of such magnitude as Medicare are being made.[1] However, technology clearly has long received the giant's share of research interest, and, more recently, social planning and legislative policy-making research have also prospered. Organizational processes, the means whereby technology can be applied, and at the same time the vehicle upon which policy makers can place new social programs, cannot be allowed to continue relatively unresearched.

Community health organizations, thanks to their omnipresence and diversity of structure and goals, offer a splendid environment in which to undertake organizational research. Principles and generalizations derived from studies in such agencies should apply to other types of organizations as well. Potential researchers in this field must soon become aware that community health programs most heavily affect those portions of the population that are economically deprived and socially incapable of taking advantage of the best that society offers. Researchers who pave the way for effective community health efforts will have the satisfaction of making socially valued contributions not only because of the character of the populations typically served, but as a result of liberating the potential power of community health agencies to change the health status of the recipient populations and the total lives of large groups of community members.

52

Organizational research in a general sense is research about agency structure and practices. This is a broad area inclusive of and in great part indistinguishable from administrative and operation research.[2-6] It encompasses the development of new knowledge about institutions, programs, operations, the people working in these activities or the individuals or communities served by them. Diseases and patients tend more to be side issues, sometimes acting as yardsticks for identifying organizational success or failure.[2]

Evaluation, which has as its objective the intellectual control over administrative efforts, is the most critically lacking day-to-day ingredient in community health practices.[1] But, it only incidentally includes the element of exploration. Therefore, it cannot be given more than passing mention even though Wylie[2,6] equates this type of effort with administrative research because it is done to provide information with which to redirect methods or choose more realistic goals. (Demonstrations or pilot runs are similarly only of tangential interest.)

This review will attempt to focus on research initiated for purposes of studying and affecting organization. Nevertheless, because of scarcity of such material, and because almost all agency research ultimately impinges on organizational structure, process or function, many areas and examples of research on programs and methods will be pointed out.

Little attention will be given to activities of federal agencies or the national voluntary health agencies which only infrequently offer community health services, even though they are responsible for stimulating and funding much of the research done by state and local agencies. The bulk of community health activities occurs at the local level even when provided by state agencies. Related research will receive the most attention whether it is initiated locally or is carried out by universities, state or national agencies.

Harsh criticism has been directed at undertaking research in the area of organization. Hard criteria are lacking for quality, continuity, suitability of care, etc., which would be the measures of organizational accomplishments. With this in mind, studies are recommended which provide statements of relationships generally applicable to most community health agencies. This involves laying out models complete with the theorctical propositions that underlie why the input or modification will result in a different outcome. Unless a research proposal may be described in terms that permit replication in other settings, or practice principles may be specified on which other settings may model programs, research about what goes on in a specific agency is probably an unjustifiable waste of resources.

The vehicles for delivering social products have not been said to lend themselves to inexpensive exploration or simple evaluation. Research will only allow an informed guess as to how workers' current relationships within the agency and with their clients will shape tomorrow's tasks. To complicate matters further, any information given to staff or clients about their yesterday may influence their tomorrow.

The extensive, unending and expensive nature of research into agency relationships does not call for its abandonment. Rather information should be arranged in a way that focuses not so much on the situation at the time of study, but on the processes at work. In this way unveiling processes, rather than objects or subjects, should reveal underlying generalizations. From these, careful predictive probes into some finite bit of the future should tell about the adequacy of the research produced model from which prognoses are launched.

Repeated *ad infinitum* today are the sad facts that performance or effective delivery of health services and information is often decades behind the actual knowledge or techniques of rendering specific services. This is apparently true over much of the nation[7-10] and strongly indicates that successful research in administrative techniques has not kept pace with research into the causes, prevention or cure of disease. In other words, the creakiest part of the health delivery service has been the administrative vehicle which is neither able to carry the necessary load nor to proceed at an adequate pace. It has not adequately distributed the lifesaving goods available from medical resources. The transport analogy may be inadequate, for many of the obvious failures seem to lie with inability to package the products seductively enough to be valued sufficiently to warrant the expenditure of energy or dollars. The element of product desirability or acceptablity is in part dependent on, and therefore amenable to, research in structure and administration. This will be seen in the discussion of multipurpose workers who might, because of comprehensive assignments, be a more effective means of providing personal services.[17]

54

Community health agencies are the major means of providing many health services and information and are themselves one of the critical bottlenecks. Therefore, they may reasonably be asked to attempt an investigation into their structure and administration upon which is dependent successful delivery of services, or to submit to research of a similar nature.

However, one cannot concentrate solely on the structure of the agency as though this were an end perfectable in itself. Rather, its appropriate structure must be determined from different research, that is, from an analysis of who needs and who is to benefit from its ministrations and what the obstacles are to the client's successful recognition and utilization of what is offered. Perhaps research into these considerations must be given precedence over that into traditionally taught approaches to the organization of agencies. In the past agencies have been seen as edifices erected according to universally applicable and learnable formulae and able to stand by themselves, even if unoccupied, because of obliviousness of the people to be served.[12]

WILL THE PAUCITY OF RESEARCH CONTINUE?

Only in community service agencies can structural and organizational research about their effectivity be validated, and in them the host of research opportunities occurs day in and day out. Why then such a niggardly output?

Indifference in the Agency

Perhaps studies on methods of testing, diagnosing or treating are often more attractive than those on organization to the medically-oriented health agency leadership. However, this is probably not relevant because few of the community health serving agencies undertake or participate in substantial research of any kind. This suggests that the health agency has not attracted personnel who are adequately inquisitive, ambitious or capable of mounting a sound investigation. Unfortunately, the more demanding or sophisticated research, and that for which the staff is least well prepared by current professional background, would concern organization.

Indifference among Policy Makers

An often overpoweringly inhibiting factor is the attitude in many local governments and voluntary agencies that research is something to be carried out by universities, or by state and national agencies. Since awareness is typically lacking of what currently most needs researching, i.e., the means of reaching the population at risk, research is regarded as pursuit of the great breakthrough in diagnosis or cure. The fact that Papanicolau smears represented such a breakthrough several decades ago and that they are utilized by or available to only a minority of those at risk has not been seen as a need for more than a handful of research projects.

Fears of Conflict

The above example suggests several other reasons why significant research may not be mounted in community health agencies. At this stage of national philosophical and political evolution such efforts are likely to bring agencies into serious collision with privately practicing medical confreres. The latter may see research into such areas as bringing services by subsidized agencies one step nearer to another of their private patient's needs, perhaps at a low or even inapparent cost because of contributions or taxes. Perhaps when poverty-segregated (separate and rarely equal) medical care disappears as a result of government acting as third party payer for groups not reasonably able to afford health services, and when this care is obtained where anyone else obtains it, that is, from the privately practicing doctor chosen by the individual himself, the problem now pertaining should evaporate.

Demands for Immediate Payoff

Perhaps research is inhibited because many feel that it must produce answers that are immediately useful. Research, whose application cannot immediately be seen, will likely be acceptable only in sophisticated communities or those having agencies large enough to acknowledge research among their goals. As a fortunate offset, many agencies and communities recognize availability of study opportunities as one way of attracting persons who bear the quality of skills necessary to solve the so-called "everyday, practical" problems.[13]

Professional Stumbling Blocks

Side by side with the ever present urges for change are the potent individual homeostatic drives to stay within the known or with what is believed. The more fundamental changes that a research project implies, the more the brakes are applied by a majority of those who feel personally involved by the proposal. These threats are perceived early by professionals and agency personnel who often oppose possibilities for research long before the public is even aware of the opportunities. This is understandable as the professionals have already secured personal success as the providers of service and are thus heavily oriented toward the status quo.

The increasing inappropriateness of the professionals' service often becomes the force for change. The aggregate recipients of services, the lay public, demand change as a result of professionally contrived obstructions to availability of appropriate services. No small number of the great breakthroughs in health services have arisen from lay demands for new approaches and new institutions, albeit on a purely empirical basis. Since public demands often set the stage for legislative plunges before the professionals carry out needed research, legislators are learning to temper public demand with a search for technical advice on how to meet it. Not uncommonly, pilot runs and research are the first legislative response, particularly when substantial professional interest is either absent or in opposition.[14]

Perhaps the growth of a value-oriented scientific era will lead to a strengthening of the professionals' motivations so that their concern for the object of their services will exceed that for the rewards of their particular school-bestowed merit badge. A rapid growth of agency interest in how to effect delivery should occur concomitantly. This state of affairs will no doubt be related to major changes in graduate school disciplines which seem far from exemplifying the situation calculated to instill values or objectives.[15]

Inherent Complexities due to Other Contemporary Forces

A major change in agency structure is expensive and often involves many political decisions. Even small modifications are often achieved only after almost unbelievable internal and external obstacles (civil service, finance, union, etc., demands) have been overcome. Struggles so engendered create unplanned realignments, enmities and resignations that can rob the intended change of much of its validity.

The difficulty of maintaining a single variable or a control situation is further compounded by new community perceptions and broad social changes. As a result the organizational research conclusions, particularly generalizations, are open to grave doubts.[16-18]

Obstacles encountered in recruiting adequately skilled persons for key jobs to spark a new structure are almost routine in terms of civil service and professional requirements and restrictions. This situation in community health agencies is generally coupled with inadequate pay and personnel shortages. As a result, planned changes make do with the wrong or inadequate skills, and jobs are juggled just to provide coverage of the most visible needs. The intended experiment is often so gerrymandered that it is a mass of unwanted changes (patches would be a better term). Any drive to do research under these conditions is soon lost, and in fact, common sense indicates it would be futile.

Even more commonly, planned change may be handicapped by inadequate financing. Clerical support, data gathering or analytical procedures become additional tasks for regular staff, or can only be undertaken so long after the change was initiated that new and obscuring changes are imminent or underway.

A relatively new factor, that of a major change as a result of new national or state policy, commonly hangs over operating agencies. Further modifications are often obviously impending and research opportunities are lost under the pressure of hastily assuming many new functions. The impact of the Economic Opportunity Act of 1964 alone is such that continuous organizational as well as program changes are inevitable in most local health and welfare agencies for years to come. This counterforce to organizational research is occurring at this very moment, in great part due to the fact that funds and horizons for organizational research are opening up in proportion to those for social purposes generally.

Certain general environmental forces may account for the dearth of research into agency organization. In view of the array of difficulties, those with research bent are likely to be steered toward a more suitable clime—the university research centers, or those state or national health agencies now unearthing new knowledge. Unfortunately, in research environments the issues which would typically be raised in a local agency as to how to deliver services would not have to be faced, perhaps would not even come to mind. The academic researchers also do not always have available the delivery structures willing to participate in research manipulations. For these or other reasons schools of public health and state health departments have, with few exceptions, been slightly less unproductive than field agencies in organizational research.

Impact of Science and Technology

Research has been utilized in the technologic areas and there its productivity has generally outstripped the means of disseminating information about the significance of its output. When research techniques are utilized to overcome deficiencies in application (which depends heavily on the consumer's being attracted to the product), will channels be created for extending consumer opportunities for health? Unfortunately, the very act of testing and of feeding back what was observed into the continued service output of the agency may well increase day to day uncertainties felt by both consumers and purveyors. Granted that research into the distribution of services is desperately needed. Still, quite possibly a third or more of the population has been so sensitized by threatening physical changes introduced by technologically slanted research such as automation, pesticides or atomic destruction, that they can only with difficulty be restrained from disowning any aspect of research.

The colloquium presented in the winter, 1965, issue of *Daedalus* suggested that the current existentialist role of science and research must be counterbalanced by a new resurgence among scientists of values not created by, but cognizant of science, research and technology.

Evidences of Research Activity

A brief screening of the contents of *Public Health Reports* and the *American Journal of Public Health* since 1950, reveals a handful of significant, specifically organizational research projects. These include a large number of discussions of new operating or staff divisions and agencies, new programs and new administrative or service techniques. Few, however, contain more than a general account and rarely is a meaningful evaluation included. Who did this research? The more significant projects with adequate evaluation were usually the product of university or federal or state agency action.

What was to be learned about the prevalence and auspices of organizational research reported in journals that covered administration generally? A brief scrutiny of the contents of four such journals since 1960, revealed that only one contained more than a few significant reports.[19-22] More frequently, articles were about the role of research, its relative importance in agency policy making and the priorities it should receive. Contributions were also heavily oriented to hypotheses with proposals for action. As in community health research, most contributions to organizational knowledge arose as by-products of investigations into new programs, methods or skill and work distribution. The reports bearing on organization, whether of a research, review, exhortative or hypothesizing nature were usually contributed by academicians and not by practitioners.

Research into hospital organization seems very active when compared to that in other community health serving agencies, probably for several reasons. The hospitals' traditional unconcern for the patient before he enters and after he leaves leads to a self-contained perception of the nature of their services. This, coupled with the public's comparable perception as well as with the rapid rise of hospital costs, has precipitated a great demand for research, primarily concentrating on effectiveness of various concise elements of service for the inpatient. Some happy exceptions are reported which point out how the occurrences outside the hospital are relevant to the distribution, kind and extent of services within the hospital.[23]

Prospects for the Growth of Organizational Research

Health agencies will find themselves increasingly pressured to improve their efficiency and effectiveness as a result of the growing sophistication of the public and its rapidly burgeoning expectations. In the face of the shortage of professional personnel, severe competition for tax funds for community service purposes and the pressure for more precise programming and more efficient use of personnel, agencies will be forced to focus more sharply on specific objectives and optimum use of different types of personnel. This means that familiar fields of work will need to be approached in new ways and new fields of performance will have to be developed.

The field of health services, as does the area of "helping others" generally, suffers from the widely prevalent attitude that anything is better than nothing. Since other alternatives are within reach, a more pertinent attitude is how to do better with what is available.

Even as agency workers feel the growing social consensus to seek out better ways of accomplishing the community charge to the agency, society itself may be intuitively afraid of many of the answers that research might reveal. Research into delivery of service implies needed changes in such things as segregation, the prospect of treating all people as individuals and of extending the opportunity for all to approach, if not vigorously participate in health. The latter must surely mean participation in society, jobs, housing and public policy making as well.

Failure or unwillingness to look at how basic social needs affect the ability to deliver or utilize services is a major reason why health departments and medicine in general have achieved so little improvement in health status for large segments of the population.[26]

Above all, then, those engaged in providing community health services will most likely be forced to concern themselves with the social factors that make people too preoccupied, unoccupied or uneducated to heed health messages. They will also become involved with the tools of change and organizational means to move the deprived whose way of life presumably allows little place for planning for tomorrow, and least of all for preventive services. These prospects no longer make agency people uncomfortable or turn their attention to pamphlets, patching plasters and clinics.[9, 10, 24, 25]

RESEARCH OPPORTUNITIES

Extensive listings of research opportunities and reported research are available.[6, 27–29]

To truly indicate the scope of research possibilities, one need only remind each administrator to record the spoken or unspoken "givens" that he applies in decision making. Each of them is probably valid only as old wives' tales are, that is, empirically and in the context in which they were originally divined. The decision that evokes their memory may involve a situation in which to test these generalizations. Everybody knows "that the client can't come because there is no public transportation," and therefore clinics must be decentralized. Has the agency tried giving clients an option of going where most people go, e.g., to a central medical location, instead of a segregated neighborhood house? In some situations other factors than transport or distance may affect the situation. Almost every easy administrative truth is an invitation to investigation. In addition, many of them would soon be revealed to be so heavily qualified that they constitute a reversal of their customary usage.[30]

Many agencies or individuals with unique relationships, assignments or research favoring climates should be reminded not to take these study opportunities for granted.

IN PROVISION OF SERVICES

Community health agencies do not of themselves take care of more than a fraction of all the health services, or provide more than a portion of the services in which they participate. Considering the frictions, discontinuities and lack of substantial relationships between many health agencies or between them and the world of private medical care, the bulk of agency research, if restricted to areas fully controlled by

61

themselves, would possibly make a rather slight impact. Moreover, meaningful success for a service agency rests on coordinated collaboration with the other service providers and an attainment of participation of clients. Morris[31] calls this "internalizing other agencies' and clients' goals." Of course, this has often been done by osmosis, by submission or by extra-sensory perception. Is a plea for a conscious facing of this area out of place?

Dealing with Peer Groups

At the interface with private practice. Agencies must be reminded that private practitioners, and their professional associations, are ill-equipped to indulge in controlled experimentation of health practices without major financial, program and statistical assistance. One of the greatest contributions that can be made by researchers in the organization of health agencies will be work directed at their interface with medical practice. This may be the means of capturing inspirations heretofore glimpsed but forgotten by busy practitioners for lack of a suitable co-partner with the time and intellectual, social, organizational and resource know-how necessary to nurture an idea into a research undertaking. Such relationships should also create many bridges between badly isolated aspects of services to the same patients.[32] From exercise of such concerns may come a deluge of elegant research ideas and opportunities to cooperate in studies about services which may be offered inside or outside of the agency.

The amazingly successful oral polio vaccine campaigns offer typical examples of failure to study significant new approaches. Not only did public agencies see "their" work well done in a few months that might otherwise have taken a decade, but private practitioners essentially reversed a customary stance about the public provision of service. No studies have been made either of what practitioners thought of their new leadership role or about its impact on their general social outlook. Similarly, none seems to have been made on what constituted the ingredients for unprecedented immunization success.

The National Vaccination Assistance Act of 1963, will no doubt provide some beginnings to study this shared frontier. This act offers opportunities for either continuous or periodic population sampling to uncover opinions about community introduced changes in health knowledge, attitudes and practices. Careful design could also help clarify whether the relationships between these latter three supposedly interdependent variables are the customarily accepted ones.[33]

Experimentation involving the disbanding of public well-baby clinics, and government purchase of this service for needy persons not reasonably able to obtain it otherwise, offers opportunities to study the effects on client participation, continuity and quality of care and private practitioner participation. The contemporary recommendations of one widely representative state health department study group call for research into just this issue.[34]

Current public health proposals for buying prenatal, delivery and postpartal care from the doctor of the patient's choice, rather than offering separate clinic and delivery services at sites exclusively created for the poor, offer further study opportunities.

Private practitioners undertaking low cost immunizing "clinics" for their own clients in their own offices need public agency support in determining the significance of such efforts on motivating as well as channeling people to more comprehensive care. Success suggests abandonment of public clinics, of new motivation and roles for private physicians in providing patient education, of the possibility of the public health nurse assisting the private physician located in her district with his clinics, referring her charges to the clinic, of government, via the health department, paying a reasonable private "clinic" cost for those whom it must otherwise serve in segregated clinics. These areas suggest the need to study the accomplishments and redistribution of functions of private practitioner-public health nurse teams reported on from Europe.[85]

The use of counsellors provided by the health department and of nurses or interviewers provided by the doctor in his office for patients with certain complicated disabilities has been tried but is rarely reported on in the United States. The reverse situation, that of providing comprehensive care in health department clinics, has occasionally been reported on.[86]

The extension of hospitals into communities, their closer relationships with patients and their educational efforts with professionals, is successfully being researched.[87]

At the interface with other public and private health, welfare and education agencies. Critical examination is needed of the customary client approach that may bring one or many categorical social workers from welfare, probation, school, case work or mental health agencies to be joined by health visitors from one or more other agencies.[11] Extensive experimentation in the related areas of utilizing psychiatric assistants, family managers, or homemaker-mother figures refers to recasting the mold of social assistance in accordance with new ways of looking at needs.[38-44] Intensive study is needed to see whether they are simply introducing additional categories of service-appliers or if they signify substitute avenues of approach that make possible heretofore unachievable levels of client motivation. The validity of a comprehensive people-oriented agency which uses a basic generalized worker as anchor person to deliver all the community provided services to families (utilizing specialists only as needed) needs exploration.[1, 10, 11]

Other interorganizational experiments that have been undertaken but rarely evaluated come to mind. Where the health department and the county, university or community hospital are separate health services in the same political jurisdiction, sharing key personnel between the agencies may serve to tie client services together.[45] Sharing the hospital chief of obstetrics or pediatrics, by giving him a major maternal and child health responsibility in the health department or vice versa, may be feasible. Using health department program directors as a regular source of medical supervision on hospital wards or outpatient clinics might facilitate an exchange of outlook on care versus prevention, and on home versus institutional care.

Utilizing field public health nurses as liaison persons attending rounds on hospital wards which receive or discharge patients who are likely to become field clients of the health department has also shown merit. The director, or a key assistant of one agency, may be invited to become a regularly attending member of the other agency's administrative staff and be given informational responsibilities. Planned interchanges of workers such as supervisors of service personnel between public and/or private agencies might enhance continuity of care for those patients who use services from one and then the other agency. The impact on residents and interns, as well as on patients, of joint efforts between teaching hospitals and health departments needs further evaluation.[46]

Examination of methods of sharing statistical skills is also needed. The use in common of biostatisticians, systems analysts and programers would not only enlarge the supply of data, but should provide the impetus to draw the sets of data into more meaningful relationships and provide for all involved a better view of health needs and services.

Public agency relationships with the voluntary promotional health agencies suggest other research possibilities. The role of planned parenthood, for so long a combination of clinic services, public information and value arousal, is now being subjected to change. Public agencies will assume operation of the clinic and to some extent of the public contraceptive education service. The variants of the planned parenthood relationships to the official agency, such as financing or conducting the latter's clinics, all substitutes for government action, offer many study situations. Does planned parenthood in the clinic operating role still serve a useful evolutionary role in popularizing this service? Does it currently offer an unsatisfactory (underfinanced and underavailable) way out for policy making officials and does it thereby retard development of overall adequate services?

Of continuing concern is the health department's relationship with voluntary agencies in their promotional and educational functions. Who shall do which piece of the reactivated thrust for control of tuberculosis? Are some lessons to be learned about the assignment of the more visible lobbying tasks in the quest for more health dollars? What allocation of responsibilities offers particular advantages in working jointly with schools and school curricula?

Research into the activities of the public agency staff is also important as they assume policy making roles on the boards of voluntary agencies. Commitments, opportunities for abuse of power, inadvertent limitation of democratic shaping of decisions by their very presence or title, limitations of voluntary agency movement for fear of compromising public officials or as a result of the voluntary agency appearing to be the mouthpiece of vested public servants, have all been postulated. Such voluntary activities take as much as 50 per cent of the time of many public agency officials, whose own organizations must somehow reflect either a loss of large amounts of executive time or an augumentation of what the agency desires to get done.

Dealing with Clients

Matching program to client attributes. The changing demands made by the shrinking and more isolated plains population who are losing their usual sources of medical care, the needs for regionalization and the use of traveling multipurpose workers representing multiple agencies are crying for investigation.[47] Studies by Weiner[48] and Barsky[49] carry more than a word of interest for health agencies. A study by Newmann analyzes beliefs about the role of the community homemaker and points out the partnership of government and voluntary agencies called for in this function, which also has an interface between the public health nursing and social casework functions as well as their disciplinary jurisdictions.[50]

Since so much of future health programming must be directed to personal preventive activities, the client must of his own volition present himself at certain intervals for various procedures, many of which are either misunderstood or may reveal dread disease. From a theoretical standpoint, not only is client autonomy desired in society, but his autonomy is essential if he is to participate in the frequent changes in his behavior which new health knowledge calls for.[33] Research into client characteristics that have a bearing on how he can be encouraged to respond to new information may not be the assignment of this paper, but it is very germane. Two excellent reports on factors influencing human behavior present an array of researched and researchable health related subjects.[27, 51]

Planning to render services at the moment when they are forcibly called to the client's attention is also an administrative matter to be studied. It may involve establishing mobile, door-to-door services for everyone, or for segments of the population currently immersed in the problems of survival from crisis to crisis, and from day to day.[10, 52]

The means of disseminating information to promote action involves in part the problem of selecting agency personnel. Persons having different skills tend to approach clients in different ways. The definition of the "significant others," although not specifically pertaining to health workers and their clients, is an example of the rewards of research done in this field.[53]

The impact of specialized programs to provide services to selected groups, particularly to the poor or other isolated groups, needs scrutiny for the risks and consequences of de facto segregation. One can also study the extent whereby specific client oriented programs socialize a patient inappropriately, e.g., teach him to become more dependent on an all-giving center for services, when what he needs is more militancy to help force changes in society to create a new niche for himself. The effect that special services for one group has upon the attitudes and goals of a more affluent group, for example, who are presently coping with minimal assistance, is also open to investigation.

Policy Making

A high proportion of all the inadequacies in the field of community health services are clearly attributable to policy rather than to technological or organizational factors. In the case of public agencies, virtually all new innovations or modifications in program require the support and approval of public officials not personally identified with the health field, as well as of various power groups in the community. In the case of voluntary agencies, lay boards and key community members have a substantial voice in even the minutiae of program development.

Research into the social policy making processes involved here suggests the need to take into account who the decision makers are and what their primary goals are when research questions are being framed and when study findings are written up. So little in the way of documented research has taken place here that the innovation of introducing boards and citizen leaders to welfare clients in their homes was positively startling.[54] A brief listing of commonly discussed practices finds only a few researched:

1. Reporting devices from agencies to governing boards and the public.

2. Client participation in planning programs or at the very least, mechanisms for client communication of complaints and imminent needs (Ombudsman).[55]

3. Other means of involving policy makers and the public.[56]

4. Sources of authority. The long range effects of autonomous local boards of health and their health departments deserve serious scrutiny because of their isolation from other sources of service. Boards of health also should be contrasted with short-lived, single-purpose advisory committees.[57, 58] The governing functions in metropolitan government, with and without multi-tier structure, have been studied in other contexts than health where they remain essentially undocumented.

5. Effects of interposing lay administrators between technical departments and policy boards.

5. Budgeting practices, and their utilization in connection with meaningful program evaluation and review.

7. Financing patterns. The state of Washington might have a lot to offer others contemplating multiple, annually negotiated, health department contracts for service to be provided various cities and schools inside the health department's jurisdiction. Collection of funds by metropolitan jurisdictions and redistribution to overcome unequal proportions of persons needing special or intensive ser-

vices (aging, alcoholics, children) appears in few, if any, analyses of metropolitan development. The long- and short-range effects of general subventions, special time limited grants, categorical and general funding which are contingent on commitments to create new services, and competitive project funding have rarely been analyzed in the health field.[59] Comparing the effects of the latter two methods operating over the same period in time in California would reveal remarkable differences of impact on community health programming that should not be ignored in future legislating or financing.

8. Patterns of legal authority. Striking differences between enforcement via warrants for law-breaking and departmental hearings for removal of operating permits deserve scrutiny not only for their effectiveness, but for evidence as to their effect on democratic processes and citizen rights.

9. Although widely heralded, the community-shared medical center[60, 61] remains relatively unstudied.

10. New approaches to recruitment,[62] training[63] and desperately needed salary increases deserve attention.

11. Role of special segments of the public, vested interests and the press require investigation. Although much has been written, little that could be called research is evident from the health fields.[64]

IN ORGANIZATIONAL PROCESSES

Performance

Is goal achievement affected by loyalty, the "one, big, happy family" environment, quality of housing and facilities and status devices such as titles, salaries, rewards or impressive quarters obvious to clients, peers and fellow employees?[45, 65, 66, 67] Of equal interest are the uses of modified competitive and cooperative devices among employees.[66]

Communications and Information Processing

Although fields unto themselves, communication and information processing may well have to be measured in terms of how they affect performance. Staff meetings, written administrative and service guides must be related to the spelled out objectives and to those implicit in observable practices. Is value indoctrination needed to free employees

68

from protocol so that they can perceive objectives and carry them out? How important is the source of indoctrination and what is the role of supervision in effective transmission?[68]

Information processing to enable agency invention and utilization of new policies to meet changing conditions is the culmination of receiving word from the field. Devices are needed to assemble information from the field into new patterns which would be most unlikely to be discovered otherwise.[69]

Patterns of communication have been shown to vary in accordance with context, and the question as to whether attributed restraints, as well as real ones, act as such have been the subject of profitable research.[70]

Supervision, Work Pressures, Tensions

The problems of leaving work priorities in the hands of the public health nurse, who has two or three times more work facing her each day than she can possibly cope with, seems to be a different kind of problem than that posed by the overburdening of clerks. Setting priorities may invoke quite different responses at different levels of the hierarchy and may be related to the degree of professionalization or freedom from supervision of the worker. Tensions originating from work overload, stressfull supervision, competition, inadequate information and tools, client demand, client disinterest and unattained or unattainable goals suggest more questions than answers and call for clarification as to which are productive and which are unproductive tensions.

Standards

Not only must standards be the measure of performance for which the agency lives, they can be the basis or common language by which significant intra- or interagency exchanges can take place. Balance between central policy making (authorized practices) and decentralized execution may be brought about in industry by establishing common standards which are understood throughout the organization (or industry), and against which each division's performance is measured.[71] The California Hospital Association, through development of its statewide uniform accounting system, has attacked one side of hospital production, that of the quantitative-cost aspect of all services offered.[72]

Concern for standards of quality ostensibly accounts for much of the research into structure and administration. Unfortunately, quality of health services is many things. One person interprets it as excellent care for illness. Another emphasizes disease prevention. To others, quality has quantitative aspects; e.g., does it reach the population widely enough to result in a decline of some undesirable condition such as infant mortality?

Undoubtedly, superlative individual care, which has enabled paraplegics to walk, can have resulted in a denial of resources to others and have worsened an overall community situation. Even the walking paraplegic may have been done a disservice, for in his work and social outlook a wheelchair may in fact be the desirable and tolerable end point. In other words, the less elegant result may be the only useful one and thus be the best quality of service. Standards of quality obviously may embody elements of comprehensiveness, continuity, prevention, effectivity and appropriateness. This one area, against which much organizational effectiveness must be measured, is itself in critical need of definitive study.

Standards of effectiveness are also in a serious state of confusion as a result of continuous intermeshing with values. The demonstrated effectiveness of a program or technique to serve one type of disorder or victim does not of itself overcome the other factors. Those conditions thought likely to terminate soon and fatally, and, particularly in our culture, if occurring in elderly persons, command little professional or public attention even though very effective methods of serving the victims are known. Witness the difficulty in promoting the very effective stroke rehabilitation programs.

Today, many communities assign tremendous resources for facilities and personnel to serve young, very visible cerebral palsy victims while they make almost no provisions to prevent recrudescences of rheumatic fever. The latter is demonstrably effective and offers a full and healthy life for the properly followed victim. The former has offered some, but not generally remarkable gains for a lifelong handicap. In this comparison of two conditions usually encompassed by crippled children's services, both the effectiveness and value are high in one, low in the other, yet society places the greater value on the lesser accomplishment.

The innumerable variants of this type of community, if not individual decision, indicate that research in other than attitudes may not always be too helpful to agencies trying to plan organizational change and program direction.

The problem remains of whether the application of some statistically supported concept of effectiveness has practical significance when incorporated into agency action. Although statistically significant, a procedure may eventually have a miniscule practical effect. In fact, it may, through unwise deployment of resources, have a harmful effect in that other and wiser uses of these resources may become impossible.

Idea and Goal Development

The many aspects of this critical area extend from the professional individual's pedagogically shaped ability to utilize new experiences[73] to the sociohistorical context in which he finds himself.[74] Anything more than giving this subject its own heading or anything less than composing a book seem unwarranted. This does not preclude utilizing everyday situations to structure experiments on the stimulation of new ideas.

The use of broad library services, abstracting services, journal clubs or in-service exchanges offer an opportunity to study their effect on the flow of ideas. The opportunity for workers to define or create different approaches to their own delivery of agency services may offer intellectual stimulation for the majority of service-oriented workers.[66]

Occupational Tools; Suitable Assignments

Although the need for studying good tools can stand by itself in the sense of technical utility, it cannot in the area of applicability under varying client needs. "Perfect" tools may never reach the client who fears, resents or cannot understand them. The visibility of research opportunities among the tools is so very high and the opportunities to create controls so good, that the bulk of health research reported on falls in this area and needs only modest encouragement. Although basically program and method research, tools research affects scope, distribution and organization of agency resources. In fact, many technologies dictate structure and/or function. The client orientation of different skills and of different individuals in one skill, and the need to relate the task to the appropriate skill, vehicle and quantity of service are among the most appealing areas for investigation.[40, 75–78]

The state of the professional "arts," as practiced in various organizational settings, is markedly volatile. The possibility of transferring skills among occupational groups in the health and social serving fields should be examined. The anchor worker who came to the job as a public health nurse may have to acquire skills quite different from those needed by her sister worker who came to the same job as a trained social worker.

Attention must also be given to problems of interpersonal arrangements between professionals in the new scheme of things. For example, in organizational settings in which health is not the primary goal orientation of most practitioners but rather a means to attain other goals such as employability or education, new status relationships will undoubtedly develop between professionals. How will they affect the work to be done?

Organizational development is taking many paths at this moment. The anchor worker, the indigenous worker, the homemaker-mother figure, the worker in the multipurpose center, all imply new kinds of worker attributes and new relationships to supervisors as well as to clients.

How are these workers to be chosen? Will the customary approaches to educational qualifications bear on the success or failure of the indigenous community worker or homemaker-mother? Will they be supplemented by estimates of "feeling" qualities for the professional worker converted into the multipurpose or anchor figure for families in crises? In fact, can the whole present system of tenure in a given agency, with promotions to supervisory and administrative rather than to leader-educator roles, do any more than hamper the development of new approaches to service?

Clearly, the researchers needed in operational agencies can rarely be recruited under existing hiring and civil service practices. The narrowness of categories, the salary limitations for personnel who plan to be on the job for only one to five years, the customary nontransferability of benefits from one government agency to another or to or between voluntary agencies, indicates that the whole field of personnel practices, classification, recruitment, benefits, duties, etc., must be the subject of varied experiments. These can point the way to alternative means for setting personnel requirements and outlining organizational structures to avoid current service stifling rigidities.

Training for the traditional disciplines and for the newer subprofessionals raises the issues of whether training can be partially or totally done on the job,[63] whether the traditional academic degree approach can be expected any longer to carry the major load, and whether, under academic auspices or not, effective training primarily in operating environments can be developed.

Structural and Process Influences

Although inevitably subtle, structured relationships undoubtedly hold the workers of an organization in their toils much as language is said to determine the ability of a culture to form ideas. The utility of combining staff and line functions in each medical position, which is so commonly done in health departments, has not been suitably contrasted with an attempt to separate programming functions into the hands of a few and production into the hands of the remainder.

The use of nonmedical health program assistants, or of nonmedical heads for line divisions employing many kinds of professionals is now becoming a popular subject of debate, but with minimal study of results.[79]

The validity of combining sizable health and welfare agencies into still larger agencies versus their maintaining independence but being responsible to one city official needs examination. The placement of ancillary service divisions such as health education, statistics or social service under an overall, lay manager is a comparable intra-agency issue.

The use of districts, their degree of autonomy, the choice of personalities that are relevant to the degree of autonomy and the status differentials implied between line and staff positions all need clarification.[80, 81] Decentralization, as a means of obtaining fast appropriate decisions in the field, may now be disappearing with the electronic data processing era. This may indicate the need to gather the mass of administrative talent in a central location, particularly in the agencies serving large populations and areas.

Organization structure may also be interpreted in terms of pursuing a goal that is customarily outside the agency's own walls, e.g., prevention of hospitalization[82, 83] or of finding the right people to whom the agency's service is to be rendered.[84, 85]

The effects of providing student training with and without utilizing school-assigned instructors have presumably had a measureable impact on agencies and their workers. Similarly, the effects of staff participation in teaching and research opportunities needs to be studied.

The use of registers and of electronic data processing devices to call attention of workers to overdue visits or activities, or to remind program directors of under usage or overextension, may seem so

73

desirable as to preclude research efforts. However, their effects on worker responsibility deserve consideration.

Utilizing mutliple, independent sources of assessing "needs" may be a substitute for departmental program-by-program interpretation of "facts." Assessment by holders of several diverse viewpoints, e.g., legislator, businessman, practitioner, nurse and householder, might offer startling new information. The antipoverty program with its insistence on broad community involvement may afford researchers the opportunity to compare traditional expert observations with assessments from the community being served.

Allocating resources is a procedure that calls for many elements already suggested as ripe for study. Basically, current alternatives must be judged on appropriate statistical estimates of their effect, and health operations policy will often be determined by the results of exploring such alternatives.[86] The work of medical economists in assigning tangible value to health maintenance must be extended so that one can tally the health benefit increases resulting from particular kinds and types of inputs, as from differing levels of skills or of multiple versus single sources of care.

HOW AND WHEN TO DO RESEARCH

Modes of Investigation

Inductive logic or the logic of discovery is the research tool which will always be available to the astute observer. Probabilities will be weighed, irrelevant details discarded and general rules divined according to events which have been observed.

Deductive logic, that of the discovered, is the research tool at hand to predict the special circumstance which should follow from the general laws. When natural or general laws from other societies, other fields or related areas of health services are made known, trials can be devised to test understanding of the law and its implied applicability, i.e., ascertain if it is really as general a natural law as is claimed.

Perhaps the most useful of all tools will be the logic of abduction or that of controlled intuition, the products of which can then be put into the customary knowledge producing framework, the seesaw of generalizing and specifying.

On first consideration organizational research poses the question, "does a given relationship of resources provide a more effective or efficient method of achieving the goal than some other?" If so, three

74

initial tasks are required. First, clearly define goals and establish specific objectives. Second, construct a control situation to contrast with the experimental one which has introduced into it one or more well circumscribed variables. Third, develop the means of comparing the two in terms of the goals and the variables.

The administrative structure of an organization (bureaucracy) has many dimensions. Its variations along these many axes can be used to describe it for a given situation. In a brilliant review and reconstruction of how to conduct organizational analysis, of which a brief outline follows, Pugh, *et al.*, clearly establish that a multidimensional analysis is necessary to be meaningful.[16]

At the most basic level the context in which the organization finds itself is critical to its being, survival and productivity. Eight major "environmental" variables that must be measured are described. Against this background which produced, and now contains and maintains constant pressure on the organization, its internal structure and function must be reviewed. Seven structural and five functional variables are studied for the degree or extent to which each occurs in the organization under scrutiny. On top of this layer of quantified description a meaningful analysis of group composition and interaction and of individual personality and behavior is undertaken. Finally, five performance variables are offered which can be used to test the success of various organizational patterns.

Even when research into organization of health service agencies can be done in this rational a manner, goals of an organization are not so easily found nor do they provide an ideal point against which to measure organizational effectivity. Etzioni[17] makes abundantly clear that goals are often mostly in the observer's head, or if in the organization's charter, may be only a few among many or be unrelated to the current goals.

Any organization must have many goals. It must be a multifunctional unit if it is to replace itself, survive various social currents and live to prosecute its ostensible or major goals. As a result, Etzioni is quite convincing that organizational performance cannot realistically be measured solely against the stated main goals. Measured in this way, performance will always fall pathetically short. The best performance measures in an organization are those which compare effectiveness at various times; not those which make a single comparison of achieved goals against stated aims at one finite point in time.[18] This makes a rational allowance for the nongoal "friction losses" and "survival" energy. It gives a picture of how well the allocation of resources permits the optimum distribution of output under more than one momentary set of conditions.

Since no organization can have all goal output without jeopardizing its survival, and must put great energy into the day-to-day nurturing of staff, maintenance of plant, compulsory bookkeeping, public acceptance, etc., subunits automatically develop around goals other than the stated agency-wide ones.[65, 96] These subunits require great quantities of energy, and none can be starved without hurting the whole. This opens the door to conflicts which sap energy and output, particularly between the professionals, or great public goal keepers, and the administrators, the keepers of the often denied or ignored survival goals.

As one recasts his mind over the researchable areas suggested in the preceding pages, he will find that few offer a simple study framework. The three workaday approaches that follow offer a clarification of what might be anticipated in organizational research.

Experimentation utilizing control or contrast situations. Superficially, research could most profitably be undertaken in those programs or services which have clearly defined goals and where alternative methods for reaching these goals can be put into practice. Among the examples given of researchable areas, desegregation of care for the poor and utilization of private practitioners through government-sponsored third party pay schemes appear to offer a reasonable fulfillment of the requirements. One's health value scheme may determine which goal elements are paramount. But, whether generally agreed to or not, they can be rather firmly described for the purposes of the experiment as being, e.g., continuous care, better doctor-patient rapport, better family-patient performance and knowledge, better infant health as measured by immunization status, more prompt medical care, defects remedied, etc. The traditional alternatives of clinics for well child supervision and private practitioner for sick care can then be tested against the new approach. Control and experimental populations can be defined and the two schemes can be run side by side. Follow-up, with measurements and comparisons can be devised to test child progress, family attitudes and information, practitioner attitudes and administrative and dollar costs of operating the two schemes. A third group which receives no well child care may offer an even firmer base from which to start, for many of the suppositions on benefits of well child care are based on poorly evaluated

76

work done in another era when the needs for such services may have been significantly different.

Evaluation may show that well child care does indeed offer significant health gains but that little can be said about differences in obtaining it from poverty-segregated clinics or private practitioners. Perhaps clinics offer government a cheaper route to the same health ends for its wards. At this point another kind of value judgment (environment at the time of the study) enters the picture. If health alone is the issue, the less expensive way becomes the obvious choice, particularly if resources are slim. On the other hand, if such things as removal of stigma for attendance at segregated clinics, or expressed patient desires for a doctor of their own choice is of great concern, even though occasioning no particular improvement of client participation or health gains, the policy bodies may for these reasons alone agree to a greater expenditure. Presumably this decision would be made because the policy board feels that this approach offers gains toward long range democratic goals which are worth the cost.

Clearly, the experiment described included no definition of what such democratic gains might be. Of course, with reasonable agreement on democractic attributes, they, as well as health, could have been tested for and measured in the experiment. Comparisons of achievement over time would then offer policy makers something more than cultural beliefs on which to base their decisions about the social as well as the health gains involved.

Controlled experimentation also raises the issue of prospective versus retrospective studies. Prospective experiments currently do not need defending, but they typically suffer from defects that retrospective studies alone are reputed to have. Many of the defects that retrospective studies are said to have simply reflect the way samples are taken. An example from a less complicated area than administration may point up the needlessness of arbitrarily defining, favoring or using retrospective or prospective studies. Something as relatively straightforward as the relationship of smoking to lung cancer and other easily defined health disabilities has not shown that retrospective studies need be any more or less adequate than prospective ones.[88] Prospective ones starting with smoking, nonsmoking or cessation, were more easily used to define the relationship of smoking to conditions other than lung cancer. However, retrospective studies need not have limited their concern to lung cancer and could have offered the same information as the prospective, and often at a significantly lower cost and in a shorter time. The surgeon general's report shows that the qualitative and quantitative effects measured were also comparable.

A lucid analysis in 1956, pointed out that many studies fit neither and many include both approaches.[89] The issue is the intelligent taking and dimensioning of samples. Obviously some situations lend themselves more easily to a forward, others to a backward glance. Elements of both should be planned for whenever possible since many of the social, value and environmental variables will not be foreseen but may be quite evident on retrospection. To illustrate these complexities, return to the private practitioner versus well-child care clinic experiment. It is occurring at a time when doctors feel tremendous pressures to defend publicly the quality of their work and to provide a broader and more significant kind of service to individuals and families rather than to diseased organ systems. One can easily imagine a selection of more socially conscious practitioners setting out both to assure the best quality care to the health department's wards and to prove that the "patient selected" doctor can and does do a better job than the well child clinic. With such determination a marked difference in quality of care could possibly be seen between the control and experimental group, but not necessarily due to the prospectively designed study variables that might be given credit.

Scrutiny of Performance in Ongoing and Newly Changed Situations
Many times legislative decision to shift responsibility from one agency to another offers opportunity to contrast the effect of such factors as auspices or organization upon the public's utilization of or compliance with the relocated program. Unfortunately, here too, switching as simple a function as rabies control services from the sheriff to the agricultural commissioner, health officer or humane society is often accompanied by more than a change in auspices. Differing attitudes and organization of agencies doing basically different kinds of jobs from different points of view, e.g., law enforcement, livestock protection, health protection or pet care, when combined with new procedures usually create something more than a switch of organization or auspices.[90] In any case, no original version usually remains and no means remains for the experimental comparison except by doing a review over time. That is, comparing the present operation with

what is remembered of its now terminated predecessor. Even when done in depth, such a study may have difficulty in tracing cause and effect. The transfer may have represented a public appeasement or relief of an agency that despised the program.

More complex examples of experimentation without a control are available, as when a health department decides to create semi-autonomous districts. Most of the goals desired can be defined, even those as idealistic as "returning policy making closer to the people." Measuring instruments can be devised to relate extent of public awareness, public response and public suggestions for change in services. The ability to reach more of the target groups or their attainment of higher levels of various health attributes can also be measured. In fact, instead of waiting for the new agency structure, all the measuring devices can be used for a year or two preceding the change and can then be continued after the change has been made.

However, determination of cause and effect or of success and failure are not that simple. Even if a control were to be created by withholding districting in a major segment of the overall jurisdiction, the very occurrence of the political climate which sponsored the districting, and the public discussion centering on the event and its purpose might have much the same effects on the control as on the districted areas.

If certain internal agency relationships are taken as the goals to be achieved by districting, and these are indeed often the major ones, similar problems of evaluation arise. Who is to say that the difficulties that plagued yesteryear would not have been ameliorated or replaced by others if the extensive departmental discussions preceding and following the actual districting were undertaken, even though the institution of districting were never implemented?

Change of operation under scrutiny offers the greatest number of research opportunities but only a modest outlook for tagging discernible variants or validating consequences. Even more than in the controlled experiment the non-participant observer-recorder should be included. His chronicle of events may shed more light than the measured effects which may otherwise be fearlessly attributed to the wrong causes.

Although not truly organizational research, program evaluation is available and presumably is a daily part of any conscientious service agency's work. Actions taken in consequence of observations can have a heavy bearing on organization at one or another level and many gratifyingly analyzable changes are on the record.[77, 91-93]

Closely related are studies on the tools of evaluation themselves. In many situations criteria of performance, definition of parts of the task or definition of degrees of accomplishment are still far from adequate to indicate the state of affairs even when applied conscientiously. Contributions made here are not in the center of the field of organizational research but help define or create measuring tools for various elements of function, interaction or performance, the measuring devices of organizational analysis.[94-96]

Historical analysis. Of all the modes of investigation, historical analysis, or the fully retrospective approach, probably offers the best tool for disentangling cause and consequence on the larger scene. The records of incidents attendant on districting large health departments, which have been done with every determination to avoid historian bias or premature interpretation, provide a series of chance samples. One, that of New York City,[97] offers a continuing history of switches toward, but never to, a decentralized authority structure. Another,[98] Philadelphia, offers a single major attempt to form semi-autonomous districts.

These historical perspectives can catch certain apparent cause and consequence pairs that lend themselves to rational and likely explanations. The presence of the same combination in another agency history, even at another but not too remote period, leads to generalizations or hypotheses.[81]

One should harbor no delusions about the ease of a backward glance over an agency's career. A perusal of Bock's collection[97] of such research or of Lincoln Steffens' autobiography[99] indicates their use of and the need for collateral consultation with other parties. Bock attempts to check the data with all apparently significant concerned parties before making any "statements of fact" or generalizations. Just the matter of timing as to which in a series of exchanges came first, may lead to quite different conclusions about cause and consequence.

The role of the diarist in all recorded history is very evident. How little it has been urged as a research tool is very surprising. Even the novel, because of the contemporary window from which the author as consumer looks upon the scene of organization provided services, may carry the germ of a generalization which can then be systematically researched.[100]

80

Decisions and Resources Necessary

Allocation of resources between administration and service. A quick comparison of general attitudes among the welfare nations (with citizens' welfare a predominant concern) of western Europe and the United States in the field of public health may produce a startling set of extremes. For example, the heavy administrative laying on of hands in a well staffed health department in the United States is commonly justified on the basis that very great efforts must be devoted to picking out the most at-risk groups on whom to concentrate services, to carefully supervise the work, and to evaluate the results of such efforts. This is quite in keeping with the "scientific" outlook and with the desire to avoid conflicts with the private practice of medicine. The funds spent on these administrative chores would, in western Europe, immediately be diverted to increasing services because essentially all of the population is to be served, a relatively much simpler administrative task. The proof of the value of their approach to service, they claim, will be in the outcome. Since their basic indices of health commonly and increasingly surpass those of the United States,[8] the realization should dawn that the allocation of available funds to administration versus service does need thorough research.

A secondary and analyzable factor at work in the allocation of resources will be the proportion of the agency's energies devoted to recruiting, training, salaries, benefits, travel, controls or public relations. An agency that is being bombarded with plaudits is more likely to make effective service contacts than one receiving stiff criticism. One that has an apathetic or newly migrated population is likely to put out much greater support efforts per service accomplished than one in a receptive community.

The decision-making task on allocation of resources to administration leads directly to the issue of what portion should go into research itself and how such decisions can best be reached. Wylie[2] discusses the arguments for administration deciding on what is to be researched and to what extent, versus the position that researchers must take the lead in opening the new frontiers and thus be the decision-making influence in allocation of resources. He also refers to industry's concern on this matter.

Setting up a research project. Research should be thought of as the result of one person's outstanding interest. This person should have at least some of the skills called for by the project, even though early participation of other specialists is required. An important requirement is a clear determination as to who will make final project decisions and whether this project director will also be the responsible principle investigator. The final decision maker should usually be the person who has the dominant and initiating interest in the project.

The idea of research guided by a committee is abhorred by many, yet it is becoming a common practice as knowledge grows more comprehensive, detailed and splintered.

The coming together of persons from many related community agencies or disciplines often produces strong interest in a research project and agreement on overall objectives. However, assignment of primary responsibility to one person with far reaching and pertinent skills who has the respect of all the participants is necessary to coordinate a community research project.

Group projects often are taken only to the broad organizational level, whereas methods, detailed objectives and definitive criteria are purposely left undeveloped by the organizing body. In these cases, the next objective must be to procure a research investigator who has adequate ability to provide or direct the skills needed. This same investigator is usually the person chosen to lead the research team. In this capacity he is given full responsibility by the overall policy setting committee of which he essentially becomes the executive.

Without the executive or research coordinator, such a committee behaves much as a group of consultants and rarely does a workmanlike job. Demands of successful research are many.[1,101] Careful statistical scrutiny is often not built in or is not applied. Much good research data are frittered away when no driving personality is in control to insist on exploring meanings and probabilities. Under dilute or absent direction, community committees rarely finish an analysis or the write-up. The results of their research become a matter of unclear legend, forgotten or misinterpreted by everyone.

Commitments also need early clarification. Relationships, pay, extent, duration, tentative dates, authorship, even place and method of publication should be in writing. Clarification of their roles is particularly needed when students or short-term trainees participate to further their education.

Since not all persons with needed skills should or can be on the committee, they are often enlisted as consultants. When to call in the expert consultant varies for different agencies, different research ideas and different consultants. The researcher's expectations of the consultant need to be outlined for him and included with his invitation, so that he can decline if he lacks interest.

Consultation may be needed to consider the value or definition of the research idea itself or of its specific technical aspects. It may be required for analysis, consideration or exploration of implications of the research. If the consultant is asked to show how to undertake the total job, rather than to clarify technical procedures or elements of the project, then the embryo researchers are probably not yet strong enough for the effort. Use of consultants, whether from the specialist staff of the agency or from outside it, does not absolve the principle investigator from the responsibility for decision making.

On occasion a consultant may represent or influence the prospective source of funds, and appropriate changes may be necessary. If a project is too badly distorted by consultant influences, one is well advised to start anew or give up for a time.

Specially designated research personnel or divisions. Judicious use of designated and qualified researchers usually requires that they act as consultants to program directors without assuming control of all departmental research activities. However, most research-oriented persons will want to direct and actively participate in studies of their own as well as to consult with operating divisions who are undertaking research. Restriction of research staff to full-time consultant roles may freeze them to their current levels of proficiency. Their enthusiasm is also likely to dull if researchers are always kept outside looking in.

This issue would probably occur whether researchers are in autonomous divisions or not. With designated research personnel the only option available is to encourage independent or self-originating research staff projects. But these have resulted in conflicts between research and operating divisions to the detriment of both, unless strong administrative leadership anticipates and prevents it.

Problems of collaboration between operational personnel and those with research assignments are extensive, whether belonging to the same organization or not. Relationships have been analyzed and several generalizations attempted.[102] The relationships of the researcher to his administrative chiefs seem to hold justifiable mutual and self-serving attractions.[103]

For the future, one may hope for a somewhat different availability pattern of research talent. Researchers will have received their training from and be based at research centers. (A few will have developed from career administrators.) They will become a mobile resource for joint work with service agencies. Some may even become service administrators for periods of their career. A freer interchange between research and service institutions should be made feasible, in fiscal and tenure terms, so that a researcher can become an active member of the organization he is investigating when that is called for (or an administrator can become part of a research institution). This approach, not unrealistically, calls for a substantial proportion of researchers to be sophisticated in the service and research arenas, willing to become involved in both and essentially unhampered in moving from one to the other.

To What Extent Should Research be Expected in Operating Agencies?

Should each health agency undertake at least an occasional carefully developed research project? To ask all health agencies to do organizational studies on themselves is probably unrealistic.

Many operating agencies do not have employees who are either interested or competent enough to focus intellectual curiosity or translate daily demands into the form of a hypothesis that could lend itself to experimentation. Such agencies, even if given outside stimulation or when selected as an ideal place in which to explore and test hypotheses, may have so little talent that their very participation may destroy attempts at accurate performance, recording or preservation of a control situation.

The cost in both dollars and travail of doing research cannot be ignored. Often the decision is made to not explore an activity because a brief estimate of the research involved reveals costs greater than that of providing the service for many years. The same decision may be reached because of inability to construct adequately definitive study criteria.

The current pressures for new programs and expansions of old ones are based on changing national values (not on research produced information). Their demands exceed most agencies' capabilities and their value burden and political origin tend to further dampen the research outlook of more traditional, nonacademic, service agency administrators.

One may predict that research on the organization of community health service agencies will consist primarily of evaluation of change. Unfortunately, much of this will apply only to the specific organiza-

84

tion being studied, and even there for only a short time, as rapidly changing values and national policies call for new services and skills whose very technology will dictate further organizational change.

Although the national pressures for change in agency services discourage local research by their weight and frequency, they do allow a chance to measure simultaneously, in many different environments and structures, the impact of the same phenomena. A series of carefully coordinated multiagency studies should ferret out basic generalizations or organizational truths and reapply such principles in specific situations so that their validity or generality can be tested.

If not seen, or if visualized but not obtainable by operating agencies, multiagency study opportunities are nonetheless beckoning the universities, federal, state and larger voluntary agencies and foundations. Most of these find fewer barriers to participation, in part because of their safe removal from pressures of directly delivering client services, than do the local front line agencies. Research elements of the former, which are also growing dramatically, will hopefully be harnessed with the service-providing agencies. In this way the thousands of new tasks and the millions of new jobs society can well afford and wants created can be undertaken by the operating agencies. The resultant activities will in turn provide the most extensive opportunities ever hoped for whereby processes of social organization can be studied and improved.

REFERENCES

[1] Blum, H. L. and Leonard, A. R., PUBLIC ADMINISTRATION, A PUBLIC HEALTH VIEWPOINT, New York, The Macmillan Company, 1963.

[2] Wylie, C. M., The Future Development of Research in Public Health Departments. A Critical Review, *Public Health Reports,* 79, 261–265, March, 1964.

[3] Miser, H. J., Operations Research in Perspective, *Operations Research,* 11, 669–677, September–October, 1963.

[4] Ackoff, R. L. and Rivette, P., A MANAGER'S GUIDE TO OPERATIONS RESEARCH, New York, John Wiley & Sons, Inc., 1963.

[5] Anderson, S., Operations Research in Public Health, *Public Health Reports,* 79, 297–305, April, 1964.

[6] School of Hygiene and Public Health, RESEARCH IN PUBLIC HEALTH ADMINISTRATION, Baltimore, The Johns Hopkins Press, Selected Abstracts I (1962), II (1963) and III (1964).

[7] Where Medicine Fits in Johnson's Great Society Plan, *Medical World News,* 66–71, December 18, 1964.

[8] Chenoweth, A. V., Perinatal Mortality in the United States, *The Journal of the American Osteopathic Society,* December, 1964, as quoted in *Briefs,* 29, 36–39, March, 1965.

[9] Yankauer, A., Maternal and Child Health Problems, *Annals of the American Academy of Political and Social Science,* 64, 112–120, September, 1964.

[10] James, G., Quoted in a Chronicle of Progress, Urban Problems, *Public Health Reports,* 80, 97, February, 1965.

[11] Blum, H. L., The Multipurpose Worker—A Family Specialist, *American Journal of Public Health,* 55, 367–376, March, 1965.

[12] Harting, D., *et al.,* The Public Health Needs and Practices in a Great Plains County, *American Journal of Public Health,* 49, 1591–1595, December, 1959.

[13] Carter, H. W., Some Observations on the Effects of Program Research in a Local Health Department, *American Journal of Public Health,* 53, 1818–1824, November, 1963.

[14] Children with Epilepsy, a Report to the State Legislature in Response to Senate Bill 739, Chapter 2033, California Statutes of 1959, State of California, Department of Public Health, Berkeley, California, January, 1963.

[15] Rogers, C. R., Graduate Education in Psychology, A Passionate Statement, Western Behavioral Science Institute, La Jolla, California, undated Mimeograph publication.

[16] Pugh, D. S., *et al.,* A Conceptual Scheme for Organizational Analysis, *Administrative Science Quarterly,* 8, 289–315, December, 1963.

[17] Kramer, M., Problems in the Interpretation of Trends in the Population Movement of the Public Mental Hospitals, *American Journal of Public Health,* 48, 1003–1019, August, 1958.

[18] Molina, G. and Noorn, I. F., Indicators of Health, Economy, Culture in Puerto Rico and Latin America, *American Journal of Public Health,* 54, 1191–1206, August, 1964.

[19] *Harvard Business Review.*

[20] *Public Administration Review.*

[21] *The Annals of the American Academy of Political and Social Science.*

[22] *Administrative Science Quarterly.*

[23] Wenkert, W., Coordinated Community Health Care Programs, *Bulletin of the New York Academy of Medicine,* 41, 92–97, January, 1965.

[24] Health and Ethnic Minorities in the Sixties, Editorial, *American Journal of Public Health,* 55, 495–498, April, 1965.

[25] Children of Families Who Follow the Crops—A Responsibility for Public Health, Editorial, *American Journal of Public Health,* 54, 520–521, March, 1964.

[26] How is a Nation's Health Level Measured? Implications of Infant Mortality Rates, Committee Report, *Journal of the American Medical Association,* 189, 321–325, July 27, 1964.

[27] Riessman, F., Cohen, J. and Pearl, A., MENTAL HEALTH OF THE POOR, New York, Free Press of Glencoe, Inc., 1964.

[28] RESEARCH IN COMMUNITY HEALTH, Public Health Service Publication 1225, Washington, Department of Health, Education and Welfare, July, 1964.

[29] Etzioni, A., COMPLEX ORGANIZATIONS, New York, Holt, Rinehart & Winston, Inc., 1961.

[30] Howe, L. P., in Bellak, L., HANDBOOK OF COMMUNITY PSYCHIATRY AND COMMUNITY MENTAL HEALTH, New York, Grune & Stratton, Inc., 1964, p. 40.

[31] Morris, R., Basic Factors in Planning for the Coordination of Health Services, *American Journal of Public Health,* 53, 248–259, February, 1963; and 53, 462–472, March, 1963.

[32] Reed, J. J. A., Future of Public Health, *British Medical Journal,* 2, 1483–1486, December, 1964.

[33] Lippitt, R., Watson, J. and Westley, B., THE DYNAMICS OF PLANNED CHANGE, New York, Harcourt, Brace & World, Inc., 1958.

[34] Department of Public Health, State of California, New Directions in Public Medical Care for Children, *Family Health Bulletin,* 7, 1–3, December, 1964.

[35] Fry, J., Dillane, J. B. and Connolly, M. M., The Evolution of a Health Team, *British Medical Journal,* 1, 181–183, January 16, 1965.

[36] Jacobziner, H., A Pediatric Treatment Clinic in a Health Department, *Bulletin of the New York Academy of Medicine,* 41, 107–116, January, 1965.

[37] Willard, H. N., The Community Hospital as a Center for Medical Care Planning, *Bulletin of the New York Academy of Medicine,* 41, 86–91, January, 1965.

[38] National Institute of Labor Education Mental Health Program, The Indigenous Non-Professional, Report Number 3, November, 1964.

[39] Shames, M., Use of Homemaker Service in Families that Neglect Their Children, *Journal of Social Work,* 9, 12–18, January, 1964.

[40] Foresman, L., Homemaker in Neglect and Abuse, *Children,* 12, 23–26, January–February, 1965.

[41] Deuschle, K. W., Training and Use of Medical Auxiliaries in a Navajo Community, *Public Health Reports,* 78, 461–469, June, 1963.

[42] Riessman, F., The Revolution in Social Work: The New Non-Professional, *Trans-Action,* (Publication of the Community Leadership Project, Washington University, St. Louis), 2, November–December, 1964.

[43] Brager, G., The Indigenous Worker: A New Approach to the Social Work Technician, *Social Work,* 10, 33–40, April, 1965.

[44] Simpson, W. and Cosand, M. E., Homemaking Teachers in Public Health, Health Department, San Bernardino County, California, paper given at San Francisco, March, 1965.

[45] Lichty, J. A., Reciprocal Benefits from Combining Academic Pediatrics with the Child Health Program of a Health Department, *American Journal of Public Health,* 48, 898–902, July, 1958.

[46] Fleming, W. L., Callahan, S. E. and Warren, S. L., Service to Discharged General Hospital Patients Through Local Health Departments, *American Journal of Public Health*, 50, 779–785, June, 1960.

[47] Kraenzel, C. F., Pillars of Service for the Emerging Community of the Plains, With Special Emphasis Upon Health Services, *Journal of Health and Human Behavior*, 5, 67–74, Summer-Fall, 1964.

[48] Weiner, H. J. and Akabas, S., The Impact of Chronic Illness on a Union Population, *Journal of Health and Human Behavior*, 5, 103–107, Summer–Fall, 1964.

[49] Barsky, P. N. and Sagen, O. K., Motivations Toward Health Examinations, *American Journal of Public Health*, 49, 515–527, April, 1959.

[50] Newmann, A. U. and Vahey, V. V., Organized Community Homemaker Services, *Journal of Health and Human Behavior*, 5, 114–118, Summer–Fall, 1964.

[51] Freeman, H. E., Levine, S. and Reeder, L. G., HANDBOOK OF MEDICAL SOCIOLOGY, Englewood Cliffs, New Jersey, Prentice-Hall, Inc., 1963.

[52] McLean, C. C. and Geekie, D. A., Operation Doorstep, *Bulletin of the National Tuberculosis Association*, 3–7, October, 1964.

[53] Katz, E. and Lazarsfield, P. F., PERSONAL INFLUENCE, New York, Free Press of Glencoe, Inc., 1955.

[54] May, E., THE WASTED AMERICANS, New York, Harper & Row, Publishers, 1964, p. 170.

[55] Rosenthal, Albert H., The Ombudsman—Swedish "Grievance Man," *Public Administration Review*, 24, 226–230, December 1, 1964.

[56] Ingraham, N. R., Public Policy on Medical Care, *American Journal of Public Health*, 51, 1144–1151, August, 1961.

[57] Senn, C. L., Use of Advisory Committees in Environmental Health, *Public Health Reports*, 78, 543–546, June, 1963.

[58] Price, J. L., The Impact of Governing Boards in Organizational Effectiveness and Morale, *Administrative Science Quarterly*, 8, 361–378, December, 1963.

[59] Erickson, H. M., Can Public Health Fragmentation be Contained or Coordinated?, *California's Health*, 22, 89–92, December, 1964.

[63] Smillie, W. G. and Curran, J. A., MEDICAL CARE IN THE STATE OF MAINE, 1956–1962, Augusta, Maine, Bingham Associates Fund, Department of Health and Welfare, 1962.

[60] American Public Health Association, The Development of Community Health Service Centers—Present and Future, *American Journal of Public Health*, 54, 140–143, January, 1964.

[61] Trussell, R. E., HUNTERDON MEDICAL CENTER, New York, The Commonwealth Fund, Harvard University Press, 1955.

[62] Bureau of Sociological Research, Evaluation of the WICHE Summer Work Study Program in Mental Health, Institute of Behaviorial Science, Boulder, University of Colorado, November, 1962 (Mimeographed).

64 Carter, R. E., The Press, the Physician and the Public Health Officer, *American Journal of Public Health,* 49, 465–472, April, 1959.

65 Fleck, A. C., Jr., Evaluation on Research Programs in Public Health Practice, *Annals of the New York Academy of Science,* 107, 717–724, May, 1963.

66 Leavitt, H. J., Unhuman Organizations, *Harvard Business Review,* 40, 90–98, July–August, 1962.

67 Etzioni, A., MODERN ORGANIZATIONS, Englewood Cliffs, New Jersey, Prentice-Hall, Inc., 1964.

68 Blum, R. H. and Downing, J. J., Staff Response to Innovation in Mental Health Service, *American Journal of Public Health,* 54, 1230–1240, August, 1964.

69 Deutsch, K., THE NERVES OF GOVERNMENT, New York, Free Press of Glencoe, Inc., 1963, p. 163.

70 Berkowitz, N. H. and Dennis, W. G., Interaction Patterns in Formal Service-Oriented Organizations, *Administrative Science Quarterly,* 6, 25–32, June, 1961.

71 Townsend, U. A., *Business Week,* 122, October 31, 1961.

72 California Hospital Association, Uniform Accounting.

73 Whitehead, A. N., THE AIMS OF EDUCATION AND OTHER ESSAYS, New York, The Macmillan Company, 1959.

74 Rosen, G., The Evolution of Social Medicine, in Freeman, H. E., Levine, S. and Reeder, L. G., HANDBOOK OF MEDICAL SOCIOLOGY, Englewood Cliffs, New Jersey, Prentice-Hall, Inc., 1963, pp. 17–161.

75 Willie, G. V., The Social Class of Patients that Public Health Nurses Prefer to Serve, *American Journal of Public Health,* 50, 1126–1136, August, 1960.

76 Pennell, M. N. and Smith, L. M., Characteristics of Families Served by Homemakers, *American Journal of Public Health,* 49, 1467–1474, November, 1959.

77 Cohart, E. M. and Willard, W. R., Functional Distribution of Working Time in Five County Health Departments—The Yale Study, *Public Health Reports,* 70, 713–719, July, 1955.

78 Andrew, G., Sibilis, J. P. and Stehman, U. A., Utility of Small Group Discussion Method as Practiced in Certain Applied Settings, *American Journal of Public Health,* 50, 785–790, June, 1960.

79 Aronson, J. B., The Non-Medical Health Officer in New Jersey State Experience, *Public Health Reports,* 77, 993–999, November, 1962.

80 Silver, G. A. and Lilienfeld, A. M., Observations on Current Practices in Municipal District Health Administration, *American Journal of Public Health,* 41, 1263–1267, October, 1951.

81 Ferrer, A. R., Regionalization in Puerto Rico. Problems and Progress, *American Journal of Public Health,* 50, 1257–1263, September, 1960.

[82] Greenblatt, M., *et al.*, THE PREVENTION OF HOSPITALIZATION, New York, Grune & Stratton, Inc., 1963.

[83] Furstenberg, F. F., Comprehensive Care for the Aging in the Outpatient Department, *Bulletin of the New York Academy of Medicine*, 41, 98–107, January, 1965.

[84] Heymann, G. M. and Downing, J. J., Some Initial Approaches to Continuous Evaluation of a County Mental Health Program, *American Journal of Public Health*, 51, 980–989, July, 1961.

[85] Yankauer, A., *et al.*, A study of Periodic School Medical Examinations, *American Journal of Public Health*, 51, 1532–1540, October, 1961.

[86] Feldstein, M. S., Operational Research and Efficiency in the Health Service, *The Lancet*, 1, 491–493, March 2, 1963.

[87] Etzioni, A., Two Approaches to Organizational Analysis: A Critique and a Suggestion, *Administrative Science Quarterly*, 5, 257–278, September, 1960.

[88] Report of the Advisory Committee to the Surgeon General of the Public Health Service, SMOKING AND HEALTH, Washington, United States Department of Health, Education and Welfare, Public Health Service, 1964.

[89] White, C. and Bailar, J. C., Retrospective and Prospective Methods of Studying Association in Medicine, *American Journal of Public Health*, 46, 35–44, January 1, 1956.

[90] Brecher, R. and Brecher, E., Nursing Homes, Part 4, *Consumer Reports*, 29, 194–198, April, 1964.

[91] Roemer, M. I., How to Put Theory into Practice in Research, *The Modern Hospital*, 93, 85–89, August, 1959.

[92] Curry, F. J., District Clinics for Outpatient Treatment of Tuberculous Problem Patients, *Diseases of the Chest*, 46, 524–530, November, 1964.

[93] Perrow, C., Research in a Home Care Program, *American Journal of Public Health*, 49, 34–49, January, 1959.

[94] Krause, A. G. and Vaughn, I. R., Development, Application and Evaluation of the Wayne County Public Health Nursing Record System, With an Analysis of the Statistical Method Used, *American Journal of Public Health*, 48, 1364–1375, October, 1958.

[95] Morris, J. G., Validating a Mental Health Scale, *American Sociological Review*, 28, 108–116, February, 1963.

[96] Burnett, F. M. and Greenhill, M. H., Some Problems in the Evaluation of an In-Service Training Program, *American Journal of Public Health*, 44, 1546–1556, December, 1954.

[97] Bock, E. A., STATE AND LOCAL GOVERNMENT, A CASE BOOK, University, Alabama, University of Alabama Press, 1963.

[98] AN INTER-UNIVERSITY CASE PROGRAM (ICP) STUDY, University, Alabama, University of Alabama Press, in preparation.

[99] Steffens, L., THE AUTOBIOGRAPHY OF LINCOLN STEFFENS, New York, Harcourt, Brace & World, Inc., 1931.

[100] Waldo, D., History as Research, Perspectives on Administration, University, Alabama, University of Alabama Press, 1956.

[101] Rosenstock, I. M. and Hochbaum, G. M., Principles of Research Design in Public Health, *American Journal of Public Health*, 50, 266-277, February, 1961.

[102] Cottrell, L. S. and Sheldon, E. B., Problems of Collaboration Between Social Scientists and the Practicing Professions, *Annals of the American Academy of Political and Social Science*, 346, 126-137, March, 1963.

[103] Glaser, B. G., Attraction, Autonomy anod Reciprocity in the Scientist-Supervisor Relationship, *Administrative Science Quarterly*, 8, 379-398, December, 1963.

DISCUSSION

The Views of the Administrator and Researcher

Of all health services research areas, the organization of local health agencies is one that could be greatly strengthened through research. Support should focus on studies with a potential for generalizability across community agencies. Blum's contention that research should concentrate on studies that lead to social policy changes rather than technological changes was seconded. However, his presentation of the specific problems could more clearly identify the priority issues in terms of social policy variables.

A more consistent research framework would offer a better orientation to a person newly entering the field, and would enable him to understand the scope of the problems facing local health agencies. Such a framework would describe the role of public agencies at the local level in terms of the larger social and political issues, would lay out a more theoretical set of definitions and would justify more specifically the particular problems proposed for research. Blum's catalog of problems might overwhelm the potentially interested researcher instead of stimulating him.

However, health services research depends upon two groups of persons and upon two points of view. Blum supplies a special point of view not found in the other papers. Health services research requires not only those who do the research, but also those who are in the practical world and need the research for practical purposes. Both groups deal with the same questions, but they package them differently. The

91

users, such as Blum, will package questions together in terms in which a decision to practice is needed. The researcher will package problems in relation to theory and methodology. What may be only one problem to the researcher might appear to the administrator to contain a large number of questions. While each of the two points of view might cover the field comprehensively, both have relevance and are needed because the health services research field can advance only when the two viewpoints are brought together and integrated.

Evaluation and Planning Studies

Blum may have underestimated the criteria that already exist for evaluating what is going on. In addition, he might profitably have discussed more specifically some other areas which he did not even mention in his paper. As an example of the kind of outcome characteristics that might be used in evaluation, one may measure the quality of the organization against its own stated goals, or in terms of what the community at large seems to identify as desirable and is willing to accept. Besides numerous outcome characteristics, one can also look at the question of feasibility in relation to initial goals and judge whether what is feasible has been achieved, given a set of personnel and facilities.

Blum's statement about statistical versus practical significance is considered a fundamental idea which the health services research field needs to explore and emphasize more fully. Hopefully, Blum will eventually carry the discussion of this subject further.

The grasp of what "planning studies" are or ought to be is still lacking. Most so-called planning studies at present are limited to demonstrations of needs and to specifications of linkages within organizations. By the very nature of the field, however, needs are endless and an infinite number of alternatives for modifying delivery systems exist. Planning studies ought to provide perspectives and propositions with a generalizability potential. They should provide information on variables pertinent to the development or modification of a policy or a program and specify the relationships between pertinent variables. Such evaluation and planning studies of an organization's structure require the close involvement of persons within that structure.

The Role and Responsibility of the Social Researcher

Besides the attitude of administrators and the separation of administration and research, the stance of the social scientists themselves may be responsible for the small number of evaluation and planning studies, as well as for the limited use made of such research in the reorganization of services. Most investigations in this field require the researcher to become an active member of the organization he is investigating.

In this field a researcher cannot assert that he will remain a scientist who stays out of the organization and yet can provide the organization with meaningful findings. Instead of seeking to remain uninvolved, social scientists need to find a more appropriate role for themselves in terms of the development of evaluation and planning studies.

If Blum had considered in more detail when and how the researcher should involve himself in operating organizations to conduct meaningful studies, he would have provided a valuable addition to his paper. He might also have dealt with the question of how to provide feedback to operating personnel during a study. Specific questions that need answers are: under what circumstances should agreements be made specifying that such interim data will be forthcoming; and under what conditions does the researcher have moral responsibility to provide knowledge of results immediately?

ACKNOWLEDGMENT

Brief excerpts are reprinted, with permission of the publisher, from Blum, Henrik L. and Leonard, A. R., PUBLIC ADMINISTRATION, New York, The Macmillan Company, 1963.

WHY PEOPLE USE HEALTH SERVICES

IRWIN M. ROSENSTOCK

INTRODUCTION

Aims of the Paper

The principal aims of this paper are 1. to increase professional health workers' knowledge of selected research findings and theory so that they may better understand why and under what conditions people take action to prevent, detect and diagnose disease; and 2. to increase awareness among qualified behavioral scientists about the kinds of behavioral research opportunities and needs that exist in public health.

A matter of personal philosophy of the author is that the goal of understanding and predicting behavior should appropriately precede the goal of attempting to persuade people to modify their health practices, even though behavior can sometimes be changed in a planned way without clear understanding of its original causes. Efforts to modify behavior will ultimately be more successful if they grow out of an understanding of causal processes. Accordingly, primary attention will here be given to an effort to understand why people behave as they do. Only then will brief consideration be given to problems of how to persuade people to use health services.

Focus and Limitations of the Paper

Kasl and Cobb recently provided a classification of various behaviors in the health area that provides a useful framework for considering the focus and limitations of the present paper.[1] They define health behavior as "any activity undertaken by a person who believes him-

94

self to be healthy, for the purpose of preventing disease or detecting disease in an asymptomatic stage." Illness behavior is defined as "any activity undertaken by a person who feels ill, for the purpose of defining the state of his health and of discovering suitable remedy." Finally, sick-role behavior "is the activity undertaken by those who consider themselves ill for the purpose of getting well." In terms of these distinctions, the present paper emphasizes research on the determinants of health behavior and to a lesser extent, research on illness behavior. No attempt will be made to treat the voluminous literature on sick-role behavior for two reasons. First, the public health worker is more centrally concerned with behavior relative to prevention, early detection and diagnosis of illness than he is with behavior in response to diagnosed illness. Second, the author's research experience is largely confined to studies of health behavior, as defined by Kasl and Cobb.

Another limitation that should be made explicit is that virtually all material to be presented has been drawn from studies of various subgroups of the population of the United States. No attention will be given to the contributions accruing from studies of other cultures.

THE DETERMINANTS OF INDIVIDUAL HEALTH BEHAVIOR

Studies of How People Use Health Services

Consideration may first be given to the relationship between studies of how health services are used and an understanding of why health services are used. Do studies of how people use services explain why people use health services? In approaching an answer to this question, a careful distinction should be drawn between studies of utilization whose findings are intended to have immediate application, and studies of utilization which are intended to serve as means to still other research ends. In the first case, information is sought to serve as a basis for formulating and implementing public policy in the health area. Utilization data obtained for such purposes have proved invaluable in the health field.[2-4]

However, studies of the use of services may also be undertaken as means to achieve the broader aim of increased understanding of why services are used. In this sense, utilization studies are intended to generate hypotheses about why services are used. Such utilization studies have generally failed to accomplish their purpose. Little can be learned from these studies about why people use or fail to use certain services. Evidence in support of this conclusion has been drawn from studies of high and low users of free medical examinations,[5] detection tests for cervical cancer,[6] polio immunization,[7] dental services,[8, 9] physicians' services,[3, 10] hospital services[11] and from studies of the characteristics of those who do and those who do not delay in seeking diagnosis and treatment of cancer.[1, 12]

Analyzing the major findings of studies on the patterns of use of preventive and detection services permits certain summary generalizations about the association of personal characteristics with the use of services. In general, such services are used most by younger or middle aged people, by females, by those who are relatively better educated and have higher income (though perhaps not the very highest levels of education and income). Striking differences may nearly always be found in acceptance rates between whites and non-whites, with whites generally showing higher acceptance rates, although occasional exceptions occur.

A review of the previously cited data on utilization of diagnostic and treatment services provided by the physician, the dentist and the hospital, suggests a pattern quite similar to that obtained in connection with preventive and detection services. In general, more females than males visit the physician and the dentist and incur hospitalization, even when hospitalization for pregnancy is excluded. Higher socioeconomic groupings (defined in terms of educational and income level) are also more likely to obtain medical, dental and hospital services, although the associations between income and utilization are becoming less marked.[2, 3]

With reference to race, whites show much higher utilization rates than non-whites in all three utilization categories (physician visits, dental visits and hospitalization).

The nature of the association between age and utilization of treatment services is generally different from that found between age and seeking preventive and detection services, probably reflecting the effect of objective medical and dental need.

With respect to characteristics of those who delay in seeking diagnosis and treatment of cancer, similar patterns emerge. In general, persons who delay are older, of low educational status and, at least in some studies, males.[12]

Although most studies of utilization do not throw light on why people use health services, one area of research can be identified in which quite sophisticated efforts have been made to understand health and illness behavior as a function of personal characteristics; an area described by Kasl and Cobb as "variables affecting the perception of symptoms." Several other workers attempt to link personal and subcultural variables to the individual's likelihood of perceiving an event as a symptom or to his mode of responding to a symptom. For instance, Koos found a social class gradient in terms of the likelihood of interpreting a particular sign as a symptom.[13] Stoeckle, Zola and Davidson and Zola studied the effects of ethnic values upon the specific decision to seek medical attention and on the differential interpretation of objectively similar symptoms.[14, 15] Freidson illustrated the different processes through which members of different social groups move in obtaining diagnosis (lay and professional) and in seeking care.[16] Suchman attempted an interesting and promising approach which links demographic factors to social structure, both of these to medical orientation and in turn to health and medical care.[17]

Studies of the kinds performed by Koos, Stoeckle, Zola, Freidson and Suchman are far superior in their ability to explain than are the more traditional analyses of relationships between demographic factors and the utilization of services. This superiority lies in the proposed linking mechanisms between personal characteristics and behavior. These studies also demonstrate that health decision making is a process in which the individual moves through a series of stages or phases. Interactions with persons or events at each of these stages influence the individual's decisions and subsequent behavior.

Yet, even these sophisticated studies limit their focus to illness behavior; that is, to behavior undertaken in response to symptoms. The findings are, thus, of unknown relevance to the situation confronting the person who must decide whether to seek preventive or detection services before the appearance of events that he interprets as symptoms. Suchman explicitly notes the failure of his concepts of social structure and health orientation to account for preventive health actions.[17] Stimulating the development of a preventive orientation in the public is the heart of most educational programs in public health.

A Model to Explain Health Behavior

Within the past decade several theoretical papers and empirical research reports have appeared which deal with a particular model for explaining health behavior in individuals who believe themselves to be free of symptoms or illness.[18-26] A comprehensive description and critique of the model[28] will be provided, as well as a presentation of research evidence that tends both to support it and to contradict it.

An analysis will be made of the questions that remain unanswered and of the kinds of research that will be needed to answer these questions. The model does not attempt to provide a comprehensive explanation of all health action. Rather, what is attempted is the specification of several variables that appear to contribute significantly to an understanding of behavior in the health area.

Considerable detail will be provided although the model is far from having been proven valid and useful. This is justified on the grounds that the model seems to provide a most promising framework for explaining large segments of behavior relevant to health and for unifying what, at the moment, are unrelated findings from several investigations. Possibly, though the attempt will not be made in this paper, the model, formulated essentially to explain health behavior (in the sense used by Kasl and Cobb[1]) can ultimately be applied as well to explaining illness behavior and sick-role behavior.

Before turning to a presentation of the model itself, a few words about some of its general characteristics are in order. The major variables in the model are drawn and adapted from general social-psychological theory, notably the work of Lewin.[27] The variables deal with subjective world of the behaving individual and not with the objective world of the physician or the physicist. The two, no doubt, are correlated, but the correlation is far from perfect. The focus in the application of the model is to link current subjective states of the individual with current health behavior.

A truism in social psychology is that motivation is required for perception and action. Thus, people who are unconcerned with a particular aspect of their health are not likely to perceive any material that bears on that aspect of their health. Even if, through accidental circumstances, they do perceive such material, they will fail to learn, accept or use the information.

Not only is such concern or motivation a necessary condition for action; motives also determine the particular ways in which the environment will be perceived. That a motivated person perceives selectively in accordance with his motives has been verified in many laboratory studies[29] as well as in field settings.[30]

The proposed model to explain health behavior grows out of such evidence. Specifically, it includes two classes of variables: 1. the psychological state of readiness to take specific action and, 2. the extent to which a particular course of action is believed, on the whole, to be beneficial in reducing the threat. Two principal dimensions define

98

whether a state of readiness to act exists. They include the degree to which an individual feels vulnerable or susceptible to a particular health condition and the extent to which he feels that contracting that condition would have serious consequences in his case.

Readiness to act is defined in terms of the individual's points of view about susceptibility and seriousness rather than the professional's view of reality. But the model does not require that individuals be continuously or consciously aware of the relevant beliefs.

Evidence from studies to be discussed subsequently suggests that the beliefs that define readiness have both cognitive (i.e., intellectual) elements and emotional elements. The author's opinion is that the underlying emotional aspects have greater value in accounting for behavior than do the cognitive elements.

Perceived susceptibility. Individuals vary widely in the acceptance of personal susceptibility to a condition. At one extreme is the individual who, during interview, may deny any possibility of his contracting a given condition. In a more moderate position is the person who may admit to the "statistical" possibility of its occurrence but to whom this possibility has little reality and who does not really believe it will happen to him. Finally, a person may express a feeling that he is in real danger of contracting the condition. In short, as it has been measured, susceptibility refers to the subjective risks of contracting a condition.

Perceived seriousness. Convictions concerning the seriousness of a given health problem may also vary from person to person. The degree of seriousness may be judged both by the degree of emotional arousal created by the thought of a disease as well as by the kinds of difficulties the individual believes a given health condition will create for him.[31]

A person may, of course, see a health problem in terms of its medical or clinical consequence. He would thus be concerned with such questions as whether a disease could lead to his death, or reduce his physical or mental functioning for long periods of time, or disable him permanently. However, the perceived seriousness of a condition may, for a given individual, include such broader and more complex implications as the effects of the disease on his job, on his family life and on his social relations. Thus a person may not believe that tuberculosis is medically serious, but may nevertheless believe that its occurrence would be serious if it created important psychological and economic tensions within his family.

Perceived benefits of taking action and barriers to taking action. The acceptance of one's susceptibility to a disease that is also believed to be serious provides a force leading to action, but it does not define the particular course of action that is likely to be taken.

The direction that the action will take is influenced by beliefs regarding the relative effectiveness of known available alternatives in reducing the disease threat to which the individual feels subjected. His behavior will thus depend on how beneficial he thinks the various alternatives would be in his case. Of course, he must have available to him at least one action that is subjectively possible. An alternative is likely to be seen as beneficial if it relates subjectively to the reduction of one's susceptibility to or seriousness of an illness. Again, the person's belief about the availability and effectiveness of various courses of action, and not the objective facts about the effectiveness of action, determines what course he will take. In turn, his beliefs in this area are doubtless influenced by the norms and pressures of his social groups.

An individual may believe that a given action will be effective in reducing the threat of disease, but at the same time see that action itself as being inconvenient, expensive, unpleasant, painful or upsetting. These negative aspects of health action arouse conflicting motives of avoidance. Several resolutions of the conflict are possible. If the readiness to act is high and the negative aspects are seen as relatively weak, the action in question is likely to be taken. If, on the other hand, the readiness to act is low while the potential negative aspects are seen as strong, they function as barriers to prevent action.

Where the readiness to act is great and the barriers to action are also great, the conflict is more difficult to resolve. The individual is highly oriented toward acting to reduce the likelihood or impact of the perceived health danger. He is equally highly motivated to avoid action since he sees it as highly unpleasant or even painful.

Sometimes, alternative actions of nearly equal efficacy may be available. For example, the person who feels threatened by tuberculosis but fears the potential hazards of x-rays may choose to obtain a tuberculin test for initial screening.

But what can he do if the situation does not provide such alternative means to resolve his conflicts? Experimental evidence obtained outside the health area suggests that one of two reactions occur. First, the person may attempt to remove himself psychologically from the conflict situation by engaging in activities which do not really reduce the threat. Vacillating (without decision) between choices may be an example. Consider the individual who feels threatened by lung cancer who believes quitting cigarette smoking will reduce the risk but for whom smoking serves important needs. He may constantly commit himself to give up smoking soon and thereby relieve, if only momentarily, the pressure imposed by the discrepancy between the barriers and the perceived benefits.

A second possible reaction is a marked increase in fear or anxiety.[32] If the anxiety or fear become strong enough, the individual may be rendered incapable of thinking objectively and behaving rationally about the problem. Even if he is subsequently offered a more effective means of handling the situation, he may not accept it simply because he can no longer think constructively about the matter.

Cues to action. The variables which constitute readiness to act, that is, perceived susceptibility and severity as well as the variables that define perceived benefits and barriers to taking action, have all been subjected to research which will be reviewed in subsequent sections. However, one additional variable is believed to be necessary to complete the model but it has not been subjected to careful study.

A factor that serves as a cue or a trigger to trip off appropriate action appears to be neccessary. The level of readiness (susceptibility and severity) provides the energy or force to act and the perception of benefits (less barriers) provides a preferred path of action. However, the combination of these could reach quite considerable levels of intensity without resulting in overt action unless some instigating event occurred to set the process in motion. In the health area, such events or cues may be internal (e.g., perception of bodily states) or external (e.g., interpersonal interactions, the impact of media of communication, knowledge that some one else has become affected or receiving a postcard from the dentist).

The required intensity of a cue that is sufficient to trigger behavior presumably varies with differences in the level of readiness. With relatively low psychological readiness (i.e., little acceptance of susceptibility to or severity of a disease) rather intense stimuli will be needed to trigger a response. On the other hand, with relatively high levels of readiness even slight stimuli may be adequate. For example, other things being equal, the person who barely accepts his susceptibility to tuberculosis will be unlikely to check upon his health until he experiences rather intense symptoms (e.g., spitting blood). On the other hand, the person who readily accepts his constant susceptibility to the disease may be spurred into action by the mere sight of a mobile x-ray unit or a relevant poster.

Unfortunately, the settings for most of the research on the model

101

have precluded obtaining an adequate measure of the role of cues. Since the kinds of cues that have been hypothesized may be quite fleeting and of little intrinsic significance (e.g., a casual view of a poster urging chest x-ray), they may easily be forgotten with the passage of time. An interview taken months or years later could not adequately identify the cues. Freidson has described the difficulties in attempting to assess interpersonal influences as cues.[33] Furthermore, respondents who have taken a recommended action in the past will probably be more likely to remember preceding events as relevant than will respondents who were exposed to the same events but never took the action. These problems make testing the role of cues most difficult in any retrospective setting. A prospective design, perhaps a panel study, will probably be required to assess properly how various stimuli serve as cues to trigger action in an individual who is psychologically ready to act.

Evidence For and Against the Model

Although many investigations have identified explanatory variables which are similar to one or another variable contained in the model, only seven major projects have been undertaken whose design was largely or entirely determined by the behavioral model. Of these, four were retrospective studies[18-21] while three were prospective studies.[22-24] The retrospective research projects have in common the crucial characteristic that data about respondents' beliefs and behavior are gathered during the same interview and the beliefs are assumed to have existed in a point in time prior to the behavior. That assumption is a questionable one at best and will be considered after a review of the retrospective research.

One other problem in the interpretation of the studies should be noted. With the exception of the Hochbaum study[18] and the National Study of Health Attitudes and Behavior,[24] the research has been based on quite small samples. Sometimes sample size has been limited by financial or other insuperable obstacles. However, in some cases difficulties in categorizing responses or in obtaining responses to every necessary item have reduced samples to dangerously low proportions.

The best documented of the retrospective studies were performed by Hochbaum[18] and Kegeles,[19] and these will be reviewed in some detail.

Hochbaum studied more than 1000 adults in three cities in an attempt to identify factors underlying the decision to obtain a chest x-ray for the detection of tuberculosis. He tapped beliefs in susceptibility to tuberculosis and beliefs in the benefits of early detection. Perceived susceptibility to tuberculosis contained two elements. It included, first, the respondent's beliefs about whether tuberculosis was a real possibility in his case, and second, the extent to which he accepted the fact that one may have tuberculosis in the absence of all symptoms. Consider first the findings for the group of persons that exhibited both beliefs, that is, belief in their own susceptibility to tuberculosis and the belief that over-all benefits would accrue from early detection. In that group 82 per cent had had at least one voluntary chest x-ray during a specified period preceding the interview. On the other hand, of the group exhibiting neither of these beliefs, only 21 per cent had obtained a voluntary x-ray during the criterion period. Thus, four out of five people who exhibited both beliefs took the predicted action, while four of five people who accepted neither of the beliefs had not taken the action.

Thus, Hochbaum appears to have demonstrated with considerable precision that a particular action is a function of the two interacting variables—perceived susceptibility and perceived benefits.

The belief in one's susceptibility to tuberculosis appeared to be the more powerful variable studied. For the individuals who exhibited this belief without accepting the benefits of early detection, 64 per cent had obtained prior voluntary x-rays. Of the individuals accepting the benefits of early detection without accepting their susceptibility to the disease, only 29 per cent had prior voluntary x-rays.

Hochbaum failed to show that perceived severity plays a role in the decision-making process. This may be due to the fact that his measures of severity proved not to be sensitive, thus precluding the possibility of obtaining definitive data.

Kegeles[19] dealt with the conditions under which members of a prepaid dental care plan will come in for preventive dental check-ups or for prophylaxis in the absence of symptoms. He attempted to measure the respondent's perceived susceptibility to a variety of dental diseases, the perceived severity of these conditions, his beliefs about the benefits of preventive action and his perceptions of barriers to those actions.

While the findings generally support the importance of the model variables, their general applicability is greatly limited by an unusually large loss in the sample. The study was initiated with a sample of 430, but those without teeth, those for whom information was not available to determine whether past dental visits had been made for preventive purposes or for treatment of symptoms and those whose positions could not be coded on all three belief variables were excluded. The crucial analysis could thus be made only on 77 individuals. Within the major limitations implied by the small sample size and by the likely nonrepresentativeness of the 77, Kegeles showed that with successive increases in the number of beliefs exhibited by respondents from none to all three, their frequency of making preventive dental visits also increased. The actual findings show that 1. of only three persons who were low on all three variables none made such preventive visits, 2. of 18 who were high on any one variable but low on the other two, 61 per cent made such visits, 3. of 38 persons high on two beliefs and low on one, 66 per cent made preventive visits and, finally, 4. of 18 persons who were high on all three variables, 78 per cent made preventive dental visits. Similar patterns of findings based on much larger samples were obtained in an analysis of relationships between behavior and each of a series of single variables, that is, susceptibility, severity, benefits and barriers.

The findings of the two remaining retrospective studies will not be reviewed in detail but are in most respects quite similar to the two that have been reviewed.[20, 21] In each case evidence that supports the model has been obtained although the sample sizes were not large.

In summary, while no one study provides convincing confirmation of the model variables, each has produced internally consistent findings which are in the predicted direction. Taken together they thus provide strong support for the model.

As indicated, any interpretations made of the findings of the retrospective studies are based on an assumption. The hypothesis that behavior is determined by a particular constellation of beliefs can only be adequately tested where the beliefs are known to have existed prior to the behavior that they are supposed to determine. However, the retrospective projects have been undertaken in situations which necessitated identifying the beliefs and behavior at the same point in time. This approach has always been known to be quite dangerous. Work on cognitive dissonance[34] supported these suspicions and suggested that the decision to accept or reject a health service

104

may in and of itself modify the individual's perceptions in areas relevant to that health action. Obviously, what was needed was a two-phase study in which beliefs would be identified at one point in time, and behavior measured later.

Such a study was undertaken in the fall of 1957, around the topic of the impact of Asian Influenza on American community life.[22] As one of a series of related studies, Leventhal, *et al.*, investigated the impact of the threat of influenza on families through the use of a design that was intended to permit a test of the model in a prospective manner. In this phase of the study, 200 randomly selected families in each of two medium size cities in the United States were interviewed twice. The first interview was intended to be made before most people had the opportunity to seek vaccination or to take any other preventive action and before much influenza-like illness had occurred in the communities. The second interview was to be made after all available evidence indicated that the epidemic had subsided.

In fact, only partial success was achieved in satisfying these conditions because community vaccination programs as well as the spread of the epidemic moved much faster than had been anticipated. For these reasons the sample on which the test could be made was reduced to 86. This sample of 86 respondents had, at the time of initial interview, neither taken preventive action relative to influenza nor had they experienced influenza-like illness in themselves or in other members of their families. Twelve of the 86 scored relatively high on a combination of beliefs in their own susceptibility to influenza and the severity of the disease.[35] Five of these 12 subsequently made preventive preparations relative to influenza. On the other hand, at the time of the first interview, the remaining 74 persons were unmotivated in the sense of rejecting either their own susceptibility to the disease or its severity or both. Of these, only eight, or 11 per cent, subsequently made preparations relative to influenza.[36] Although the samples on whom comparable data could be obtained were very small and possibly not representative, the differences are statistically significant beyond the one per cent level of significance. Analysis of the available data thus suggest that prior beliefs are instrumental in determining subsequent action.

A second prospective study was a follow-up by Kegeles[23] on the study reported earlier.[19] Three years after the initial collection of data on a sample of more than 400 in 1958, a mail questionnaire was sent to each person in the sample as well as to a comparable control group to obtain information about the three most recent dental visits. The objective of the follow-up was to determine whether the beliefs identified during the original study were associated with behavior during the subsequent three-year period.

Kegeles found that perceptions of seriousness, whether considered independently or together with other variables, were not at all associated with subsequent behavior. Perceptions of benefits taken alone were not related to subsequent behavior. However, the perception of susceptibility did show a correlation with making subsequent preventive dental visits. Of those who had earlier seen themselves as susceptible, 58 per cent made subsequent preventive dental visits while 42 per cent who had not accepted their susceptibility made such visits. When beliefs about susceptibility and benefits were combined, a more accurate prediction was possible of who would or would not make preventive dental visits. Considering only those who scored high on susceptibility, and cross-tabulating against beliefs in benefits, 67 per cent of those high on both beliefs made subsequent preventive visits while only 38 per cent low in benefits made such visits. Thus, the combination of susceptibility and benefits is demonstrated to be important in predicting behavior.

The results of the six studies cited above lend support to the importance of several of the variables in the model as explanatory or predictive variables. However, a seventh major investigation,[24] currently in progress and not yet published, conflicts in most respects with the findings of earlier studies. The study includes analyses of beliefs and behavior of a probability sample of nearly 1500 American adults studied in 1963, and the subsequent behavior of a 50 per cent subsample studied 15 months later. Although the analysis is not complete, it already clearly shows that perceived susceptibility, severity, and benefits, whether taken singly or in combination, do not account for a major portion of the variance in subsequent preventive and diagnostic behavior, although predictions based on the belief in benefits taken alone frequently approaches significance. The study findings do not disclose any explanation for the failure to obtain findings similar to those of the earlier described studies, but the current national study has been conducted in a setting which distinguishes it from all the other reported studies in one respect that may be crucial. In the earlier described studies, the settings were such that the population in each case had been offered the opportunity

106

to take action through directed messages and circumstances that could have served as cues to stimulate action. In Hockbaum's study,[18] mass media had been used in the three study cities to urge the population to obtain chest x-rays. The Kegeles studies,[19, 23] offered every member of the population free or inexpensive dental treatment and urged them to use it. In the Levanthal, *et al.*, study,[22] the population had been alerted by newspapers and by public health officials to the desirability of obtaining influenza immunizations. In the Heinzelmann study,[20] the patients had been urged to use penicillin prophylactically. The Flach study[21] offered the population a free test for cervical cancer. In short, in all the prior studies the population had been exposed to information which both indicated the availability of a health procedure and which, in most cases, urged them to avail themselves of that procedure.

In contrast, no such condition obtained for the national sample in the study currently in progress. With respect to the several health problems covered in the study, neither the sample nor the United States adult population which it represents, had been uniformly exposed to intensive campaigns to inform them about available services and to persuade them to use such services. Nor can the assumption reasonably be made that preventive and diagnostic services were equally available to all. The absence of clear-cut cues to stimulate action as well as unequal opportunity to act may in large measure account for the failure to replicate the earlier results. However, those possibilities must be treated as hypotheses which will need to be tested in new research.

Critique of the Model and Needed Additional Research

The place of the model in the health decision-making process. As indicated earlier, health decision-making is a process in which the individual moves through a series of stages or phases in each of which he interacts with individuals and events. The nature of the interactions at any one of these stages may increase or decrease the probability that a particular subsequent response will be made. Freidson[16] and Zola[15] have illustrated some of these stages. The individual's relevant health beliefs as described in this paper are presumed to serve as a setting for his subsequent responses at other stages in the decision process. For example, individuals who accept their susceptibility to a particular condition and are aware of actions that might be beneficial in reducing their susceptibility may well exhibit what Freidson terms "cosmopolitan" rather than "parochial" orientations toward health services. They may be more prone to learn about and seek out professional diagnosis rather than using the "lay referral" system. In such a case the initial set of beliefs would itself determine subsequent choices in the decision-making process.

What have here been termed "cues" are probably identical with Zola's "critical incidents."[15] One can not but agree heartily with his recommendation that the role of such triggers to action be much more thoroughly investigated than has previously been done. This is urged despite the forbidding difficulties in identifying cues that have already been described.

Operational definitions of the variables. No two studies of the model's variables have used identical questions for determining the presence or absence of each belief. This raises the possibility that the concepts being measured may also vary from study to study. For example, Hochbaum's questions on perceived susceptibility apparently tapped a dimension of perceived *possibility* or risk of contracting a disease.[18] On the other hand, Kegeles[19] asked questions oriented toward *probability* or likelihood of occurrence. The two approaches cannot be assumed to measure a single psychological dimension.

In an effort to bring some order into this area the current National Study of Health Attitutdes and Behavior was undertaken.[24] In that study alternative methods were used to identify beliefs about the severity of and susceptibility to four diseases: dental decay, gum trouble, tuberculosis and cancer. Four different question formats were developed, differing simultaneously on two dimensions: 1. "self-reference" versus "reference to men-women your age;" 2. fixed-alternative versus more open items. A two by two design was used with approximately one-quarter of the total sample randomly assigned to each of the four question formats.

The preliminary findings demonstrate that the question types obtain different distributions of responses. However, since in the present study no clear relationship is demonstrated between possession of the beliefs, however measured, and health behavior, no decision can be made on which method of questioning is most valid.

Quantification. The model implies that certain levels of readiness are optimal in stimulating behavior but neither theory nor research have disclosed what the levels are. In most of the studies limitations in sample size have necessitated dichotomizing scores on the variables into categories of "high" and "low." Until data can be collected on

108

at least an ordinal scale the problem of determining optimal quantities will not be solved.

Stability and reliability of the beliefs. Little is known about the stability of the beliefs although they may vary from time to time as a function of situational changes. Learning that a friend or a president has suffered a serious illness may well raise personal levels of readiness to act based on increases in subjective susceptibility. Research is needed to determine how stable the beliefs are.

Similarly, little information is available on the reliability of the measures of beliefs. More work is also needed in this area. The appropriate approach to testing reliability depends on the stability of the beliefs. If the beliefs do change from time to time, test-retest measures of reliability would not be as appropriate as split-half measures of reliability.

Perceived seriousness. Hochbaum,[18] Kegeles[23] and Rosenstock, et al.,[24] failed to demonstrate the importance of perceived severity in determining behavior. Flach[21] did not measure severity since he assumed that cancer was universally seen as severe in the group of women studied. On the other hand, the studies by Heinzelmann,[20] the first Kegeles study[19] and Leventhal, et al.,[22] did support the importance of perceived severity. Since the latter three studies suffer from greatly attenuated samples, greater doubt must be maintained about the importance of perceived severity as an explanatory factor than about the other variables.

Genesis of the beliefs. Nothing is known about the genesis of the beliefs, nor of the conditions under which they are acquired. Moreover, no research has been done on how an individual's position on the three health beliefs is related to other comparable beliefs he holds. For a given person, how is the level of concern created by serious and probable disease related to threats caused by other hazards, such as the possibility of unemployment, the possibility of atomic bombing, etc.? Seemingly, the potential value of the model would be greatly enhanced if the origins and development of the health beliefs were specified and if the beliefs were placed within a broader theoretical framework that would account for responses to a wide variety of stimuli.

The need for experimental studies. Convincing demonstrations of cause and effect can rarely, if ever, be provided through cross-sectional surveys of the kind thus far employed to study the model. This is true because the survey is highly susceptible to errors in judging which of two associated factors preceded the other in time and because the possibility is great that apparent relationships may be spurious. For these reasons, experimental studies must be undertaken to determine the causal role of the relevant health beliefs. For example, an effort could be made to modify the health beliefs of a randomly assigned experimental group while holding constant the beliefs of a comparable control group. Both groups would then be offered a particular health service and observations taken of the relative responsiveness of the groups to the health appeal. A variety of specific experiments could be devised to assess the contribution of the health beliefs to behavior.

Susceptibility of the beliefs to modification. Even if the model did predict behavior, its ultimate usefulness would depend upon the extent to which the health beliefs can be modified in a planned way. Two efforts to attempt such change have been reported. Guskin,[37] through the use of a film, has succeeded in modifying the reported beliefs of fifth and sixth grade students relative to their perceived susceptibility to and severity of tuberculosis, although no changes in perceived benefits took place. In a study of fear arousal and persuasion, which will be discussed in some detail in a subsequent section, Haefner[38] has obtained data, as yet unpublished, which show that the health beliefs of ninth graders can be modified. High fear messages tended to have more favorable effects on beliefs about severity and preventability (benefits) than did low fear messages. One of two effects was observed: 1. high fear messages led to a greater increase in each of the two beliefs than low fear messages, or 2. high fear messages led to a smaller reduction in the beliefs than did low fear messages.

Results for perceived susceptibility were not clear; in one experimental treatment a high fear message led to a greater increase in perceived susceptibility than did a low fear message while in a second experimental treatment, a high fear message resulted in no change or even led to a reduction in susceptibility.

Universality of model. 1. Voluntary, symptom free health behavior. To date, the model has been applied exclusively in situations in which the behavior in question is purely voluntary and the individuals studied do not believe themselves to have symptoms. These criteria are not met in a variety of situations in which people obtain health services. For instance, social pressures may be effective in stimulating action. Legal compulsion and job requirements also account for

110

much health behavior. Finally, the appearance of clear symptoms is a most frequent instigator to health action. The likelihood is, therefore, that only a minority of the population currently takes voluntary preventive action or action to detect disease in the absence of distinct symptoms. Despite these facts, continued work with the model may have great ultimate benefit. The aim in public health is to increase the proportion of people who consistently, rationally and freely take preventive actions or actions to check on the presence of disease while free of symptoms. Careful analysis of the health decision processes in what is currently a small group of people may well be useful in subsequent planning of efforts to modify the behavior of very large groups of people. Studying the exceptional case may have vast practical implications for working with the more typical.

2. Health beliefs and social class. The health belief model would seem to have greater applicability to middle class groups than to lower status groups since possession of the health beliefs implies an orientation toward the future, toward deliberate planning, toward deferment of immediate gratification in the interest of long-run goals. The fact has frequently been noted, e.g., by Simmons,[39] that, unlike middle class groups, lower status people probably accord greater priority to immediate rewards than to long-range goals. This difference in the time orientation of the different social classes may well have implications for the planning of preventive health programs. But these implications are far from obvious ones. Hochbaum and Kegeles, in earlier cited studies, have indeed shown that social classes differ in the frequency with which the beliefs are held. But they have also shown that where the proper constellation of beliefs exists, the probability is greater that the recommended behavior will occur irrespective of social class. Thus, public health workers must recognize that members of the lower social classes are not as prone to accept health beliefs of the kind described as are members of the higher classes. But they must also recognize that many members of the lower classes do accept such beliefs, indicating their ability to adopt a long range perspective. Subjective time horizons are thus not immutable.

3. Health habits. A third possible limitation in the ultimate applicability of the model is in the case of habitual behaviors and in styles of behavior. Patterns of behavior that are developed in early life most likely are not motivated by the kinds of health concerns that may guide the adult's behavior. During the socialization process,

children learn to adopt many health related habits and practices which will permanently influence their adult behavior, e.g., brushing teeth, visiting the physician or dentist regularly and adopting unique nutritional practices. Yet, these patterns of adjustment can not be explained by applying the explanatory model to the children themselves. The habitual behavior of the child cannot be explained with certainty by applying the model to his parents. Preliminary data suggest that health behavior undertaken on behalf of children may not be explainable by reference to the present model.[19] Research is clearly needed on the determinants of health habits.

The Relationship Between Health Beliefs and Demographic Factors

Typical demographic analysis of utilization rates was previously criticized, partially on the grounds that few attempts have been made to show the mechanisms that link behavior with fixed, personal characteristics. However, two published studies are relevant in this connection. Kegeles, et al.,[6] investigated relationships among the use of Papanicolaou tests, demographic factors and beliefs in the benefits of early detection of cancer. Beliefs in benefits were measured by responses to questions on the perceived importance of early versus delayed treatment for cancer and on opinions as to whether medical check-ups or tests could detect cancer before the appearance of symptoms. An analysis of the findings discloses that personal characteristics and beliefs each make independent contributions to the understanding of behavior. Tests were much more likely to have been taken by women who were relatively young, age 35–44, white, had higher income, married, relatively well educated and who reported higher occupational levels (using husband's occupation in the case of married women).

The study also showed that accepting the benefits of early professional detection and treatment was highly associated with having taken the test. However, the joint analysis is of most interest. Within every demographic grouping those who held a belief in benefits were much more likely to have taken the test than those not holding that belief. Similarly, within each of the belief categories those with the appropriate demographic characteristics were much more likely to have taken the action than those who did not. Clearly, the joint effect of the beliefs and the personal characteristics is much greater than the effects of either alone.

112

In Hochbaum's earlier study,[18] a similar finding was obtained. Socioeconomic status (education and income) and the combination of beliefs in susceptibility and benefits were independently associated with having taken voluntary chest x-rays in the absence of symptoms. Within each socioeconomic status category, however, those who scored high on the combination of beliefs were much more likely to have taken the x-ray than those scoring medium or low.

An interpretation of the findings of the two studies suggests that certain of the beliefs may be necessary for taking preventive or screening tests, but that they are distributed unevenly in the population, tending to be more prevalent among white females, of higher socioeconomic status and the relatively young. Why this is so is not known. Perhaps the earlier described information on differences in subjective time horizons of the different social classes may help to explain the unequal distribution of specific health beliefs.

INDUCING BEHAVIORAL CHANGE

The major focus in this paper has been on identifying factors that help to explain why people use health services. Since, however, the ultimate aim of understanding behavior in the health area is an applied one, the problem of persuading people to use health services may appropriately be considered.

Material presented earlier indicates that a decision to take a health action is influenced by the individual's state of readiness to behave, by his socially and individually determined beliefs about the efficacy of alternative actions, by psychological barriers to action, by interpersonal influences and by one or more cues or critical incidents which serve to trigger a response. No *a priori* reason may be found to indicate that action directed toward any one of these will in the long run prove more effective than action directed toward the others. Therefore, action programs to modify behavior could legitimately focus on any one or more of the determinants. Only systematic investigation will demonstrate the conditions under which one or another of the determinants is most susceptible to effective manipulation.

Despite the lack of definitive research findings, a few practical considerations may clarify the problem. Ordinarily, to change people is much more difficult than to change their environment (though the latter may itself represent no simple task). Therefore efforts to increase public response should always aim at minimizing the barriers to action, increasing the opportunities to act (which will increase perceived benefits) and providing cues to trigger responses. Some simple but important environmental features may be modified with good effect, e.g., minimizing inconvenience by reducing financial costs of services and distances that have to be traveled to obtain them, and setting hours for service that are convenient. Moreover, cues may frequently be arranged to trigger responses, e.g., reminders from dentists and physicians, spot announcements in the mass media.

Fairly simple situational changes of the kinds described may well increase the rate of preventive and diagnostic behavior. However, their effect is probably limited, if current views of the determinants of health behavior are at all correct. Probably, after all situational improvements are made, a large number of individuals remain who are not in a state of readiness to act, and, other things being equal, will not. Concerning such people, one must ask whether a direct effort to increase the readiness can be successful and efficient or whether success is more likely through an indirect effort to stimulate the behavior as, for example, through the use of social pressures. Again, the question is empirical; definitive research has not been performed. However, some research material affecting a decision on this matter can be drawn from studies of communication and persuasion.

The Effects of Mass Communications

Literature and experience in communication of health information clearly demonstrate that large groups of individuals stand ready to take action on any given issue and merely lack the information or cue necessary to make the action possible. Mass media are undoubtedly effective in bringing to such groups all that is necessary to insure a response. Mass communications are thus effective in imparting information. However, in respect to changing opinions, Klapper has indicated that "Communication research strongly indicates that persuasive mass communication is in general more likely to reinforce the existing opinion of its audience than it is to change such opinions . . ."[40] Klapper's conclusions are based on the analysis of research findings on the effects of the 1940 and 1948 presidential campaigns upon changes in voter preference, efforts to improve attitude toward the oil industry or toward the TVA and many others. Research is required to show whether these conclusions are applicable to attempts to change opinions in the health area. Until that research has been done, one must maintain a skeptical position regarding the likelihood that mass media will provide the mechanism for changing rather than reinforcing health beliefs and behavior, especially if the beliefs are deeply embedded.

Self-Selection

Another fact of considerable importance for health and health research is that people tend to expose themselves to communications media and content in highly selective ways.

Lazarsfeld and Kendall have demonstrated that lower educational groups do not read newspapers, magazines, and books to the same extent as do groups with more education.[41] Moreover, even when groups are exposed to the same medium, they may attend to and learn different things from the same material.

Some of the data reported in the studies of poliomyelitis vaccination campaigns reinforce that conclusion.[7] Belcher found that the non-whites in his sample obtained their information on poliomyelitis and vaccination from personal sources (teachers, children, public health officials), while whites tended to get their information through impersonal sources. Similarly, Deasy showed that all women in her sample had been exposed to an identical brochure on the 1954 field trials, which had been brought home by their children. Practically all women in the sample had been exposed to daily papers which were featuring intensive coverage of the field trials. Nevertheless, the women differed in knowledge and acceptance of the program, acceptance being associated with amount of education.

Katz and Lazarsfeld conclude that people who are reached by educational programs through the mass media are very largely those who do not need the education. Those who do need the education tend to stay away. In their words, "Those groups which are most hopefully regarded as the target of the communication are often least likely to be in the audience. Thus, educational programs . . . are very unlikely to reach the uneducated . . ."[42]

The mass media have, and always have had, an important role in communication. However, the communication studies reviewed here suggest that the assets and liabilities of the traditional approach should be considered in the light of the particular needs that face health workers in attempting to reach the lower income family, the family with little formal education, and the non-white family.

Emotional Appeals

Health workers have long been interested in the question of the role that fear-arousing messages may have in inducing attitude and behavior change. A 1963 publication which reviews research studies on the effects of fear-arousing communications concludes: ". . . on the basis of the evidence that has been cited it seems reasonable to conclude that fear is an unsatisfactory motive to employ in public health education."[43] That conclusion was based largely on a 1953 study by Janis and Feshbach[44] who showed that messages arousing little or no fear were more successful than messages arousing high fear in stimulating ninth grade children to change their attitudes and reported practices in the area of personal dental hygiene practices. Other related studies have obtained findings that low fear arousal is superior,[45] that high fear arousal is superior[46] or that no difference exists between low and high fear arousal.[47]

In 1964, Haefner performed a replication and extension of the Janis and Feshbach study.[38] Using Janis and Feshbach's original experimental material in one experiment (as well as revised material in another), Haefner obtained main effects that were opposite to those of the earlier study—high-fear arousal being much more effective than low-fear arousal. Through secondary analysis, controlling on social class, Haefner was able to reconcile the results of his study with the results of the Janis and Feshbach study. In Haefner's study, children from families of relatively high social class were more influenced by low-fear messages, while children of lower social class were more influenced by high-fear messages. His initial finding, which had shown the greater power of high fear, was attributed to the fact that his ninth grade sample was preponderately lower class. If, as seems likely, Janis and Feshbach's sample in Greenwich, Connecticut, was primarily drawn from upper class families, the apparently discrepant findings of the two studies are readily reconciled.

Thus, to conclude that fear is uniformly to be eschewed in educational programs is premature. If Haefner's findings can be replicated, especially in settings using other health content, and with other age groups, the attempts to induce fear might, for certain subgroups of the population, be much more effective than a more neutral or, as sometimes called, a more "positive" approach.

Personal Influence and the Resolution of Cognitive Dissonance

A great deal has been written about the potential power of personal influence techniques (i.e., those stressing face to face contacts) in communication and persuasion, especially with lower-socioeconomic groups. Many studies have been conducted in laboratory settings[48] and in natural field settings.[42] However, relatively little research has been reported which clearly demonstrates the potency of personal influence on health behavior. Two well known studies[49,50] demonstrated that a group discussion-decision method is apparently superior to a lecture in persuading women to alter certain nutritional practices and in persuading women to undertake periodic breast self-examination. However, in both studies information is lacking about the long-term duration of the effect. The superiority of the group discussion approach extends to at least a matter of weeks, but whether the effects continue over months and years is not known. Moreover, the interaction of socioeconomic status with educational method is not clear. Although the superiority of personal influence over mass communication techniques has so long been proclaimed, oddly enough, only few follow-up studies have been made. Studies are needed not merely to demonstrate that group methods are superior. The greater need is to specify the conditions under which the superiority, if any, may be enhanced.

One such potential enhancing condition is implied by Festinger's theory of cognitive dissonance.[34] When an individual has been induced to behave in a way that conflicts with a prior belief he holds, the conflict or dissonance has to be reduced. Frequently, the dissonance is reduced by changing the initial belief. One can only speculate that the application of group pressure upon the individual in a state of dissonance might provide a powerful inducement to modify certain of his beliefs.

The application of imagination and ingenuity could provide highly practical programs of research in health education utilizing the potential power of personal influence and the need to reduce cognitive dissonance. Research on these techniques might profitably be applied to problems in preventing or reducing cigarette smoking in teen-agers and adults, in weight reduction programs and in the prevention of automobile accidents.

Implications

The foregoing brief review suggests a key research question. Can more imaginative use be made of communications approaches to increase their power to persuade? Combinations of mass communications approaches and personal influence techniques, using emotional appeals with specified subgroups, might pay far greater dividends in modifying health beliefs and behavior than has yet been obtained with the sole use of any one approach.

In the light of traditional difficulties in modifying opinion and behavior of adults, an interesting note is that the two reported successful efforts to modify health behavior through the use of emotional appeals were both performed on children.[38,44] Also, Guskin's successful effort to change positions on the health beliefs of the model was performed on children.[87] Unusual opportunities apparently exist in primary and secondary education to influence children both to develop desirable health habits and to acquire desired health beliefs. Curricula could be planned to emphasize the value of specific health habits and to provide rewards for performing them. Other possibilities would be to build on theories of the natural causation of disease and germ theory and to deal specifically with the topics of susceptibility to various diseases, with the personal and social consequences of unchecked disease and with approaches to the prevention, early detection and control of diseases. Much could be done in this process to lay the basis for later minimizing in the adult the psychological barriers to accepting an otherwise beneficial service.

To some extent school systems have approached some of these goals through their increasing emphasis on health, science and physical education. Unquestionably, relatively younger groups and better educated groups more often exhibit preventive health behavior than do older or poorly educated groups. Similarly, they more often exhibit related health beliefs. Yet, few systematic efforts have been made to develop curricula specifically and explicitly to stimulate the acquisition of desired health beliefs. Such systematic efforts should be planned on an experimental basis to determine the extent to which school health programs can exert a significant and lasting effect on the acquisition of health beliefs and behavior.

SUMMARY AND CONCLUSIONS

Only a beginning has been made toward a systematic explanation of health and illness behavior. Many studies of the utilization of preventive and treatment services, while valuable for formulating public policy, do not throw light on the determinants of behavior. On the other hand, recent sociological research is demonstrating that health decision making is best thought of as a process in which the individual moves through each of a series of stages or phases. Events occurring at any of these stages influence choices at subsequent stages. Even such research is currently limited to explaining circumscribed aspects of health behavior.

A specific model to account for personal health decisions that are made in the absence of clear-cut symptoms shows promise of providing a means of explaining preventive health behavior. The model hypothesizes that a decision to obtain a preventive or detection test in the absence of symptoms will not be made unless the following conditions are satisfied:

1. The individual is psychologically ready to take action relative to a particular health condition. The extent of readiness to act is defined by whether the individual feels susceptible to the condition in question and the extent to which its possible occurrence is viewed as having serious personal consequences.

2. The individual believes that the preventive or test in question is both feasible and appropriate for him to use, would reduce either his perceived susceptibility to or the perceived severity of the health condition and no serious psychological barriers to the proposed action are present.

3. A cue or stimulus occurs to trigger the response.

The strengths of the model are that it has appeared adequate to account for major variations in behavior in groups of individuals studied in a variety of settings, is composed of a small number of elements, appears to be capable of application to a wide variety of health actions and beliefs along the dimensions included in the model are, at least in principle, capable of change through education.

Some defects have appeared in the model to date. Experimental manipulation of the variables has not been undertaken to any marked extent, data are lacking on the role of cues in explaining health behavior, many of the studies which lend support to the model were based on small and possibly non-representative samples, a number of supporting studies were necessarily done retrospectively although the model implies a prospective design, operational definitions of the model's concepts have not been uniform, the variables have not yet been quantified beyond the nominal scale and the stability of the beliefs and reliability of the measures are not known.

In short, considerable research is still needed to demonstrate the model's true explanatory value. However, evidence to date justifies continued support of such research.

Since health decisions are determined by a variety of personal, interpersonal and situational factors, attempts to induce people to change their health actions may successfully be undertaken at various points in the decision process. Efforts to minimize barriers to action, to maximize convenience and to provide intensive cues to action are believed to increase public acceptance of health programs. However, after all such attempts have been made, a group will remain which is not psychologically ready to act and which will, therefore, not respond to cues to seek health services. For that group persuasive efforts will need to be focused directly on their beliefs or their behavior.

The beliefs identified in the model (as well as the use of associated preventive health measures) are not distributed equally in the population. The beliefs and the behavior tend more to be exhibited by upper socioeconomic groups than by lower. Educational programs designed to increase the acceptance of the beliefs as well as the adoption of preventive health behavior should be directed primarily to the poorly educated, to those of lower income and to non-white groups. However, the very groups to be reached tend, through a process of self-selection, not to expose themselves to scientific and health information transmitted through the mass media. Also, the mass media have not been notably effective in changing existing beliefs and behavior, although sufficient research has not been done in health contexts. More emphasis should be placed on methods that employ personal influence in face-to-face contacts, an approach which is widely held to be effective in educating members of the affected groups, though very little relevant research evidence can be cited. Some new approaches described might be used in enhancing the effects of group discussion techniques. Moreover, research and demonstration are needed to determine the extent to which school health programs can exert a significant and lasting effect on the acquisition of health beliefs and behavior.

The critical review presented in this paper suggests a need for research on the following unsolved problems.

With respect to the explanatory model, more evidence, especially experimental evidence, is needed on the validity and relative contributions of each of the model variables to personal health decision making, including data on the importance of cues. Operational definitions of each of the model variables are needed which are related to the concepts covered, which correlate with criterion measures of behavior, which can be measured reliably, and which are quantified on at least an ordinal scale.

With respect to the problem of inducing behavioral change, research on mass communication and personal influence methods needs to be extended to determine the principles by which individuals, especially those in lower socioeconomic groups can be persuaded to alter their health opinions, attitudes and behavior. More extensive research in health settings is needed to resolve inconsistencies which can be experimentally induced between beliefs and behavior. Recent research suggests the desirability of more intensive study of the role of emotionally arousing factors in education and on the conditions which increase the effects of emotionally arousing messages upon attitude and behavior change.

REFERENCES

[1] Kasl, Stanislav V. and Cobb, Sidney, HEALTH BEHAVIOR, ILLNESS BEHAVIOR, AND SICK-ROLE BEHAVIOR, (Unpublished review), Ann Arbor, The University of Michigan, Institute for Social Research, 1965, p. 2.

[2] Lerner, Monroe and Anderson, Odin W., HEALTH PROGRESS IN THE UNITED STATES, 1900–1960: A REPORT OF THE HEALTH INFORMATION FOUNDATION, Chicago, University of Chicago Press, 1963.

[3] Somers, Herman M. and Somers, Anne R., DOCTORS, PATIENTS, AND HEALTH INSURANCE: THE ORGANIZATION AND FINANCING OF MEDICAL CARE, Washington, The Brookings Institution, 1961.

[4] United States Department of Health, Education and Welfare, Office of the Secretary, HEALTH, EDUCATION, AND WELFARE TRENDS, 1963 Edition, Washington, United States Government Printing Office, 1963.

[5] Borsky, Paul N. and Sagen, Oswald K., Motivations Toward Health Examinations, *American Journal of Public Health,* 49, 514–527, April, 1959.

[6] Kegeles, S. Stephen, *et al.,* Survey of Beliefs About Cancer Detection and Taking Papanicoloau Tests, *Public Health Reports,* 80, 815–824, September, 1965.

[7] Rosenstock, Irwin M., Derryberry, Mayhew and Carriger, Barbara K., Why People Fail to Seek Poliomyelitis Vaccination, *Public Health Reports,* 74, 98–103, February, 1959.

[8] United States Department of Health, Education and Welfare, Public Health Service, HEALTH STATISTICS FROM THE U.S. NATIONAL HEALTH SURVEY: DENTAL CARE, INTERVAL AND FREQUENCY OF VISITS, UNITED STATES, JULY 1957–JUNE 1959, Public Health Service Publication Number 584-B14, Washington, United States Government Printing Office, 1960.

[9] Kegeles, S. Stephen, Lotzkar, Stanley and Andrews, Lewis W., "Dental Care for the Chronically Ill and Aged. II. Some Factors Relevant for Predicting the Acceptance of Dental Care by Nursing Home Residents," (Unpublished manuscript), United States Department of Health, Education and Welfare, Public Health Service, 1959.

[10] United States Department of Health, Education and Welfare, Public Health Service, HEALTH STATISTICS FROM THE U.S. NATIONAL HEALTH SURVEY: VOLUME OF PHYSICIAN VISITS, UNITED STATES, JULY 1957–JUNE 1959, Public Health Service Publication Number 584-B19, Washington, United States Government Printing Office, 1960.

[11] United States Department of Health, Education and Welfare, Public Health Service, HEALTH STATISTICS FROM THE U.S. NATIONAL HEALTH SURVEY, HOSPITAL DISCHARGES AND LENGTH OF STAY: SHORT-STAY HOSPITALS, UNITED STATES, 1958–1960, Public Health Service Publication Number 584-B32, Washington, United States Government Printing Office, 1962.

[12] Blackwell, Barbara, The Literature of Delay in Seeking Medical Care for Chronic Illnesses, *Health Education Monographs,* 16, 3–31, 1963.

[13] Koos, Earl L., THE HEALTH OF REGIONVILLE—WHAT THE PEOPLE THOUGHT AND DID ABOUT IT, New York, Columbia University Press, 1954.

[14] Stoeckle, John D., Zola, Irving K. and Davidson, Gerald E., On Going to See the Doctor, the Contributions of the Patient to the Decision to Seek Medical Aid, A Selected Review, *Journal of Chronic Diseases,* 16, 975–989, 1963.

[15] Zola, Irving K., Illness Behavior of the Working Class: Implications and Recommendations, Shostak, Arthur and Gomberg, William (Editors), BLUE COLLAR WORLD, Englewood Cliffs, New Jersey, Prentice-Hall, Inc., 1964, pp. 351–361.

[16] Freidson, Eliot, PATIENTS' VIEWS OF MEDICAL PRACTICE, New York, Russell Sage Foundation, 1961.

[17] Suchman, Edward A., Social Patterns of Illness and Medical Care. *Journal of Health and Human Behavior,* 6, 2–16, Spring, 1965.

[18] Hochbaum, Godfrey M., PUBLIC PARTICIPATION IN MEDICAL SCREENING PROGRAMS: A SOCIOPSYCHOLOGICAL STUDY, Public Health Service, Public Health Service Publication Number 572, Washington, United States Government Printing Office, 1958.

122

[19] Kegeles, S. Stephen, Some Motives for Seeking Preventive Dental Care, *Journal of the American Dental Association*, 67, 90–98, July, 1963.

[20] Heinzelmann, Fred, Determinants of Prophylaxis Behavior with Respect to Rheumatic Fever, *Journal of Health and Human Behavior*, 3, 73–81, 1962.

[21] Flach, Elizabeth, Participation in Case Finding Program for Cervical Cancer, Administrative Report, Cancer Control Program, United States Public Health Service, Washington, D.C., 1960.

[22] Leventhal, Howard, *et al.*, Epidemic Impact on the General Population in Two Cities, in THE IMPACT OF ASIAN INFLUENZA ON COMMUNITY LIFE: A STUDY IN FIVE CITIES, United States Department of Health, Education and Welfare, Public Health Service, Publication Number 766, 1960.

[23] Kegeles, S. Stephen, Why People Seek Dental Care: A Test of a Conceptual Formulation, *Journal of Health and Human Behavior*, 4, 166–173, Fall, 1963.

[24] Rosenstock, Irwin M., *et al.*, A NATIONAL STUDY OF HEALTH ATTITUDES AND BEHAVIOR, (In progress), Ann Arbor, The University of Michigan, School of Public Health, 1965.

[25] Rosenstock, Irwin M., What Research in Motivation Suggests for Public Health, *American Journal of Public Health*, 50, 295–302, March, 1960.

[26] Rosenstock, Irwin M., Hochbaum, Godfrey M. and Kegeles, S. Stephen, "Determinants of Health Behavior," Working paper prepared for the Golden Anniversary White House Conference on Children and Youth, 1960, (Mimeographed).

[27] Lewin, Kurt, A DYNAMIC THEORY OF PERSONALITY, London, McGraw-Hill Book Company, Inc., 1935.

[28] The model was originally developed in the Behavioral Science Section of the Public Health Service, principally by Hochbaum, Leventhal, Kegeles and Rosenstock. The present statement of the model is the author's and may or may not fully reflect current points of view of others who have been working with it.

[29] Bruner, Jerome and Goodman, Cecile C., Value and Need as Organizing Factors in Perception, *Journal of Abnormal and Social Psychology*, 42, 37–39, 1947.

[30] Rosenstock, Irwin M. and Hendry, Jean, Epidemic Impact on Community Agencies, in *The Impact of Asian Influenza on Community Life: A Study in Five Cities, op. cit.*

[31] Robbins, Paul, Some Explorations Into the Nature of Anxieties Relating to Illness, United States Department of Health, Education and Welfare, Public Health Service, *Genetic Psychology Monographs*, 66, 91–141, 1962.

[32] Miller, Neal E., Experimental Studies of Conflict, *in* Hunt, J. McV., PERSONALITY AND THE BEHAVIOR DISORDERS, New York, The Ronald Press, 1944, pp. 431–465.

[33] Freidson, *op. cit.*, p. 144.

[34] Festinger, Leon, A THEORY OF COGNITIVE DISSONANCE, Evanston, Illinois, Row Peterson, 1957.

[35] Other analyses showed that no more than 12 per cent of all respondents accepted both beliefs.

[36] Beliefs in the benefits of preventive actions were not introduced into the analysis since most people expressed generally positive feelings about the vaccine.

[37] Guskin, Samuel L., The Measurement of Change in Beliefs About Tuberculosis, in PROCEEDINGS OF THE FIRST ANNUAL CONFERENCE ON BEHAVIORAL ASPECTS OF TUBERCULOSIS CONTROL, Atlanta, Georgia, Tuberculosis Branch, Communicable Disease Center, Public Health Service, in press.

[38] Haefner, Don P., Arousing Fear in Dental Health Education, *Journal of Public Health Dentistry*, 25, 140–146, 1965.

[39] Simmons, Ozzie G., *Social Status and Public Health*, Social Science Research Council, Pamphlet number 13, New York, 1958.

[40] Klapper, Joseph T., THE EFFECTS OF MASS COMMUNICATION, Glencoe, Illinois, The Free Press of Glencoe, 1960, pp. 49–50.

[41] Lazarsfeld, Paul F. and Kendall, Patricia, The Communication Behavior of the Average American, in Schramm, Wilbur L., (Editor), MASS COMMUNICATIONS, Urbana, Illinois, University of Illinois Press, 1960, pp. 425–437.

[42] Katz, Elihu and Lazarsfeld, Paul F., PERSONAL INFLUENCE, Glencoe, Illinois, The Free Press of Glencoe, 1955, p. 41.

[43] Society of Public Health Educators Research Committee, Review of Research Related to Health Education Practice, *Health Education Monographs*, 1, 70, 1963.

[44] Janis, Irving L. and Feshbach, Seymour, Effects of Fear Arousing Communications, *Journal of Abnormal and Social Psychology*, 48, 1953.

[45] Goldstein, Michael J., The Relationship Between Coping and Avoiding Behavior and Response to Fear-Arousing Propaganda, *Journal of Abnormal and Social Psychology*, 60, 37–43, 1960.

[46] Leventhal, Howard and Kafes, Patricia N., The Effectiveness of Fear Arousing Movies in Motivating Preventive Health Measures, *New York State Journal of Medicine*, 63, 867–874, 1963.

[47] Radelfinger, Sam, Some Effects of Fear-Arousing Communications on Preventive Health Behavior, *Health Education Monographs*, 19, 2–15, 1965.

[48] Cartwright, Dorwin and Zander, Alvin, GROUP DYNAMICS RESEARCH AND THEORY, Second edition, Evanston, Illinois, Row, Peterson and Company, 1960.

[49] Lewin, Kurt, Group Decision and Social Change, in Newcomb, T. M. and Hartley, E. L., (Editors), READINGS IN SOCIAL PSYCHOLOGY, New York, Henry Holt and Company, 1947, pp. 330–344.

[50] Bond, Betty W., Group Discussion-Decision: An Appraisal of Its Use in Health Education, *International Journal of Health Education*, 1, 1958.

124

DISCUSSION

The uncertain relationship of beliefs to behavior. The paper presents a highly developed model of medical decision-making and the author himself provides the most cogent critique of the model. In view of the relative lack of systematic data in the field for its support, discussants question the appropriateness of singling out this particular model as the reference point for organizing most of the research strategy on use of health services. While the published studies show impressive correlations between beliefs and actions, they do not demonstrate that beliefs are instrumental in determining action. Questions were raised about Dr. Rosenstock's decision to ignore the past behavior of the subjects in his model, as well as the situational settings conditioning behavior. Those who, in the past, have taken preventive actions may have adopted appropriate rationales for their behavior, or may continue to observe preventive behavior because of the operation of factors leading to the earlier actions. To establish that beliefs and perceptions have impact on behavior independently of the force of habit, research would have to control for past behavior.

More knowledge is needed concerning the limits of applicability of findings correlating particular beliefs and actions. Perceived susceptibility and preventive action have been correlated only in populations recently exposed to directed messages or to cues to action. Beliefs and behavior might be less closely correlated in populations where an appreciable segment is compelled to engage routinely in preventive behavior. Any number of other external factors could weaken or strengthen the degree of consonance found, and without reference to the concrete situation only limited links may connect beliefs and actions.

The objective health care situation as a factor in behavior. While the model presented in the paper appears useful for understanding the development of individual health behavior, many discussants question its fruitfulness for developing intervention models to improve preventive practices and to change behavior. The intervention model associated with Dr. Rosenstock's theory seems to call for the conversion of those individuals who take poor care of their health to the ideology of those who take better care of it. In view of the lack of evidence that the strengthening of beliefs would produce widespread improvement in health care, as well as in view of the constraints of the research economy, the belief system does not seem to warrant as much attention as it receives in the paper. While the manipulation of the environmental as well as the belief systems of people raises serious questions in the minds of the speakers, several believe that greater gains per given research expenditures might accrue if study designs concentrated more on those elements of the situation most susceptible to alteration, namely, the medical care setting itself. Systematic and extended observation of what people do when given access to new and experimental forms of care could extend the knowledge and predictability of people's health behavior.

Dr. Rosenstock's model implicitly seems to entail a research strategy in which the individual person is the ultimate unit of analysis. But public health programs, in the opinion of one discussant, are conducted on a mass basis and require knowledge of the population's aggregate behavior. Whether knowledge based on individual behavior would be directly applicable at the population level was questioned. Since the prevailing responses to health problems vary from population to population and in accordance with the institutional frameworks in effect, stress should be placed on those research strategies which make possible the understanding of the diversity of response and how it varies with population characteristics. While in cross-national comparisons differences in cultural norms would be confounded with institutional differences, even these studies would be helpful because they would lead to a separation from the restrictive influences of the immediate United States situation and provide new research and action perspectives.

The concept "everybody is a case." Considerable reflection took place on the limited concepts of illness and of health decision-making that characterize most of current health services research. Illness and symptoms tend to be conceived as knowable and specifiable entities and the population categorized in terms of the sick and the well, with health decisions regarded as single, isolable incidents. Whereas health itself is in reality an elusive concept, in much of research the stages involved in seeking medical care are conceived as completely distinct. The health professions are becoming increasingly aware of the lack of clarity in the definition of health. People may not think primarily in terms of disease states and symptoms; which of the vast array of symp-

126

toms they heed and why is not clear. In this broad perspective everybody, in Leighton's terms, would appear to be a case, and exhaustive studies of the total process of seeking care would appear most timely. To other speakers, however, the construct "everybody is a case" and the corresponding research strategy appear to involve a serious loss of research perspective and disregard for research economy. In health behavior research, as in other research areas, focus should be placed on the important issue, which is how to motivate populations at risk to more appropriate health behavior.

Perceptions of health services benefits. Arguments are also presented for a broader concept of the potential benefits patients expect from health services. Dr. Rosenstock appears to have defined perceived benefits essentially in terms of their medical significance. Yet published research findings increasingly point out the many psychological and related problems patients bring to physicians and for which they expect help. Some services might even be used too much. To investigate this problem seriously, more information is needed from the medical profession about what constitutes appropriate use of health services. Such a definition in turn would depend on the extent to which physicians transcend their functions of technical experts for the treatment of organic disorders and accept additional responsibilities for some aspects of psychotherapeutic care. More definite criteria are definitely needed about the use of health resources in relation to meeting specified needs. In conclusion, patients are not the only ones who should be studied in connection with the use of health services. Although physicians are a major influence on the behavior of their patients, Dr. Rosenstock's paper does not emphasize their role enough. Knowledge of the effects of health services personnel on the utilization of services is important because findings from studies of public health programs in other countries indicate that altering the perceptions and behavior of health personnel may be easier than altering those of their clientele.

RESEARCH ON THE DEMAND FOR HEALTH SERVICES

PAUL J. FELDSTEIN

INTRODUCTION

A Framework for Analysis

The sharp rise in the prices of medical care services and expenditures on medical care over the past 20 years has been the major cause for concern over the adequate provision and financing of health services.[1] If each person's consumption of medical care services were small and the prices charged for these services were low, the welfare aspects of the problem would diminish as would the costs of misallocation of medical care resources. Time could then be spent analyzing other problems of concern to society. Unfortunately, the converse is largely true. Therefore, to avoid costly errors in planning and to minimize the hardships of any unmet needs, the factors that influence prices and utlization in the medical care market must be understood.

Interpreting the trend in health service usage and explaining variations in usage during any one year are difficult tasks. This paper approaches these difficulties by dividing them into two areas: the first is one of definition; the second is the development of an analytical framework. Part of the observed variation in the utilization of health services can be explained by changes in how services have been defined and how their use has been measured over time. Adjusting for changes in the product definition will not, however, explain all the variations in use of health services. Therefore, a framework must be developed to explain such variations.

128

This paper will describe an economic framework for explaining variations in the demand for health services. Lack of such a framework hinders, or even prevents a survey of the literature and research in this field to show where it fits in, on what parts of the framework knowledge is available and also where future research is needed. The framework should also serve as an aid in evaluating the findings of present research to the extent that such research does or does not incorporate into its analyses relevant parts of the framework.

A demand analysis is only one-half of the analysis needed to explain variations in the use of medical care services. If private expenditures for medical care services were plotted on a chart, using a series of points for the years, each point would be higher than the previous one. The height of a given point, or the magnitude of expenditures in any one year, is the result of many factors which the economist classifies according to those that affect the demand for care and those that affect the supply of care. To understand why the price of medical care is at a certain level or why the utilization of medical care is what it is, both the demand and supply factors must be known. A change in the quantity of medical care used between any two periods could result from a change in the demand for care, a change in the supply of care or, more likely, a change in both conditions. For example, if the number of persons covered by hospital insurance were to increase from one period to the next while all other factors remained constant, an increase in the demand for hospital care would be expected (assuming a positive causal relationship exists). If, however, along with this increase in insurance coverage changes occurred also in the costs of providing care, in the number and type of facilities and personnel, etc., then utilization in the next period would be difficult to predict. Changes are always occurring in the conditions affecting both the supply of care and the demand for care. The interaction of these sets of conditions determines the level of care provided in any period. Examining the factors affecting the demand for care, which this paper will do, is only one part of the problem of determining the health service utilization level and will not, by itself, enable a prediction of actual use to be made. A more complete study to explain the trends in utilization over the past 20 years would have to examine the changes in both demand and supply.

129

The Uses of Demand Analysis

Studies of demand generally have two purposes. The first is explanation; the ability to specify and estimate the relationship between use of a product or service and the factors influencing this use increases understanding of usage variations. Furthermore, identification and measurement of the "explanatory variables" are useful when formulating policies aimed at increasing or decreasing the use of services and also when assessments are being made on probable effects of public policy measures aimed at any of the explanatory factors.

The other important application of this kind of study is prediction of future demand. Forecasting utilization of medical care services depends essentially upon finding relationships between the variables to be forecasted and the other factors which determine the variables' magnitude. Projections are then made for the explanatory factors. These projections, when related to utilization, make possible an estimate of the demand for a future period. Such estimates can serve, for example, as guides for determining the number and types of personnel and the number of hospital beds or other medical care facilities needed in the future.

Demand and need for care are not necessarily the same. Need is the amount of care believed necessary by medical authorities while demand is the actual use of medical care services. Several factors account for discrepancies between the need and the demand for care. For instance, an individual may demand more care than is medically required. Conversely, he could be unaware of the value of medical care, or specialized facilities and services could be unavailable to him or he could be without the financial resources for the medical care he needs. Therefore, to plan for future use of a community's health facilities and personnel, the demand rather than the need for such resources must be projected. The need may be very great, but if it is not reflected in usage, facilities based on need will remain empty.

Private and "Public" Demand for Medical Care

The demand framework to be described does not cover a community's total demand for medical care. Excluded are aspects of demand involving externalities and indivisibilities. For example, certain services which can only be provided in large units, e.g., water fluoridation, are difficult, if not impossible, to purchase on an individual basis.

Moreover, the purchase of some services provides benefits to persons other than the purchasers, e.g., knowledge derived from medical research. Services of external or indivisible characteristics have traditionally been provided by governments through public health programs since, if left to the market, a smaller than optimal amount of such services might be provided. Although individual variations may occur in the demand for these services, the means by which they are provided and financed eliminate individual choice of usage. Hence, to incorporate this demand into the demand for personal health services would be incorrect. The role of the government should not be excluded completely from studies of the private demand for medical care, however. In addition to governmental provision of "public" goods, one may also find some public provision of what are normally considered private goods and services in medical care. Spending for personal health care by federal, state and local units of government totalled 6118.9 million dollars in the 1962–63 fiscal year. Of this amount, 4131.1 million, or 14 per cent, was allocated to programs which were not related to government employment.[2] Governmental provision of personal health care as a form of public assistance may be accomplished either through the existing medical care market, by means of subsidies, such as payments to a general hospital for welfare patients, or through the provision of such care outside the existing market, by the Veterans Administration, for example. Since the care being provided may be, to some extent, a substitute for care purchased by families and individuals, it should be included in the analysis of the demand for personal health services.

The way in which this care is provided—whether through subsidies or through direct provision of the services—will affect empirical estimates of the personal demand for health care. In either case, however, a complete model of the demand for medical care in the private sector should include the personal services aspects of public programs but exclude services, such as public health programs, which offer no individual choice other than the ballot box.

Expenditures on public health programs may be substituted to some extent for private health expenditures; e.g., the demand for private dental care is probably affected by water fluoridation. The decision to include public health programs in an analysis of the private demand for health services depends on the specific content and variety of public programs and on the study's level of aggregation. That is, a study of private demand for dental care in a community with water

131

fluoridation may exclude such a program. If, however, the study were being made in several communities, some with fluoridation and some without, the existence of fluoridation programs should be included in the analysis. (The choice in these situations is a collective choice.) Similarly, an analysis of private health services demand in different countries must allow for differences in expenditures on public programs when they may be substituted for private expenditures. This paper assumes that excluding public health programs that may be substituted for private expenditures has little or no effect on explaining variations in private demand.

THE PRODUCT—MEDICAL CARE

Until now, the general terms of supply and demand have been used for "health services." If the factors affecting the demand for health care are to be specified, a more precise definition of the "product" demanded must be found along with a better understanding of how the various components of care are used in its production. Furthermore, if empirical work on the estimation of demand is to be evaluated, more attention must be given to the interpretation of the various indices used to measure medical care demand.

Definition of the Product

Expenditures for medical care represent the purchase of a conglomeration of services. Drugs, hospital and physician care, for example, are all included. In empirical work, quality differences may not usually be distinguished in the same type of care or in differences in expenditures that reflect only differing amenities, such as private accommodations, that are not medically required. Medical care is not purchased merely for a hospital admission or a physician visit. Rather, it is purchased with the hope of receiving something more basic; good health. Good health, however, may also result from expenditures for food, clothing and housing. Thus, a more precise definition of "medical care" is needed.

One possible definition of the medical care product is that "medical care is the service consisting of the control and/or management of diseases (or other unwanted physical or mental conditions) be they actual or potential."[8] (Preventive care is included in this definition since it represents the management of a potential disease.) The different components of medical care services have traditionally been

132

analyzed separately without regard for the use of other components. According to the above definition, the components are used together when treating an illness and must therefore be considered both complementary and interchangeable. For example, hospital care may be used together with physician care in the treatment of an illness, and the two would thus be considered complementary. On the other hand, nursing home care and outpatient care may to some extent be substituted for hospital care.

Depending upon the degree to which components may be substituted for each other, analyses which examine the use of one care component without considering the extent to which the other components are used must be held incomplete for the purpose of explaining usage variations in medical care or in any one component of care. In many instances, the above definitional framework of the medical care product would have helped explain apparent differences in hospital use. Since a patient may be treated for an illness with different combinations of hospital care, physician visits, etc., different lengths of hospital stay may conceivably represent use of the other components of care in varying proportions. That is, higher hospitalization rates may reflect relatively less use of the other "inputs" in the production of a treatment. The reason for relatively greater use of some components will be discussed below. However, without consideration of all the components of care used in a particular treatment, conclusions cannot be drawn regarding the "proper" amount of care received from one component. To explain variations in that component's use would also be impossible if the factors influencing the relative mix of a treatment's components are not explicitly included in the analysis.[4]

Thus, to have as precise a definition of medical care as possible is important. In addition to using this definition to analyze the differential usage rates of any care component, the definition facilitates an explanation (and prediction) of what will happen when a change occurs in any of the factors affecting the demand for care. For example, if economic resources increase, are treatments of a different type demanded, or is an increase in the quality of treatment demanded? Which components will be used more? Although empirical problems are involved in holding the distribution of illness constant and measuring changes in treatment quality, a theoretical definition of medical care is still useful to see where current research fits in and whether any theoretical criticisms of the research can be made.

Measurement Problems

An empirical measure of medical care also becomes important when deriving estimates for the effect of the various factors that influence demand. Empirical measures of demand have generally been expressed as units of service such as hospital admissions, patient days, length of stay and physician visits. One writer has suggested that the appropriate dependent variable for medical care demand studies is the dollar amount a person spends, since for a given expenditure the physician will provide a set of components for treatment.[5] However, an empirical measure such as medical care expenditures may bias the effects of the factors believed to influence demand (prices and income), if it is not first adjusted for price changes and for changes in the product itself, e.g., quality changes. These problems, of developing a price index for medical care and adjusting for quality changes, are present in both time series and cross-section analyses.[6] For example, medical care expenditures are a combination of both the price charged for the treatment and the number of treatments purchased. If a rise in a patient's economic resources is accompanied by a rise in medical care expenditures, the latter may be merely the result of either an increase in the price to the patient or an increase in his consumption of comfort aspects. This would have different policy implications than an increased demand for treatments of higher quality or purchase of a different distribution of treatments.

The use of index number techniques in studies of medical care may help solve some problems. For instance, allowances might be made for the fact that the types of patients and the types of diseases being treated today are not the same as they were in the past. But a more important problem in arriving at an empirical measure of the product is eliminating differences in quality. For example, the results of a treatment for a particular illness today generally differ from the treatment results for that same illness ten or 15 years ago because the probability of recovery is greater, length of stay has been reduced or a lesser amount of other care is needed. An index of price changes over time, such as the medical care price index, that does not allow for these quality changes will greatly overestimate the price rise that has occurred and hence bias the estimates of the factors believed to affect demand. Measuring quality is not easy. A change in a person's chances of recovery from tuberculosis, for example, may take the form of a change in death rates from tuberculosis. Finer measurements would be desired, however, because some of those who would have died from tuberculosis in the past may now contribute to an increase in the death rates from cardiovascular diseases. A change in death rates in one diagnostic category will generally affect the death rates in other categories.

Although measurement is difficult, a clear advantage may be gained by discussing the price of medical care in terms of treatment price, allowing for quality changes that have occurred, rather than by merely observing the changes in prices for the components of medical care.

Some research has been conducted on the measurement of medical care prices and on the estimation of quality changes. Scitovsky[7] has undertaken a study to price a treatment as a whole, rather than studying only one care component, such as room rates, as has been and still is the more usual approach. Griliches[8] has conducted a study in which he attempts to estimate the bias introduced in the automobile price index by an inadequate allowance for the changes in automobile quality over time. The estimation of quality change in medical care is a particularly difficult problem, but an attempt to estimate the extent to which the rise in medical care prices has been offset by changes in quality would be worthwhile. Several surveys of changes in the distribution of inputs for a treatment have been made. "Changing Patterns of Care"[9] was an attempt to measure the change in distribution of inputs for provision of hospital care over a 15-year period. Unfortunately, data on the other components of care (other than hospitals) were not available.

The purpose of this section has been to define more clearly the medical care product that is being demanded. When empirical demand studies are later described, attempts to explain variations in use of the components of care should be considered in terms of this definitional framework. When the theoretical definition, which may be difficult to measure empirically, is related to the various empirical measures presently being used, the definition itself may explain some of the observed variations in use and expenditures.

A FRAMEWORK FOR ANALYZING
DEMAND FOR HEALTH SERVICES

At any time innumerable factors may influence a person's decision to make an expenditure for medical care and the amount he spends. To investigate variations in utilization of medical care, the first step is to decide upon an approach. To gather data and analyze relationships in a meaningful way a "model," based on hypotheses about the expected relationships, could be constructed. Therefore, before discussing empirical research on factors affecting the demand for medical care, a framework will be described within which the empirical work may be placed. Assuming the framework to be an accurate skeletal model of the demand for medical care, a discussion of the work done to date should indicate the areas in which some knowledge exists of the underlying relationships and the area lacking information on the importance of certain relationships. To discuss research without reference to some such framework might result in placing too much emphasis on those areas in which more research has been conducted—not because that area is more important but because it is more easily subject to quantification or because particular disciplines were interested in it.

The economic framework to be developed does not exclude noneconomic factors, but it does attempt to distinguish between those factors that affect supply and those that affect demand. Both the demand and supply factors must be known to predict actual use, and a study of demand is a study of only one part of the complete model. With a knowledge of demand the net change in demand may be forecast if a change occurs in any one of the factors affecting demand while all else is unchanged. The value for all the demand and supply factors must be known to say what actual use will be.

The demand approach, simply stated, is that the demand for medical care is determined by several economic and cultural-demographic factors, prevailing medical practice, as well as the incidence of illness. Before developing this framework and all its interrelationships in greater detail, the "product" and the concept of "choice" in the medical care market should be discussed.

The demand for medical care is the demand for a treatment, and variations in demand are variations in either number of treatments or in their quality. Moreover, this demand is typically initiated by the patient. (For simplicity, those instances where a physician discovers new illnesses in a patient that has come for treatment of another condition are considered as patient-initiated.) The physician combines the "inputs"—his own services, hospital services, etc.—to provide a treatment of a given quality. The demand for these "inputs" then become "derived" demands; that is, they are determined largely by the initial demand for a treatment. For example, a patient does not demand prescription drugs; he demands treatment for an illness. In

136

treating this illness the physician is aware of the patient's financial resources and how much he can afford to spend, and this, in addition to the physician's medical knowledge (and other constraints to be discussed), influences the kinds of "inputs" he will prescribe. If the physician decides home care and drugs would be a better alternative than prolonged hospital care, he will then prescribe the necessary drugs.

Therefore, empirical demand studies should first describe the manner in which different factors affect the patient's demand for medical care, and secondly, how the physician then decides what care components to use in caring for the patient. (Although the patient and physician phase is discussed sequentially, they occur at the same time.) Once this general process or framework has been described, an estimate should then be made of the various relationships between these factors and utilization of medical care. For example, how important are the patient's financial resources as a factor in determining the components of care to be used in treatment, or what is the impact of the extent of the physician's knowledge of the efficiency of various forms of treatment on his choice of care components? The empirical research, then, is the estimation of the above theoretical relationships of the demand for care.

Assumptions Underlying an Economic Approach: the Role of Choice in the Medical Care Market

Implicit in studies of demand is the assumption of choice. In studies of the demand for medical care, the element of choice exists both in the amount of medical care purchased and in the way which the components of care are combined to produce a given treatment. If choice in these areas were not possible, much less variation would be expected in the use of medical care in relation to economic factors, e.g., income and prices, and less variation in the manner in which a treatment is provided.

The degree of choice, whether on the part of the patient or his physician, depends on two factors—knowledge and the availability of substitutes. If a person were cognizant of the benefits from annual checkups or good dental hygiene, for example, his utilization of these services would be different, other things being equal, than if he did not have the knowledge. (Similarly, he may incorrectly attribute too great a benefit to some forms of treatment; however, this would increase the observed variations in use, which is the interest of this paper.) People often assume that no close substitutes for medical care exist. Even if this is true, families may still differ in their use of these services because they attach different values to the expected benefits of increased use and/or have varying knowledge of these benefits.

When discussing the degree of choice exhibited by the physician, remember that the physician, not the patient, combines the components of care into a treatment. In other markets the consumer, with varying degrees of knowledge selects the goods and services he desires from the available alternatives. In medical care, however, the patient does not usually make this choice directly. He does not usually decide, for example, which hospital he is to enter nor the form of treatment he is to receive; instead, he selects a physician who then makes these choices for him. Presumably, the physician has an element of choice available to him that produces observed variations in usage. Medical practice differs among doctors, as does their knowledge of the benefits of certain treatments. These differences, however, are not great enough in themselves to enable one to relate patient characteristics to variations in use. Another assumption is necessary, namely that the physician is cognizant of the patient's financial resources as well as of his medical needs, and thus acts in a manner consistent with the way the patient would behave if he were able to make the decisions. Evidence that this assumption is not wholly unrealistic may be seen from the numerous studies that relate hospital utilization to economic resources such as insurance coverage.

Implicit in the above assumption concerning the behavior of the physician is the belief that, in producing a form of treatment for the patient, he combines the components of care, depending upon their availability (closeness of substitutes) and their cost to the patient and to himself, to produce a treatment that is relatively low in cost to both the patient and himself. Also, the physician is assumed to be aware not only of the patient's needs and resources, but also of the various ways of combining the components of care to produce given treatments. Further, the physician presumably is cognizant of the increase in benefits that may be expected from an increase in use of any component, and he combines these components with regard to their relative cost to both the patient (insurance coverage, for example, would affect the relative prices to a patient) and to himself. (He would not combine components to result in the lowest cost to the patient if that combination increased his costs.)

In the studies that follow, these assumptions of choice in the medical care market need not be as clear-cut as described above each time a patient sees a physician and each time a physician treats a patient. However, to the extent that the above choices do exist and the physician acts with regard to the patient's financial resources, a greater empirical relationship should be observed between the patient's economic variables (financial resources) and utilization of medical care services. Further, a closer correlation may be expected between usage and economic variables if the following occurs: 1. knowledge of medical benefits to the patient and to the physician increases (the physician is able to combine the components of care differently with increased knowledge); 2. closer substitutes to be used in treatment are developed, e.g., the trend to use nursing homes as a partial substitute for hospital care.

Needless to say, much of the discussion of choice and the extent to which it exists is speculative. However, studies in this area would profitably increase understanding of the assumptions which are relevant to much empirical work and certainly to questions of public policy.[10]

The general framework of the demand for medical care within which the empirical research will be discussed is presented in Table 1.

TABLE 1. A MODEL OF DEMAND FOR MEDICAL CARE

Patient	*Physician*	*Derived Demands for the Components of Care*
Factors affecting a patient's demand for treatments	Factors affecting a physician's use of the components of care	hospital care physician care
Incidence of Illness	Patient characteristics includes	referrals to specialists
Cultural-demographic	relative cost to the patient	nursing home care
factors	from using different com-	etc.
Economic factors	ponents of care	
	Institutional Arrangements	
	Physician's knowledge	
	Relative costs to the physician	
	from using alternative sets of	
	components of care	

Briefly stated, the first phase is the patient's demand for care which is influenced by a number of factors, some of which imply an element of choice. The second phase involves the physician combining the inputs to produce a treatment. The way in which he uses these components is also determined by several factors, some of which also imply an element of choice available to him. In arriving at the demand for any one of the components of care, therefore, both the patient and physician influences must be considered. As a means of further describing this multifaceted process that results in the demand for medical care and for each of its components, each facet will be discussed together with some research findings to indicate the influence of some of the factors involved.

Factors Affecting the Patient's Demand for Medical Care

The factors that affect a patient's demand for medical care may be generally categorized as incidence of illness, cultural-demographic characteristics and economic factors.

The first two of these factors may be considered to shape a family's "desire" for medical care, and depend primarily upon the family's perception of a health deficiency and belief in the efficacy of medical treatment. In translating this desire into expenditure, the family is limited by the extent of its financial resources, as care cannot generally be obtained free of charge. Determining the amount to be spent for personal health services, then, becomes a part of the problem of allocating scarce financial resources among alternative desires. The amount spent would thus partially depend on the amount of income and wealth available and also on the price of medical care relative to the prices of other goods and services.

Medical care has been said to be solely a "need" rather than a "want" and economic considerations such as income and price therefore have little or no influence in determining the amount used. For care which is expected to substantially improve well-being and which can be obtained at a cost which does not strain a family's financial resources, this may well be the case. Often, however, the type of illness present and its prognosis are uncertain. For example, the distinction between a severe cold and pneumonia is not clear-cut, at least to the untrained mind. Chest pains may indicate either indigestion or a serious heart condition. In these and similar instances, income and price would be expected to affect decisions involving the purchase of medical care. Also, even after treatment is initiated, economic considerations may influence its extent. The gain from palliating the discomfort associated with a chronic condition will not always be worth the cost.

140

Each of these general categories that affect demand are more fully discussed below.

The incidence of illness. Need is generated by the incidence of illness while demand is generated by the interrelationship of illness with other factors.

The onset of illness and the use of the hospital is to many people an unexpected occurrence. Thus, for individuals, illness may be considered as a random event. However, for the population as a whole, illness has a fair degree of predictability, given certain characteristics of the population such as age, sex, etc. (Since age and sex are also demographic factors, a discussion of them is postponed until the next section.)

The concept of illness being considered as random among individuals but having greater predictability for population groups has been the basis for planning medical care services through the use of mortality rates, bed/population ratios, and physician/population ratios as indications of need. The use of incidence rates together with standards of care were used for developing standard ratios of facilities to population, and these ratios were then prescribed throughout the country.[11]

The unexpected nature of illness to individuals and the fluctuating or random element in demand on a day-to-day basis with respect to individual hospitals have prompted a number of studies that deal with predicting demand. Persons with a knowledge of operations research have reasoned that if they could ascertain the underlying probability distribution of "need" that best fits the utilization data, they will have developed an explanatory model as well as an accurate predictive device. Some interesting work in this area has been done in both the United States and the United Kingdom. These studies have used essentially the same technique for examining utilization in a hospital department as for examining the utilization of the hospital itself or the use of all the hospitals in a community.[12]

A basic assumption underlying the use of these studies in predictions of hospitalization is that admission is based on incidence of illness and that length of stay in the hospital, except for scheduling problems, is also based on medical necessity. If these studies were based on other assumptions, a stochastic distribution should not be used to describe or simulate it.

In a lecture before the Research Seminar in Hospital and Medical

Systems, Long made several points about the use of the random component of demand for planning hospital facilities. If at any time utilization is random, having large facilities brings certain economies. This random component should also be used for determining the number of beds to be built, for if facilities are built according to the mean expected level of use, the cost is a penalty of not being able to satisfy demand in excess of that mean level. This penalty cost will vary according to the community—the existing level of facilities, available substitutes, etc.—and will depend upon what the unsatisfied demand consists of, e.g., emergency versus elective cases. The optimum number of beds in a community is the point where the penalty cost to a community of not having an additional bed is equal to the long-run costs of adding an additional bed.

To be able to estimate what amount of medical care is solely a "need," i.e., may be considered as either emergent or urgent care, is important. If this quantity is very large in relation to the total demand for medical care, variations in medical care demand with reference to cultural-demographic and economic factors cannot be explained even with the possibility of determining why some components of care are used more in treatment.

Some studies attempt to estimate the size of this random element. According to the admission records of one particular hospital studied, patients classified as "emergent" (admitted immediately) and "urgent" (admitted within 24–48 hours) consisted of less than 20 per cent of the total admissions each month, the rest being classified as "elective" patients.[13] Anderson, reporting on a study of Massachusetts hospitals, said that, excluding maternity cases, 32 per cent of admissions were same-day emergency ones and 33 per cent were for illnesses that had been present for more than a year.[14]

The studies conducted by the operations researchers described above estimate the probability distribution of this random component with regard to only one componet of care—namely, hospitals. These studies are generally confined to a moment in time, that is, the other factors affecting demand are unchanged. In addition to the cultural-demographic and economic factors being constant, the factors affecting the physician's use of any components should also be considered as being constant. If these factors were to change, i.e., if the demand for medical care or the demand for any one component were to be examined over a period of years, using stochastic distributions could not explain variation as well as a method that holds other factors, such as patient and physician factors, constant and then fits a stochastic distribution to the unexplained variation.

Assuming a large random component in medical care has been the basis for many policy and planning decisions concerned with such matters, for example, as the location and size of facilities. Hence, the determination must be made of whether the nature and extent of this random component are changing. The percentage of total demand considered to be random is probably decreasing. This would be expected as the discretionary amount spent on medical care increases. If this is the case, then limiting the size of the hospital for reasons of accessibility decreases in importance, and greater advantage may be taken of economies of scale. Also, the cost of maintaining peak-period facilities and the means by which they are financed, might be re-examined.

Cultural-demographic factors. Cultural-demographic factors affecting a patient's demand for medical care represent physiological condition, perception of illness and attitudes toward seeking medical care. Since these factors can seldom be measured directly, specific population characteristics are substituted as indicators. Some of the characteristics commonly used in demand studies are age, sex, marital status, family size, education and residence (urban or rural). Differences in utilization of medical care services according to these characteristics have been documented in a number of studies. The relationship between the characteristics and the utilization of the various components of care, however, has not necessarily been similar. For example, the relationship between age and utilization of hospital services is different from that between age and utilization of dental services. A difference also exists in the relationship of the various characteristics to hospital admissions and lengths of stay. Although these population characteristics may not affect each of the components of health services in the same way, they are important in explaining variations in use of these services.

As individuals age, incidence of illness increases and morbidity patterns change; accidental injuries and chronic diseases become more frequent causes of death.[15] In considering the average difference in utilization of health care services between men and women, both marital status and age must be taken into account. Medical care expenditures are approximately the same for both sexes in the early years of life. Later on, the expenditures incurred by women exceed those incurred by men, mainly because of obstetrical charges. The

143

difference persists, however, far beyond the normal child-bearing age. Also, the relationship between age and use of medical care services is not a simple linear one. Tables reproduced from the various surveys would show the relationship between all the cultural-demographic factors mentioned and the utilization of each component of care with the different measures used for each category. However, because, for instance, hospital care may be represented by expenditures on hospitals, number of admissions, patient days and length of stay, reproducing such tables would not be feasible. Instead, the interested reader is referred to the original sources for such information.[16]

Marital status is also considered to affect the consumption of certain components of medical care. For example, unmarried persons generally consume more total days of hospital care than married persons. The availability of persons in the home to care for married persons may account for their using the hospital less.

Together with marital status, the size of the family will be an important influence on demand. The increase in demand, however, is not expected to be proportional to the number of persons in the family. Also important in the use of the various components of care is the age distribution of the family members.

A direct correspondence does not necessarily exist between physiological condition and desire for medical care. An actual need for care may not be perceived in some instances, while a nonexistent or imaginary "need" may be perceived in others. Also, a recognized health deficiency may not be translated directly into expenditure because of variations in disposition toward risk-taking and differences in belief in the effectiveness of medical treatment. Variables which might explain these factors include education and area of residence. Whether the prompt translation of physiological need to medical care spending results in higher or lower ultimate demand for medical care is difficult to foretell. A person who is well aware of the dangers of ill health and is desirous of treatment is likely to incur relatively large expenditures for preventive services, but may incur lower expenditures for treatment of morbid physiological conditions because they have been prevented. On the other hand, one who tends to ignore the symptoms of disease will have low expenditures for preventive services and care of noncritical conditions, but may well spend more for treatment in the long run (unless he succeeds in avoiding medical care entirely).

The interest of this paper is not in developing a theoretical model

144

of demand that will explain variations in demand for each individual family. Innumerable factors determine whether or not a person seeks medical care, the type of medical care he selects and the amount of medical care he uses. Demand studies do not attempt to specify all the many factors that might be important in individual cases; rather, they attempt to relate only those factors that are considered on the average to be most important in influencing usage of medical care services. For this reason the above list of factors has been kept fairly short.

Much of the knowledge of the factors affecting the use of health services has come from survey data. These data are usually presented by classifying utilization of a component according to some population characteristics. The ability to cross-classify tables according to more than one population characteristic or to use one characteristic in greater detail, e.g., an age breakdown for both males and females, increases understanding of the net effect of a particular factor on utilization. However, gross relationships between variables are generally presented because detailed subclassifications are limited by the size of the page and the reader's ability to comprehend them. Only within the last few years has a statistical technique long in use in other fields been applied to the interpretation of utilization data. This technique, multivariate analysis, holds promise to enable the determination of the net effect of any one characteristic on utilization.

A number of studies have used this technique on survey data and derived estimates of the effects of some cultural-demographic variables on utilization. The purpose of these studies was to determine the effect of a particular variable on utilization while holding constant the effects of other variables. The studies have been conducted for total medical care expenditures for a particular component of care, as well as for subclassifications within a component, such as pediatric, obstetric or medical-surgical utilization in a hospital, and also for a finer breakdown such as hospital diagnosis.[17]

Multivariate studies have been few and have differed widely with regard to the variables included, the method by which the same variables were represented, the data used, the components of care studied, etc. Therefore, the results on the net effects of the variables studied cannot be used with any high degree of confidence. More multivariate studies, however, would be very worthwhile, and greater consensus on the effects of the particular variables might be reached in a few years.

Though determining the effect of cultural-demographic factors on use of health services is important to increase understanding, cultural-demographic factors are not usually subject to sudden changes. The age composition changes gradually, and abrupt changes in cultural-demographic factors are unlikely over short periods of time. Also, for policy purposes, affecting utilization by changing these variables is difficult. With regard to the next set of factors to be discussed, information on their net effects can have more immediate value for policy and prediction.

Economic factors. Prices and income theoretically affect not only a person's decision whether or not to seek medical care, but also the extent of the care once treatment is undertaken. For example, the effect of prices or of income may or may not have much effect on whether or not a maternity patient goes to the hospital (although it may influence the choice of hospital), but once she has been admitted, it may affect the length of her stay.

Economic theory hypothesizes that, other things being equal, the consumption of any commodity or service varies inversely with the price of the service. That is, as the price of the service is lowered, consumption increases. As applied to the discussion of the cultural-demographic factors, however, not only the direction but also the extent of the effect of a price change must be known. Economists use the term "elasticity" to indicate the responsiveness of changes in consumption to a change in one of the factors affecting consumption. An estimate of elasticity greater than one means that the percentage change in consumption will be greater than the percentage change in the factor that brought about this change. An estimate of zero elasticity means that consumption of a particular service is unaffected by changes in the factor being studied.

Those in the health field have generally assumed that changes in prices have little effect on the use of medical care services. That is, price elasticity is considered to be less than one because of the few substitutes for medical care. Adequate data to test this belief have been lacking. To estimate a price effect empirically a "net" price variable must be used, that is, the "out-of-pocket" price to the patient and not the stated price. To arrive at this estimate, the effect of health insurance, "free" care and the tax deductibility aspects would first have to be eliminated, for these factors actually reduce the price the patient pays for services. Some of the empirical demand studies have used a price variable in their analyses, and their findings show that the price elasticity of the components of care studied is much less than one. However, these results may be criticized on the grounds that the price variable was either not a true "net" price to the patient,[18] or that the manner used for constructing a "net" price to the patient had biased the derived estimates.[19]

In theory, health insurance acts as a proxy price variable, i.e., it lowers the price the patient pays for the covered service. Insurance will therefore have two effects: 1. it reduces the over-all price of medical care to the patient with insurance, hence increasing his consumption of medical care services (this is an "income" effect), and 2. it causes components of care that are covered to be substituted for those that are not (this is the "price" effect). Both these effects are difficult to empirically measure.

A number of studies have related the existence of health insurance in one form or another to the use of health services, primarily hospitals. These studies have varied in their degree of sophistication from single cross-tabulations of how much persons with and persons without insurance use hospitals, to studies attempting to adjust insurance by its benefit structure and to hold constant the effects of other cultural-demographic and economic factors believed to have an effect on utilization. Generally these studies show that insurance is positively related to both medical care expenditures and hospital use, but that the elasticity of insurance with respect to both is less than one.

In some empirical studies in this area, economic and cultural-demographic variables have been related to the different components of care, and different measures, such as admissions, length of stay and total patient days, have been used to represent hospitalization. The effect of the factors representing patient characteristics will differ according to which variables are used to represent hospitalization. For example, Cardwell, Reid and Shain[20] found that the birth rate now largely determines the obstetrical admission rate, but that economic factors exert the most influence on how long women stay in the hospital after childbirth.[21]

A number of questions are still unanswered, and further research in this area would be fruitful. For example, is the relationship between insurance and utilization in fact a causal one, or do persons who expect to use health services buy health insurance? Also, since age, education, income, etc., are correlated with the holding of insurance, determining the net effect of insurance on utilization is difficult. Part of the so-called insurance effect may really be the effect of these other

147

factors. Further, how large are the substitution effects between use of the components of care according to the range of insurance benefits?

In empirical studies of the demand for medical care, the price effect must be eliminated to derive accurate estimates of the effects of the other factors influencing demand, such as income. This is because of the relation between pricing practices and income in the provision of medical services. The use of the "sliding-scale" in setting fees, as well as other price-related factors such as "free" care, health insurance and tax deductibility of medical expenditures, are examples.[22]

If those in higher income groups pay higher prices for the same services, and if higher prices result in greater expenditures (and expenditures are used as a proxy measure for quantity), then estimates of the income effect based on expenditure data will be biased upward. Statistical evidence of the effect of the sliding scale on prices paid by those at different income levels is lacking, probably because differences in prices are difficult to separate from variations in the amount of service and amenity received. Medical care cannot easily be considered a service of homogeneous quality, and therefore, even with similar "quantities" of service, a person with a relatively high income paying a higher price may be receiving a somewhat different product. Because of this element of "trading-up," income elasticities calculated from expenditure data will result in higher estimates than elasticities based on quantities as they are usually measured, e.g., dental visits.

The relationship between family income and consumption of medical care services has been examined in a number of studies. In general, these studies indicate that families with higher incomes have higher expenditures—signifying higher consumption—for medical care, but the percentage of income spent on medical care decreases with higher levels of income. In other words, the consensus of these surveys and multivariate analyses is that the income elasticity is less than one.[23] The paper by Feldstein and Carr[24] contains a summary of the income-expenditure relationships derived from a number of surveys. For a number of such surveys, from 1917 to 1960, income elasticity was estimated by means of regression analysis and summarized in that paper. The calculated estimates from these surveys all indicate an income elasticity of less than one. A number of other studies have calculated the relation between income and medical care expenditures or between income and some component of care. Many of the studies, however, are not comparable with regard to the data used, components of care studied, technique used, etc.[25]

148

The manner in which family income is measured must be understood if the estimate of the effect of income derived from surveys and analyses in the health field is to be interpreted correctly. A family's income in any given year may be abnormally low or high because of temporary loss of employment, windfall gains or other unexpected events. Empirical evidence suggests that total consumption (that is, the use of products and services) is not generally raised or lowered to correspond with temporary changes in income. Rather, a family's level of consumption is determined primarily by its expected normal or "permanent" income.[26] Nearly all categories of consumption, including the total, probably exhibit this unresponsiveness to temporary fluctuations in income.

In general, then, transitory income is hypothesized to have little or no effect on the consumption level. Thus, if all income differences were transitory and people spent only according to their permanent incomes, no relationship between income and expenditures for medical care could be found. On the other hand, if incomes differed but contained no transitory components, the regression line would approximate the effect of normal income. Empirical observations of incomes of individual families are mixtures of normal and transitory components. Regression lines fitted to them will therefore lie somewhere between these two extremes. In terms of Figure 1, the slope of a line based on reported income (AA) would be less steep than the slope of a line based on normal income (BB), but steeper than the nearly horizontal line which would be derived from data containing only transitory income differences (CC).

Another way of looking at this is to consider the distribution of the transitory components of income. One postulate of the permanent-income theory is that transitory income is not correlated with normal income. Therefore, families with negative transitory incomes (e.g., people who are sick are likely to be below their "normal" income) are most likely to be found in the lower portion of the distribution of reported incomes, while those with positive transitory incomes most probably lie in the upper part. In terms of normal income, incomes in the lower portion of the distribution thus tend to be understated while those in the upper part are likely to be overstated. To this extent, a regression analysis of expenditures and total income will underestimate the effect of differences in normal income on medical care spending. (Random errors in the amount of income reported will also bias the income expenditure regression in the same direction as differences

FIGURE 1.

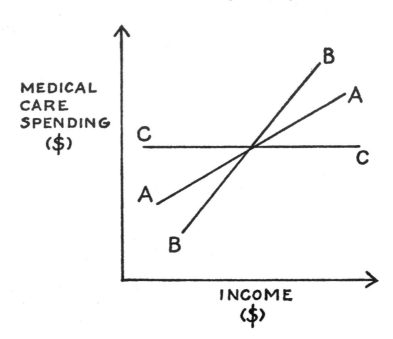

MEDICAL CARE SPENDING ($)

INCOME ($)

in transitory income because they affect the level of income reported but not the level of expenditure.)

The relationship presented by survey data and by multivariate analyses compares medical care expenditures with total income, which includes both permanent and transitory components. A more useful estimate would be based on the relationship between expenditures and normal (permanent) income alone. Since transitory income is included in the income variable, but presumably has little effect on the level of expenditure, the indicated relationships presented in the above mentioned analyses provide a biased estimate of the effect of normal income on medical care spending. Therefore, removing the effects of transitory income would considerably improve estimates of the effect of normal income.

Another important income-related consideration is that physiological condition may affect both expenditure and income. Illness may result in higher medical care spending and, at the same time, reduce family income by causing the disability of a wage earner. This may occur in either the permanent or transitory sense. In both cases, the result is to lower the measured effect of income on medical care spending. To the extent that physiological condition does not depend upon income, it should be held constant among income groups in calculating the income-expenditure relationship, or else income estimates based on family survey data will also be biased downward by this factor.

Another factor which must be taken into account in analyzing the income effect is that employer and other third-party contributions to health insurance premiums are not normally included in family expenditure data. To determine the over-all elasticity of private medical care spending, these expenditures must be included in the analysis. Although spending for group plans is probably fairly independent of individual families' incomes within a given plant or company, the average income of the group as a whole exhibits a strong influence on third-party expenditures for health insurance. In addition, tax considerations provide an incentive for increased employer contributions at higher average levels. Employers' contributions toward the payment of health insurance premiums do not constitute taxable income to the recipients. Thus, the higher the average income tax bracket, the larger the potential tax saving to the employee and the greater his incentive to have payments made by the employer. Rice has estimated that roughly one-half of total health insurance premiums are paid by third parties, and that the income elasticity of third-party payments must be much greater than one. To some extent, these employer contributions act as substitutes for family payments. Any estimate of the over-all income elasticity of medical care spending will therefore be biased downward if third-party payments of health insurance premiums are not included. The bias would be expected to be even greater in recent years because the percentage of private medical care expenditures accounted for by insurance rose from 12.8 in 1950, to 29.7 per cent in 1960.[27]

In the study by Feldstein and Carr, in which the effect of transitory income and the growth in health insurance enrollment were allowed for, the estimate of income elasticity increased to approximately one. In other words, the percentage of income spent on medical care is approximately constant at higher levels of income. These conclusions, which differ from those presented earlier, must still be considered tentative since the effect of prices and price-related factors correlated with income could not be completely eliminated.[28]

Additional research on the effect of economic factors on use of medical care should be in two general areas. First, continued effort should be made to estimate the net effects of each economic factor on use. As the above discussion shows, difficulty lies not only in separating the effects of the economic factors from each other, as with prices, but also in separating them from the cultural-demographic factors. However, this separation must be accomplished to understand the effects of either the economic or the cultural-demographic factors on the use of health services. Second, further studies in this area should attempt to examine utilization in terms of the illnesses being treated at different income levels and to classify them according to their discretionary aspects. A shift in the distribution of illnesses with increased family income will have important policy implications with regard to financing health care.[29]

Factors Affecting the Physician's Use of the Components of Care

Earlier the hypothesis was made that the physician knows the patient's needs and financial resources and that, other things being equal, he acts as a purchaser for the patient. Therefore, the patient characteristics, both economic and cultural-demographic, are expected to be related to the use of medical care services. In other words, the physician is making the decisions that the patient would make if he had the knowledge to do so. In this role, the physician can be thought of as a firm combining the inputs (components of care) for producing a treatment. When choosing the components of care to be used in treatment, he will be guided not only by their efficacy in treatment but also by their relative prices to the patient. For example, if care in a nursing home could be substituted for additional care in a hospital but the patient's insurance coverage provides only for hospital care, the physician would probably provide care in the hospital, not in the nursing home. (Providing the set of components of care least expensive to the patient but not to the community may cause the physician to act against the interests of the community, as in the above example.) Though this behavior of the physician will be limited by factors to be discussed later, this assumption has enough basis in fact to be useful in predicting use of the other components if other factors are unchanged. An example of the discretion a physician can exercise in choosing alternatives to hospitalization is the following:

Surgical admissions accounted for 49 per cent of the total, medical for 35 per cent, admissions for diagnostic tests for 14 per cent, and other sorts of admissions for the remaining 2 per cent . . . Physicians were . . . asked to choose among four alternatives in the handling of each patient in an attempt to determine the size of the area of discretion open to them . . . Physicians felt that there was much less leeway in performing surgery outside of the hospital than for appropriate handling of medical patients and those admitted for diagnostic purposes: for 76, 46 and 45 per cent, respectively, of three categories of patients, hospital admission was absolutely necessary according to the admitting physician.[30]

Other forces affecting the physician, however, may prevent his using the set of components that would result in lowest cost to the patient. He may be limited by institutional arrangements. For example, if two hospitals in a community provide about the same care to their obstetrics patients, but one hospital is more expensive than the other, unless the physician has a staff appointment at the lower-priced hospital, his obstetrics patient will be limited to the more expensive one.[31]

Another factor which will limit a physician in providing his patient with a set of components at lowest cost is the extent of his knowledge of different methods of treatment. For example, if recent developments suggest that patients should be ambulatory in shorter time, but the physician is not aware of these developments, he will probably keep his patient in the hospital longer than is necessary.[32]

Further, some hospitals have sanctions preventing the physician from prolonging a patient's stay unnecessarily when other forms of care are available, e.g., utilization committees reviewing admissions and length of stay for each of the physicians on the staff. If this occurs, little relationship could be observed between the patient's economic characteristics and the use of the components of care.[33]

Another factor not explicitly mentioned above greatly affects the manner in which the physician uses the components of care. Presumably, if certain institutional arrangements, the physician's knowledge, and possible sanctions were not present, the physician would combine the components of care in a manner to produce a treatment at lowest cost to the patient. Therefore, one would expect patient characteristics and the demand for medical care and its components to be closely related. However, in combining the components of care, the physician is acting not only in the patient's interest but also in his own. Since physician care is also a component of treatment, the extent to which this care is used depends not only on the patient characteristics and patient cost for this care relative to alternative combinations, but also on the cost (implicit or otherwise) to the physician of using relatively more or less of his care. For example, if hospitals were to lower their weekend rates drastically to raise the occupancy over this period (assuming staff costs are similar for both weekend and weekday use), the physician could, in elective cases, reduce the patient's hospital bill by admitting him over the weekend. However, the cost to the physician must be considered in terms of loss of leisure time if he is required to work over the weekend to achieve a lower hospital bill to the patient. The result might actually be a higher *total* bill to the patient, if the physician charges him a higher rate for his own loss of leisure.[34]

Different forms of organizing medical care have their affect on the manner in which physicians use the components of care. To affect a lower total cost of care to the community, new forms of organization must first enable the physician to produce care of given quality with lower cost components, e.g., to substitute outpatient care for hospitalization when medically possible. At the same time, organization forms must allow the physician to act in the patient's interest, e.g., to substitute insured for uninsured services. Second, they must not change the relative cost to the physician for using a new set of components of care unless the change is downward, e.g., by requiring less of his time, increasing his convenience of performing his tasks, increasing his productivity, resulting in economies of scale, etc. The important point is that if a change in organization is to be accepted, it must result in a lower cost to the patient, the physician or both.

Therefore, the effect of both prepaid group practice plans, and also increases in the availability of facilities, is largely through their effect on the costs to either the patient or the physician. The use of specific components of care will be influenced by changes in their relative costs. Studies of the effect that prepaid group practice has had on hospital utilization and on the other components of care have been subject to varying interpretations because of the difficulty in examining organizational structure's net effect on use, while holding constant insurance coverage changes and the resultant additional case finding by physician.[35]

As for the availability of facilities, the question whether changes in the supply of beds affect the demand for them or whether beds are built essentially in response to changes in demand has been much discussed.[36] The author's opinion is that increases in bed supply affect the relative cost to the physician for providing care. For example, if other influences, such as the patient's financial resources, are constant, then an increase in the bed supply in an area with few physicians will probably

154

increase the physician's use of the hospital. The physician will substitute hospital beds for his own time in treating the patient because he can see more patients in a given time.

The point here is that patient characteristics, such as economic and cultural-demographic factors, influence the amount and type of medical care a physician will prescribe. The effects of these factors, however, are muted by institutional arrangements, the extent of the physician's knowledge and possible sanctions against him. An important factor which will also influence his behavior in use of the components of care is the relative costs to himself. Therefore, he will tend to substitute some components for others according to his own needs or convenience. In this latter context organizational arrangements may have, and accessibility of beds will have, their effect. (In addition to the above explanation on the effect changes in bed supply have on hospital use, beds also set an upper limit to use. Other increases in bed supply either are responses to an already present demand or would have resulted given the trend in demand over time. For these reasons bed supply was not included as a separate factor affecting demand, as some persons might suggest.)

CONCLUSION

This paper has presented a framework for analyzing the factors affecting people's demand for medical care and for its components. Within this framework, previous research has been surveyed to show where, in this writer's opinion, research fits into the over-all model and also to indicate the sections of the framework with little or no knowledge of the theoretical relationships.

Others may well suggest modifications in the proposed framework. Such suggestions are welcome, for unless a researcher has an understanding of the over-all set of relationships that are assumed to exist, his study may exclude relevant relationships, or he may concentrate on a relatively insignificant aspect of the problem. Apparently, in this age when computers and bountiful sums of money are available for data collection, less effort is spent on specifying in advance the theoretical relationships and their interrelationship. Because of this, studies of demand for health care are by themselves incomplete. To achieve a more complete understanding of why use of health services is at a certain level and why it is changing, all the demand relationships must be specified and a framework for explaining variations in the conditions affecting supply must be developed. Additional work will hopefully be directed toward developing a more complete general model of the market for medical care services and of the factors causing changes in both the amount of services provided and their prices. (In the framework presented, the economic factors have been emphasized. Economic incentives are strong even in medical care. Also, economic factors are relatively easier to affect, and they will respond much more quickly when changes are desired in the use or the provision of services.)

Once a set of hypotheses has been developed, the next step is to collect data on them and test them. One way to collect data to test the framework is presented here; namely, to study the entire treatment of an illness and not merely a hospital episode or the use of any particular component of care. Interest should be in the factors influencing the demand for treatments and, therefore, knowledge of what treatments are being demanded is necessary.

Unless the illness pattern and how it might shift with changes in income levels, for example, are known, whether future differences in expenditures between high- and low-income persons represent unfilled medical needs cannot be determined. Differences in expenditures on medical care may represent a shift from inelective to more discretionary utilization, or a shift to increased quality of care, or to more comfort, or differences may merely represent higher prices to the high-income family for essentially the same care.

Even a study of only one component of care should consider the factors affecting the use of the other components that could be or are being used for treatment. Changes in economic variables, such as a change in insurance coverage of previously uncovered illnesses, may change either the patterns of use or the relative prices to the patient of the alternative forms of care. Therefore, the substitutability and complementary nature of the components of care must be known along with the effect that changes in their relative prices have on component usage, and the factors influencing the physician in his use of these components.

Once data representing theoretical relationships have been collected, techniques of estimation should be used that will provide the net effects of any one factor on demand, while holding constant the effects of the other factors. The usual method of presenting survey data does not

156

accomplish this. When so many factors are interrelated, such as education, income, insurance coverage, etc., one cannot be certain which effect or combination of effects he is observing. Multivariate analyses are beginning to be used in health studies and the results look promising. A word of caution, however. Results derived by statistical techniques, no matter how highly sophisticated, cannot give substance to poorly formulated hypotheses and are no more reliable than the raw data. One further comment on the expected benefits from estimation techniques. Showing that a certain relationship exists is not enough. An estimate of the magnitude of the relationship is needed. For example, one must know, for policy and predictive purposes, not only that a given change in the insured population will cause a change in demand, but also how much the demand will change.

A final point in the discussion of the role and effect of information and knowledge on demand for health services: the demand for health services is dynamic. Progress in medical science increases the possible benefits from health care, while also changing the costs of providing services. Thus, empirical relationships may change drastically. One should know whether this information is transmitted to those making decisions on health care so that they may decide on the basis of the most complete knowledge possible. Consider this knowledge transmission in two areas. First, how informed is the practitioner of changes in medical practice and on the use of alternative forms of care in treatment? Rapid dissemination of information to the physician will enable him to produce better medical care at lowest cost to his patient and, hopefully, to the community. Also, to the extent that variations in use are a result of differences in information, increased information will decrease these variations. Second, what is the discrepancy between medical need and demand for care? To the extent that financial resources are not a constraint, an increase in information about the benefits of care would help reduce the difference between need and demand for medical treatment in circumstances in which the apparent benefits to the individual from undertaking such treatment greatly exceed the expected cost.

Further increases in medical knowledge and in its dissemination can only serve to increase the demand for health services in the future. Perhaps through greater use of preventive care and early diagnosis, the demand for certain forms of treatment will decrease; however, offsetting increases will probably occur in the demands for other treat-

157

ments, such as with chronic diseases and mental illness. New knowledge, however, and its widespread dissemination can help increase the choices available to the physician in providing care, and at least in this manner a given treatment may be provided at lowest cost.

REFERENCES

[1] Reed, Louis S., Private Consumer Expenditures for Medical Care and Voluntary Health Insurance, 1948–63, *Social Security Bulletin,* 27, 15, December, 1964.

[2] *See* Merriam, Ida C., Social Welfare Expenditures, 1963–64, *Social Security Bulletin,* 27, 10, October, 1964.

[3] Baer, D. V. T., The Economics of Medical Care, unpublished paper, March 20, 1963, p. 18.

[4] Another case in which failure to consider the components of care as being the inputs for a treatment, and hence substitutable, can lead to faulty reasoning is in interpreting the rise in hospital expenses per patient day. Part of this rise is merely a result of the fact that relatively more of the treatment is being provided in the hospital than formerly. If no other changes had occurred, a rise in the cost of the hospital component of care could be expected, while the total bill for the treatment remained the same.

[5] Friedman, M. and Kuznets, S., INCOME FROM INDEPENDENT PROFESSIONAL PRACTICE, New York, National Bureau of Economic Research, 1945, pp. 157–158.

[6] For a number of reasons time series analysis is of limited value for analyzing the demand for medical care. Historically, the trend reflects the influence of a multitude of factors which cannot be separated. A more promising approach for studies of medical care demand is cross-section analysis. By examining data for a cross-section of families in the same time period, the effect of factors influencing their expenditure over a wide range of values can be assessed while holding constant the state of technology and other conditions which change over time but cannot easily be quantified. The precision of the analysis is thereby increased and the complexities substantially reduced. The approach used in this paper is essentially cross-sectional.

[7] Scitovsky, Ann A., An Index on the Cost of Medical Care—A Proposed New Approach, *in* ECONOMICS OF HEALTH AND MEDICAL CARE, School of Public Health, Ann Arbor, The University of Michigan Press, 1964. *See also* the Comment by Margaret Reid in the same volume.

[8] Griliches, Zvi, Hedonic Price Indexes for Automobiles: An Econometric Analysis of Quality Change, *in* Joint Economic Committee hearings, Government Price Statistics, 87th Congress, May, 1961, pp. 173–196.

[9] Changing Patterns of Care, *in* REPORT OF THE COMMISSION ON COST OF MEDICAL CARE, Chicago, American Medical Association, Volume 4, 1964.

[10] The discussion of "choice," which is crucial to any economic analysis, may be criticized as being incomplete and an unrealistic approximation of behavior in medical care markets. Relevant to this is the following:

A hypothesis is important if it "explains" much by little, that is, if it abstracts the common and crucial elements from the mass of complex and detailed circumstances surrounding the phenomena to be explained and permits valid predictions on the basis of this alone. . . . the relevant question to ask about the "assumptions" of a theory is not whether they are descriptively "realistic," for they never are, but whether they are sufficiently good approximations for the purposes at hand. And this question can be answered only by seeing whether the theory works, which means whether it yields sufficiently accurate predictions.

In Friedman, M., the Methodology of Positive Economics, *in* ESSAYS IN POSITIVE ECONOMICS, Chicago, The University of Chicago Press, 1953, pp. 14–15.

[11] Palmer, Jeanne, MEASURING BED NEEDS FOR GENERAL HOSPITALS: HISTORICAL REVIEW OF OPINIONS WITH ANNOTATED BIBLIOGRAPHY, Washington, United States Department of Health, Education and Welfare, Public Health Service, October, 1956, Mimeographed; Lee, R. I. and Jones, L. W., THE FUNDAMENTALS OF GOOD MEDICAL CARE, (Publication number 22 of the Committee on the Costs of Medical Care), Chicago, The University of Chicago Press, 1933; Lerner, Monroe, Mortality and Morbidity in the United States as Basic Indices of Health Needs, *Annals of the American Academy of Political and Social Science,* September, 1961.

[12] Thompson, John D. and Fetter, Robert B., Economics of the Maternity Service, *The Yale Journal of Biology and Medicine,* August, 1963; Newell, D. J., Statistical Aspects of the Demand for Maternity Beds, *Journal of the Royal Statistical Society,* 127, 1–40, 1964; Blumberg, Mark DPF Concept Helps Determine Bed Needs, *The Modern Hospital,* December, 1961; Young, John P., A Queuing Theory Approach to the Control of Hospital Inpatient Census, Johns Hopkins Hospital, Operations Research Division, July, 1962; Balintfy, Joseph L., Mathematical Models and Analysis of Certain Stochastic Processes in General Hospitals, Johns Hopkins University, Operations Research Division, 1962; ————, Outline of a Census-Predictor Model for General Hospitals, Tulane University, School of Business Administration, 1964 (unpublished); Bailey, Norman T. J., Calculating the Scale of Inpatient Accommodations, *in* the Nuffield Provincial Hospitals Trust, TOWARDS A MEASURE OF MEDICAL CARE, London, the Oxford University Press, 1962; Robinson, G. H., *et al.*, A Simulation Model for the Evaluation of Scheduling Decision Rules for Hospital Elective Admissions, The Human Factors in Technology Research Group, Berkeley, The University of California, February, 1964; As an aside, some other predictive techniques should be briefly mentioned at this point. These techniques are not explanatory approaches, but merely predictive devices. Fitting trends to utilization ratios has been suggested for use in planning health facilities and for estimating manpower requirements. The use of trend data for predictive purposes says little as to the underlying reasons for utilization. Examples of such methods may be found in: Division of Hospital and Medical Facilities, AREAWIDE PLANNING MANUAL FOR HOSPITALS AND RELATED HEALTH FACILITIES, Washington, United States Department of Health, Education and Welfare, Public Health Service, August, 1962; Cardwell, Rosson L., How to Measure Hospital Bed Needs, *The Modern Hospital,* 103, August, 1964; Some British Studies in this regard are: Forsyth, Gordon and Logan, Robert F. L., THE DEMAND FOR MEDICAL CARE, A STUDY OF THE CASE-LOAD IN THE BARROW AND FURNESS GROUP OF HOSPITALS, London, The Oxford University Press, 1960; Airth, A. D. and Newell, D. J., THE DEMAND FOR HOSPITAL BEDS, RESULTS OF AN ENQUIRY ON TEE-SIDE, Newcastle on Tyne, Kings College, 1961; Newell, David

J., Problems in Estimating the Demand for Hospital Beds, *Journal of Chronic Diseases*, 17, September, 1964; Brotherston, J. H. F., CONFERENCE ON RESEARCH IN HOSPITAL USE, Publication number 930-E-2, Washington, United States Department of Health, Education and Welfare, 1963.

[13] Feldstein, Paul, A Note on the Pricing of Hospital Services, *in* AN EMPIRICAL INVESTIGATION OF THE MARGINAL COST OF HOSPITAL SERVICES, Graduate Program in Hospital Administration, Chicago, University of Chicago Press, 1961, p. 67.

[14] Division of Hospital and Medical Facilities, CONFERENCE ON RESEARCH IN HOSPITAL USE, Publication number 930-E-2, Washington, United States Department of Health, Education and Welfare, Public Health Service, 1962.

[15] United States National Center for Health Statistics, THE CHANGE IN MORTALITY TREND IN THE UNITED STATES, Washington, United States Department of Health, Education and Welfare, Public Health Service, Publication number 1000, March, 1964, pp. 10–36.

[16] Falk, I. S., Klem, Margaret C. and Sinai, Nathan, THE INCIDENCE OF ILLNESS AND THE RECEIPT AND COSTS OF MEDICAL CARE AMONG REPRESENTATIVE FAMILIES: EXPERIENCES IN TWELVE CONSECUTIVE MONTHS DURING 1928–1931, Publication number 26 of the Committee on the Costs of Medical Care, Chicago, University of Chicago Press, 1933; Anderson, Odin W. and Feldman, Jacob J., FAMILY MEDICAL COSTS AND VOLUNTARY HEALTH INSURANCE: A NATIONWIDE SURVEY, New York, McGraw-Hill Book Company, 1956; Anderson, Odin W., Collette, Patricia and Feldman, Jacob, CHANGES IN FAMILY MEDICAL CARE EXPENDITURES: A FIVE-YEAR RESURVEY, Cambridge, Harvard University Press, 1963; United States Department of Health, Education and Welfare, National Health Survey, HOSPITAL DISCHARGES AND LENGTH OF STAY: SHORT-STAY HOSPITALS, UNITED STATES, 1958–1960, Washington, United States Department of Health, Education and Welfare, April, 1962; National Center for Health Statistics, MEDICAL CARE, HEALTH STATUS AND FAMILY INCOME, Series 10, number 9; Weeks, Ashley H., FAMILY SPENDING PATTERNS AND HEALTH CARE, Cambridge, Harvard University Press, 1961; In addition to the above, many local surveys have been taken. References for many of these may be found in Anderson and Feldman, *op. cit.*, pp. 1–2, footnote 3, and Anderson, Collette and Feldman, *op. cit.*, p. 3, footnote 6. Other articles of interest are: Kirk, Dudley, Anticipating the Health Needs of Americans: Some Demographic Projections, *Annals of the American Academy of Political and Social Science*, September, 1961; Odoroff, M. E. and Abbe, L. M., Use of General Hospitals; Demographic and Ecological Factors, *Public Health Reports*, 72, 397–403, May, 1957; Coe, Rodney M. and Wessen, Albert F., Social-Psychological Factors Influencing the Use of Community Health Resources, paper presented at the 92nd annual meeting of the American Public Health Association, New York City, October, 1964; An excellent review and description of the field and its problems is contained in Klarman, Herbert E., THE ECONOMICS OF HEALTH, New York, Columbia University Press, 1965. The chapters on Demand in this publication are particularly recommended.

[17] These studies have also included a number of economic factors in addition to cultural-demographic variables; these will be discussed in the next section of the paper; Wirick, Grover and Barlow, Robin, Social and Economic Determinants of the Demand for Health Services, *in* THE ECONOMICS OF HEALTH AND MEDICAL CARE, Ann Arbor, The University of Michigan Press, 1964; Feldstein, Paul, The Demand for Medical Care, *in* REPORT OF THE COMMISSION ON COST OF MEDICAL CARE, Chicago, The American Medical Association, June, 1964, volume 1; London, Morris, Variations in Post-Operative Study Among Appendectomy Patients, *Hospital Management*, 49–52, November, 1963 and 45–57, December, 1963; Rosenthal, Gerald, THE DEMAND FOR GENERAL HOSPITAL

FACILITIES, Chicago, The American Hospital Association, Monograph number 14, 1964; Cardwell, R., Reid, M. and Shain, M., HOSPITAL UTILIZATION IN A MAJOR METROPOLITAN AREA, Chicago, Hospital Planning Council for Metropolitan Chicago, 1964 (mimeographed); Berry, Charles, Family Medical Expense: Estimates and Projections, *in* VOLUNTARY MEDICAL INSURANCE AND PREPAYMENT, Ottawa, Royal Commission on Health Services, 1965; Riedel, Donald C. and Fitzpatrick, Thomas B., PATTERNS OF PATIENT CARE: A STUDY OF HOSPITAL USE IN SIX DIAGNOSES, Ann Arbor, The University of Michigan Press, 1964.

[18] Rosenthal, *op. cit.*

[19] Feldstein, *op. cit.*

[20] Cardwell, Reid and Shain, *op. cit.,* p. 130.

[21] Anderson, Collette and Feldman, *op. cit.,* p. 178; United States National Health Survey, PROPORTION OF HOSPITAL BILL PAID BY INSURANCE: PATIENTS DISCHARGED FROM SHORT-STAY HOSPITALS, Washington, United States Government Printing Office, 1961, pp. 1–40; Weisbrod, B. A. and Fiesler, R. J., Hospitalization Insurance and Hospital Utilization, *American Economic Review,* 51, 126–132, March, 1961; some studies that have used insurance in a multivariate analysis to derive its net effect are: Wirick and Barlow, *op. cit.,* 117–119; Feldstein, The Demand for Medical Care, *op. cit.,* pp. 73–74; Rosenthal, *op. cit.,* p. 35; Feldstein, Paul J. and Carr, W. John, The Effect of Income on Medical Care Spending, *Proceedings, American Statistical Association,* 38 and 42, 1964; some articles of interest in this regard are: Arrow, Kenneth, Uncertainty and the Welfare Economics of Medical Care, *American Economic Review,* December, 1963; Lees, D. S. and Rice, R. G., Uncertainty and the Welfare Economics of Medical Care: Comment, *American Economic Review,* 55, 140–154, March, 1965, and Arrow, Kenneth, Reply, in the same issue; Weisbrod, Burton, Anticipating the Health Needs of Americans: Some Economic Projections, *Annals of the American Academy of Political and Social Science,* September, 1961; Brewster, Agnes W., Voluntary and Health Insurance and Medical Care Expenditures, 1948–58, *Social Security Bulletin,* 22, 3–11, December 25, 1959; McNary, W. S., Controlling Hospital Use Through Prepayment Benefit Provisions and Reimbursement Formulas, *in* WHERE IS HOSPITAL USE HEADED, Proceedings of the Fifth Annual Symposium on Hospital Affairs, Chicago, University of Chicago Press, pp. 64–68; Roemer, M. and Shain, M., HOSPITAL UTILIZATION UNDER INSURANCE, Chicago, The American Hospital Association, 1959; Odoroff, Maurice E. and Abbe, Leslie M., Use of General Hospitals: Variations with Methods of Payment, *Public Health Reports,* 74, 316–24, April, 1959.

[22] Kessel, Reuben, Price Discrimination in Medicine, *Journal of Law and Economics,* October, 1958.

[23] A number of surveys have collected data on family income and expenditures on medical care. Examples of the income-expenditure relationship from a few of the better known surveys are Falk, Klem and Sinai, *op. cit.,* pp. 151 and 206; Anderson, Collette and Feldman, *op. cit.,* pp. 17–18; see also MEDICAL CARE, HEALTH STATUS AND FAMILY INCOME, National Center for Health Statistics, series 10, number 9; National Center for Health Statistics, LENGTH OF CONVALESCENCE AFTER SURGERY, Washington, United States Department of Health, Education and Welfare, Public Health Service, July, 1963.

[24] Feldstein and Carr, *op. cit.*

[25] Wirick and Barlow, *op. cit.,* p. 117; Cardwell, Reid and Shain, *op. cit.,* pp. 128–136; Friedman and Kuznets, *op. cit.,* pp. 163–169; Stigler, G., THE THEORY OF PRICE, New York, The Macmillan Company, 1952, pp. 50 and 52.

[26] The distinction between permanent and transitory components of income and their relationship to consumption is set out in Friedman's permanent-income theory of consumption. A statement of this theory, along with empirical evidence to support it, is contained in Friedman, Milton, A THEORY OF THE CONSUMPTION FUNCTION, Princeton, New Jersey, Princeton University Press, 1957.

[27] Reed and Rice, *op. cit.*, p. 4, Table 2.

[28] For a more complete review of this paper, see the comments by Rothenberg, J. and Klarman, H., PROCEEDINGS OF THE SOCIAL STATISTICS SECTION, American Statistical Association, 1964, pp. 106–112.

[29] Rothenberg, Jerome, Welfare Implications of Alternative Methods of Financing Medical Care, *American Economic Review, Papers and Proceedings,* 677, May, 1951.

[30] Physicians, Patients and the General Hospital: Patterns of Use in Massachusetts, *Progress in Health Services,* X15, 3, January–February, 1965.

[31] Multiple staff appointments would increase the availability of choice to the physician. This might be one method of achieving some of the benefits of competition among hospitals.

[32] One area where knowledge is incomplete, that of drugs, has resulted in the patient paying prices higher than necessary. Steele, after demonstrating that different firms sold the same drug at prices varying from $1.75 to $17.90 a bottle, commented: "In the absence of extremely imperfect market information, such great differences in prices would be impossible." Steele, Henry, Monopoly and Competition in the Ethical Drugs Market, *Journal of Law and Economics,* 5, October, 1962.

[33] For studies of "proper use" to be effective, an identity of interests must be arrived at to insure that the physician provides care at lowest cost to the patient and to the community; this might involve changes in insurance coverage.

[34] For a more complete discussion of peak and off-peak pricing of hospital services, *see* Feldstein, Paul J., A Note on the Pricing of Hospital Services, *in* AN EMPIRICAL INVESTIGATION OF THE MARGINAL COST OF HOSPITAL SERVICES, Graduate Program in Hospital Administration, Chicago, University of Chicago, 1961, Appendix C.

[35] For an excellent summary and discussion of studies of prepaid group practice and their conclusions, *see:* Klarman, Herbert E., Effect of Prepaid Group Practice on Hospital Use, *Public Health Reports,* 78, November, 1963; Densen, Paul M., Balamuth, Eve and Shapiro, Sam, PREPAID MEDICAL CARE AND HOSPITAL UTILIZATION, Chicago, The American Hospital Association, 1958; Densen, Paul M., et al., Prepaid Medical Care and Hospital Utilization, *Hospitals,* 36, November 16, 1962; Roemer, Milton I., The Influence of Prepaid Physicians' Service on Hospital Utilization, *Hospitals,* October 16, 1958; Anderson, Odin W. and Sheatsley, Paul B., Comprehensive Medical Insurance; A Study of Costs, Use and Attitudes Under Two Types of Plans, Research Series number 9, Health Information Foundation, 1959; Commission on the Cost of Medical Care, Solo and Group Practice, *in* THE REPORT OF THE COMMISSION ON THE COST OF MEDICAL CARE, Chicago, The American Medical Association, 1964, Volume I, Chapter 5.

[36] Shain, M. and Roemer, Milton, I., Hospital Costs Relate to the Supply of Beds, *Modern Hospital,* 92, April, 1959; Sigmond, Robert M., Does Supply of Beds Control Costs?, *Modern Hospital,* 93, August 2, 1959; Roemer, Milton I., Bed Supply and Hospital Utilization: A Natural Experiment, *Hospitals,* 35, November 1, 1961; Rosenthal, *op. cit.,* pp. 55–62.

162

ACKNOWLEDGMENTS

I wish to acknowledge the helpful comments of A. Alhadeff, J. Carr, J. German, M. Long and G. Rosenthal.

DISCUSSION

The economist's point of view. In the interests of interdisciplinary discussion, demand in the economist's language is specifically defined as a set of relationships between a few economic aspects of the consuming public and their likelihood of making or not making particular decisions—in this case, using health services. Economists are primarily interested in relating changes in consumption to changes in prices and in the income circumstances of the consumer. Economic analysis thus begins from the point where the tastes and preferences of the consumer are already set. In their analyses, most economists do not consider social and demographic factors. Since patient preferences are known to be relevant to their demand for services, such an orthodox point of view is admittedly a limited one. However, when the economist does include other factors in his framework, as Dr. Feldstein has done, he is not *qua* economist concerned with *why* people use health services. He is interested instead in *how* people use health services and how certain sets of circumstances, in a consistent and predictable way, create a likelihood that certain amounts of health services will be consumed.

The relationship of economic and other social science approaches. The task of analyzing ways in which the behavioral patterns in question are generated within society belongs to social psychology and sociology. The implicit framework, however, in terms of which the sociologist and the economist view utilization is basically the same. The tools at the disposal of each are applicable to different and limited aspects of the whole phenomenon of utilization. Dr. Rosenstock's paper, for example, helps to clarify important aspects of health economics problems about demand, aspects not explicitly considered by economic techniques. The economic model, in turn, is not only useful for analyzing the traditional economic aspects of demand, but for integrating other demographic and cultural factors as well. By ignoring

163

the theoretical framework of economics, research designs may neglect important relationships and lead to misinterpreted findings.

The physician's role in the demand for care. Researchers, in the opinion of some speakers, frequently appear to reify relationships between patient characteristics and to overlook the ramifications of the individual physician's decision to choose alternatives in the treatment of illness and the factors influencing him. The two basic dimensions of Dr. Feldstein's framework—the factors affecting a patient's demand and those affecting a physician's use of the several components of care—seem to succeed in highlighting the magnitude of the physician's role in the demand for medical care. To determine the amount and significance of variation in physician standards and the patient care reflected in them seem to constitute an important research area. A related research priority appears to be for some national benchmarks on physicians' office practices, supplemented with more detailed analyses of "patient-flow" in smaller geographic areas. The practical usefulness of Dr. Feldstein's model would be increased if more specific knowledge were available of what the "office visit" entails.

Methodological problems posed by the model. Dr. Feldstein's attempt to conceive demand for health services as derived demand is novel and interesting. However, in the opinion of some he may have overemphasized the assumption that the physician has sole responsibility for combining the various components of patient care. Patients can exercise considerable influence. The nature of the physician's practice, such as entrepreneurial or salaried, is also thought to affect demand. These factors might be considered in future refinements of the model.

Dr. Feldstein should have analyzed the difficulties of using the concept of "total treatment" to measure demand. The paper appears to recommend collecting data on prices for each component of care rendered during the entire course of treating an illness, correcting each of these prices for "quality" differences, and then aggregating these values in some way to come up with corrected estimates of demand. Several questions have been raised concerning the implications of this approach. In the area of prepayment, per capita utilization per year rather than the illness episode is proposed as a more likely unit of output.

Doubts were expressed about the practicability, though not the desirability, of Dr. Feldstein's suggestion to estimate the extent to which the rise in medical care prices has been offset by changes in quality. Relying on utilization data to estimate demand on the one hand and supply on the other also seems to pose difficulties, with which Dr. Feldstein would have been extremely well qualified to deal.

Use of the model in long-term planning. The model, while perhaps intended to operate on a longitudinal basis, appears to several speakers to be too cross-sectionally oriented to forecast responses to long-term changes. How economists would use, for planning purposes, the notion of random variation associated with the impact of demand on a given institution at a certain time is questioned. So far only operations researchers, rather than economists, appear to have used the random aspects of demand, and essentially only for predicting short-term reactions. Economists, however, are basically interested in predicting for randomness and in determining future demand under specified sets of circumstances. Future research and model-building should emphasize time-series orientations and the collection and analysis of longitudinal data rather than concentrate on cross-sectional analyses.

In the opinion of some speakers, health services research to date have emphasized data gathering and description of perceived relationships. Rarely have results been placed in the context of the broader behavioral relationships in which individual studies should fit. Economists in particular have difficulty in evaluating existing research related to demand for health services because it is not presented in terms of the analytic structures familiar to them. Even if an individual study should answer its own questions, the overall product, in the absence of some structure for integrating diverse findings, would be a conglomeration of fragmentary results. Dr. Feldstein's paper is an excellent theoretical basis on which to begin to evaluate the results as well as the methodological usefulness of demand studies.

Since most available research findings in the area of demand concern the private market, economic theory is called upon to develop models of demand for the governmental and philanthropic sectors as well.

EVALUATING THE QUALITY OF MEDICAL CARE

AVEDIS DONABEDIAN

INTRODUCTION

This paper is an attempt to describe and evaluate current methods for assessing the quality of medical care and to suggest some directions for further study. It is concerned with methods rather than findings, and with an evaluation of methodology in general, rather than a detailed critique of methods in specific studies.

This is not an exhaustive review of the pertinent literature. Certain key studies, of course, have been included. Other papers have been selected only as illustrative examples. Those omitted are not, for that reason, less worthy of note.

This paper deals almost exclusively with the evaluation of the medical care process at the level of physician-patient interaction. It excludes, therefore, processes primarily related to the effective delivery of medical care at the community level. Moreover, this paper is not concerned with the administrative aspects of quality control. Many of the studies reviewed here have arisen out of the urgent need to evaluate and control the quality of care in organized programs of medical care. Nevertheless, these studies will be discussed only in terms of their contribution to methods of assessment and not in terms of their broader social goals. The author has remained, by and large, in the familiar territory of care provided by physicians and has avoided incursions into other types of health care. Also, consideration of the difficult problem of economic efficiency as a measurable dimension of quality has been excluded.

Three general discussions of the evaluation of quality have been

166

very helpful in preparing this review. The first is a classic paper by Mindel Sheps which includes an excellent discussion of methods.[1] A more recent paper by Peterson provides a valuable appraisal of the field.[2] The paper by Lerner and Riedel discusses one recent study of quality and raises several questions of general importance.[3]

Definition of Quality

The assessment of quality must rest on a conceptual and operationalized definition of what the "quality of medical care" means. Many problems are present at this fundamental level, for the quality of care is a remarkably difficult notion to define. Perhaps the best-known definition is that offered by Lee and Jones[4] in the form of eight "articles of faith," some stated as attributes or properties of the process of care and others as goals or objectives of that process. These "articles" convey vividly the impression that the criteria of quality are nothing more than value judgments that are applied to several aspects, properties, ingredients or dimensions of a process called medical care. As such, the definition of quality may be almost anything anyone wishes it to be, although it is, ordinarily, a reflection of values and goals current in the medical care system and in the larger society of which it is a part.

Few empirical studies delve into what the relevant dimensions and values are at any given time in a given setting. Klein, et al.,[5] found that 24 "administrative officials," among them, gave 80 criteria for evaluating "patient care." They conclude that patient care, like morale, cannot be considered as a unitary concept and ". . . it seems likely that there will never be a single comprehensive criterion by which to measure the quality of patient care."

Which of a multitude of possible dimensions and criteria are selected to define quality will, of course, have profound influence on the approaches and methods one employs in the assessment of medical care.

APPROACHES TO ASSESSMENT: WHAT TO ASSESS

The outcome of medical care, in terms of recovery, restoration of function and of survival, has been frequently used as an indicator of the quality of medical care. Examples are studies of perinatal mortality,[6,7] surgical fatality rates[8] and social restoration of patients discharged from psychiatric hospitals.[9]

167

Many advantages are gained by using outcome as the criterion of quality in medical care. The validity of outcome as a dimension of quality is seldom questioned. Nor does any doubt exist as to the stability and validity of the values of recovery, restoration and survival in most situations and in most cultures, though perhaps not in all. Moreover, outcomes tend to be fairly concrete and, as such, seemingly amenable to more precise measurement.

However, a number of considerations limit the use of outcomes as measures of the quality of care. The first of these is whether the outcome of care is, in fact, the relevant measure. This is because outcomes reflect both the power of medical science to achieve certain results under any given set of conditions, and the degree to which "scientific medicine," as currently conceived, has been applied in the instances under study. But the object may be precisely to separate these two effects. Sometimes a particular outcome may be irrelevant, as when survival is chosen as a criterion of success in a situation which is not fatal but is likely to produce suboptimal health or crippling.[10]

Even in situations where outcomes are relevant, and the relevant outcome has been chosen as a criterion, limitations must be reckoned with. Many factors other than medical care may influence outcome, and precautions must be taken to hold all significant factors other than medical care constant if valid conclusions are to be drawn. In some cases long periods of time, perhaps decades, must elapse before relevant outcomes are manifest. In such cases the results are not available when they are needed for appraisal and the problems of maintaining comparability are greatly magnified. Also, medical technology is not fully effective and the measure of success that can be expected in a particular situation is often not precisely known. For this reason comparative studies of outcome, under controlled situations, must be used.

Although some outcomes are generally unmistakable and easy to measure (death, for example) other outcomes, not so clearly defined, can be difficult to measure. These include patient attitudes and satisfactions, social restoration and physicial disability and rehabilitation.[11] Even the face validity that outcomes generally have as criteria of success or failure, is not absolute. One may debate, for example, whether the prolongation of life under certain circumstances is evidence of good medical care. McDermott, *et al.*, have shown that, although fixing a congenitally dislocated hip joint in a given position is considered good medicine for the white man, it can prove crippling for the Navajo Indian who spends much time seated on the floor or in the saddle.[12] Finally, although outcomes might indicate good or bad care in the aggregate, they do not give an insight into the nature and location of the deficiences or strengths to which the outcome might be attributed.

All these limitations to the use of outcomes as criteria of medical care are presented not to demonstrate that outcomes are inappropriate indicators of quality but to emphasize that they must be used with discrimination. Outcomes, by and large, remain the ultimate validators of the effectiveness and quality of medical care.

Another approach to assessment is to examine the process of care itself rather than its outcomes. This is justified by the assumption that one is interested not in the power of medical technology to achieve results, but in whether what is now known to be "good" medical care has been applied. Judgments are based on considerations such as the appropriateness, completeness and redundancy of information obtained through clincial history, physical examination and diagnostic tests; justification of diagnosis and therapy; technical competence in the performance of diagnostic and therapeutic procedures, including surgery; evidence of preventive management in health and illness; coordination and continuity of care; acceptability of care to the recipient and so on. This approach requires that a great deal of attention be given to specifying the relevant dimensions, values and standards to be used in assessment. The estimates of quality that one obtains are less stable and less final than those that derive from the measurement of outcomes. They may, however, be more relevant to the question at hand: whether medicine is properly practiced.

This discussion of process and outcome may seem to imply a simple separation between means and ends. Perhaps more correctly, one may think of an unbroken chain of antecedent means followed by intermediate ends which are themselves the means to still further ends.[13] Health itself may be a means to a further objective. Several authors have pointed out that this formulation provides a useful approach to evaluation.[14, 15] It may be designated as the measurement of procedural end points and included under the general heading of "process" because it rests on similar considerations with respect to values, standards and validation.

A third approach to assessment is to study not the process of care itself, but the settings in which it takes place and the instrumentalities of which it is the product. This may be roughly designated as the assessment of structure, although it may include administrative and related processes that support and direct the provision of care. It is concerned with such things as the adequacy of facilities and equipment; the qualifications of medical staff and their organization; the administrative structure and operations of programs and institutions providing care; fiscal organization and the like.[16,17] The assumption is made that given the proper settings and instrumentalities, good medical care will follow. This approach offers the advantage of dealing, at least in part, with fairly concrete and accessible information. It has the major limitation that the relationship between structure and process or structure and outcome, is often not well established.

Sources and Methods of Obtaining Information

The approach adopted for the appraisal of quality determines, in large measure, the methods used for collecting the requisite information. Since these range the gamut of social science methods, no attempt will be made to describe them all. Four, however, deserve special attention.

Clinical records are the source documents for most studies of the medical care process. In using them one must be aware of their several limitations. Since the private office practice of most physicians is not readily accessible to the researcher, and the records of such practice are generally disappointingly sketchy, the use of records has been restricted to the assessment of care in hospitals, outpatient departments of hospitals and prepaid group practice. Both Peterson[18] and Clute[19] have reported the prevailing inadequacies of recording in general practice. In addition, Clute has pointed out that, in general practice, ". . . the lack of adequate records is not incompatible with practice of a good, or even an excellent quality. . . ." On the other hand, a recent study of the office practice of a sample of members of the New York Society of Internal Medicine[20] suggests that abstracts of office records can be used to obtain reproducible judgments concerning the quality of care. But to generalize from this finding is difficult. It concerns a particular group of physicians more likely to keep good records than the average. Moreover, for one reason or another, the original sample drawn for this study suffered a 61 per cent attrition rate.

170

Assuming the record to be available and reasonably adequate, two further issues to be settled are the veracity and the completeness of the record. Lembcke[10] has questioned whether key statements in the record can be accepted at face value. He has questioned not only the statements of the physician about the patient and his management, but also the validity of the reports of diagnostic services. The first is verified by seeking in the record, including the nurses' notes, what appears to be the most valid evidence of the true state of affairs. The second is verified by having competent judges re-examine the evidence (films, tracings, slides) upon which diagnostic reports are made. Observer error tends to be a problem under the best of circumstances.[21] But nothing can remove the incredulity from the finding by Lembcke, in one hospital, that the true incidence of uterine hyperplasia was between five and eight per cent rather than 60 to 65 per cent of uterine curettages, as reported by the hospital pathologist. In any case, the implications of verification as part of the assessment of quality must be carefully considered. Errors in diagnostic reports no doubt reflect particularly on the quality of diagnostic service and on the care provided by the hospital, in general. But the physician may be judged to perform well irrespective of whether the data he works with are or are not valid. This is so when the object of interest is the logic that governs the physician's activities rather than the absolute validity of these activities.

Much discussion has centered on the question of the completeness of clinical records and whether, in assessing the quality of care based on what appears in the record, one is rating the record or the care provided. What confuses the issue is that recording is itself a separate and legitimate dimension of the quality of practice, as well as the medium of information for the evaluation of most other dimensions. These two aspects can be separated when an alternative source of information about the process of care is available, such as the direct observation of practice.[18, 19] In most instances, however, they are confounded. Rosenfeld[22] handled the problem of separating recording from care by examining the reasons for downrating the quality of care in each patient record examined. He demonstrated that the quality of care was rated down partly because of what could have been poor recording ("presumptive" evidence) and partly for reasons that could not have been a matter of recording ("substantial" evidence). He also found that hospitals tended to rank high or low on both types of errors, showing that these errors were correlated. Since routine recording is more likely to be complete in the wards, comparison of ward and private services in each hospital by type of reason for downrating might have provided further information on this important question. Other investigators have tried to allow for incompleteness in the record by supplementing it with interviews with the attending physician and making appropriate amendments.[23-25] Unfortunately, only one of these studies (length of stay in Michigan hospitals) contains a report of what difference this additional step made. In this study "the additional medical information elicited by means of personal interviews with attending physicians was of sufficient importance in 12.6 per cent of the total number of cases studied to warrant a reclassification of the evaluation of necessity for admission and/or the appropriateness of length of stay."[3, 25] When information obtained by interview is used to amend or supplement the patient record, the assumption may have to be made that this additional information has equal or superior validity. Morehead, who has had extensive experience with this method, said, "Many of the surveyors engaged in the present study employed the technique of physician interview in earlier studies without fruitful results. . . . The surveyor was . . . left in the uncomfortable position of having to choose between taking at face value statements that medical care was indeed optimal, or concluding that statements presented were untrue."[26] Even in an earlier study, where supplementation by interview is reported to have been used,[24] verbal information was discarded unless it was further corroborated by the course of action or by concrete evidence.[27]

Another question of method is whether the entire record or abstracted digests of it should be used as a basis for evaluation. The question arises because summaries and abstracts can presumably be prepared by less skilled persons allowing the hard-to-get expert to concentrate on the actual task of evaluation. Abstracting, however, seemingly involves the exercise of judgment as to relevance and importance. For that reason, it has been used as a first step in the evaluation of quality only in those studies that use very specific and detailed standards.[10] Even then, little information is available about how reliable the process of abstracting is, or how valid when compared with a more expert reading of the chart. The study of New York internists, already referred to, demonstrated a high level of agreement between physicians and highly trained non-physicians abstracting the same office record.[20]

172

While the controversy about the record as a source of information continues, some have attempted to reduce dependence on the physician's recording habits by choosing for evaluation diagnostic categories which are likely to be supported by recorded evidence additional to the physician's own entries.[28] This explains, in part, the frequent use of surgical operations as material for studies of quality.

In general practice, patient records are too inadequate to serve as a basis for evaluation. The alternative is *direct observation* of the physician's activities by a well qualified colleague.[18, 19] The major limitation of this method would seem to be the changes likely to occur in the usual practice of the physician who knows he is being observed. This has been countered by assurances that the physician is often unaware of the true purpose of the study, becomes rapidly accustomed to the presence of the observer, and is unable to change confirmed habits of practice. Even if changes do occur, they would tend to result in an overestimate of quality rather than the reverse. These assurances notwithstanding, measuring the effect of observation on practice remains an unsolved problem.

Those who have used the method of direct observation have been aware that the problem of completeness is not obviated. The practicing physician often knows a great deal about the patient from previous contacts with him. Hence the need to select for observation "new" cases and situations that require a thorough examination irrespective of the patient's previous experience. Moreover, not all of the managing physician's activities are explicit. Some dimensions of care, not subject to direct observation, must be excluded from the scheme of assessment. Selective perception by the observer may be an additional problem. The observer is not likely to be first a neutral recorder of events and then a judge of these same events. His knowledge and criteria are likely to influence what he perceives, and thus to introduce a certain distortion into perception.

An indirect method of obtaining information is to study *behaviors* and *opinions* from which inferences may be drawn concerning quality. A *sociometric* approach has been reported by Maloney, *et al.,* which assumes that physicians, in seeking care for themselves and their families, exhibit critical and valid judgments concerning the capacity of their colleagues to provide care of high quality.[29] Such choices were shown to identify classes of physicians presumed to be more highly qualified than others. But both sensitivity and specificity, using as criterion more rigorous estimates of the quality of care, lack validation. Georgopoulos and Mann[30] used what might be called an *auto-reputational*[31] approach in assessing the quality of care in selected community hospitals. This grew out of previous studies showing that people are pretty shrewd judges of the "effectiveness" of the organizations in which they work.[32] The hospitals were rated and ranked using opinions concerning the quality of medical care, and other characteristics, held by different categories of managerial, professional and technical persons working in, or connected with, each hospital, as well as by knowledgeable persons in the community. The responses were sufficiently consistent and discriminating to permit the hospitals to be ranked with an apparently satisfactory degree of reliability. This in spite of the generally self-congratulatory nature of the responses that classified the quality of medical care in the hospitals as "very good," "excellent," or "outstanding" in 89 per cent of cases, and "poor" in almost none. The authors provide much evidence that the several opinions, severally held, were intercorrelated to a high degree. But little evidence supports the validity of the judgments by using truly external criteria of the quality of care.

SAMPLING AND SELECTION

The first issue in sampling is to specify precisely the universe to be sampled, which, in turn, depends on the nature of the generalizations that one wishes to make. Studies of quality are ordinarily concerned with one of three objects: 1. the actual care provided by a specified category of providers of care; 2. the actual care received by a specified group of people and 3. the capacity of a specified group of providers to provide care. In the first two instances representative samples of potential providers or recipients are required, as well as representative samples of care provided or received. In the third instance a representative sample of providers is needed, but not necessarily a representative sample of care. A more important aspect is to select, uniformly of course, significant dimensions of care. Perhaps performance should be studied in certain clinical situations that are particularly stressful and therefore more revealing of latent capacities or weaknesses in performance. Hypothetical test situations may even be set up to assess the capacity to perform in selected dimensions of care.[33-35] The distinctions made above, and especially those between the assessment of actual care provided and of the capacity to provide care, are useful in evaluating the sampling pro-

174

cedures used in the major studies of quality. By these criteria, some studies belong in one category or another, but some seem to combine features of several in such a way that generalization becomes difficult. For example, in the first study of the quality of care received by Teamster families, the findings are meant to apply only to the management of specific categories of hospitalized illness in a specified population group.[28] In the second study of this series, somewhat greater generalizability is achieved by obtaining a representative sample (exclusive of seasonal variation) of all hospitalized illness in the same population group.[26] Neither study is meant to provide information about all the care provided by a representative sample of physicians.

The degree of homogeneity in the universe to be sampled is, of course, a matter of great importance in any scheme of sampling or selection. The question that must be asked is to what extent the care provided by a physician maintains a consistent level. Do specific diagnostic categories, levels of difficulty or dimensions of care exist in which a physician performs better than in others? Can one find, in fact, an "overall capacity for goodness in medical care,"[18] or is he dealing with a bundle of fairly disparate strands of performance? One might, similarly, ask whether the care provided by all subdivisions of an institution are at about the same level in absolute terms or in relation to performance in comparable institutions. Makover, for example, makes an explicit assumption of homogeneity when he writes, "No attempt was made to relate the number of records to be studied to the size of enrollment of the medical groups. The medical care provided to one or another individual is valid evidence of quality and there should be little or no chance variation which is affected by adjusting the size of the sample."[23] Rosenfeld began his study with the hypothesis "that there is a correspondence in standards of care in the several specialties and for various categories of illness in an institution."[22]

The empirical evidence concerning homogeneity is not extensive. Both the Peterson and Clute studies of general practice[18, 19] showed a high degree of correlation between performance of physicians in different components or dimensions of care (history, physical examination, treatment, etc.). Rosenfeld demonstrated that the differences in quality ratings among several diagnoses selected within each area of practice (medicine, surgery and obstetrics-gynecology) were not large. Although the differences among hospitals by area of practice appeared by inspection to be larger, they were not large enough to alter the rankings of the three hospitals studied.

The two studies of care received by Teamster families[26, 28] arrived at almost identical proportions of optimal and less than optimal care for the entire populations studied. This must have been coincidental, since the percent of optimal care, in the second study, varied greatly by diagnostic category from 31 per cent for medicine to 100 per cent for ophthalmology (nine cases only). If such variability exists, the "diagnostic mix" of the sample of care must be a matter of considerable importance in assessment. In the two Teamster studies, differences in "diagnostic mix" were thought to have resulted in lower ratings for medicine and higher ratings for obstetrics-gynecology in the second study than in the first. That the same factor may produce effects in two opposite directions is an indication of the complex interactions that the researcher must consider. "The most probable explanation for the ratings in medicine being lower in the present (second) study is the nature of the cases reviewed." The factor responsible is less ability to handle illness "which did not fall into a well recognized pattern." For obstetrics and gynecology the finding of the second study ". . . differed in one major respect from the earlier study where serious questions were raised about the management of far more patients. The earlier study consisted primarily of major abdominal surgery, whereas this randomly selected group contained few such cases and had more patients with minor conditions."[26] In studies such as these, where the care received by total or partial populations is under study, the variations noted stem partly from differences in diagnostic content and partly from institutionalized patterns of practice associated with diagnostic content. For example, all nine cases of eye disease received optimal care because "this is a highly specialized area, where physicians not trained in this field rarely venture to perform procedures."[26]

Sampling and selection influence, and are influenced by, a number of considerations in addition to generalization and homogeneity. The specific dimensions of care that interest one (preventive management or surgical technique, to mention two rather different examples) may dictate the selection of medical care situations for evaluation. The situations chosen are also related to the nature of the criteria and standards used and of the rating and scoring system adopted. Attempts to sample problem situations, rather than traditional diagnoses or operations, can be very difficult, because of the manner in which

176

clinical records are filed and indexed. This is unfortunate, because a review of operations or established diagnoses gives an insight into the bases upon which the diagnosis was made or the operation performed. It leaves unexplored a complementary segment of practice, namely the situations in which a similar diagnosis or treatment may have been indicated but not made or performed.

Measurement Standards

Measurement depends on the development of standards. In the assessment of quality standards derive from two sources.

Empirical standards are derived from actual practice and are generally used to compare medical care in one setting with that in another, or with statistical averages and ranges obtained from a larger number of similar settings. The Professional Activities Study is based, in part, on this approach.[36]

Empirical standards rest on demonstrably attainable levels of care and, for that reason, enjoy a certain degree of credibility and acceptability. Moreover, without clear normative standards, empirical observations in selected settings must be made to serve the purpose. An interesting example is provided by Furstenberg, *et al.,* who used patterns of prescribing in medical care clinics and outpatient hospitals as the standard to judge private practice.[37]

In using empirical standards one needs some assurance that the clinicial material in the settings being compared is similar. The Professional Activities Study makes some allowance for this by reporting patterns of care for hospitals grouped by size. The major shortcoming, however, is that care may appear to be adequate in comparison to that in other situations and yet fall short of what is attainable through the full application of current medical knowledge.

Normative standards derive, in principle, from the sources that legitimately set the standards of knowledge and practice in the dominant medical care system. In practice, they are set by standard textbooks or publications,[10] panels of physicians,[25] highly qualified practitioners who serve as judges[26] or a research staff in consultation with qualified practitioners.[22] Normative standards can be put very high and represent the "best" medical care that can be provided, or they can be set at a more modest level signifying "acceptable" or "adequate" care. In any event, their distinctive characteristic is that they stem from a body of legitimate knowledge and values rather than from specific examples of actual practice. As such, they depend for their validity on the extent of agreement concerning facts and values within the profession or, at least, among its leadership. Where equally legitimate sources differ in their views, judgments concerning quality become correspondingly ambiguous.

The relevance of certain normative standards, developed by one group, to the field of practice of another group, has been questioned. For example, Peterson and Barsamian report that although spermatic fluid examination of the husband should precede surgery for the Stein-Leventhal syndrome, not one instance of such examination was noted, and that this requirement was dropped from the criteria for assessment.[38] Dissatisfaction has also been voiced concerning the application to general practice of standards and criteria elaborated by specialists who practice in academic settings. The major studies of general practice have made allowances for this. Little is known, however, about the strategies of "good" general practice and the extent to which they are similar to, or different from, the strategies of specialized practice in academic settings.

Some researchers have used both types of standards, normative and empirical, in the assessment of care. Rosenfeld used normative standards but included in his design a comparison between university affiliated and community hospitals. "Use of the teaching hospital as a control provides the element of flexibility needed to adjust to the constantly changing scientific basis of the practice of medicine. No written standards, no matter how carefully drawn, would be adequate in five years."[22] Lembcke used experience in the best hospitals to derive a corrective factor that softens the excessive rigidity of his normative standards. This factor, expressed in terms of an acceptable percent of compliance with the standard, was designed to take account of contingencies not foreseen in the standards themselves. It does, however, have the effect of being more realistically permissive as well. This is because the correction factor is likely to be made up partly of acceptable departures from the norm and partly of deviations that might be unacceptable.

Standards can also be differentiated by the extent of their specificity and directiveness. At one extreme the assessing physician may be very simply instructed as follows: "You will use as a yardstick in relation to the quality of care rendered, whether you would have treated this particular patient in this particular fashion during this specific hospital admission."[26] At the other extreme, a virtually watertight "logic system" may be constructed that specifies all the decision

178

rules that are acceptable to justify diagnosis and treatment.[38,39] Most cases fall somewhere in between.

Highly precise and directive standards are associated with the selection of specific diagnostic categories for assessment. When a representative sample of all the care provided is to be assessed, little more than general guides can be given to the assessor. Lembcke, who has stressed the need for specific criteria, has had to develop a correspondingly detailed diagnostic classification of pelvic surgery, for example.[10] In addition to diagnostic specificity, highly directive standards are associated with the preselection of specific dimensions of care for evaluation. Certain diagnoses, such as surgical operations, lend themselves more readily to this approach. This is evident in Lembcke's attempt to extend his system of audits to nonsurgical diagnoses.[40] The clear, almost rule-of-thumb judgments of adequacy become blurred. The data abstracted under each diagnostic rubric are more like descriptions of patterns of management, with insufficient normative criteria for decisive evaluation. The alternative adopted is comparison with a criterion institution.

Obviously, the more general and nondirective the standards are, the more one must depend on the interpretations and norms of the person entrusted with the actual assessment of care. With greater specificity, the research team is able, collectively, to exercise much greater control over what dimensions of care require emphasis and what the acceptable standards are. A great deal appears in common between the standards used in structured and unstructured situations as shown by the degree of agreement between "intuitive" ratings and directed ratings in the Rosenfeld study,[22] and between the "qualitative" and "quantitative" ratings in the study by Peterson, et al.[18] Indeed, these last two were so similar that they could be used interchangeably.

When standards are not very specific and the assessor must exercise his own judgment in arriving at an evaluation, very expert and careful judges must be used. Lembcke claims that a much more precise and directive system such as his does not require expert judges. "It is said that with a cookbook, anyone who can read can cook. The same is true, and to about the same extent, of the medical audit using objective criteria; anyone who knows enough medical terminology to understand the definitions and criteria can prepare the case abstracts and tables for the medical audit. However, the final acceptance, interpretation and application of the findings must be the responsibility of a physician or group of physicians."[41] The "logic system"

179

developed by Peterson and Barsamian appears well suited for rating by computer, once the basic facts have been assembled, presumably by a record abstractor.[38, 39]

The dimensions of care and the values that one uses to judge them are, of course, embodied in the criteria and standards used to assess care.[42] These standards can, therefore, be differentiated by their selectivity and inclusiveness in the choice of dimensions to be assessed. The dimensions selected and the value judgments attached to them constitute the operationalized definition of quality in each study.

The preselection of dimensions makes possible, as already pointed out, the development of precise procedures, standards and criteria. Lembcke[10] has put much stress on the need for selecting a few specific dimensions of care within specified diagnostic categories rather than attempting general evaluations of unspecified dimensions which, he feels, lack precision. He uses dimensions such as the following: confirmation of clinical diagnosis, justification of treatment (including surgery) and completeness of the surgical procedure. Within each dimension, and for each diagnostic category, one or more previously defined activities are often used to characterize performance for that dimension as a whole. Examples are the compatibility of the diagnosis of pancreatitis with serum amylase levels or of liver cirrhosis with biopsy findings, the performance of sensitivity tests prior to antibiotic therapy in acute bronchitis, and the control of blood sugar levels in diabetes.

In addition to the extent to which preselection of dimensions takes place, assessments of quality differ with respect to the number of dimensions used and the exhaustiveness with which performance in each dimension is explored. For example, Peterson, et al.,[18] and Rosenfeld[22] use a large number of dimensions. Peterson and Barsamian,[38, 39] on the other hand, concentrate on two basic dimensions, justification of diagnosis and of therapy, but require complete proof of justification. A much more simplified approach is illustrated by Huntley, et al.,[43] who evaluate outpatient care using two criteria only: the percent of work-ups not including certain routine procedures, and the percent of abnormalities found that were not followed up.

Judgments of quality are incomplete when only a few dimensions are used and decisions about each dimension are made on the basis of partial evidence. Some dimensions, such as preventive care or the

180

psychological and social management of health and illness, are often excluded from the definition of quality and the standards and criteria that make it operational. Examples are the intentional exclusion of psychiatric care from the Peterson study[18] and the planned exclusion of the patient-physician relationship and the attitudes of physicians in studies of the quality of care in the Health Insurance Plan of Greater New York.[27] Rosenfeld[22] made a special point of including the performance of specified screening measures among the criteria of superior care; but care was labeled good in the absence of these measures. In the absence of specific instructions to the judges, the study by Morehead, *et al.*,[26] includes histories of cases, considered to have received optimal care, in which failure of preventive management could have resulted in serious consequences to the patient.

Another characteristic of measurement is the level at which the standard is set. Standards can be so strict that none can comply with them, or so permissive that all are rated "good." For example, in the study of general practice reported by Clute,[19] blood pressure examinations, measurement of body temperature, otoscopy and performance of immunizations did not serve to categorize physicians because all physicians performed them well.

Measurement Scales

The ability to discriminate different levels of performance depends on the scale of measurement used. Many studies of quality use a small number of divisions to classify care, seen as a whole, into categories such as "excellent," "good," "fair" or "poor." A person's relative position in a set can then be further specified by computing the percent of cases in each scale category. Other studies assign scores to performance of specified components of care and cumulate these to obtain a numerical index usually ranging from 0–100. These practices raise questions relative to scales of measurement and legitimate operations on these scales. Some of these are described below.

Those who adhere to the first practice point out that any greater degree of precision is not possible with present methods. Some have even reduced the categories to only two: optimal and less than optimal. Clute[19] uses three, of which the middle one is acknowledged to be doubtful or indeterminate. Also, medical care has an all-or-none aspect that the usual numerical scores do not reflect. Care can be good in many of its parts and be disastrously inadequate in the aggregate due to a vital error in one component. This is, of course, less often a problem if it is demonstrated that performance on different components of care is highly intercorrelated.

Those who have used numerical scores have pointed out much loss of information in the use of overall judgments,[38] and that numerical scores, cumulated from specified subscores, give a picture not only of the whole but also of the evaluation of individual parts. Rosenfeld[22] has handled this problem by using a system of assigning qualitative scores to component parts of care and an overall qualitative score based on arbitrary rules of combination that allow for the all-or-none attribute of the quality of medical care. As already pointed out, a high degree of agreement was found between intuitive and structured ratings in the Rosenfeld study[22] and between qualitative and quantitative ratings in the study by Peterson, et al.[18]

A major problem, yet unsolved, in the construction of numercial scores, is the manner in which the different components are to be weighted in the process of arriving at the total. At present this is an arbitrary matter. Peterson, et al.,[18] for example, arrive at the following scale: clinical history 30, physical examination 34, use of laboratory aids 26, therapy 9, preventive medicine 6, clinical records 2, total 107. Daily and Morehead[24] assign different weights as follows: records 30, diagnostic work-up 40, treatment and follow-up 30, total 100. Peterson, et al., say: "Greatest importance is attached to the process of arriving at a diagnosis since, without a diagnosis, therapy cannot be rational. Furthermore, therapy is in the process of constant change, while the form of history and physical examination has changed very little over the years."[18] Daily and Morehead offer no justification for their weightings, but equally persuasive arguments could probably be made on their behalf. The problem of seeking external confirmation remains.[44]

The problem of weights is related to the more general problem of value of items of information or of procedures in the medical care process. Rimoldi, et al.,[34] used the frequency with which specified items of information were used in the solution of a test problem as a measure of the value of that item. Williamson had experts classify specified procedures, in a specified diagnostic test setting, on a scale ranging from "very helpful" to "very harmful." Individual performance in the test was then rated using quantitative indices of "efficiency," "proficiency" and overall "competence," depending on the frequency and nature of the procedures used.[35]

182

A problem in the interpretation of numerical scores is the meaning of the numerical interval between points on the scale. Numerical scores derived for the assessment of quality are not likely to have the property of equal intervals. They should not be used as if they had.

Reliability

The reliability of assessments is a major consideration in studies of quality, where so much depends on judgment even when the directive types of standards are used. Several studies have given some attention to agreement between judges. The impression gained is that this is considered to be at an acceptable level. Peterson, *et al.*,[18] on the basis of 14 observer revisits, judged agreement to be sufficiently high to permit all the observations to be pooled together after adjustment for observer bias in one of the six major divisions of care. In the study by Daily and Morehead, "several cross-checks were made between the two interviewing internists by having them interview the same physicians. The differences in the scores of the family physicians based on these separate ratings did not exceed 7 per cent."[24] Rosenfeld[22] paid considerable attention to testing reliability, and devised mathematical indices of "agreement" and "dispersion" to measure it. These indicate a fair amount of agreement, but a precise evaluation is difficult since no other investigator is known to have used these same measures. Morehead, *et al.*,[26] in the second study of medical care received by Teamster families, report initial agreement between two judges in assigning care to one of two classes in 78 per cent of cases. This was raised to 92 per cent following reevaluation of disagreements by the two judges.

By contrast to between-judge reliability, very little has been reported about the reliability of repeated judgments of quality made by the same person. To test within-observer variation, Peterson, *et al.*,[18] asked each of two observers to revisit four of his own previously visited physicians. The level of agreement was lower within observers than between observers, partly because revisits lasted a shorter period of time and related, therefore, to a smaller sample of practice.

The major mechanism for achieving higher levels of reliability is the detailed specification of criteria, standards and procedures used for the assessment of care. Striving for reproducibility was, in fact, a major impetus in the development of the more rigorous rating systems by Lembcke, and by Peterson and Barsamian. Unfortunately, no comparative studies of reliability exist using highly directive versus nondirective methods of assessment. Rosenfeld's raw data might permit a comparison of reliability of "intuitive" judgments and the reliability of structured judgments by the same two assessors. Unreported data by Morehead, et al.,[26] could be analyzed in the same way as those of Rosenfeld[22] to give useful information about the relationship between degree of reliability and method of assessment. The partial data that have been published suggest that the post-review reliability achieved by Morehead, et al., using the most non-directive of approaches, is quite comparable with that achieved by Rosenfeld who used a much more directive technique.

Morehead, et al., raised the important question of whether the reliability obtained through the detailed specification of standards and criteria may not be gained at the cost of reduced validity. "Frequently, such criteria force into a rigid framework similar actions or factors which may not be appropriate in a given situation due to the infinite variations in the reaction of the human body to illness. . . . The study group rejects the assumption that such criteria are necessary to evaluate the quality of medical care. It is their unanimous opinion that it is as important for the surveyors to have flexibility in the judgment of an individual case as it is for a competent physician when confronting a clinical problem in a given patient."[26]

The reasons for disagreement between judges throw some light on the problems of evaluation and the prospects of achieving greater reliability. Rosenfeld found that "almost half the differences were attributable to situations not covered adequately by standards, or in which the standards were ambiguous. In another quarter differences developed around questions of fact, because one consultant missed a significant item of information in the record. It would therefore appear that with revised standards, and improved methods of orienting consultants, a substantially higher degree of agreement could be achieved."[22] Less than a quarter of the disagreements contain differences of opinion with regard to the requirements of management. This is a function of ambiguity in the medical care system and sets an upper limit of reproducibility. Morehead, et al., report that in about half the cases of initial disagreement "there was agreement on the most serious aspect of the patient's care, but one surveyor later agreed that he had not taken into account corollary aspects of patient care."[26] Other reasons for disagreement were difficulty in adhering to the rating categories or failure to note

184

all the facts. Of the small number of unresolved disagreements (eight per cent of all admissions and 36 per cent of initial disagreements) more than half were due to honest differences of opinion regarding the clinical handling of the problem. The remainder arose out of differences in interpreting inadequate records, or the technical problems of where to assess unsatisfactory care in a series of admissions.[27]

A final aspect of reliability is the occasional breakdown in the performance of an assessor, as so dramatically demonstrated in the Rosenfeld study.[22] The question of what the investigator does when a well defined segment of his results are so completely aberrant will be raised here without any attempt to provide an answer.

Bias

When several observers or judges describe and evaluate the process of medical care, one of them may consistently employ more rigid standards than another, or interpret predetermined standards more strictly. Peterson, et al.,[18] discovered that one of their observers generally awarded higher ratings than the other in the assessment of performance of physical examination, but not in the other areas of care. Rosenfeld[22] showed that, of two assessors, one regularly awarded lower ratings to the same cases assessed by both. An examination of individual cases of disagreement in the study by Morehead, et al.,[26] reveals that, in the medical category, the same assessor rated the care at a lower level in 11 out of 12 instances of disagreement. For surgical cases, one surveyor rated the care lower than the other in all eight instances of disagreement. The impression is gained from examining reasons for disagreement on medical cases that one of the judges had a special interest in cardiology and was more demanding of clarity and certainty in the management of cardiac cases.

The clear indication of these findings is that bias must be accepted as the rule rather than the exception, and that studies of quality must be designed with this in mind. In the Rosenfeld study,[22] for example, either of the two raters used for each area of practice would have ranked the several hospitals in the same order, even though one was consistently more generous than the other. The Clute study of general practice in Canada,[19] on the other hand, has been criticized for comparing the quality of care in two geographic areas even though different observers examined the care in the two areas in question.[45] The author was aware of this problem and devised methods for comparing the performance of the observers in the two geographic areas, but the basic weakness remains.

Predetermined order or regularity in the process of study may be associated with bias. Therefore, some carefully planned procedures may have to be introduced into the research design for randomization. The study by Peterson, *et al.*,[18] appears to be one of the few to have paid attention to this factor. Another important source of bias is knowledge, by the assessor, of the identity of the physician who provided the care or of the hospital in which care was given. The question of removing identifying features from charts under review has been raised,[8] but little is known about the feasibility of this procedure and its effects on the ratings assigned. Still another type of bias may result from parochial standards and criteria of practice that may develop in and around certain institutions or "schools" of medical practice. To the extent that this is true, or suspected to be true, appropriate precautions need to be taken in the recruitment and allocation of judges.

Validity

The effectiveness of care as has been stated, in achieving or producing health and satisfaction, as defined for its individual members by a particular society or subculture, is the ultimate validator of the quality of care. The validity of all other phenomena as indicators of quality depends, ultimately, on the relationship between these phenomena and the achievement of health and satisfaction. Nevertheless, conformity of practice to accepted standards has a kind of conditional or interim validity which may be more relevant to the purposes of assessment in specific instances.

The validation of the details of medical practice by their effect on health is the particular concern of the clinical sciences. In the clinical literature one seeks data on whether penicillin promotes recovery in certain types of pneumonia, anticoagulants in coronary thrombosis, or corticosteroids in rheumatic carditis; what certain tests indicate about the function of the liver; and whether simple or radical mastectomy is the more life-prolonging procedure in given types of breast cancer. From the general body of knowledge concerning such relationships arise the standards of practice, more or less fully validated, by which the medical care process is ordinarily judged.

Intermediate, or procedural, end points often represent larger

186

bundles of care. Their relationship to outcome has attracted the attention of both the clinical investigator and the student of medical care organization. Some examples of the latter are studies of relationships between prenatal care and the health of mothers and infants[46,47] and the relationship between multiple screening examinations and subsequent health.[48] An interesting example of the study of the relationship between one procedural end point and another is the attempt to demonstrate a positive relationship between the performance of rectal and vaginal examinations by the physician, and the pathological confirmation of appendicitis in primary appendectomies, as reported by the Professional Activities Study.[49]

Many studies reviewed[18,19,23,26,28] attempt to study the relationship between structural properties and the assessment of the process of care. Several of these studies have shown, for example, a relationship between the training and qualifications of physicians and the quality of care they provide. The relationship is, however, a complex one, and is influenced by the type of training, it duration and the type of hospital within which it was obtained. The two studies of general practice[18,19] have shown additional positive relationships between quality and better office facilities for practice, the presence or availabilty of laboratory equipment, and the institution of an appointment system. No realtionship was shown between quality and membership of professional associations, the income of the physician or the presence of x-ray equipment in the office. The two studies do not agree fully on the nature of the relationship between quality of practice and whether the physician obtained his training in a teaching hospital or not, the number of hours worked or the nature of the physician's hospital affiliation. Hospital accreditation, presumably a mark of quality conferred mainly for compliance with a wide range of organizational standards, does not appear, in and of itself, to be related to the quality of care, at least in New York City.[26]

Although structure and process are no doubt related, the few examples cited above indicate clearly the complexity and ambiguity of these relationships. This is the result partly of the many factors involved, and partly of the poorly understood interactions among these factors. For example, one could reasonably propose, based on several findings[26,38] that both hospital factors and physician factors influence the quality of care rendered in the hospital, but that differences between physicians are obliterated in the best and worst hospital and express themselves, in varying degrees, in hospitals of intermediate quality.

An approach particularly favored by students of medical care organization is to examine relations between structure and outcome without reference to the complex processes that tie them together. Some examples of such studies have been cited already.[6-9] Others include studies of the effects of reorganizing the outpatient clinic on health status,[50] the effects of intensive hospital care on recovery,[51] the effects of home care on survival[52] and the effect of a rehabilitation program on the physical status of nursing home patients.[53, 54] The lack of relationship to outcome in the latter two studies suggests that current opinions about how care should be set up are sometimes less than well established.

This brief review indicates the kinds of evidence pertaining to the validity of the various approaches to the evaluation of quality of care. Clearly, the relationships between process and outcome, and between structure and both process and outcome, are not fully understood. With regard to this, the requirements of validation are best expressed by the concept, already referred to, of a chain of events in which each event is an end to the one that comes before it and a necessary condition to the one that follows. This indicates that the means-end relationship between each adjacent pair requires validation in any chain of hypothetical or real events.[55] This is, of course, a laborious process. More commonly, as has been shown, the intervening links are ignored. The result is that causal inferences become attenuated in proportion to the distance separating the two events on the chain.

Unfortunately, very little information is available on actual assessments of quality using more than one method of evaluation concurrently. Makover has studied specifically the relationships between multifactorial assessments of structure and of process in the same medical groups. "It was found that the medical groups that achieved higher quality ratings by the method used in this study were those that, in general, adhered more closely to HIP's Minimum Medical Standards. However, the exceptions were sufficiently marked, both in number and degree, to induce one to question the reliability[56] of one or the other rating method when applied to any one medical group. It would seem that further comparison of these two methods of rating is clearly indicated."[23]

Since a multidimensional assessment of medical care is a costly and laborious undertaking, the search continues for discrete, readily measurable data that can provide information about the quality of medical care. The data used may be about aspects of structure, process or outcome. The chief requirement is that they be easily, sometimes routinely, measurable and be reasonably valid. Among the studies of quality using this approach are those of the Professional Activities Study,[56] Ciocco, et al.,[57] and Furstenberg, et al.[37]

Such indices have the advantage of convenience; but the inferences that are drawn from them may be of doubtful validity. Myers has pointed out the many limitations of the traditional indices of the quality of hospital care, including rates of total and postoperative mortality, complications, postoperative infection, Caesarian section, consultation and removal of normal tissue at operation.[58] The accuracy and completeness of the basic information may be open to question. More important still, serious questions may be raised about what each index means since so many factors are involved in producing the phenomenon which it measures. Eislee has pointed out, on the other hand, that at least certain indices can be helpful, if used with care.[56]

The search for easy ways to measure a highly complex phenomenon such as medical care may be pursuing a will-o'-the-wisp. The use of simple indices in lieu of more complex measures may be justified by demonstrating high correlations among them.[1] But, in the absence of demonstrated causal links, this may be an unsure foundation upon which to build. On the other hand, each index can be a measure of a dimension or ingredient of care. Judiciously selected multiple indices may, therefore, constitute the equivalent of borings in a geological survey which yield sufficient information about the parts to permit reconstruction of the whole. The validity of inferences about the whole will depend, of course, on the extent of internal continuities in the individual or institutional practice of medicine.

Some Problems of Assessing Ambulatory Care

Some of the special difficulties in assessing the quality of ambulatory care have already been mentioned. These include the paucity of recorded information, and the prior knowledge, by the managing physician, of the patient's medical and social history. The first of these problems has led to the use of trained observers and the second to the observation of cases for which prior knowledge is not a factor in current management. The degree of relevance to general practice of standards and strategies of care developed by hospital centered and academically oriented physicians has also been questioned.

Another problem is the difficulty of defining the segment of care that may be properly the object of evaluation in ambulatory care. For hospital care, a single admission is usually the appropriate unit.[59] In office or clinic practice, a sequence of care may cover an indeterminate number of visits so that the identification of the appropriate unit is open to question. Usually the answer has been to choose an arbitrary time period to define the relevant episode of care. Ciocco, et al.,[57] defined this as the first visit plus 14 days of follow-up. Huntley, et al.,[43] use a four-week period after the initial work-up.

CONCLUSIONS AND PROPOSALS

This review has attempted to give an impression of the various approaches and methods that have been used for evaluating the quality of medical care, and to point out certain issues and problems that these approaches and methods bring up for consideration.

The methods used may easily be said to have been of doubtful value and more frequently lacking in rigor and precision. But how precise do estimates of quality have to be? At least the better methods have been adequate for the administrative and social policy purposes that have brought them into being. The search for perfection should not blind one to the fact that present techniques of evaluating quality, crude as they are, have revealed a range of quality from outstanding to deplorable. Tools are now available for making broad judgments of this kind with considerable assurance. This degree of assurance is supported by findings, already referred to, that suggest acceptable levels of homogeneity in individual practice and of reproducibility of qualitative judgments based on a minimally structured approach to evaluation. This is not to say that a great deal does not remain to be accomplished in developing the greater precision necessary for certain other purposes.

One might begin a catalogue of needed refinements by considering the nature of the information which is the basis for judgments of quality. More must be known about the effect of the observer on the practice being observed, as well as about the process of observation itself—its reliability and validity. Comparisons need to be made between direct observation and recorded information both with and without supplementation by interview with the managing physician. Recording agreement or disagreement is not sufficient. More detailed study is needed of the nature of, and reasons for, discrepancy in various settings. Similarly, using abstracts of records needs to be tested against using the records themselves.

The process of evaluation itself requires much further study. A great deal of effort goes into the development of criteria and standards which are presumed to lend stability and uniformity to judgments of quality; and yet this presumed effect has not been empirically demonstrated. How far explicit standardization must go before appreciable gains in reliability are realized is not known. One must also consider whether, with increasing standardization, so much loss of the ability to account for unforeseen elements in the clinical situation occurs that one obtains reliability at the cost of validity. Assessments of the same set of records using progressively more structured standards and criteria should yield valuable information on these points. The contention that less well trained assessors using exhaustive criteria can come up with reliable and valid judgments can also be tested in this way.

Attention has already been drawn, in the body of the review, to the little that is known about reliability and bias when two or more judges are compared, and about the reliability of repeated judgments of the same items of care by the same assessor. Similarly, very little is known about the effects on reliability and validity, of certain characteristics of judges including experience, areas of special interest and personality factors. Much may be learned concerning these and related matters by making explicit the process of judging and subjecting it to careful study. This should reveal the dimensions and values used by the various judges and show how differences are resolved when two or more judges discuss their points of view. Some doubt now exists about the validity of group reconciliations in which one point of view may dominate, not necessarily because it is more valid.[1] The effect of masking the identity of the hospital or the physician providing care can be studied in the same way. What is proposed here is not only to demonstrate differences or similarities in overall judgments, but to attempt, by making explicit the thought processes of the judges, to determine how the differences and similarities arise, and how differences are resolved.

In addition to defects in method, most studies of quality suffer from having adopted too narrow a definition of quality. In general, they concern themselves with the technical management of illness and pay little attention to prevention, rehabilitation, coordination and continuity of care, or handling the patient-physician relationship. Presumably, the reason for this is that the technical requirements of management are more widely recognized and better standardized. Therefore, more complete conceptual and empirical exploration of the definition of quality is needed.

What is meant by "conceptual exploration" may be illustrated by considering the dimension of efficiency which is often ignored in studies of quality. Two types of efficiency might be distinguished: logical and economic. Logical efficiency concerns the use of information to arrive at decisions. Here the issue might be whether the information obtained by the physician is relevant or irrelevant to the clinical business to be transacted. If relevant, one might consider the degree of replication or duplication in information obtained and the extent to which it exceeds the requirements of decision making in a given situation. If parsimony is a value in medical care, the identification of redundancy becomes an element in the evaluation of care.

Economic efficiency deals with the relationships between inputs and outputs and asks whether a given output is produced at least cost. It is, of course, influenced by logical efficiency, since the accumulation of unnecessary or unused information is a costly procedure which yields no benefit. Typically it goes beyond the individual and is concerned with the social product of medical care effort. It considers the possibility that the "best" medical care for the individual may not be the "best" for the community. Peterson, *et al.*, cite an example that epitomizes the issue. "Two physicians had delegated supervision of routine prenatal visits to office nurses, and the doctor saw the patient only if she had specific complaints."[18] In one sense, this may have been less than the best care for each expectant mother. In another sense, it may have been brilliant strategy in terms of making available to the largest number of women the combined skills of a medical care team. Cordero, in a thought provoking paper, has documented the thesis that, when resources are limited, optimal medical care for the community may require less than "the best" care for its individual members.[60]

In addition to conceptual exploration of the meaning of quality, in terms of dimensions of care and the values attached to them, empirical studies are needed of what are the prevailing dimensions and values in relevant population groups.[5] Little is known, for example, about how physicians define quality, nor is the relationship known between the physician's practice and his own definition of quality. This is an area of research significant to medical education as well as quality. Empirical studies of the medical care process should also contribute greatly to the identification of dimensions and values to be incorporated into the definition of quality.

A review of the studies of quality shows a certain discouraging repetitiousness in basic concepts, approaches and methods. Further substantive progress, beyond refinements in methodology, is likely to come from a program of research in the medical care process itself rather than from frontal attacks on the problem of quality. This is believed to be so because, before one can make judgments about quality, one needs to understand how patients and physicians interact and how physicians function in the process of providing care. Once the elements of process and their interrelationships are understood, one can attach value judgments to them in terms of their contributions to intermediate and ultimate goals. Assume, for example, that authoritarianism-permissiveness is one dimension of the patient-physician relationship. An empirical study may show that physicians are in fact differentiated by this attribute. One might then ask whether authoritarianism or permissiveness should be the criterion of quality. The answer could be derived from the general values of society that may endorse one or the other as the more desirable attribute in social interactions. This is one form of quality judgment, and is perfectly valid, provided its rationale and bases are explicit. The study of the medical care process itself may however offer an alternative, and more pragmatic, approach. Assume, for the time being, that compliance with the recommendations of the physician is a goal and value in the medical care system. The value of authoritarianism or permissiveness can be determined, in part, by its contribution to compliance. Compliance is itself subject to validation by the higher order criterion of health outcomes. The true state of affairs is likely to be more complex than the hypothetical example given. The criterion of quality

193

may prove to be congruence with patient expectations, or a more complex adaptation to specific clinical and social situations, rather than authoritarianism or permissiveness as a predominant mode. Also, certain goals in the medical care process may not be compatible with other goals, and one may not speak of quality in global terms but of quality in specified dimensions and for specified purposes. Assessments of quality will not, therefore, result in a summary judgment but in a complex profile, as Sheps has suggested.[1]

A large portion of research in the medical care process will, of course, deal with the manner in which physicians gather clinically relevant information, and arrive at diagnostic and therapeutic decisions. This is not the place to present a conceptual framework for research in this portion of the medical care process. Certain specific studies may, however, be mentioned and some directions for further research indicated.

Research on information gathering includes studies of the perception and interpretation of physical signs.[61,62] Evans and Bybee have shown, for example, that in interpreting heart sounds errors of perception (of rhythm and timing) occurred along with additional errors of interpretation of what was perceived. Faulty diagnosis, as judged by comparison with a criterion, was the result of these two errors.[62] This points to the need for including, in estimates of quality, information about the reliability and validity of the sensory data upon which management, in part, rests.

The work of Peterson and Barsamian[38,39] represents the nearest approach to a rigorous evaluation of diagnostic and therapeutic decision making. As such, it is possibly the most significant recent advance in the methods of quality assessment. But this method is based on record reviews and is almost exclusively preoccupied with the justification of diagnosis and therapy. As a result, many important dimensions of care are not included in the evaluation. Some of these are considerations of efficiency, and of styles and strategies in problem solving.

Styles and strategies in problem solving can be studied through actual observation of practice, as was done so effectively by Peterson, et al., in their study of general practice.[18] A great deal that remains unobserved can be made explicit by asking the physician to say aloud what he is doing and why. This method of réflexion parlée has been used in studies of problem solving even though it may, in itself, alter behavior.[63] Another approach is to set up test situations, such as those

194

used by Rimoldi, *et al.*,[34] and by Williamson,[35] to observe the decision making process. Although such test situations have certain limitations arising out of their artificiality,[64] the greater simplicity and control that they provide can be very helpful.

At first sight, the student of medical care might expect to be helped by knowledge and skill developed in the general field of research in problem solving. Unfortunately, no well developed theoretical base is available which can be exploited readily in studies of medical care. Some of the empirical studies in problem solving might however, suggest methods and ideas applicable to medical care situations.[63-67] Some of the studies of "troubleshooting" in electronic equipment, in particular, show intriguing similarities to the process of medical diagnosis and treatment. These and similar studies have identified behavioral characteristics that might be used to categorize styles in clinical management. They include amount of information collected, rate of seeking information, value of items of information sought as modified by place in a sequence and by interaction with other items of information, several types of redundancy, stereotypy, search patterns in relation to the part known to be defective, tendencies to act prior to amassing sufficient information or to seek information beyond the point of reasonable assurance about the solution, "error distance" and degrees of success in achieving a solution, and so on.

Decision making theory may also offer conceptual tools of research in the medical care process. Ledley and Lusted,[68,69] among others, have attempted to apply models based on conditional probabilities to the process of diagnosis and therapy. Peterson and Barsamian[38,39] decided against using probabilities in their logic systems for the very good reason that the necessary data (the independent probabilities of diseases and of symptoms, and the probabilities of specified symptoms in specified diseases) were not available. But Edwards, *et al.*,[70] point out that one can still test efficiency in decision making by substituting subjective probabilities (those of the decision maker himself or of selected experts) for the statistical data one would prefer to have.

A basic question that has arisen frequently in this review is the degree to which performance in medical care is a homogeneous or heterogeneous phenomenon. This was seen, for example, to be relevant to sampling, the use of indices in place of multidimensional measurements, and the construction of scales that purport to judge total performance. When this question is raised with respect to individual physicians, the object of study is the integration of various kinds of

195

knowledge and of skills in the personality and behavior of the physician. When it is raised with respect to institutions and social systems the factors are completely different. Here one is concerned with the formal and informal mechanisms for organizing, influencing and directing human effort in general, and the practice of medicine in particular. Research in all these areas is expected to contribute to greater sophistication in the measurement of quality.

Some of the conventions accepted in this review are, in themselves, obstacles to more meaningful study of quality. Physicians' services are not, in the real world, separated from the services of other health professionals, nor from the services of a variety of supportive personnel. The separation of hospital and ambulatory care is also largely artificial. The units of care which are the proper objects of study include the contributions of many persons during a sequence which may include care in a variety of settings. The manner in which these sequences are defined and identified has implications for sampling, methods of obtaining information, and standards and criteria of evaluation.

A final comment concerns the frame of mind with which studies of quality are approached. The social imperatives that give rise to assessments of quality have already been referred to. Often associated with these are the zeal and values of the social reformer. Greater neutrality and detachment are needed in studies of quality. More often one needs to ask, "What goes on here?" rather than, "What is wrong; and how can it be made better?" This does not mean that the researcher disowns his own values or social objectives. It does mean, however, that the distinction between values, and elements of structure, process or outcome, is recognized and maintained; and that both are subjected to equally critical study. Partly to achieve this kind of orientation emphasis must be shifted from preoccupation with evaluating quality to concentration on understanding the medical care process itself.

REFERENCES

[1] Sheps, M. C., Approaches to the Quality of Hospital Care, *Public Health Reports,* 70, 877–886, September, 1955.
This paper represents an unusually successful crystallization of thinking concerning the evaluation of quality. It contains brief but remarkably complete discussions of the purposes of evaluation, problems of definition, criteria and standards, various approaches to measurement, the reliability of qualitative judgments and indices of quality. The bibliography is excellent.

[2] Peterson, L., Evaluation of the Quality of Medical Care, *New England Journal of Medicine,* 269, 1238–1245, December 5, 1963.

[3] Lerner, M. and Riedel, D. C., The Teamster Study and the Quality of Medical Care, *Inquiry,* 1, 69–80, January, 1964.
The major value of this paper is that it raises questions concerning methods of assessment including the sampling of populations and diagnostic categories, the use of records and the need for supplementation by interview, the value of detailed standards, the need for understanding the auditing process, the definition of terms and concepts (of "unnecessary admission," for example), and the problems of defining the relevant episode of care.

[4] Lee, R. I. and Jones, L. W., THE FUNDAMENTALS OF GOOD MEDICAL CARE, Chicago, University of Chicago Press, 1933.

[5] Klein, M. W., *et al.,* Problems of Measuring Patient Care in the Out Patient Department, *Journal of Health and Human Behavior,* 2, 138–144, Summer, 1961.

[6] Kohl, S. G., PERINATAL MORTALITY IN NEW YORK CITY: RESPONSIBLE FACTORS, Cambridge, Harvard University Press, 1955.
This study, sponsored by the New York Academy of Medicine, was an examination by an expert committee of records pertaining to a representative sample of perinatal deaths in New York City. Preventable deaths were recognized and "responsibility factors" identified, including errors in medical judgment and technique. The incidence of both of these was further related to type of hospital service, type of professional service and type of hospital, indicating relationships between structure and outcome as modified by the characteristics of the population served.

[7] Shapiro, S., *et al.,* Further Observations on Prematurity and Perinatal Mortality in a General Population and in the Population of a Prepaid Group Practice Medical Care Plan, *American Journal of Public Health,* 50, 1304–1317, September, 1960.

[8] Lipworth, L., Lee J. A. H. and Morris, J. N., Case Fatality in Teaching and Nonteaching Hospitals, 1956–1959, *Medical Care,* 1, 71–76, April-June, 1963.

[9] Rice, C. E., *et al.,* Measuring Social Restoration Performance of Public Psychiatric Hospitals, *Public Health Reports,* 76, 437–446, May, 1961.

[10] Lembcke, P. A., Medical Auditing by Scientific Methods, *Journal of the*

American Medical Association, 162, 646–655, October 13, 1956. (Appendices A and B supplied by the author.)

This is perhaps the single best paper that describes the underlying concepts as well as the methods of the highly structured approach developed by Lembcke to audit hospital records. Also included is an example of the remarkable effect that an "external audit" of this kind can have on surgical practice in a hospital.

[11] Kelman, H. R. and Willner, A., Problems in Measurement and Evaluation of Rehabilitation, *Archives of Physical Medicine and Rehabilitation,* 43, 172–181, April, 1962.

[12] McDermott, W., *et al.,* Introducing Modern Medicine in a Navajo Community, *Science,* 131, 197–205 and 280–287, January 22 and 29, 1960.

[13] Simon, H. A., ADMINISTRATIVE BEHAVIOR, New York, The Macmillan Company, 1961, pp. 62–66.

[14] Hutchinson, G. B., Evaluation of Preventive Services, *Journal of Chronic Diseases,* 11, 497–508, May, 1960.

[15] James, G., EVALUATION OF PUBLIC HEALTH, Report of the Second National Conference on Evaluation in Public Health, Ann Arbor, The University of Michigan, School of Public Health, 1960 pp. 7–17.

[16] Weinerman, E. R., Appraisal of Medical Care Programs, *American Journal of Public Health,* 40, 1129–1134, September, 1950.

[17] Goldmann, F. and Graham, E. A., THE QUALITY OF MEDICAL CARE PROVIDED AT THE LABOR HEALTH INSTITUTE, ST. LOUIS, MISSOURI, St. Louis, The Labor Health Institute, 1954.
This is a good example of an approach to evaluation based on structural characteristics. In this instance, these included the layout and equipment of physical facilities, the competence and stability of medical staff, provisions made for continuity of service centering around a family physician, the scheduling and duration of clinic visits, the content of the initial examination, the degree of emphasis on preventive medicine and the adequacy of the medical records.

[18] Peterson, O. L., *et al.,* An Analytical Study of North Carolina General Practice: 1953–1954, *The Journal of Medical Education,* 31, 1–165, Part 2, December, 1956.
Already a classic, this study is distinguished by more than ordinary attention to methods and rather exhaustive exploration of the relationship between quality ratings and characteristics of physicians, including education training and methods of practice. The findings of this study, and others that have used the same method, raise basic questions about traditional general practice in this and other countries.

[19] Clute, K. F., THE GENERAL PRACTITIONER: A STUDY OF MEDICAL EDUCATION AND PRACTICE IN ONTARIO AND NOVA SCOTIA, Toronto, University of Toronto Press, 1963, chapters 1, 2, 16, 17 and 18.
Since this study uses the method developed by Peterson, *et al.,* it offers an excellent opportunity to examine the generality of relationships between physician characteristics and quality ratings. In addition, the reader of this elegantly written volume gets a richly detailed view of general practice in the two areas studied.

[20] Kroeger, H. H., *et al.,* The Office Practice of Internists, I. The Feasibility of Evaluating Quality of Care, *The Journal of the American Medical Association,* 193, 371–376, August 2, 1965.
This is the first of a series of papers based on a study of the practice of mem-

bers of the New York Society of Internal Medicine. This paper reports findings concerning the completeness of office records, their suitability for judging quality and the degree of agreement between abstracts of records prepared by physicians and by highly trained non-physicians. Judgments concerning the quality of care provided are not given. Other papers in this series currently appearing in the *Journal of the American Medical Association* concern patient load (August 23), characteristics of patients (September 13), professional activities other than care of private patients (October 11), and background and form of practice (November 1).

[21] Kilpatrick, G. S., Observer Error in Medicine, *Journal of Medical Education*, 38, 38–43, January, 1963. For a useful bibliography on observer error *see* Witts, L. J. (Editor), MEDICAL SURVEYS AND CLINICAL TRIALS, London, Oxford University Press, 1959, pp. 39–44.

[22] Rosenfeld, L. S., Quality of Medical Care in Hospitals, *American Journal of Public Health*, 47, 856–865, July, 1957.
This carefully designed comparative study of the quality of care in four hospitals addresses itself to the problems of methods in the assessment of quality. Here one finds important information about the use of normative and empirical standards, reliability and bias in judgments based on chart review, the correlation between defects in recording and defects in practice and homogeneity in quality ratings within and between diagnostic categories.

[23] Makover, H. B., The Quality of Medical Care: Methodological Survey of the Medical Groups Associated with the Health Insurance Plan of New York, *American Journal of Public Health*, 41, 824–832, July, 1951.
This is possibly the first published report concerning an administratively instituted, but research oriented, program of studies of the quality of care in medical groups contracting with the Health Insurance Plan of Greater New York. Unfortunately much of this work remains unpublished. A particular feature of this paper is that it describes, and presents the findings of simultaneous evaluation of structure (policies, organization, administration, finances and professional activities) and process (evaluation of a sample of clinical records).

[24] Daily, E. F. and Morehead, M. A., A Method of Evaluating and Improving the Quality of Medical Care, *American Journal of Public Health*, 46, 848–854, July, 1956.

[25] Fitzpatrick, T. B., Riedel, D. C. and Payne, B. C., Character and Effectiveness of Hospital Use, in McNerney, W. J., *et al.*, HOSPITAL AND MEDICAL ECONOMICS, Chicago, Hospital Research and Educational Trust, American Hospital Association, 1962, pp. 495–509.

[26] Morehead, M. A., *et al.*, A STUDY OF THE QUALITY OF HOSPITAL CARE SECURED BY A SAMPLE OF TEAMSTER FAMILY MEMBERS IN NEW YORK CITY, New York, Columbia University, School of Public Health and Administrative Medicine, 1964.
This study and its companion[28] perform a very important social and administrative function by documenting how frequently the care received by members of a union through traditional sources proves to be inadequate. These studies also make a major contribution to understanding the relationships between hospital and physician characteristics and the quality of care they provide. Considered are physician classifications by specialty status and admission privileges, as well as hospital classifications by ownership, medical school affiliation, approval for residency training and accreditation status. The interactional effects of some of these variables are also explored. In addition, the second of the two studies[26] pays considerable attention to questions of method, including representative versus judgmental sampling of hospital admissions and the reliability of record evaluations by different judges.

[27] Morehead, M. A., Personal communication.

[28] Ehrlich, J., Morehead, M. A. and Trussell, R. E., THE QUANTITY, QUALITY AND COSTS OF MEDICAL AND HOSPITAL CARE SECURED BY A SAMPLE OF TEAMSTER FAMILIES IN THE NEW YORK AREA, New York, Columbia University, School of Public Health and Administrative Medicine, 1962.

[29] Maloney, M. C., Trussell, R. E. and Elinson, J., Physicians Choose Medical Care: A Sociometric Approach to Quality Appraisal, *American Journal of Public Health,* 50, 1678–1686, November, 1960.
This study represents an ingenious approach to evaluation through the use of "peer judgments" in what is believed to be a particularly revealing situation: choice of care for the physician or members of his own family. Some of the characteristics of the physicians and surgeons selected included long-standing personal and professional relationships, recognized specialist status, and medical school affiliation. An incidental pearl of information is that although nine out of ten physicians said everyone should have a personal physician, four out of ten said they had someone whom they considered their personal physician, and only two out of ten had seen their personal physician in the past year!

[30] Georgopoulos, B. S. and Mann, F. C., THE COMMUNITY GENERAL HOSPITAL, New York, The Macmillan Company, 1962.
The study of quality reported in several chapters of this book is based on the thesis that if one wishes to find out about the quality of care provided, all one might need to do is to ask the persons directly or indirectly involved in the provision of such care. Although physicians may find this notion rather naive, the stability and internal consistency of the findings reported in this study indicate that this approach deserves further careful evaluation. A second study of a nationwide sample of general hospitals will attempt to confirm the validity of respondent opinions by comparing them to selected indices of professional activities in each hospital. The findings will be awaited with great interest.

[31] One of the author's students, Mr. Arnold D. Kaluzny, helped the author to coin this word.

[32] Georgopoulos, B. S. and Tannenbaum, A. S., A Study of Organizational Effectiveness, *American Sociological Review,* 22, 534–540, October, 1957.

[33] Evans, L. R. and Bybee, J. R., Evaluation of Student Skills in Physical Diagnosis, *Journal of Medical Education,* 40, 199–204, February, 1965.

[34] Rimoldi, H. J. A., Haley, J. V. and Fogliatto, H., THE TEST OF DIAGNOSTIC SKILLS, Loyola Psychometric Laboratory Publication Number 25, Chicago, Loyola University Press, 1962.
This study is of interest because it uses a controlled test situation to study the performance of medical students and physicians. Even more intriguing is the attempt to approach the question of the value or utility of diagnostic actions in a systematic and rigorous manner. While this particular study does not appear to contribute greatly to understanding the quality of care, this general approach appears to be worth pursuing.

[35] Williamson, J. W., Assessing Clinical Judgment, *Journal of Medical Education,* 40, 180–187, February, 1965.
This is another example of the assessment of clinical performance using an artificial test situation. The noteworthy aspect of the work is the attachment of certain values ("helpful" or "harmful") to a set of diagnostic and therapeutic actions and the development of measures of "efficiency," "proficiency" and "competence" based on which actions are selected by the subject in managing the test case. Differences of performance between individual physicians were detected using this method. An unexpected finding was the absence of systematic differences by age, training or type of practice in groups tested so far.

[86] Eislee, C. W., Slee, V. N. and Hoffmann, R. G., Can the Practice of Internal Medicine Be Evaluated?, *Annals of Internal Medicine,* 44, 144–161, January, 1956.
The authors discuss the use of indices from which inferences might be drawn concerning the quality of surgical and medical management. The indices described include tissue pathology reports in appendectomies, diabetes patients without blood sugar determinations and without chest x-rays, and pneumonia without chest x-rays. A striking finding reported in this paper, and others based on the same approach, is the tremendous variation by physician and hospital in the occurrence of such indices of "professional activity."

[37] Furstenberg, F. F., *et al.,* Prescribing as an Index to Quality of Medical Care: A Study of the Baltimore City Medical Care Program, *American Journal of Public Health,* 43, 1299–1309, October, 1953.

[38] Peterson, O. L. and Barsamian, E. M., An Application of Logic to a Study of Quality of Surgical Care, Paper read at the Fifth IBM Medical Symposium, Endicott, New York, October 7–11, 1963.
This paper and its companion[39] present a fairly complete description of the "logic tree" approach to the evaluation of quality. Examples are given of the logic systems for the Stein-Leventhal Syndrome and uterine fibromyoma. No data are given on empirical findings using this method.

[39] ———, Diagnostic Performance, in Jacquez, J. A. (Editor), THE DIAGNOSTIC PROCESS, Ann Arbor, The University of Michigan Press, April, 1964, pp. 347–362.

[40] Lembcke, P. A. and Johnson, O. G., A MEDICAL AUDIT REPORT, Los Angeles, University of California, School of Public Health, 1963 (Mimeographed).
This is an extension of Lembcke's method of medical audit to medical diagnostic categories as well as a large number of surgical operations. Although this volume is a compendium of fairly raw data, careful study can provide insights and limitations of the method used by the author.

[41] Lembcke, P. A., A Scientific Method for Medical Auditing, *Hospitals,* 33, 65–71, June 16 and 65–72, July 1, 1959.

[42] The dimensionality of the set of variables incorporating these standards remains to be determined.

[43] Huntley, R. R., *et al.,* The Quality of Medical Care: Techniques and Investigation in the Outpatient Clinic, *Journal of Chronic Diseases,* 14, 630–642, December, 1961.
This study provides an example of the application of a routine chart review procedure as a check on the quality of management in the outpatient department of a teaching hospital. Fairly often routine procedures were not carried out and abnormalities that were found were not followed up. A revised chart review procedure seemed to make a significant reduction in the percent of abnormalities not followed up.

[44] Peterson, *et al., loc. cit.,* attempted to get some confirmation of weightings through the procedure of factor analysis. The mathematically sophisticated are referred to their footnote on pp. 14–15.

[45] Mainland, D., Calibration of the Human Instrument, Notes from a Laboratory of Medical Statistics, Number 81, August 24, 1964 (Mimeographed).

[46] Joint Committee of the Royal College of Obstetricians and Gynecologists and the Population Investigation Committee, MATERNITY IN GREAT BRITAIN, London, Oxford University Press, 1948.

201

[47] Yankauer, A., Goss, K. G. and Romeo, S. M., An Evaluation of Prenatal Care and its Relationship to Social Class and Social Disorganization, *American Journal of Public Health,* 43, 1001–1010, August, 1953.

[48] Wylie, C. M., Participation in a Multiple Screening Clinic with Five-Year Follow-Up, *Public Health Reports,* 76, 596–602, July, 1961.

[49] Commission on Professional and Hospital Activities, MEDICAL AUDIT STUDY REPORT 5: PRIMARY APPENDICTOMIES, Ann Arbor, The Commission on Professional and Hospital Activities, October, 1957.

[50] Simon, A. J., Social Structure of Clinics and Patient Improvement, *Administrative Science Quarterly,* 4, 197–206, September, 1959.

[51] Lockward, H. J., Lundberg, G. A. F. and Odoroff, M. E., Effect of Intensive Care on Mortality Rate of Patients with Myocardial Infarcts, *Public Health Reports,* 78, 655–661, August, 1963.

[52] Bakst, J. N. and Marra, E. F., Experiences with Home Care for Cardiac Patients, *American Journal of Public Health,* 45, 444–450, April, 1955.

[53] Muller, J. N., Tobis, J. S. and Kelman, H. R., The Rehabilitation Potential of Nursing Home Residents, *American Journal of Public Health,* 53, 243–247, February, 1963.

[54] These studies also include data on the relationships between structural features and procedural end points. Examples are the effect of clinic structure on the number of outpatient visits,[50] and the effect of a home care program on hospital admissions.[52]

[55] Getting, V. A., *et al.,* Research in Evaluation in Public Health Practices, Paper presented at the 92nd Annual Meeting, American Public Health Association, New York, October 5, 1964.

[56] Assuming the direct evaluation of process to be the criterion, the issue becomes one of the implications of reliability measures for validity.

[57] Ciocco, A., Hunt, H. and Altman, I., Statistics on Clinical Services to New Patients in Medical Groups, *Public Health Reports,* 65, 99–115, January 27, 1950.
This is an early application to group practice of the analysis of "professional activities" now generally associated with the evaluation of hospital care. The indices used included the recording of diagnosis and treatment, the performance of rectal and vaginal examinations, the performance of certain laboratory examinations and the use of sedatives, stimulants and other medications subject to abuse. As is true of hospitals, the groups varied a great deal with respect to these indicators.

[58] Myers, R. S., Hospital Statistics Don't Tell the Truth, *Modern Hospital,* 83, 53–54, July, 1954.

[59] Even for hospital care the appropriate unit may include care before and after admission, as well as several hospital admissions.[3]

[60] Cordero, A. L., The Determination of Medical Care Needs in Relation to a Concept of Minimal Adequate Care: An Evaluation of the Curative Outpatient Services in a Rural Health Center, *Medical Care,* 2, 95–103, April–June, 1964.

[61] Butterworth, J. S. and Reppert, E. H., Auscultatory Acumen in the General Medical Population, *Journal of the American Medical Association,* 174, 32–34, September 3, 1960.

[62] Evans, L. R. and Bybee, J. R., Evaluation of Student Skills in Physical Diagnosis, *Journal of Medical Education*, 40, 199–204, February, 1965.

[63] Fattu, N. C., Experimental Studies of Problem Solving, *Journal of Medical Education*, 39, 212–225, February, 1964.

[64] John, E. R., Contributions to the Study of the Problem Solving Process, *Psychological Monographs*, 71, 1957.

[65] Duncan, C. P., Recent Research in Human Problem Solving, *Psychological Bulletin*, 56, 397–429, November, 1959.

[66] Fattu, N. A., Mech, E. and Kapos, E., Some Statistical Relationships between Selected Response Dimensions and Problem-Solving Proficiency, *Psychological Monographs*, 68, 1954.

[67] Stolurow, L. M., *et al.*, The Efficient Course of Action in "Trouble Shooting" as a Joint Function of Probability and Cost, *Educational and Psychological Measurement*, 15, 462–477, Winter, 1955.

[68] Ledley, R. S. and Lusted, L. B., Reasoning Foundations of Medical Diagnosis, *Science*, 130, 9–21, July 3, 1959.

[69] Lusted, L. B. and Stahl, W. R., Conceptual Models of Diagnosis, in Jacquez, J. A. (Editor), THE DIAGNOSTIC PROCESS, Ann Arbor, The University of Michigan Press, 1964, pp. 157–174.

[70] Edwards, W., Lindman, H. and Phillips, L. D., Emerging Technologies for Making Decisions, in Newcomb, T. M. (Editor), NEW DIRECTIONS IN PSYCHOLOGY, II, New York, Holt, Rinehart & Winston, Inc., 1965, pp. 261–325.

ACKNOWLEDGMENTS

Included among the reviewed authors who read the manuscript and made corrections or comments are Georgopoulos, Makover, Morehead, Peterson, Riedel, Rosenstock, Rosenfeld, Sheps and Weinerman. The author is especially indebted to Dr. Mildred A. Morehead and to professors Basil S. Georgopoulos, Herbert E. Klarman and Charles A. Metzner for taking time to make extensive comments. The official critics, Mr. Sam Shapiro and Dr. Jonas N. Muller were helpful in sharpening some of the issues in the assessment of quality. Since the author was unable to use all the excellent advice he received, he alone is responsible for defects in this paper.

This review has been supported, in part, by Grant CH-00108 from the Division of Community Health Services, United States Public Health Service.

DISCUSSION

The feasibility of individual vs. population level studies. Most of this discussion concentrates on the choice of the aspect of quality set forth in Dr. Donabedian's paper. While his focus on quality in the individual patient-physician relationship was acknowledged to be a traditional concern, a research approach from the standpoint of total target populations was advocated as a broader and more needed framework for studying quality in the future. In such a case the assessment of quality should include such factors as the distribution, accessibility and use of medical services, relating, among other things, to the efficiency of providing and delivering services. Even though no new facilities become available, the quality of medical care received by particular population groups may change simply through a different pattern of use. While Dr. Donabedian provides examples of how the best quality of care for the individual may not be the best care for a community, unfortunately he does not develop this concept further, but remains within the framework of the behavior of the individual patient and physician.

In reply Dr. Donabedian contends that if quality of care were defined to include the total medical care system and target populations, all research in health services involving values would become research into "quality." The meaning of "quality" would lose the little precision it has and would be even more difficult to study than it is already. Introducing utilization and other socioeconomic variables would greatly multiply the factors to be integrated. Emphasis now should be placed on studies at the individual patient-physician level or on studies of the kinds of medical services offered to the public; the more complex variables could be introduced in subsequent investigations.

The most reputable findings in the social sciences appear to stem from studies of groups rather than of individuals. Likewise, the natural sciences deal with the interactions of large populations. Similarly, while studies of the educational process at the individual pupil-teacher relationship have not been revealing, they have succeeded with remarkable precision in replicating relationships between settings, administrative structures and outcomes. Since the whole patient care process cannot be brought into view and related even to a profile of outcomes, the study of process at the level of individual interactions would have to stop at immediate microcriteria and would not be fruitful. While complex variables do enter into the study of both the individual patient-physician relationship and populations at risk, the research problem is more within the investigator's grasp if populations rather than individuals are the object of study.

The importance of medical care outcomes. Also disputed is Dr. Donabedian's assumption that the more promising research strategy lay in studying process rather than outcome. The overall social circumstances in which medical care is provided today requires concentration on the issues and goals of the system and on outcomes rather than process. While the discussion brought out the difficulties of using the outcome approach, the obstacles are not considered insuperable. The difficulties cited by Dr. Donabedian reflected more on the ability of the investigators to define criteria relevant to the populations studied than on the power or desirability of the outcome approach. Divorced from the issue of context, any branch of study could be overwhelmed with methodological problems. Acceptance of a margin of error is basic to all research and the real methodological issue for investigation concerns the degree of interference that bias can exert on conclusions concerning quality of care. Such determinations of the significant methodological problems cannot be made in the abstract, without discussion of the specific issues and goals of evaluating quality of care. Had Dr. Donabedian concentrated more on the issues and values of the medical care system he might have been led to a less pessimistic view of the importance of the outcome approach and to its more extensive treatment. In addition, he might have further clarified the gaps in methodology currently deterring research progress, the compromises that have to be accepted, and the priorities for sharpening existing research tools. While Dr. Donabedian agrees to the validity of introducing organizational changes, for example, and then observing the outcome in terms of care, he feels that such studies possess inherent limitations. The unknown variables involved prohibit generalizations about the ways such outcomes occur. The relationships between changes in settings and changes in outcomes can only be validated through studies of process. Also, outcomes may reflect the effects of two different processes; one which furthers, the other which detracts from good outcome. By themselves, outcome studies cannot take account of such cancellation effects.

Since numerous variables other than medical care affect outcome, much more research should be devoted to identifying the proportion of outcome that is related to medical care variables. The study of process at the individual level, aggregated to the population, is proposed as a way to define the contribution that medical care makes to outcome. Seen in this way, the study of process at the population level would no longer be considered as an inferior substitute for the study of outcome.

The need to separate values from the elements of the process. In Dr. Donabedian's opinion, the issue is not one of process vs. outcome, but of choosing in any particular situation what is the most productive thing to do. While the ultimate concern in this field is indeed with outcomes, from certain vantage points he advocates concentrating on process and leaving the validation of the relationship between process and outcome to different kinds of investigators, clinicians in particular.

Furthermore, he avoids reference to content issues and to the goals and values of medical care because he specifically argues for the need to separate value judgments from descriptions of the elements of the process. In Dr. Donabedian's opinion, the approach to quality which maintains that, for example, continuity of care must constitute good care, is a very naive approach. Research ought to transcend this limited stance and develop methods to define operationally what continuity means and to study its natural history, how and when it manifests itself. The study of the values and goals of the medical care process needs to be approached from a completely different and radically empirical point of view. Particularly important is the need to discover to what extent values in the medical care system agree or contradict each other. Whenever values conflict, medical care cannot be described as simply either good or bad. It can only be characterized as good in terms of certain specific dimensions and bad in terms of other dimensions. The elements of the process must therefore be dissected and understood much more clearly before any value judgments can be attached to them in terms of their contribution to certain goals.

206

RESEARCH INTO HOSPITAL MANAGEMENT AND ORGANIZATION

REGINALD W. REVANS

INTRODUCTION

This paper suggests that those in charge of hospitals are the persons best fitted to pursue research into the operational problems of hospital management. To do this they may need the help of social scientists, and the main thesis of the paper is in no way intended to suggest that university staffs and other academics have no effective contribution to make in raising the standards of hospital organization and control.

But, the problems of action—of real men striving to change real situations—are but partially accessible to those who neither carry the responsibility for the outcome of that action nor can be the victims of any misunderstandings which the action may create. The external worker may often help to prepare what others may decide, but his research interests are frequently so far from the necessities of practical operation as to seem, to the responsible administrator, positively harmful in the demands they may make upon managerial time. Nor is this all. If hospital administrators are to use what the external research worker has to say to them, they should both intellectually and emotionally understand his approach, his methods, his criteria, his austerity. This they will do best when they themselves are closely joined in research into their own problems.

Finally, this thesis is not new; the hospital literature is filled with examples of how those in operational authority have successfully embarked unaided upon the misty waters of self-analysis. Also, their

207

discoveries may well help to form new concepts of administration, to be used in fields far removed from the care of the sick. The professional scholars must lend a hand whenever it may be needed in this exciting search.

SOCIAL RESEARCH AND HOSPITAL ADMINISTRATION

At the end of "The Community General Hospital," its authors, Georgopoulos and Mann, state:

> The community general hospital could easily claim the dubious honor of being one of the least researched modern large-scale organisations In spite of its crucial function of aiding the integration and stability of society, through the maintenance of a level of health that permits other social institutions to accomplish their objectives, and in spite of its far-reaching impact upon nearly every facet of everyday life—particularly our economy, standards of living and community welfare—the community general hospital has not received more than a fraction of the scientific attention that its importance as an organisation would warrant. As yet our understanding of its functioning, problems and characteristics is extremely limited . . . and the same is true, only more so, regarding comparative studies of hospitals.[1]

The significance of this comment cannot be allowed to escape attention, since research in the field of health itself—the diagnosis, treatment and prevention of disease—must rank among the oldest of quests for security, not only among the sciences as they are established today, but in the previous epochs of alchemy, magic and superstition through which they all, including medicine, have passed. Why, when the history of medicine itself is so richly documented and, of later years, so suggestive for the other sciences, has so little regard been paid to the development of hospital organization itself?

To some extent the answer is that studies of hospitals were not needed. In the past the hospital created no serious problems for those whose hands were on the levers of social control, for only the poor were driven to seek its shelter. The rich were nursed at home and died in their own beds. The demand for hospitals for the middle classes needed to await the rise of the middle classes. By the second half of the nineteenth century they provided their own abundance of daughters to nurse in the hospitals, and charity enough in their more successful members, including the doctors, to guarantee that, judged by the standards of the times, the hospitals were well run and well staffed.

208

Someone in this day and age would have difficulty in understanding the expansive and benevolent amateurism with which these hospitals were established. The suggestion that research might be needed either to identify their problems or to point their solutions would have been so remote from their patronizing self-confidence as to lack all meaning. The Encyclopedia Britannica for 1911, for example, in its article on nursing, remarks that whatever other problems the profession may face in the future, it will never be short of recruits. Who, in their senses, would spend years examining the role and status of nurses, given this happy state of affairs? Bullock, in his 1954 report on the profession's needs for self-realization would, to the first daughters of Florence Nightingale, have sounded not only pretentious but also indecent. Nor did the hospitals have none of the problems by which they are now bedevilled. So long as they were run by amateurs only for the deserving poor they made no demands upon official consciences and so called for no official examination. Even if he had existed the research worker had no channel of entry either from the university or the government department. To grasp how amateur and uninstructed was the world of hospital management only a generation back is difficult. This extract from a letter written by a hospital vice-president may afford some insight. It advises the public upon more effective ways of financing hospital activities than the sale of foil wrappers stripped from chocolate and tobacco:

> The metal of accumulator [storage battery] plates contains antimony, which renders them more valuable than ordinary scrap lead. Also hospitals selling collections of old accumulators in quantity direct to the smelters would be able to get a far better price for them than could be obtained for only one or two. No doubt there would be people to organise collections of old accumulators in their district for the local hospital.[2]

A culture in which an educated man would write such a letter and one of the world's leading newspapers would print it probably had neither the time nor the inclination for self-analysis.

This was half a lifetime ago and Britain, for all its preoccupation with the past, is changing quickly. The spirit of the National Health Service today, although austere, is in a businesslike and athletic way, very different from this ethic of charity and old lead plates. But one does not create overnight a tradition of hospital research. The fact that a better understanding is needed of present-day problems no longer needs emphasis. But resources to carry out the search for understanding are practically nonexistent. Few studies get to the heart of the problem of "what makes for a good hospital," on which alone a tradition of hospital research is built. Nor does one have to look far back into American history to find equally telling illustrations of how little progress has been made in eliminating the ignorance of these vital problems in the best use of precious resources. The Commonwealth Fund, only 20 years ago, produced a report upon the small community hospital and, in its chapter on organization and administration, said of the doctors:

> Men already accustomed to having their own way in a proprietory situation promptly identify the hospital with themselves, thinking of the operating room as *their* operating room, the nurses as *their* nurses, the superintendent as *their* agent . . . these attitudes may lead to irritability in the staff and early friction with the superintendent, if not with the business men who stand behind him. There is a good deal of jockeying for position and much depends upon the tact and firmness with which the hospital is run during this period. . . . Perhaps a local disaster—a tornado or a fire— throws into relief the advantage of the hospital to the community and shows the doctors their own capacity for a quick and smooth cooperation . . .[3]

The author of these lines has nothing to learn about one of the most obstinate of all hospital problems—the cult of individualism among the medical staff—but his drastic remedy, teamwork in disaster, is one on which the resources of social science should be able to improve. Nor is this all. A full program of research into the organization and management of hospitals would help to understand this distressing condition among the medical staff, not merely to ameliorate or even cure it, but to prevent it by adequate methods of emotional inoculation in early life. But, judged against what is needed in the way of social therapy, present knowledge is pitiably slender. The advantage to this is that in this field no misconceived theory need be disproven before contact can be made with what may prove useful. Also, a very wide variety of ideas can be adapted from other fields, from mechanical engineering to political science, and from nonparametric statistics to social psychology. But, the main research problem remains that of defining, analyzing and modifying the attitudes of those who, in the hospitals, command the heights of power. All three must be achieved—definition, analysis and modification—for in the real world of suffering and anxiety (shared by staff no less than by patients) academic or scholarly studies that do not lend themselves to improving the human condition have but a secondary place.

210

They may be brilliant excursions into the fields of statistics, anthropology, economics or social theory, but if they do not help to resolve the problems of hospital effectiveness they are not research into management or organization. These management problems can be understood only if and when those who are actually managing personally join or take over the research needed to resolve the problems. This demands a radical change of view, to recognize that, while help is available, salvation will not be by outside experts. Action research alone, in the final analysis, can win the race.

RESEARCH INTO OPERATIONAL PROBLEMS

Presumably, a hospital exists primarily to help those admitted to it as patients, and to provide this help through a program of stimuli —clinical, intellectual, social and emotional (if these factors are in fact so readily distinguishable)—best calculated to encourage the patients' recovery. The special administrative problems of the many hospitals which do not seem to conform to this description, such as those whose administration is preoccupied with clinical research or the training of medical students, cannot be treated as special cases. Even in such as these the management is still responsible to insure the use of resources in the best interests of the patients.

All programs of treatment demand two major sets of resources from the hospital: on the one hand, human or professional; on the other, physical or technical. In addition, demands are made upon the families of patients, or upon their employers, insurance funds or other agencies external to the hospital. These two classes of resources are not unrelated, since the capacity of a physical asset, such as a bed or a pathology laboratory, depends upon the skill of the professionals in charge of it. In the same way, the capacity of a nurse or of a pathologist depends in turn upon the physical means made available to them.[4] The deployment of these resources is, in general, the task of the hospital management. Although in practice the two sets seem inextricable, an attempt will be made in describing the research literature, to discriminate between them, although studies of the articulation of the professional skills will be the area of concentration rather than studies of the best use by managements of buildings and facilities.

One cannot resist the temptation to illustrate the difference in terms of the early career of Florence Nightingale. The difference struck her during the first hours of her arrival at Scutari. Of improving the use of her physical resources, she records the problems of clearing the remains of a dead horse from the cesspits beneath the floors on which her soldiers lay. Of the best use of the professional skills of the band of nurses she had brought with her she observed "the strongest arms will be needed at the washtub."

Ridding the hospital of dead horses may no longer be necessary and the triumphs of detergent science have freed many nurses for occupations loftier than washing the patients' clothes. But, a major aim of operational research now is to remove costly delays in the treatment of patients by more efficiently balancing the sequential use of keys assets such as operating theatres and x-ray rooms. The underlying logical structures of many of these operational problems in the hospital are no different from those of industry. Every hospital administrator should mark among his engineering or scientific friends those sufficiently imaginative to have followed the progress of management technology, operational research, work analysis, systems theory, industrial dynamics, human engineering, ergonomics or by whatever other name the rationalization of work has become known—work, in this context, being narrowly defined as the visible operations that decide what is actually achieved. No doubt, even at this level, hospitals can do a great deal to improve their efficiency, whether by such simple steps as rationalizing the filing system or the case notes, or the even humbler ones of better organizing the pig bins. Yet experience shows that the obstacles to improvement are rarely failures in the expertise of work simplification. They are a fatal inertia in applying it, through a long familiarity with a *status quo* that has forgotten how to question the obvious. Thus the challenge of using resources better is returned to those who use them. For all that, the National Health Service, at its headquarters, its regional board levels and in the hospitals themselves, has clearly demonstrated what can be done to improve work organization. The establishment of ACME (Advisory Committee on Managerial Efficiency) under the chairmanship of Sir Ewart Smith, was a major event. It has accelerated the period of cultural preparation during which hospital management has learned that operational success demands an organic approach, rather than a dependence upon energetic competition, however good for the reputation of individuals, among its leading members. The references at the end of this article list some of the projects and publications of this branch of the Health Service.[5] Sharing the effort to effect small changes in any ongoing system, whether to vary the day of the month on which a committee meets or to use the hospital vehicles more economically, can be a useful learning process for administrators preparing to take in hand the larger problems with which they are faced. For this reason, as much care needs to be given to the introduction of minor changes by work rationalization as to the architectural design of a new ward block. Given the authoritarian culture that the modern hospital has inherited, these minor cooperations in efficiency improvement or increased productivity may be an essential transition.

HOSPITALS AS ORGANIC SYSTEMS

Of interest, no doubt, is to talk of hospitals as organic systems. Georgopoulos and Mann, for example, say of their research:

> Both theoretically and methodologically, it has tried to capture the image of the total hospital as a complex organisational system, and to examine some of the problems and characteristics of hospital organisation that are system-wide in nature, or at least have direct system-wide implications. . . . Most of the concepts and variables with which it is concerned were defined and measured at the organisational or group level, and not at the individual level.[1]

Such an approach demands a definition, for the benefit of hospital staff, of the system-concept in the hospital, as this concept is being developed by workers in other fields. It encourages an examination of the models of operational research. This suggests that essentially five steps mark the progress of the patient through the hospital, just as five steps are necessary in any rational action.

First, the patient, on sufficiently convincing evidence, is admitted to the hospital. Secondly, on a detailed and specific examination, a diagnosis is made of his condition. Thirdly, based on this diagnosis, he is launched upon a program of treatment. Fourthly, his response to this treatment is continuously observed and compared with the response anticipated when the treatment was selected. Finally, in accordance with the results of this comparison, the patient is either discharged, his treatment amended or prolonged or his condition rediagnosed. To simplify the model still further, the five patient-stages may be listed as 1. admission, 2. diagnosis, 3. treatment, 4. inspection and 5. control. These stages are locked together in two dimensions: by the availability and capacity of the physical resources themselves;

213

and, by the network of power and communications through which are generated and transmitted the decisions that, in effect, control the experiences of the patient in any one stage and his transfer to the next. This model is not only effective for the operational worker seeking to improve some particular aspect of the organization, but may also form the framework for building some sophisticated simulation of the entire hospital to be manipulated by a digital computer.

Consider, for example, a patient in the second or diagnostic stage. If coordination between this and the first stage is poor a patient may have been admitted without an adequate case history, so that time is wasted over his diagnosis in trying to find his private doctor. Also, he may have been admitted when no doctor will be available to examine him for many hours. The time spent on this diagnostic stage will also depend upon the speed with which the pathology laboratory or the x-ray department produce the results of the tests demanded by the doctors, and so must depend upon the physical assets available. In British hospitals patients occupying surgical beds have been known to wait up to two weeks for a barium meal because the x-ray department is said to be overloaded. Also, a patient may undergo a major surgical operation and, after recovery from it, to be sent for the chest x-ray that was supposed to have determined whether or not the anaesthetic with which the patient had already long since been treated could be safely administered.

These unhappy errors, on close study, turn out to be largely inherent in the system rather than the product of temporary human carelessness or irresponsibility. The errors arise in the system largely because, by unstable design, it soon gets out of balance. But apart from the analysis of errors, some hospital admission systems have been shown to be significantly more efficient than that of others. The reasons for the differences can be suggested by the operational research worker teamed with the administration. Given the most complex state of affairs that is hospital reality, as compared with this grossly over-simplified five-stage model, the interest now being taken in these program aspects of patient-care by the systems analysts, such as Fetter,[6] Howland[7] and Flagle,[8] is gratifying.

Most of these workers first learned their craft by examining the operational networks of industry. The general question that they can be expected to answer for and with the administrator is: "Given the probability that a certain number of patients are likely to enter this hospital next year, distributed in such and such proportions between age, sex, diagnostic group and so forth, what would be the effect upon total performance should this or that facility be improved at such and such a cost?" Or the question could be put in slightly different words: "What elements within this five-stage sequential system called patient care should be improved first for greatest benefit to the total?" In the example quoted, how should any extra resources that become available be divided so as to improve both the barium meal facilities and the system for collecting case histories to the greatest total effect? What means could be used other than that of pressure bargaining between the two departmental heads concerned, with perhaps the hospital secretary or house governor having the final word? The answer is that such means are almost certainly worth seeking, and that the operational research workers, when enough have been trained within the hospital service, will soon have constructive ideas about how to trace them. An interesting case was presented by Fetter and Thompson in 1964.[6]

The power of these new methods should not be overrated. No doubt, in the foreseeable future, a large number of possible decisions may be tested in advance by methods of system simulation that cannot now be tested at all, but which can be only the fruits of intuition[9] and opportunity. Moreover, these efforts to study the hospital as a system of sequential steps very soon suggest an analysis of each step. The cooperation of a number of British hospitals to examine their admission systems at once demands their close and individual analysis by methods of work study. These techniques, first developed in Britain to assess the problems of supervisors in cotton mills having to handle looms no less temperamental than living persons, are now being applied to the sampling of ward activities, to determine, for example, the fluctuation of loads upon nurses and patterns of patient care under different loads. Outstanding examples of such studies, attentive to questions of methodology as well as to results, are due to the Oxford Regional Hospital Board and the Nuffield Provincial Hospitals Trust.[10] The Oxford Board has also made an important contribution to the simulation of the maternity hospital using these methods. But many such studies are clearly needed. For example, increasing the number of nurses available to a ward may not in any way increase the amount of attention devoted to the patient. It may merely increase the extent to which the nurses talk to each other. How far and why this effect varies from hospital to hospital is not known. The staff of particular hospitals have probably accepted ideas upon how much care a patient ought to get, and so the nursing system beyond a traditional threshold rejects extra care as the body rejects a surfeit of vitamins.

An interesting example of how the organic nature of the hospital may thrust itself upon the attention of the research worker comes in the study by Pantall and Elliott of an administrative change in Birmingham.[11] They set out to determine a favorable administrative scheme for forming a "large, busy, developing multi-purpose hospital group." As they tackled not only the rationalization of the committee structure, but such practical tasks as the integration of the services offered by the pathology laboratories, pharmacies, x-ray departments, physiotherapists, storekeepers and gardeners, they became aware of the need for measurement and order at the ultimate point of application, namely, the ward itself. This is now being examined at a double level: the study of bedside activity, linked with a recording of patient dependency, and the study of the tasks of the sister in charge of the ward. A third stage, the integration of the wards themselves and the parallel ancillary services, under the senior management of the hospital, will presumably follow. These examinations of what actually occurs where the patient meets the system are being carried out with attitude surveys and the results are fed back into the working of the system through discussion groups among the hospital staff generally.

Now that this and similar studies in Britain have revealed how much interest can be aroused within a nursing service traditionally seen as responding only by a submissive obedience to orders, to find that the medical staff seem to remain, in general, comparatively indifferent to these questions of social analysis and organizational therapy is disappointing. Perhaps the authors of the Commonwealth Fund study, in suggesting that nothing serves as well as "a local disaster, such as tornado or fire, to show the doctors their own capacity for quick and smooth cooperation," were not aware either that Britain is mercifully off the track of tornados or that it has extremely efficient fire service.[12]

Twelve years ago a group of hospitals in Detroit made an equally elaborate study of the conditions under which they might raise their operational efficiency to meet their rising demand. Wright[13] reported an attempt made by the hospitals themselves, helped by the faculty of a local business school and by industrial staff skilled in the analysis of production problems, to find out what needed to be done in the hospital, what seemed in fact to be done, and what the patients

216

thought about it. Some long and painstaking surveys of staff and patient opinion, to which nearly 100 doctors contributed, suggested that, among other things, more than 500 distinct groups of tasks were to be done. The staff then sat down to work out among themselves who should do which of them. In determining this the views of the patients, subscribed by a questionnaire circulated after they had been five days in the hospital, were taken as an objective standard of effectiveness. Those who were brought into these systematizing discussions about the ward tasks, of which 250 were identified, included not only the practical nurses, nursing aides and ward clerks, but the dietary maids, the laundry staff, the purchasing office, the maintenance engineers and half a dozen others. The exercise, in addition to fulfilling its purpose of serving more beds with fewer professional staff,[14] taught the lesson, to be learned afresh by every generation of managers, that hospital staff seems to seek these four operational goals:

1. to use their talents, however modest, to the maximum possible extent;
2. to seek training of any kind that may help them to develop these talents;
3. not to be unnecessarily interrupted in the course of any given task, or in other words, to have time to complete whatever they have started;
4. to work out a set of procedures within which cooperation with other persons or departments is readily possible.

This project, although starting as an exercise in individual task rationalization, finished as a major contribution to the literature of communication and social learning. It can be seen as a complement to the work of Pantall and Elliott[11] who, beginning with the administrative structure, are now microscopically examining the ward activities. To get those in charge of the hospitals both enthusiastic and informed about how more clearly to perceive, and more effectively to treat, their own problems where they exist, Wright is unsurpassed.

The success of these and of other examples of what can be done to reorganize single hospitals, or parts of single hospitals, is an essential field of study of the research worker interested in the spread of new ideas and of fresh powers among the administrative class. In Britain, where a national health service is able to insinuate these innovations into hospitals that would otherwise rarely be exposed to them, more than 1300 such studies have been completed in the last few years, nearly all by the hospitals themselves with their own work-study teams. An impressive example was the re-allocation of dental chairs at the Royal Dental Hospital,[5] where, by a different paperwork system of appointments, a proposed new building was shown to be unnecessary. While, as in starting anything that challenges existing ideas, the simpler forms of work organization are best to begin with, these excursions into systems analysis have now reached some fairly sophisticated levels. One study, of great interest not only to the hospital architect and accountant, but also to the medical staff, is that of interdepartmental traffic within a hospital (or the movement of patients, information, staff and supplies between the five stages) with a view to bringing closely together those services of the hospital that most interact. This study, with the same logical structure as the classical linear programming exercises of industry and commerce, is being assisted by the computer in the University of London. But its concealed importance, as an effort of cooperative self-evaluation, may prove greater than any immediate saving of costs. For the moment, encouraging the gradual encroachment of these organic ideas throughout a great national service is no less important than to aim at the specific technical achievement of the here and now.

HOSPITAL INTERNAL COMMUNICATIONS

Imagine that, in this model of the patient's progress through the system, his transfer from one stage to the next is in a horizontal dimension (admission ward; x-ray department; operating theatre; surgical ward; convalescent home). The transparency of this can be investigated and improved by these new methods of operational research. The vertical dimension, then, transmits the decisions of the professional staff controlling this progress. The medium through which their authority is exercised is the hospital communication system. The material with which this system is supplied is information about the patients and about the resources of the hospital available to serve them. The information has several major uses. First, it provides the working material of the carpenter. Second, it is, or should be, the influence by which the views and the skills of those in charge are systematically improved and adjusted to the constantly changing demands of the hospital and of the community it serves.

218

Third, apart from providing for the effective treatment of individual patients or the economic use of physical assets, it should inform the managment about the organic disabilities from which the hospital system itself is likely to be suffering. These include, on the one hand, the anemia of nurse wastage, and the many obstructions of the administrative circulatory system, such as conflict between ward and pharmacy or between lecture theory and bedside practice; and, on the other hand, the many fantasies or misinterpretations of reality, identified as institutional parataxis, that individuals, or classes of individuals, within the hospital seem to harbor about their roles, their powers and their relations with those who share their tasks.

To describe the labyrinthine traffic in facts and misunderstandings between, say, 2000 employees and 1000 patients as a "communication system" is, of course, a gross euphemism. The expression, moreover, is not only too gross, but also tends to give objectivity to what is essentially highly subjective. As a result, many of those who appear most conscious of failures within the communication system—without being too confident of the precise nature of these failures—imagine that the solution is to be found in the improvement of the physical means of assembling and transmitting messages, such as in training a corps of ward clerks or by installing a computer. These methods of the systems expert, transferred from the horizontal progress of the patient, through the physical services offered by the hospital, to the vertical flow of information and authority, from patient to staff, from nurse to doctor, from administrator to committee, have some application, and indeed large hospitals cannot be managed effectively without taking advantage of them. But they are by no means the most important weapons for a general campaign to improve this vertical dimension of hospital effectiveness.

Research into the administrative problems of hospitals over the last 20 years shows that their successful solution, while undoubtedly depending upon improved objective communications, is nevertheless largely to be created by subjective changes within the staff. The important elements in the communication system are not the material channels of transmission—the forms, the files, the telephones, the colored lights nor even the subcommittee structures; but the input and output mechanisms of those at the ends of such channels. The perception they hold of their place in the system, their awareness of how this role is seen by others and their capacity to make themselves clear, not in some absolute language of objective precision, but to the person in front of them, determine most strongly whether their efforts at communication will succeed.

Even supposing communication in this fundamental sense has been successful, the subjective capacity of those within the system to evaluate realistically what they are doing will determine two further things: first, whether the action they propose to take is likely to be effective (for communication without action is no communication at all) and, second, whether from that action they are likely to learn anything that may help them to perceive more clearly, to interpret more realistically and to act more effectively on a future occasion. For research into hospital management and organization has, more than research in any other field, demonstrated that administrative action itself is not any exact and mechanical application of formal rules laid down by experts, but may of itself be both a cure and an education. It is not, as many imagine, merely a medium enabling therapy to be applied; it is the very process of therapy itself. It is not just the messenger of enlightenment; it is in itself that enlightenment and is to be found, not in the formal teaching of rules or principles, but in what Burling, Lentz and Wilson, with brilliant insight, call "The Give and Take in Hospitals."[15]

This is the title of the book that everyone interested, not only in the hospital research of others, but also in how to do their own, should read. For give and take, or what the control engineer calls two-way communication or feedback, is the core of all learning. These may strike the practical hospital administrator as extravagant and even romantic claims, and he might well ask what has occurred in the past 20 years to make possible these achievements. To some extent they were determined by the very rigidity of hospital administration itself.

That western culture, which had nearly destroyed itself in two wars, but had learned in survival the cardinal importance of cooperation between ordinary and undistinguished persons, would continue to tolerate a medical ethic suggesting that only when faced with disaster could doctors learn to work together was inconceivable. Western culture, of course, has no official spokesmen. It is a way in which several hundred million people look at life, and among those observers are to be found many doctors no less perceptive than any other latter day prophets. High, therefore, in the list of critics of the manner in which American and British hospitals have been

220

managed in the past are the names of many distinguished doctors, most of whom have professional psychological or psychiatric training. They and their collaborators include T. F. Main (to whom is first due the expression "therapeutic community"), Maxwell Jones[17] and D. H. Clark[18] in Britain, and, in America, A. H. Stanton and M. S. Schwartz,[19] John and Elaine Cumming,[20] Esther Lucille Brown[21] and other workers for such agencies of liberal ideas as the Russell Sage Foundation or the Commonwealth Fund. The writings of these and of other pioneers may not yet have received the full attention they deserve, but all are prophetic signs that hospital administration on both sides of the Atlantic has embarked upon an anticipatory program of cultural change. Furthermore, this research will provide a new view of the processes of management general to all institutions, not to hospitals alone, and will have a profound effect upon the conduct of organisms as varied as universities and department stores.

The concept of the "therapeutic community," namely, an institution in which the governing element not only knows what is actually going on but is also itself capable of learning from this knowledge, as well as teaching its subordinates, may prove to be one of the discoveries of the mid-century, a broom strong enough to sweep the administrative ceilings clear of the last cobwebs of such once-powerful ideas as the charismatic leader, the Divine Right of Kings, the philosopher crown-princes of Plato's Republic and even, perhaps, some of the sterile ratiocinations taught in contemporary schools, such as "the principles of management."

COMMUNICATIONS IN MENTAL HOSPITALS

The report of the Commonwealth Fund upon the small community hospital may have appeal as a historical document suggesting the enormous changes in outlook that have taken place since the second world war, but it is one of considerable perspicacity, full of homely wisdom deserving the objective scrutiny of the social scientist. After some very general and *a priori* observations upon the ownership and financial control of the hospital, the form of its membership corporation and board of directors, the authors turn to the qualities and duties of the superintendent. They supposed that, from the salary offered, women would predominantly apply for this post, and specified that their qualities should include tact, initiative, courage, administrative finesses, personality and a fund of sound technical knowledge—qual-

221

ities that would generally be expected of any candidate to command an institution dealing with the public, especially if, as with a hospital, this might occur in distressing circumstances. But a strong note of realism is soon struck, when the authors describe the tasks facing the superintendent.

> In some respects nurse training is a positive handicap in becoming a good superintendent. Doctors are accustomed to give orders to nurses and even like a nurse to rise when they enter a room. Many physicians are puzzled and irritated at finding a nurse in a position of authority in a hospital. It is hard for them to talk seriously with her about administrative matters. . . . Only a nurse who, by virtue of temperament or a broad experience, is at ease in the administrative situation is likely to handle these difficulties successfully. . . . She embodies for the doctors a strange new order in which rules and regulations imposed by laymen impinge on the most individualistic of professions. She stands between her staff and the petulant physician who expects a nurse to be fired on the spot if she displeases him. . . . She bars the operating room to the bustling surgeon who, in defiance of schedule and without benefit of orderly diagnosis, is rushing his patient to the table. And usually, in the course of a year or two, she has become thoroughly unpopular.[22]

After some pages of homiletic advice upon the number and duties of office staff, the qualities to be looked for in the resident physician and so forth—all the essentials of a sound management—the report has some observations upon relations with the public.

> Good hospital technique is incompatible with the huddling of wide-eyed relatives in a corner of the operating room to watch the gory details of surgical treatment, but many proprietary hospitals have permitted this sort of visiting so long that the clients of the community hospital are puzzled when it is forbidden. These difficulties wear off as the hospital and its ways become familiar.

Such was the general level at which problems of hospital management were discussed when, in 1954, the scene was suddenly illuminated by the monograph of Stanton and Schwartz.[19] This is an exhaustive study of the interplay of emotions, hopes, fears, skills, interests, values and so forth, between staff and patients in the ward. Its lessons might, at first sight, appear remote from the grander policies of management and organization, and the study, having been made in a mental hospital, might seem to have still less relevance to the administrative problems of the general or community hospital. This is not so. The human organism, like truth, is a seamless garment, and bits of it cannot be taken out for examination or repair without effect upon the system as a whole. The response of the individual to stress, whether in body, mind or spirit, is one and undivided and his behavior under one disability should be instructive as to his possible behavior under another. However this may be, the work of Stanton and Schwartz can be read with profit by students of administration from every field. In Chapter 18, they say this:

> . . . the hospital suffered conspicuous inadequacies in its organisation of decision making; the whole subject was rarely discussed and then was usually treated in a most unrealistic way. A corollary of this was the inadequate arrangements for locating difficulties, diagnosing them and changing the conditions that had brought them about. Appraisal was informal and unplanned; it had to occur and it did occur almost continuously, but it was a most bungling process—inaccurate, poorly directed, hit or miss and unnecessarily painful. The emotional cost of this and similar inadequacies in the hospital was heavy; it would have been at least partly avoided if a clearer understanding of its origin had existed . . .

The contribution of Stanton and Schwartz was to discover the nature and origin of the confusion in the ward they studied. The disease had been recognizable to Southmayd and Smith[3] in 1944, but Stanton and Schwartz were among the earliest to identify its cause. Together with Main of the Cassell Hospital they laid the foundations of a new science of institutional self-help. They showed that much of the frustration and poor morale in the mental hospital was due to a lack of clear thinking about those problems that should be resolved by group rather than individual decisions. The idea behind the "therapeutic community," or what Clark has called "administrative therapy," is that the collective solution of problems may be a burden, but it is nevertheless an educative burden. All, to the limit of their capacity, learn by doing things and especially by helping to do those things that they themselves want to get settled. If one lives within a system that prevents defining what needs doing, or that discourages one from doing it should it have become defined, then one learns nothing.

A failure to solve today's problems not only leaves that same problem tomorrow, but it actually even further precludes seeing what the fresh problems of tomorrow may be. Thus the hospital (or factory, or coal mine or university) that has no clear problem-defining system from which all decision takers may learn by practice, is characterized by unintelligibility, confusion, frustration and withdrawal.

The mental hospitals, by and large, had sunk into a condition of apathetic custodialism from which the only ladder of escape was a revival of learning, a renaissance that was to be carried forward, not by a small corps of specialist training officers exercising the professional skills of the pedagogue, but by everybody in the hospital who had decisions to be taken, either at his own level or, better still, with the active cooperation of those at subordinate levels who would be affected by their outcome. And this reaching downward was to be done, not out of some charitable adhesion to the principles of egalitarianism or the Brotherhood of Man, but for the practical necessity of helping people to master their situations by understanding them.

This cultural cooperativeness is the sign of the times, a social ethic demanded by the rise of science and technology. For, if the advantages of commanding the physical environment are to be fully exploited, each must understand, not only the role in the operational systems that technology requires him to occupy, but the means by which he can improve his understanding of the role, since the changes constantly imported by scientific and economic innovation into the system demand from all a mobile and discriminating capacity to adjust. The Tower of Babel failed because its artificers could not understand their role in its construction, and the myth of Babel offers fruitful lessons to the specialists, not in the modern hospital alone, but in all institutions that depend for their success upon exploiting the secrets of modern science. Hence the importance, in these mental hospital studies, of the stress put on communication, not solely for transmitting the necessary operational facts, but for engendering the more necessary social processes of individual learning.

RESISTANCE TO INNOVATION

The studies of Cumming and Cumming[20] are an extension of the theme uncovered by Stanton and Schwartz.[19] Cumming and Cumming show how the traditional mental hospital is a rigidly granulated social system, crosscut horizontally by caste divisions and vertically by the functional autonomy of its many specialists, and, within specialties, by the many local units.[24] The older staff within such a matrix become vitally concerned with maintaining the *status quo,* and their natural enemy is the young and enthusiastic doctor. Their method of dealing with the revolutionary is characteristic: namely, to deprive him of information about what is going on, or to obscure from him any procedural rules by which the institution is normally guided. Their professional behavior is characterized by a minimal interaction with patients. Their principal shared belief is that the wards must be kept clean, tidy and inactive, and, if this is done, nothing else is either possible or necessary.

The Cummings' purpose was to examine under what conditions these attitudes could be changed, and with what effect upon the patients. Their belief was that the nursing and attendant staff could be motivated to improve their therapeutic influence upon the patients and hence reduce their length of stay. This had been tried before; an attempt had been made about eight years earlier to train the new nurses in these ideas of enhanced patient-staff interaction. But this program affected only these beginners, who were in any case of low status only, and so not likely to transmit their influence into the wards. The original training program had thus been effectively sabotaged by the senior culture-bearers, quick to prove that such change was against the laws of nature.[25]

But, that change was possible if it were encouraged had also been demonstrated previously by two doctors in the same hospital. They showed that deteriorated and chronic schizophrenics improved significantly if placed in a sympathetic social environment, whether or not they also received physical treatment of any kind.

The first problem to be tackled was the clarification of the communication channels, and the choice of a practical move to ensure this demanded resolution. Previously all decisions that affected the conduct of the hospital had been made centrally, between the superintendent, the head nurse and the business office. No department, for example, was allowed its own budget. This system of government, by a triumvirate apparently as harmonious as it was powerful created in practice a self-perpetuating avalanche of unparalleled misery. The hospital staff had become little more than a corporation of scroungers, characterized by suspicion and aloofness.

To tackle this deplorable condition a new group of coordinators were appointed within the nursing service, primarily to improve the quality of nursing by the better integration of ward activities, both between wards and with the central administration. These coordinators, two seniors and six juniors, were nominated by staff ballot throughout the hospital, and, before starting on their new tasks, were formed into small groups to examine a variety of existing ward procedures. The program of nurse training was also taken away from

225

the independent functional office where it had been placed by the triumvirate, and returned to the nursing service. Only after much argument was the agreement reached that the senior male and female nursing staff could be interchanged, and that the tradesmen who provided occupations for the patients should be brought into the discussions so that they might contribute their practical wisdom to the other resources available to the hospital for helping its patients.

In parallel with these management changes, a series of daily discussions was started on the wards aimed at analyzing and, as far as possible, resolving local ward problems; and at teaching the concepts of social behavior and of group psychotherapy. An aim of these discussions, which eventually were reduced to three times a week, was to define and overcome hidden resistances as well as to collect and employ constructive suggestions.

No doubt all innovators will easily recognize the problems encountered by these radical measures. For example, the resistance of the majority of the nursing staff to change was derived from the hard core of intractables whose morale was heightened and hostility multiplied under the experimental pressure. Those given new roles and invited to join in new decision procedures were held up to constant ridicule by this core, who seized upon every difficulty to advertise their unshakeable beliefs in custodialism and noninteraction. Since the agent of innovation can never be entirely sure where his changes are going to lead, while the defender of the *status quo* is confident of his familiar ground, these efforts to define new roles and to reassign old tasks often ended in chaos and exasperation. It is a serious dilemma to resolve: should the old guard be discharged if they refuse to cooperate?

The resistance from the doctors was less expected and thus more interesting. Those with traditional and descriptive psychiatric training were more difficult to convince than those without psychiatric training at all, and a couple with Kraepelinian orientations remained completely hostile. Other doctors interfered with the experiment by removing individual patients from the therapeutic groups as soon as their membership in such groups began to prove visibly rewarding. The only practicable solution to this problem shows the irretrievable depth of professional commitment. It was to deprive such doctors of their line authority.

This, as the authors say, was a most unsatisfactory decision, the counterpart of discharging the old-guard nursing staff who, if for less de-

226

fensible reasons, also refused to cooperate. An interesting secondary problem was created by a feeling of loneliness that overcame the staff in general once they had embarked upon the unknown. They could compare experience with no other hospital. Real involvement in such experiment may engender deep emotional stress, when the old familiar landmarks have sunk below the horizon. The authors point to the need for projects of this kind to be carried out simultaneously by several hospitals close enough to each other that visits may easily be organized, for the exchanges that result from these are important elements in the learning processes that alone will guarantee success. (This important result has been used in the design of the London Project described below.)

Another interesting discovery was that, contrary to expectations (and also to one so-called principle of management), wards below a certain size made little progress, even though under an enthusiastic nurse. Apparently without a true work-group and with insufficient staff-to-staff interaction, no norm-creating process can develop. Only by such exchanges may those who begin outside the group learn the criteria of the success for which they strive.

The results of the experiments described by the Cummings include the following: a significant reduction in the size of a hospital population that had slowly been mounting for many years; the closure of several of the least satisfactory wards; a decline in the occasions of physical treatment of patients, whether by restraint, seclusion or shock; a significant rise in the level of patient activity and recreation, accompanied by improved interdepartmental cooperation, such as the maintenance foremen seeking advice from the nursing staff about the therapeutic content of work programs; an improvement in handling the domestic problems of patients, because the nursing staff, being by social class closer to the general average of patients, understood better than the doctors the disturbances created within their homes and families. No evidence was found to indicate that the greater work load, that these changes brought down upon the hospital staff, produced any increase in stress, whether measured by sickness, by voluntary absence or by staff turnover.

The significance, in the progress of research, of this and related studies needs no detailed explanation. Four cardinal points may be stressed, however. The first is the need to re-awaken the learning process, among staff and patients alike, by participation in decision making over matters of perceived importance. The second is that of modifying

227

the power structure so that such decisions, once taken, can be put into effect, for if the participants have no access to the resources of a budget the experiment is to contemplate a fiction. The third, following from both of these, is that senior members of any hierarchy should be genuine in their support of the proposed changes. The fourth is that those whose roles are changed should be able to support each other during the stresses that arise.[26]

THE COMMUNITY GENERAL HOSPITAL

The work of Georgopoulos and Mann[1] deserves a section on its own, not only from the thoroughness of its presentation and the standing of the university school that produced it, but because it is one of the few research projects also to stress the essentially organic nature of the community or acute general hospital. The processes of learning and adjustment that so effectively interact with those of communication to determine the quality of the mental hospital are no less decisive among those whose needs are medical or surgical. Their monumental study is basically a comparison of ten hospitals. If some of these derived their better qualities from organizational factors pervading their whole being, these factors must be known in specific terms to help those in charge of other hospitals to influence them for the better.

Georgopoulos and Mann examined both the set of formal rules, which define the official relationships between the members of the hospital (described as programed coordination), and the way they get on together as people (or nonprogramed coordination). Programed coordination shows how the organization should function as an administrative machine. Nonprogramed coordination depends on the voluntary efforts of individuals and groups to adjust to one another and cooperate for common ends. This kind of cooperation develops where the members of the team caring for the patient understand each other and share the same attitudes and expectations.

The purpose of the study was to see whether organizational features of the hospital, such as the degree of coordination between groups, made it more or less efficient at doing its job. This demands evaluation and to evaluate the work of any hospital is difficult. Judging whether one hospital provides a higher level of care than another cannot be done objectively. A great deal of discussion has taken place about this, but no simple standard answer has emerged and further research is needed.

228

One figure may be chosen and used as an indicator of the hospital's performance. The intent is not to produce an absolute standard, but to find a way of distinguishing the better hospitals from the not so good, so that they could be ranked from the best to the worst. The team considered possible ways of evaluating patient care and decided that a measure which included several approaches would put the hospitals in the most accurate order.

One might expect a relationship between the sort of material facilities available in the hospital and the quality of patient care. Such things as the layout of the hospital and physical plant, the amount of space and number of beds and the equipment and supplies seem important at first sight, particularly if staff are struggling on with inadequate facilities. Surprisingly, no significant connection was found between the level of facilities and patient care. Perhaps this was because all the hospitals had reached a certain minimum standard, but nonetheless the considerable differences between them did not appear to influence patient care. "Material facilities *per se* do not play as crucial a role as do social and psychological facilities or the skill and competence of organisational members, in so far as patient care is concerned."

The team also asked if the quality of patient care might depend on the amount of money available. But they did not find that the higher income hospitals provided better care. In fact, "considered as a whole, the results indicate that the quality of patient care, particularly the quality of nursing care, tends to be lower in the higher-income hospitals." The team suggests that perhaps the hospitals that provide better care are also better managed financially. They did find, however, a connection between the proportion of income spent on salaries and the level of patient care. Where more was devoted to payroll expenses, the level of care was higher, but it was not such a strong association that it could not be simply the result of chance.

The size of an organization is known to affect its performance. Because the hospitals in this sample were all of medium size (100 to 350 beds), Georgopoulos and Mann did not expect to find any startling results on the connection between size and patient care, but thought it was worth examining. Hospitals with more beds tend to have a lower level of care, but the correlation was not significant; that is, it could have been due to chance factors. However, in hospitals with more admissions per bed, i.e., a more rapid turnover, no indication could be found that the patients received a poorer level of care.

Many writers (including the author) have used turnover and absenteeism among nurses as a measure of stability in the hospitals. The results of the Michigan study in this context are not very illuminating because it looked at the figures of turnover and absenteeism for only a three month period, the last quarter of 1957. The results indicated that the incidence of nurses being absent once or twice did not distinguish the hospitals from one another. But when considering nurses who were absent three or more times, significant differences were found between hospitals. High absenteeism depends on the particular hospital, not on the groups of nurses within it. Nurses are more at risk in some hospitals than others and the proportion of nonsupervisor registered nurses absent twice or more was significantly associated with poorer quality care.

The major objective of this study was to consider the relationship between coordination and patient care. The authors examined the purely mechanical aspects of coordination—the way the parts combine, and the way people cooperate for common ends.

They asked the different groups in each hospital to score seven questions on a five-point scale and found that the answers to the questions were sufficiently consistent to give them a measure of coordination within the hospitals. They considered various factors that might affect coordination: how well the organization is planned, how clearly rules are defined and how efficiently work is scheduled are all related to coordination, and so is the extent to which personnel see eye to eye and share their expectations. Strain, where tension existed between groups and where people felt unreasonable pressure to work, had an adverse effect on coordination. Ease of communication helps coordination, but simply communicating without feeling free to say what one desires is often no help at all. The extent to which people feel decisions are adequately explained is equally important. If people are aware of each others' problems and cooperate to solve them, coordination is likely to be good. Hospitals where the board of trustees have comparatively little understanding of the problems and needs of the medical staff are likely to score poorly on coordination.

The attitude and behavior of the administrator also influence communication. As one doctor stated in an interveiw, "Naturally, the administrator does not handle everything, but he is the key to a smooth-running hospital."

When they had found out about coordination in the hospitals and seen what sort of things improve it, they tested their idea that coordination influences the level of patient care. They found it was important for nursing care, overall patient care and comparative patient care, but

230

that did not significantly affect the level of medical care. This may be because doctors are rather more independent of the organization of the hospital than are the other people who work in it. They are not there all the time and, in certain spheres, are largely autonomous.

Nonprogramed coordination was particularly important. As one might expect, "positive attempts toward better coordination are much more crucial for effective organisational functioning than the efforts of members toward avoiding disruptive behaviour in the system." Where people do not understand each others' needs and yet make positive efforts to cooperate, strain is likely. High strain and inadequate coordination seem to go hand in hand, each reinforcing the other, both adversely affecting patient care.

They also found that the quality of care was not significantly affected by the performance of the various paramedical departments considered one by one, but that the way they worked together was important. "It seems that the quality of patient care is more a function of the performance of all the various departments taken together and considered jointly and simultaneously than a matter of how good a job the several departments do individually." The extent to which medical and nursing staff understand each others' problems is significantly related to the level of care. That is, when nurses say the doctors understand their problems, and vice versa, the patient fares better. But if the doctor claims that he understands the nurses, without their feeling that he does, it does not have a good effect on patient care. Thus the claims to understanding are not significant, but the extent to which people feel they are understood, is significant.

Georgopoulos and Mann also made an analysis of supervisory and administrative behavior, examining supervisory skills at various levels and how satisfactory the kinds of supervision were thought to be. They asked questions that would distinguish between the technical, administrative and human aspects of supervision. They found that the extent to which the superior was adept at dealing with people became more important for the satisfaction of the lower levels of personnel. Of importance at higher levels was to convey one's own ideas to the immediate superior and to feel that he understood the subordinate point of view. Middle and higher levels needed to feel free to discuss personal problems and to be sure that they were being kept informed of changes. Lower level personnel did not much want to take part in decision making, but expected their superiors to do most of the necessary planning, organizing and scheduling for them. Human relations skills are par-

231

ticularly valued, in so far as they relate to competent communication about work.

Mann and his team also made an intensive study of the communication pattern of registered nurses in relation to nursing activity and performance. Only nonsupervisory registered nurses were sampled because they have a central role in nursing activity. Communication takes place either in formal channels or in informal channels. Formal channels are the official means of communication set up by the organization. Informal channels, e.g., the grape vine, are those which arise from personal and unofficial relationships within the organization. The structure of the organization is undermined by the extent to which communication takes place in informal rather than formal channels, and the worse communications are, the more likely this is to happen.

To examine the formal channels of communication, the team asked the nonsupervisory registered nurses how often they communicated with their immediate superior and what they talked about. To get some idea of the informal channels the nurses were asked about the person with whom they communicated most, how much time they spent talking to him or her, whether they discussed work and what position the two persons held in the structure of the hospital. They found that the more adequate the nurses feel the communication from their superior to be, the more highly they evaluate both her performance and their own satisfaction. They are more likely to talk to their superiors about work and patient care, and thus communication is centered in formal channels. However, if they feel that they are receiving unnecessary communication from their superiors, or that it is predominantly critical, then conversation about work goes into informal channels. The more communication about work is concentrated in formal rather than in informal channels, the better the level of nursing performance and the more committed nurses feel to the team on the ward. If the person with whom the nurse communicated most was someone on a level different from herself, whether her superior or not, the effect on patient care was better than if she confined her communication to her own group. Co-ordination was better, with less tension, where communication was vertical rather than horizontal. The authors state that their study

. . . may be viewed as one which has attempted to investigate certain problems of the Community General Hospital from a *synoptic* point of view, to use Professor Revans' term. Both theoretically and methodologically, it has tried to capture the image of the total hospital as a complete organisational system, and to examine some of the problems and characteristics of hospital organisation that are system-wide in nature, or at least have direct system-wide implications.

As the massive text suggests, this is not easy to do but, the whole is is much more than the sum of the parts. This, then, is illustrated by a further quotation from the book:

> The admistrator and the director of nursing, considered together, are more likely to be aware of problems that arise in the organisation, and are more effective in solving conflicts. But it is their combined problem awareness and problem solving effectiveness, rather than their individual performances in these respects, which is positively and significantly related to coordination.

The Commonwealth Fund report on community hospitals stated "At bottom, however, the development of staff solidarity rests on day-to-day experience in a setting provided by the community for the benefit of the patient, in which the physician finds himself a collaborator rather than a solitary entrepreneur."[3]

These words sum up, no doubt, the values and the experience of most students of management. But such utterances contain not only so much that is seen to be true, but is also accepted as obvious, and only unusual people pause to examine the obvious. Too much knowledge exists on some subjects, for they are the themes of daily experience, and these most obvious truths are those most readily forgotten or accepted without question. Hence, students of administration can write about collaboration without attempting to define its observable structure, or they can stress the importance of staff solidarity without pausing to ask what, in real life, this desirable quality may be. Studies like those of Georgopoulos and Mann should be more widely known, not only for the good of the hospitals and their patients, but as part of a wider assault upon those arsenals of revealed dogma known as theories of management, often hampering efforts to better understand how, in practice rather than in theory, members of the human race can most effectively contribute their several skills for the benefit of all.

HOSPITAL ORGANIZATION AND THE PATIENT

A monograph on research into the problems of managing and organizing the hospital may hardly seem the place to review studies of the problems created for those obliged to enter it as patients. Yet some reference to the inquiries being made about patient responses is desirable, even if only as a reminder to those engaged in hospital research that comparable patients respond to one hospital very differently than to another. The perception that a medical or surgical patient gains of the novel and complex situation into which he is thrust can have, no less than of a mental patient, the most profound bearing upon his hospital prognosis and upon his further progress to recovery after discharge.

In Britain, McGhee[27] interviewed nearly 500 patients from a large Scottish hospital within two weeks of their discharge. Cartwright[28] studied the responses of an even larger sample drawn from all over Britain. These two studies showed the very large percentage of patients who were not only dissatisfied with the amount of information given to them, but who were more dissatisfied on this issue than upon any other of their hospital experience. These results, consonant with those of other workers, are important not only because they show that the feelings of patients are so deeply affected, but because of the potential damage they suggest to the public image of the medical profession. An essential factor in medicine is the degree of confidence that the patient is able to display in those who care for him.

Although the public image of the nurse is steadily improving, that of the doctor has suffered, at least in Britain, a sharp and decisive decline. That a profession which can demonstrate so triumphantly its advancing technical efficiency in curing disease and in prolonging life should not also be rising in public esteem is ironical. Whitehorn[29] argues that this is largely due to the doctors ignoring the personal and psychological factors in health and disease, while concentrating on what seem to be the impersonal and mechanical. However, much of this impression is due to defective hospital organization and more attention must be given to the obstructions that this can place between the profession and the public. Wilson,[30] again examining the image of the doctor as seen by the patient, stresses the contrast between the charismatic and authoritarian approach traditionally demanded by the patients of their doctors, and that envisioned by the more sophisticated members of a technologically oriented society, namely, a role based upon team work, the sharing and integration of knowledge and a rigorous analysis of observable information.

These excursions into the sidelines of doctor-patient relationship have produced still more interesting food for administrative thought.

The work of Shiloh[31] describes the two main types of patient, designated as equalitarian and hierarchal (*sic*). The former actively demands technical information about his present condition and progress, the latter passively expects the hospital to take care of his future. Both types are influenced by the perceptions they hold of their treatment. Some children learn better from particular teachers than they do from others, as a result of differences, not of skill or intelligence, but of temperament. Perhaps one significant area of organizational research still largely unexplored is the matching of personality types between those in the bed and the others who serve at the side of it.

RELATED AREAS OF RESEARCH

Among the more interesting aspects of this subject is the wide variety of academic or professional skills needed to advance the understanding of it. As do Stanton and Schwartz,[19] many qualified medical practitioners have psychiatric or psychological training. But, as early as 1949, Smith made a comparative sociological study of three general hospitals.[32] Operational research workers and statisticians are represented by Charles Flagle of Johns Hopkins and Alex Barr of the Oxford Regional Hospital Board. The team under Daniel Howland at Ohio State University represents the engineers, an excellent illustration of the multidisciplinary approach by a school originally built up around the study of complex production problems.

Business administrators are represented in their support to the massive self-analysis of operating efficiency undertaken by the four Detroit hospitals.

Although, perhaps not considered true research by university professors, many orderly presentations of the interesting experiences of hospital matrons are on record. For example, Weddell,[33] of the Cassel Hospital, wrote on the vital triangular relationship between matron, sister and tutor. A more recent move by the Hospital Centre of the King Edward VII Fund for London is to encourage the matrons, tutors and nurses of British hospitals to undertake comparative studies of common problems and to meet at the Centre to discuss their findings and sustain each other in the consequent stresses of discovery. For whatever can be done to make a profession conscious of self-development, as has been traced earlier, must help the hospitals throughout.

This initiative now comes from the institutions of British nursing, and their press supports them by widely publishing their results, as in the report of a study to examine the size of ward best suited for the general hospital of the future.[34] The nurses both of America and of Britain have so long been the objects of criticism that for the profession itself to take in hand the study of its own problems is for them a major success. That the profession has both ability and motivation enough to undertake studies of this kind has been shown by more than one sociologist. The following extract from a report by Bullock,[35] after interviewing 500 hospital nurses, not only shows how long an important channel of understanding has remained unexplored, but also for how long the potential of the profession has been misunderstood:

> In determining job satisfaction (among nurses) the most significant factors were perceived leader-behaviour, work group adjustment and personal aspirations in that order . . . the vital characteristics associated with satisfaction in the profession are those related to independence of action and self-direction. . . . Nurses seek recognition as professionals worthy of trust and responsibility. They resent, or are dissatisfied with, a status that entails obedience and the acceptance of criticism without complaint, rather than a status that involves cooperative effort and participation in planning and decision. . . . It is sometimes asserted that secure personal adjustment among nurses is not desirable, since their individual peculiarities and compulsions can be utilised by the physician, the administrator and the director of nursing service. Further it appears that different criteria of effectiveness are used, for example, by hospital administrators, by physicians, by patients and by nurses themselves. So long as such a condition obtains, nurses remain all things to all people. It is important that members of the profession know how the occupation is viewed, not only by the public but also by physicians, administrators and other groups with which nurses must deal.

This extract, and others from a wide range of nursing research, may at first sight seem to have little to do with the task of managing or organizing a hospital. The next section, however, shows that, of all the influences that bring themselves to bear upon the adjustment of the nurse, whether senior or junior, the most important to her work is the organic influence of the hospital in which she works. This influence is supposedly of outstanding concern to the hospital management also.

"STANDARDS FOR MORALE"
AND THE LONDON HOSPITAL PROJECT

Among the great variety of approaches the work of the Manchester College of Science and Technology deserves mention. As emphasized by Stanton and Schwartz, the Cummings, Hoffman and others, support for change programs must be both accepted and seen to be accepted from the top downwards. The project now to be described began by securing the personal interest of the Minister of Health himself.

In 1955, a group of research workers, including a psychologist, a chemist and a mathematical physicist, all from the department of industrial administration at the University of Manchester,[36] were invited by the local Regional Hospital Board to examine the statistics of student nurse wastage, which, at the time, had a national average of about 50 per cent. Thus of every 100 student nurses who joined training programs, only 50 successfully completed their course to become state registered nurses three years later.

The research team chose hospitals that, as far as possible, were comparable not only by internal features, such as size and distribution by specialty of beds, but which were situated in similar industrial towns, also comparable in size and social class. The team showed that the differences between the mean total wastage rates of the individual hospitals were highly significant, and that these wide differences could be almost entirely attributed to one principal factor—the voluntary withdrawal of students. Rejections by the hospital, marriage, severe illness and other apparent causes of leaving were not statistically different between hospitals. Moreover, the voluntary wastage rates bore no relation to the ease of securing alternative local employment, as measured from the recruitment figures of the local factories and department stores. What was more striking, in all hospitals the girls who withdrew exhibited sickness rates significantly higher than those who either completed their training or were rejected for inadequate progress. Coming events were casting their shadows before them. The hospitals in the sample with high wastages of student nurses also had high wastages of senior nursing staff, and vice versa. Statistical methods showed that the association between these rates among four different ward nursing grades (sister, registered nurse, student nurse, assistant nurse) could not have occurred by chance once in a thousand times, and so was probably caused.

Thus, the researchers thought that each hospital should be regarded as an entity, embracing all wards and all classes of staff, with its own characteristic social metabolism. Moreover, in pursuit of this idea, the capacities of the hospitals, not only to retain nursing staff but to treat patients, judged by the inverse of the average length of stay, were found to be significantly in accord with this concept. In statistical jargon, the variations between hospitals in length of patient stay for any specific condition were significantly greater than variations within them, and hospital means were not only concordant among themselves for different conditions in the same hospital but were concordant with the four staff turnover rates.

The search for the social mechanism responsible for this effect was strongly influenced by other research then being carried out in the department, on the attitudes and perceptions of industrial supervisors and, later, the interactions between teachers and children in a classroom. This led at once to an examination of the tasks and opinions of the ward sisters, as the central junctions of the hospital communication system, and to the development of attitude surveys across the whole hospital. By slow stages standard questionnaires were designed for quantitatively assessing the perceptions of ward sisters.

The answers confirmed, beyond all doubt, first, that each of these sisters tended to pass on to her junior nurses the perception she had formed of her own treatment at the hands of her superiors; and second, that, however much within the same hospital the views of one sister on the manner of her particular treatment might differ from those of another, these differences were small compared with the differences, averaged over all sisters, between one hospital and another. In jargon, the variance *between* hospitals in the sisters' perceptions of authority was significantly greater than the variance *within* them. The organic nature of attitudes, characteristic of an entire hospital, was adequately confirmed. This result was interpreted to mean that where, because communications with those above her were defective, the ward sister either could not readily adjust to changes of hospital method or did not feel able to make an effective use of her abilities, she herself was unable to offer wholehearted support to her junior nurses.[37] Thus, if the junior nurses felt the sisters evasive and unhelpful in resolving their own problems, the juniors, being in consequence unable to learn, would develop anxieties and, for a mounting sickness record, would withdraw from training. The reason they gave for doing so was not material to their resignation. In one management group, in which the younger nurses moved sequentially from one hospital to another, the study showed that, while serving at one particular hospital, the sickness rate among the same students was significantly higher than when they served at the others, both by frequency and severity. At this hospital the girls, in free interview, expressed the greatest fear of being assigned difficult or unexplained tasks.

The concept of the intelligibility of the work situation—in the sense that it could, by first being understood, be at least partially controlled by those within it—which had emerged in studying innovation in factories was now seen strongly reflected within the hospitals. Those whose system of management and organization offered ready learning opportunities, to nurse and patient alike, seemed both better able to keep their staff and to help their patients than those whose learning opportunities, by the infirmities of communication, left much to be desired. Finally, within a set of 15 general hospitals, five parameters were quantitatively measured: the perception that sisters held of their superiors, their attitude to their juniors, the stability of the body of all qualified nurses, including sisters, the mean length of stay of general surgical patients and the mean length of stay of general medical patients. When these opinions and values were placed in rank order (favorable perceptions, high stabilities and short stays scoring from one to 15 downwards) the concordance was so great that it could have occurred, if by chance, only once in a thousand times. It was thus assumed to be inherent. As in the mental hospitals, therefore, this research suggests that staff stability and patient recovery are functions of the communication system, and, in particular, of the learning opportunities that the system offers.

At this point the research began to take on the complexion of the department of its origin, namely, industrial administration. The results were of interest only if they could be used by practical administrators, and in securing this two major problems are confronted: first, to establish more widely the validity or underlying logical structure of the results themselves; second, to diffuse their acceptance through a hospital service existing within a world of reality. The second problem is the greater, since it immediately leads into the arenas of hospital action and so of hospital politics.

A new field of research has thus been opened up. Upon the findings of this study (which merely confirm what had already been indicated by others), a group of ten London hospitals have now formed an operational consortium, with the financial support of the Ministry of Health, to develop among themselves a program of self-analysis and therapy. No description of this optimistic venture can be more eloquent than the words of the minister himself, The Right Honourable Kenneth Robinson, on launching one of the short courses by which its participants are to secure a small opening balance of research skill.

> I have had some difficulty in finding a single word to describe your work. It is partly a research project, partly an experiment in education, partly a management adventure, but like a hospital, so much more than the sum of its parts. Enterprise, in both senses of the word, seems most fitting. My part in the enterprise is to strengthen you in your resolve as you embark upon it today, to support it through my Department, now and in the future, and to incorporate appropriately successful features in the day to day working of the Hospital Service. . . . Let me take each part of this three-fold task in turn. . . . The first part of the way is the easiest, for the courses themselves are certain to interest and stimulate you; the second part might be disconcerting or even disappointing when you see the problems and attitudes unearthed by your own studies and of those of Professor Revans' team; but it is during the third part, when you are trying to answer problems in group discussion and by group action, that you will need all the resolve you can muster. You will face unusual stresses, anxieties, frustrations and disappointments at this stage, and the success of the enterprise will depend upon how well you weather them. It is so much easier in the short run to be authoritarian rather than participative in management, especially as participative management, in spite of its natural appeal, has not yet been accepted generally as the more effective method.

This address by the minister, as the person ultimately responsible for the expenditure of both the effort and the money that this project will demand, also stresses an aspect of research that (at least in universities) is not always clearly held in mind—"the principal research element . . . will be the attempt to measure the effect upon . . . hospital efficiency (of what) you will be engaged upon. . . . We must be able to judge at the end the degree of success you have achieved. . . ." These words, suggesting that abstract truth, not necessarily the overture to practical achievement, is no adequate dividend, represent a sharp reversal of research policy, even a return to the pragmatism of William James and John Dewey.[39]

This same approach, but for a single organism, has been used at the Roosevelt Hospital, New York City,[40] in a series of projects by a firm of management consultants in collaboration with the hospital staff. These began with interviews within separate departments to

240

identify problems, to suggest goals for improvement, to assign the study of the problems to working groups and to launch a series of discussion meetings to review progress. Then departments chose assignments. Each demanded a statement of the problem and of the goal, the target date for the first report and the form of subsequent reports. An opening major objection, soon shown to be unrealistic, was that nobody had time for anything other than his daily job. The pressures were felt to allow no freedom for working out changes. But after showing that improvements were possible on very modest tasks, the confidence of the participants has grown until major reorganizations, such as the control of nursing equipment, have been undertaken by the nurses themselves. The hospital has discovered its concealed resources by forcing itself to use them. It has four lessons from this experience:

1. A successful project must make a significant demand for organization or management within it, or, in other words, it must oblige both individuals and groups to work together.

2. Its goal must be realistic, and, when reached, suggest further goals.

3. It must produce action, not merely recommendations for action; an immense difference is found, between producing a report upon what ought to be done, on the one hand, and, on the other, completing the actions of doing it.

4. Demands should be set high enough for those in charge to recognize the need for seeking help outside their own sections.

Operational results seem to confirm three of the conclusions drawn from the earlier work of, for example, Stanton and Schwartz and the Cummings. First, working improvements go hand in hand with the personal development of the managers who bring them about. Second, although the projects demand hard work they also evoke a corresponding motivation. Third, the managers discover abilities to cooperate with others in problem identification and solution in ways that the canonical development program has largely overlooked. Thus, even if the total program cannot be called research in the academic sense (e.g., that it produces no doctoral dissertation or is nursed by no professor) it has proved, in the strictest sense, a fertile and suggestive exercise in how those in charge of an institution may improve not only the execution of the task itself, but also the personal qualities that they continue to bring to it.

THE FUTURE OF RESEARCH IN HOSPITAL ORGANIZATION

What does all this effort suggest for the future of research into hospital management and organization? This question may be answered by treating it as an exercise in decision theory and so asking three essential subquestions: What do administrators want to do? What is stopping them from doing it? What means have they at their disposal?

The answer to the first is that what is wanted is to stimulate as effectively as possible the natural recovery processes of the individual by bringing to bear on him that program best suited to his condition and to the resources of the hospital. The second is that the principal handicap is an inadequate command of those sciences and arts that determine both the relations of individuals to the systems in which they work, and the interactions between the elements of those systems. The third is that in the last 20 years two lessons have been taught: to seek ideas from any school interested in how human beings interact with each other, and to realize that only by action can the hard and existential world be mastered. By these three questions the choice of future studies should be made.

REFERENCES

[1] Georgopoulos, B. S. and Mann, Floyd C., THE COMMUNITY GENERAL HOSPITAL, New York, The Macmillan Company, 1962.

[2] Farrow, E. Pickworth, letter in *The Times,* London, March 25, 1930.

[3] Southmayd, H. J. and Smith, G., SMALL COMMUNITY HOSPITALS, New York, The Commonwealth Fund, 1944.

[4] The relationship is by no means direct. When, in the financial crisis of 1931, the Cavendish Laboratory, with its ten Nobel prizewinners, prematurely came to the end of its meager budget, Lord Rutherford was heard to remark, "Well, the money's gone. We'd better try thinking."

[5] Mason, L. G. S., THE ROLE OF THE MINISTRY OF HEALTH IN ORGANISATION AND METHOD STUDY AND IN WORK STUDY, London, Ministry of Health, 1964; Abstracts of Efficiency Studies in the Hospital Service, London, Ministry of health, 1961 (and later); List of Assignments undertaken by O & M and Work Study officers of Regional Hospital Boards and Teaching Hospitals, London, Minister of Health, 1965.

[6] Fetter, Robert B. and Thompson, John D., The Simulation of Hospital Systems, Paper presented at a meeting of the Operational Research Society of America, Minneapolis, October, 1964.

[7] The Development of a Methodology for the Evaluation of Patient Care, Engineering Experiment Station, Ohio State University, Parts I–III.

[8] Flagle, C. D., OPERATIONS RESEARCH IN A HOSPITAL, Baltimore, The Johns Hopkins Press, 1960, Chapter 25.

[9] Research of this kind, leading to new methods of problem definition and resolution, will never entirely replace intuition—thought below the level of consciousness—but it will certainly free the experienced administrator to use his precious time and judgment where it is needed most and upon issues that have been fairly clearly defined for him. The systems analyst will always face a residue of questions demanding the judgment of experience other than his own, and this residue is the true province of the administrator. This is, perhaps, too clear an illustration of the defference between the science and the art of administration to need elaboration at this point, but research into the behavior of complex sequential systems shows that human intuition is singularly unable to forecast at all accurately how they are likely to respond to different forms of managerial intervention.

[10] Nursing Care in a Modern Hospital (number 2), The Computer Simulation of a modern Hospital (number 6), The Scheduling of Student Nurses with the aid of a Computer (number 7), Operational Research Unit Publications, Oxford, Oxford Regional Hospital Board; Duration of Stay in Dependency Groups (number 5), The Optimal Use of Nursing Staff (numbers 66 and 75), Variations in the Composition of the Work Load (number 72) and Patient Observation Survey (number 76), Miscellaneous Reports, Oxford, Oxford Regional Hospital Board.

[11] Pantall, John and Elliott, James, Can Research Aid Management?, Studies at East Birmingham Hospital, University of Manchester, 1965, The Hospital, 301–305, June, 349–352, July, 422–424, August, 1965.

[12] The Minister of Health has, however, recently established an advisory committee on medical education that will supposedly consider remedies of a more refined character.

[13] Wright, Marion, THE IMPROVEMENT OF PATIENT CARE, New York, G. P. Putnam's Sons, 1954.

[14] From 550 to 635 Beds with a reduction of ward staff from 385 to 376, and of these totals, a professional percentage from 38 to 29.

[15] Burling, T., Lentz, E. M. and Wilson, R. N., THE GIVE AND TAKE IN HOSPITALS, New York, G. P. Putnam's Sons, 1956.

[16] Main, T. F., The Hospital as a Therapeutic Institution, Bulletin of the Menninger Clinic, 10, 66–70, May, 1946; ———, The Social Structure of a Mental Hospital, Royal Medico-Psychological Association, January, 1956; ———, Hospital Sociology, in Paul, Routledge and Paul, Kegan, SOCIETY, PROBLEMS AND METHODS OF STUDY, London, 1962.

[17] Jones, Maxwell, SOCIAL PSYCHOLOGY IN THE COMMUNITY, IN HOSPITALS AND IN PERSONS, Springfield, Illinois, Charles C Thomas, Publisher, 1962; ———, Therapeutic Community Practice, a Paper presented at the Annual Meeting of the American Psychiatric Association, New York, 1965.

[18] Clark, D. H., Administrative Therapy, *Lancet*, 1, 805, 1958; ———, ADMINISTRATIVE THERAPY: THE ROLE OF THE DOCTOR IN THE THERAPEUTIC SOCIETY, London, Tavistock Publications, 1964; ———, Principles of Administrative Therapy, *American Journal of Psychiatry*, 117, 506, December, 1960.

[19] Stanton, A. H. and Schwartz, M. S., THE MENTAL HOSPITAL, New York, Basic Books, Inc., Publishers, 1954.

[20] Cumming, John and Cumming, Elaine, Social Equilibrium and Social Change in a Large Mental Hospital, *in* Greenblatt, M., Levinson, D. T. and Williams, R. H., THE PATIENT AND THE MENTAL HOSPITAL, Glencoe, Illinois, The Free Press of Glencoe, 1957.

[21] Brown, Esther L., NEWER DIMENSIONS IN PATIENT CARE, New York, The Russell Sage Foundation, 1961.

[22] Southmayd and Smith, *op. cit.*, pp. 57–58.

[23] *Ibid.*, p. 77.

[24] This is by no means confined to mental hospitals. Much of what the Cummings have to say would be equally true of shipyards, coal mines, factories, professional firms and universities, at least in Britain.

[25] University professors in a specialty occasionally fail to understand the cultural influences of the industrial and commercial environments where their students are to work. This makes much of what is called management education less effective than it need be.

[26] Hoffman, Jay L., Problems of Administration in a Large Mental Hospital, *in* Greenblatt, Levinson and Williams, *op. cit.*

[27] McGhee, Anne, THE PATIENT'S ATTITUDE TO NURSING CARE, Edinburgh, E. & S. Livingstone, 1961.

[28] Cartwright, Ann, HUMAN RELATIONS AND HOSPITAL CARE, London, Institute of Community Studies, 1963.

[29] Whitethorn, J. C., The Doctor's Image of Man, New York, Monograph IV of the New York Institute of Social and Historical Medicine, 1963.

[30] Wilson, R. N., The Physician's Changing Role, *Human Organization*, 18, 177–183, Winter 1959.

[31] Shiloh, Ailon, Equilibrium and Hierarchal Patients; an Investigation Among Hadassah Hospital Patients, *Medical Care*, 3, 87–95, April, 1965.

[32] Smith, H. L., The Sociological Study of Hospitals, Doctoral Dissertation, University of Chicago, 1949; Two lines of Authority, One too Many, *Modern Hospital*, 84, 59–64, March, 1955.

[33] Weddell, D., Human Relations in Nursing Administration, *Nursing Times*, 51, 1474–1477, December 30, 1955.

[34] King, Joan, How Many Beds?, *Nursing Times*, 61, 1110–1111, August, 1965.

[35] Bullock, R. P., WHAT NURSES THINK OF THEIR PROFESSION, Columbus, Ohio State University Press, 1954.

[36] Revans, R. W., STANDARDS FOR MORALE: CAUSE AND EFFECT IN HOSPITALS, Oxford, Nuffield Provincial Hospitals Trust, 1964.

[37] Other studies in the department show that children's attitudes to school teachers reflect the perceptions held by those teachers of the system of authority under which they work, and that workers in factories resistant to innovation do not believe their managers know how to listen.

[38] Learning opportunities are reciprocal. If the subordinate at one end of a communication system learns policy (i.e., is not simply told what the policy is) the management at the other end will learn the subordinate's difficulties of implementing them.

[39] Decision making and adaption to Change by Management in the Hospital Service, London, Institute for Operational Research (unpublished).

[40] Neiman, R. A. and Newman, H., Need Better Managers?, *Hospitals,* 39, 55, April 16, 1965.

Dr. Revans' presentation of the main hospital research problem as one of analyzing and modifying the attitudes of those in power was generally admired as the humanistic expression of a very civilized man who had found in practice how beneficial it is for hospital leaders and staff to recognize the individual needs and dignity of their colleagues and patients. It was questioned, however, whether the paper itself provided a relevant framework for research as distinct from administration. Whereas Dr. Revans had emphasized the need to integrate research and administration, many speakers questioned the value of this approach.

Criteria for choosing research problems. Revans' implicit model of the good hospital resembles the human relations approach of industrial sociology in which the goal of the system is the happiness of the participants rather than the quality of the product. Such an approach identifies the good of the system with the management viewpoint, whereas the function of research may be precisely to question the premises of those who run the system. Furthermore, while admittedly the researcher can learn much by working with administrators, the latter, as committed participants in the system, may not always be able to identify its important problems as easily as those not connected with the system. If the researcher is restricted to a consultant role, he will constantly be involved in firefighting attempts and propelled from one pressing problem to another.

Revans does not agree that his point of view resembles the human relations approach. In his view, people are not looking for happiness but for intelligibility. People want to understand what is going on around them rather than be plunged into an emergency by the scruff of the neck. In the course of his research Revans has found that those hospital systems that arrange employees intelligently, assigning functions in a manner understandable to the workers, not only retain staff longer but discharge patients more quickly. Outcome is thus not neglected in his approach. In turn the system that lends intelligibility to the hospital and its communications systems can only be discovered if the administrators whose hands are on the levers of power understand

and accept intelligibility as their aim. Lectures will not convince the administrators of such a course. They themselves must begin to manipulate the system by bringing intelligibility into the work of their staff.

The point of departure for hospital management research should, therefore, not be the theoretical problems within the sciences but the practical problems as perceived by administrators. The traditional concept of the research process should be expanded and in addition to model-building and analysis should include the stages of problem recognition and of implementation. Although the latter two stages are more time consuming, they have been neglected by academicians. For this reason, these are the stages Revans emphasized in his paper.

Importance of theory for action research. Revans appears to have underestimated the importance of theoretical frameworks, as well as the time required for the model-building stage of the research process. Action research has suffered precisely because rigorous theory has been lacking. To assign exclusive priority to action research at the expense of theory development, as Dr. Revans has apparently proposed, would be detrimental to action research itself. The latter is the application of pre-established principles to more concrete settings and thus presuppose the existence of theory. Theoretical concepts and models are not only ways to organize armchair thinking but also ways in which people see others in organizations and relate themselves to organizations. These theoretical concepts also organize and guide, implicitly or explicitly, the selection of hospital management areas for study. Action research itself does not seem to be the appropriate strategy for arriving at such concepts and propositions, since it tends to account for a situation in all its complexity, whereas theory development involves the production of simplified and general relationships. Finally, while the stage of problem recognition, as advocated by Revans, appears to be a legitimate part of the research process, many question whether the stage of implementation and application should be considered as part of the research process.

Special nature of management and social science research. To others however, the absence of rigorous management and social science theory implied different conclusions about research strategy. Although in other sciences research may be separated from implementation and demonstration, it cannot be so differentiated in the management and social science fields. Action research appears to be indispensable for testing and developing social science and management theories. Because of the lack of agreement among social scientists in the field of management and of the lack of demonstrations of the greater effectiveness of one management theory in comparison with another, theory alone today cannot provide a basis for introducing changes in hospital systems. Research studies into hospital management will only carry weight if they include means of testing whether the new theory and method of working will ultimately be more effective than the old one and help the workings of the whole system. Thus research designs in this field should incorporate means for measuring outcomes. Both the production of hypotheses and their testing in practice should thus be encouraged.

Further uses of the model. Revans' model could possibly be expanded into a more comprehensive and ecological one. In addition to patient flow, the model could include the flow into the system of human resources (for these also pass through stages of recruitment, training, and attrition) and the flows of facilities and dollars (considered in other papers in this series). The result would be an ecological system in which some balance ought to be established among the many populations and capacities within it. Specific research studies and problems could then be devised within the framework of such an ecological model. Revans appears to overemphasize the subjective aspects of the communications process between superiors and subordinates. Subjective aspects might preferably be examined simultaneously with the objective channels and contents of communications. By no means, however, should quantitative studies be pursued at the expense of psychosocial inquiry. Indeed, Revans' plea for more knowledge of the relationship of the individual to systems, and for interdisciplinary studies of human interaction, might provide a philosophy of survival to hospitals in the midst of the extraordinary social and technological changes taking place around them. Administrators and systems developers face pressures for change and may be forced to accept whatever advice is at hand. Unless the researcher, particularly the social science researcher, cooperates closely with the administrator in the development of needed studies, he may be leapfrogged by the systems analyst exploiting new techniques. New techniques may then be adopted without a deep enough appreciation of what makes a good hospital.

248

FACILITIES AND EQUIPMENT
FOR HEALTH SERVICES
NEEDED RESEARCH

LORD LLEWELYN-DAVIES

INTRODUCTION

The Achievements of Research

Serious research into the needs of the health services in building and equipment began about 20 years ago, at the conclusion of the war. In several countries, including the United States, Great Britain, Holland and Sweden, established research groups have been at work during this period. These groups have been characterized by a multidisciplinary approach, that is to say the research teams have been composed of people from several disciplines, including architects, engineers, doctors and nurses, as well as social scientists and operational research analysts. The combined output of these groups constitutes a considerable body of knowledge and a great deal of published work is available. Further, research findings have been widely discussed at international conferences and the interaction of research and practice has been considerable. The World Health Organization will shortly publish a substantial manual on hospital planning which will summarize the practical conclusions of research since the war.[1]

Research carried out so far has covered a fairly wide area, but shows a heavy concentration on certain types of problems. Other important areas have, for one reason or another, been relatively neglected. The present paper is directed toward the discussion of the areas so far not dealt with, or only partially dealt with, by such research as is already completed or in progress. Areas where present research is already concentrated will not be discussed in detail in this paper.

Up to the present research has concentrated mainly on the facilities needed in the care of the acutely ill. Most of the work bears on the design and equipment of medium- or large-size hospitals, including teaching hospitals, caring for short-term patients with acute conditions. Other areas of the health service, including the sectors covered by private or individual doctors, the care of the mentally ill and the care of long-stay patients, have been touched on much more lightly. Within the general area in which research has been concentrated the focus has been on the detailed needs of individual hospital departments, such as the nursing unit or the surgical block. But some work has been done on the general arrangement, or grouping, of departments to form the whole hospital. Much work has taken the form of close study of the function of various hospital services. The methods of operational research and analysis have been central to very many projects. Many studies have taken the following general pattern:

A particular hospital function, for example radiodiagnosis, is selected for study. The research team is set up containing people with an appropriate range of disciplines. The team first observes work going on in existing plant and evolves a method of systematically describing the work process. Then the design of facilities is examined and criticized from a functional point of view. At the same time account is taken of the fact that existing functional patterns may have come into use as a result of the out-dated plant and facilities, and that a new, properly designed plant might open up completely new concepts of function. Often, at the end of the study, a critique of existing methods and plant is given along with suggestions for improvements in both.[2]

Studies of this general type have been carried out over the whole field of functions in the traditional acute hospital and the design of the plant and facilities can now be undertaken with the benefit of much sophisticated research material.

Apart from research specifically directed toward the study of plant and facilities, a considerable body of research is also directed toward the problems of manpower and management. This work has had to take account of plant and facilities as an element in management and manpower questions. As a result studies of this sort have yielded a substantial by-product of information valuable for the design and provision of the plant.

Evaluating the extent to which available research data has been

250

made use of in practice is not easy, but its impact appears to have been considerable. Few major hospital authorities and few specialist architects and engineers today work in ignorance of the research material available. Nevertheless, available knowledge is not always completely understood or wisely applied. Plans for new hospitals in most countries show the influence of research into function, but sometimes a particular research finding is seized on and given a priority out of all proportion to its real worth. For example, certain studies of limited aspects of function in nursing units have been held to justify circular and star shaped buildings. Elsewhere national or local hospital authorities have sometimes used the umbrella of research to justify rather rigid standards. But, on the whole, failures in practice come from lack of wisdom and limited breadth of vision in those applying research results, rather than any intrinsic weakness in research material itself.

One shortcoming must be noted. In most of the studies of the type just described, attempts have been made to bring in the element of cost and to compare alternative methods of operation in terms of cost as well as in terms of efficiency of function. Cost comparisons would, of course, be of the greatest value in the practical application of this sort of research, but efforts to provide valid techniques for cost study have had only limited success. As a result the practical administrator, engineer or architect is left without much means of weighing up this important aspect of the alternatives among which he must choose.

Research has also attempted to solve the problem of grouping different elements which go to compose a hospital. Various ways of assembling the different services have been studied and compared in relation to various criteria. Most work has been done on methods of circulation, with the aim of finding arrangements which will minimize time and cost of journeys (and goods movement) from point to point within a building or complex of buildings. Some consideration has also been given to the relative capital and running costs arising from different types of planning, and to their aesthetic effect. For example, some discussion has been given to the psychological effect of very tall or very massive buildings and their relationship to very much smaller buildings which normally surround them. These studies into the general arrangements of hospital services have been less conclusive than those on the provision for each service individually.

Recently conclusions drawn from the study of communications and traffic movement have been strongly challenged by another school of thought which regards the primary consideration in general planning to be provision for growth and change for each element of the hospital plan.[3]

The research described above had its starting point at the patient. It began with the problem of providing for some element in the patient's care and worked upward from that to considering the plant needed, first at the level of the individual service and later at the level of the hospital as a whole. A completely different area of study has also had an influence on health plant, although not originally undertaken with this end in view. This is the investigation of the needs of a given population for the provision of health care. In many countries attempts have been made with varying degrees of sophistication to predict the demands of a given population for total health care. In many countries attempts have been made with varying degrees of sophistication to predict the demands of a given population for total health care. These studies have had, as their main aim, broad budgetary planning in terms of manpower and capital investment which a nation or region may need to direct toward health care. Two methods have been used. One has been medicosocial, by sampling the population an attempt can be made to predict morbidity and hence the need for care. Such studies have had to accept very far reaching assessments about the future of medicine and about social and economic change and the validity of their results depends on the validity of these sweeping assessments. Another method, applicable only in countries where the health service is already fairly close to an adequate standard, has been the statistical examination of the use made of existing facilities and the projection on to this use of assumed changes in morbidity, patterns of medical care, etc.[4] This latter group of studies has produced as a useful by-product quite a lot of criticism of the existing plant seen as a system, although not originally directed towards this end.

Hence the present position may be summed up somewhat as follows:

1. A substantial body of research has already been carried out and is still in progress for the provision of plant and facilities for individual services to the patient. This work is well established and by and large covers the need effectively. Some work on the general

design problem of hospitals as a whole is going on. This work can be extended with advantage, to deal more fully with facilities for psychiatric and long stay care. Further study of cost is needed.

2. Studies of the demand for medical care shed some, largely accidental, light on health plant as a whole and its function as a system.

This paper argues the present need for research in areas not adequately covered by current work.

DESIGN OF HEALTH PLANT IN RELATION TO HUMAN COMFORT AND BEHAVIOR

The impact of the built environment on human beings is, of course, a general problem affecting architecture as a whole and its study lies at the center of the architect's work. Health building is particularly suitable for study in this regard for several reasons. First, the primary purpose of health facilities is to benefit the individual patient, and the environment created by the architect has as its specific goal the well-being of the patient. Secondly, health care often requires the systematic monitoring of human reactions both physiological and psychological. Therefore, the health building is a convenient place in which to study the impact of architecture on people.

Most research to date on the effect of environment on the human being has been done in relation to extreme conditions. For example, a great volume of work in space medicine concerns human reaction under conditions in space craft. But neither the results nor the methods of this work can readily be transferred to the very different question of studying the design for optimum conditions at the other end of the scale. Some work has however already been done, and the most interesting is probably that of Hopkinson.[5]

Hopkinson has worked principally on lighting and has carried out a series of studies on the natural and artificial lighting of hospital interiors. Whereas most previous studies of lighting have been conducted entirely in terms of physical measurements, Hopkinson has successfully introduced subjective, psychological measurements. Using a systematic series of experiments with observers, he produced subjective scales by which the conditions created in the illumination of an interior can be measured. Further he has been able to relate the subjective measurements to the objective description, by physical measurement of the environment under observation. His work has been directed to an inquiry into the conditions which create visual comfort or visual discomfort, and particularly into analyzing what is meant by the concept of glare. Hospital design in Great Britain has been considerably affected by his work. However, the repercussions of Hopkinson's work have not been solely on the design of lighting fittings or lighting installations or on the design of windows. They have had a deeper effect and have influenced the ideas of architects as to room shape and the use of color and have led to new concepts in hospital design. This result has come from the fact that Hopkinson has worked closely with hospital research teams at the Nuffield Foundation. Research on daylighting has now reached a point where a projected hospital building can be tested in model form under an artificial sky, and the daylighting conditions predicted in terms of human comfort with a very high degree of accuracy. Some of the buildings designed in this manner have since been built, and observations made within them after completion have confirmed the predictions made.

One aspect of this work, which has not been followed very far, is the influence of color. Something has been discovered of the subjective effect of black and white and of various shades of grey but less is known about the influence of hues. This subject could now be fruitfully explored.

Less work has been done so far on specifying the acoustic environment in terms of human comfort. Some crude measures have been developed both in the United States and in Great Britain. But most studies on noise have dealt with extreme conditions where noise, for instance, from aircraft, is of sufficient volume to seriously interfere with human capacity to work. Very little has been done concerning the noise climate which should be maintained in hospitals or buildings for health care. Clearly, eliminating all noise altogether is not desirable. Equally, many existing buildings are known to provide conditions which are highly disagreeable to their occupants and inimical to their comfort and well-being. The physical methods of noise control are fairly well understood and, given sufficient money, any prescribed acoustic conditions can generally be produced. But what should be the aim? Studies designed to bring out the human subject's reaction to various noise climates in buildings seem to be necessary prerequisites to successful prescription of the acoustic environment.

A substantial volume of work exists on thermal environment. The physiological mechanisms by which the human subject remains in homeostasis with his surroundings have been extensively investigated. The needs of the heating and ventilating industry, particularly in relation to air-conditioning systems, has given rise to a substantial volume of research. But knowledge is lacking of the more subtle and sophisticated effects of particular forms of thermal climate. For example, human body temperature is affected both by the temperature and humidity of the circumambient air and by radiation exchange with the enclosing walls of the room in which the person finds himself. Technically a comfortable body temperature may be maintained at very low air temperature, provided that the radiation exchange is favorable. The psychological and physiological effects of possible variations in methods by which the thermal environment is controlled are not fully understood.

Prescribing building environment for health buildings would be on much firmer ground if subjective scales as good as those already developed by Hopkinson in the field of lighting were available for the acoustic and thermal elements in the environment. But, in addition to studying these three principal elements in the physical environment within a building, the environment as a whole must be considered. The well-being, or ill-being, of the human subject in a room will depend not merely on the elements of the physical environment discussed above, but also on the visual characteristics of the room as he sees them. He will be affected by the size, shape and proportion of the space which surrounds him and by the colors which he sees. The total effect of the environment as a whole will not be entirely described by dealing separately with each individual component.

Very little has been done on human reactions to size, shape, proportion or color of building interiors. Ames and other workers[6] have studied human perception of shape. Some work has also been done on space perception in relation to spastic children, and to psychotic patients who may have disorders in space perception.[7,8]

This is a difficult field for research. One of the best areas in which this could be tackled would be in institutions which care for patients who have diminished powers of spatial perception. These institutions must often build up in patients a greater ability to conceive and handle space. More knowledge of how buildings affect the people in them will be of great practical value in the design of buildings for these purposes. Also, a considerable fallout from such work will be available for the whole body of architecture.

Research in the area just described will need to be undertaken by multidisciplinary teams. Architects and artists will be needed to design experimental situations and to help assess them. Physicists will be needed to describe the environment in physical terms, and psychologists and physiologists will be needed to organize and carry out the studies with human subjects. Architects and artists are greatly interested in the possibility of scientific work in this area and finding appropriate people to participate in research will not be difficult. The main difficulty to be anticipated is formulating an adequate basis in what is a new and, in some respects, a very difficult field. This will probably necessitate leaning heavily on psychological and psychiatric approaches.

The studies described above are concerned with the relation of the built environment to the individual human being. But the built environment will also affect the behavior of human groups. The study of group dynamics has brought out some well known examples of the effect of the environment on group behavior. Group behavior is a critical factor in many aspects of health care. In much of the therapy used in mental illness groups of patients play a critical role. In all branches of medical care working groups are involved and in many cases the success of the program of care depends on successful relationships within the working group. A working group generally comprises people with widely different backgrounds and unrelated disciplines. In contrast with business, industrial and military situations, health care often involves collaboration between people belonging to independent hierarchies but with no clear-cut structural realtionship to one another. Thus, problems of group relationship and group function tend to be particularly acute in health care. Owing to the fact that buildings are relatively long lasting, many social functions have to be performed in buildings designed for another purpose. Thus buildings influence group behavior in an accidental and often undesirable way. More knowledge about the interaction of the shape and arrangement of rooms with group behavior might reveal building design to be a valuable tool to promote desirable patterns of human action.

Little research has yet been carried out on this topic. A certain amount of discussion and speculation and one or two empirical experiments have taken place. Osmond[9] has discussed the design of psychiatric hospitals in relation to the type of space which may be most useful to the patient at various stages in his cure. He suggests a form of hospital in which the patient proceeds during his recovery from a space which is a single cell to areas in which he interacts with continuously larger groups of patients and staff. In Great Britain the

Nuffield Research Unit investigated group functioning in hospital wards and reached the conclusion that small groups of nurses should focus their work on comparatively small groups of patients. As a result an experimental hospital unit was built with what has since become known as *bifocal* wards. In this building each nursing unit was split into two, each half unit being the basis for a small nursing group working with a small group of patients.[10] The operation of this unit was subsequently observed and reported.[11]

In striking contrast to these two examples, experiments have been carried out in Germany in the provision of completely undifferentiated interior space in buildings. This was not done in a hospital context but in an office block. Complete freedom was allowed in placing furniture, partitions, etc. so that the human groups occupying the building were able to colonize such areas as they needed. The form of interior division hopefully followed the functional requirements of the working groups. This experiment[12] suggests a possible research method. Another approach has been explored by Cowan.[13] He charted a considerable range of human activity as carried on in buildings and considered the limiting sizes of space needed for each. He then considered the range of possible room sizes and found a steep rise in the number of functions which could be carried on in a room of any given size up to a limit of about 150 square feet. After this size the additional number of functions which could be performed in rooms of increasing size rapidly declined. He then investigated the distribution of room size in a considerable number of plans for health buildings and found a very sharp peak at the same point, i.e., about 150 square feet. These studies suggest a concentration of human activity about a group size consisting of a fairly small number of people. On these grounds a highly flexible building could consist of rooms of standard size, each equally accessible to all others by means of an appropriate communications network. Somewhat similar considerations have led Bridgman[14] to propose the concept of l'hospital banale.

This is apparently an important field of work. Perhaps the biggest question is whether or not the planning of health buildings should encourage a particular pattern of group function by their users. Buildings can be planned so that they can only be used in a predetermined way. Or they can be planned in a manner which permits a variety of patterns of use. While on broad general grounds the latter approach seems the right one, important examples might possibly exist where buildings should be deliberately used to encourage certain modes of behavior. Research in this area will need to use both architects and social scientists. Among the latter, social psychologists and social anthropologists will probably prove to be the most useful members of a research team. Research will need to be closely linked with broader inquiry into the functioning of health programs as a whole. The relation of building design to human behavior will be meaningful only with a clear view of what the aims of the health service really are. Hence, studies in this area should be linked to and follow on more general inquiries into the pattern of medical care in its various aspects. Apart from this, however, further studies of the type undertaken by Cowan may be useful, but with closer reliance on observational data in existing institutions. Such studies could provide a picture of how function and building design appear to react on one another in current situations.

THE HEALTH PLANT AS AN INTEGRATED SYSTEM

Until now research has tended to concentrate on individual sectors of care, such as the general hospital or the doctor's office, and to study each without much regard to their interrelation. But, in fact, each element is closely linked with the other, and the role of the hospital depends on the role of the other elements in the health service. From the point of view of the patient the doctor with whom he has his first consultation, the diagnostic service to which he is referred, the hospital or other institution where he may go for treatment and the rehabilitation center which takes care of the adjustment between a stay in hospital and a patient's return to normal living, are all part of a continuous system. Some countries may have some centralized control of the whole service, nationally or by regions, but in most countries a number of more or less autonomous services go to make up the total pattern. But the role of the various elements in the service are strikingly similar, whether they are centrally controlled or not. Flagel in America, Bailey in England, and two French research organizations, CREDOC and SEMA,[23] have been concerned with the study of health systems as a whole. In all cases the object of research has been to consider the role of the different elements in the system with a view of improving the service to the patients and reducing the cost to the community. Most of these studies have been principally concerned with clinical and organizational aspects of the problem. Obviously, the health plant is an important element in such inquiries.

A strong economic element in these studies is directed toward making the best use of scarce resources, particularly manpower. But the capital devoted to the health plant is also important. Therefore, in the future development of these studies, consideration of the health plant involved in the system should be taken into account. In a general systems analysis of the health services for a region, not only social and medical parameters must be taken into account, but also the cost and distribution of the health plant. Comparisons of alternative systems must consider not merely the best employment of available manpower, but also the best form which capital investment can take. Where services depend on buildings or equipment the utilization of expensive capital items, and their disposition geographically in relation to the population served, must clearly be taken into account. For example, distributing some diagnostic functions may be socially desirable, but the extent to which these can be distributed may well depend on the nature of the plant and buildings required to do the work effectively. The cost of moving patients or medical staff must be balanced against cost of installing a plant which will not be fully utilized. In this area the need is not so much to establish special research projects concerned with plant and equipment, but to make sure that wherever a study is being made of the health service as a whole proper account is taken of the problems of buildings and plant. This will mean the association of some architectural and engineering skill within a team engaged in a general systems analysis of the health services.

Vital as studies of this sort obviously are, very little has yet been done. French studies are exploratory and theoretical. Flagel's work is on a comparatively narrow front and Bailey's work in Great Britain is only just beginning. But these studies are urgently necessary and will be vigorously pursued. Indeed the feeling in many countries now is that, without some general analysis of the health system as a whole, national resources may well be wasted in the provision of piecemeal services. But to produce effective results will be a formidable task as the complexity of the system and the interlocking character of the decisions that have to be made render effective description very difficult. The most likely form which this research will take will probably be in the design of mathematical models. These models will aim to simulate the system as a whole and to show how a patient needing care can progress through it. Hopefully, with the help of these models, a range of different designs of health systems may be compared and their effects on patient care and on cost measured. Very likely a health system is too complex to form the basis for a single mathematical model. The solution may well be a series of linked models with the output of one acting as the input of another. Some of these models will be concerned with the problems of the health plant. The two research areas next discussed in this paper might well provide the basis for two submodels forming part of a general model system describing the health services as a whole.

STUDIES OF THE STOCK OF HEALTH PLANT

The area now to be discussed has hardly attracted any attention as yet, but it is of intrinsic importance and affects several other areas of research.

Any proposals for action in developing health services must obviously be based on the situation as it is. New developments and new provisions never exist in isolation. Thus, when considering a health system and planning its development a full account should obviously be taken of what already exists. This is done as a matter of course when planning the development of an individual hospital. Existing buildings and facilities on the site are taken into account and the development plan will allow the gradual replacement over a period of time of different buildings and different facilities according to the rate necessary to renew them. But similar consideration has rarely, if ever, been given to health facilities of a region or a nation. Any given region, at any one time will have a large number of buildings and a mass of equipment, fulfilling various roles, of different ages and with different life expectancy. Ideally, any new proposal should be seen as a constructive element in the development of the whole system over a period of time. Any authority providing health care for a region, before investing capital in any particular development, should be able to consider the effect of this development on the whole system. Failure to do this must obviously result in some wastage of scarce resources, whether manpower, money or land. No business concern would invest in new production capacity or office accommodation except in relation to the activities of the business as a whole, and to the investment policy of the business as a whole. What is true for a business must also be true for the health service.

The first necessity for any study of plant stock must obviously be some system of inventory. Surprisingly enough, even in countries where substantial parts of the health service are under integrated national or regional control, no complete inventory of buildings or equipment usually exists. In general, important elements of the health systems are often under separate ownership and control. For example, in many countries, while the hospitals are under some sort of regional or national administration the individual doctors' offices, health clinics or the ambulance system will be owned and operated by different private or public organizations. Hence in no country at the present time is anything like an adequate inventory maintained of health plant and equipment covering the needs of the population in an area or region. Of course, in most countries the information exists, but it is buried in the records and files of a number of different organizations within the area. Hence the first object in this study must be the establishment of an effective system of inventory taking and record keeping for health equipment and health buildings.

To begin with, a survey must be made in which rather detailed information for the area under study is collected and this material will have to be put onto punch cards or tape to make use of effective data processing methods. The study of this material should lead to the proposals for a system of inventory in which the minimum essential amount of data is embodied. A few pilot inventories made in different regions should enable some general proposals for the organization of this kind of data to be developed and brought forward for consideration. The inventory of building stock would have to include not merely data relating to size, situation and cost of buildings, but also their age, probable future life and some measure of their degree of flexibility in use. Buildings and equipment exist in time as well as in space and at any given moment they have only a limited range of future life ahead of them. Not long ago social change and technical development were so slow that many buildings were able to work out their natural life. Under such circumstances the rate of decay of the fabric of a building was the principal measure of the date at which it would have to be replaced. Aging and decay are not solely controlled by the deterioration of structural elements, such as walls and roofs. The built-in mechanical services—plumbing, electricity, lifts, etc.—have their own life span. This is usually shorter than that of the fabric and may be a controlling factor.

Recently, particularly in health buildings, functional obsolescence has taken place very much more rapidly than structural decay. Many buildings in the prime of life, as far as fabric is concerned, have had to be torn down and replaced simply because they were designed for a function which has become out of date. But not all buildings are equally vulnerable to functional obsolescence. Cowan[15] has been able to show that various parts of hospital buildings have much longer periods of functional life than others. For example, ward buildings can continue to function more or less effectively for the care of patients for a considerably longer period than, for example, operating rooms or x-ray departments. Hence any inventory of structural stock would have to include as part of the description of any building some measure of its predicted functional life as well as its structural age. A first object of research, therefore, will be to establish appropriate concepts and measures for the aging problems of hospital buildings.

Another important indicator which will have to be taken into account is the probable requirement for growth. Here again, studies in Great Britain have shown that various functional elements in medical care have in the past shown variable patterns of growth. Hence, the utility of a building for a particular function may depend in part on the availability of some additional site area so that it can absorb the need for change by appropriate expansion. The building with room for growth may well have a longer useful life ahead of it than a similar building which cannot be expanded. Another indicator which will have to be included in the inventory would be some measure of the service capacity of each element in the building. This will generally take the form of a number showing the number of patients which will be processed through the particular service for which the building was designed, in a given time.

Once the conceptual basis for an inventory of the health plant has been established and the inventory of a particular region made, the way would be open for constructing, perhaps by means of a mathematical model, a picture of the health plant of the area both in space and time. Then any proposed change in the function of organization of the health system could be considered in relation to its effect on the plant. Whatever changes are necessary in the plant to meet the new demands of the system could be seen. Conversely, how any change in the plant would affect the performance of the system and what organizational or administrative changes it might give rise to could also be seen. Certainly, a description, on lines somewhat following those just discussed, of the health plant of an area is an absolute prerequisite for any wise decisions as to how to alter, extend or modify the system as a whole.

Although no existing examples of work in this area can be advanced, no insuperable intellectual difficulties are obvious. Almost certainly many analogies can be drawn between what is proposed and what is often done in any major business. As a first step, pilot studies should be encouraged in one or two limited areas. The research manpower involved would have to include people sophisticated in the use of modern data processing equipment as well as hospital administrators, architects and engineers who would know how to survey and describe the various items of building and equipment with which the inventory was concerned.

The development of effective methods of describing building stock and considering its impact on the system generally would be of very considerable benefit to many fields of current interest in health plant research. One example is the present interest in the pros and cons of providing various kinds of service centrally. For example, studies are in progress into the desirability of providing catering, sterilization, laundry, bulk purchasing and other facilities at various levels of area or regional organization. Obviously such inquiries will depend in great measure on the capital costs of the equipment and buildings involved in varying levels of centralization and studies of these topics will be largely futile unless these matters can be taken into account. Another area of considerable current interest concerns the question of diffusing the care of psychiatric patients more widely over the population served by a psychiatric service. The argument has been advanced that the concentration of psychiatric patients in large centralized institutions is undersirable on medicosocio grounds. Against this the main argument generally adduced is the greater economy in providing care in massive centralized institutions. The validity of this argument and the weight it should be given are open to question, but the matter cannot really be debated at all without some effective description of the health plant involved in centralized and in decentralized situations. These are only two examples of the wide range of questions in which decisions cannot be reached with wisdom unless adequate information on the existing stock of health plant and its expectancy of life and functional performance is part of the material to be considered.

LOCATION OF PLANT

Very little study has been made with regard to the location of health buildings. Little is known as to how the present patterns of location developed, nor as to what patterns would be desirable for the future. But obviously in considering the service to a given community the location of the various elements of the health plant are critical. The lack of study of this topic is striking when the literature of urban planning and development is examined. This literature will be found to be full of discussion on the location of almost every form of building except those used for health purposes. Housing, industry, the central business area are obvious topics, but, in addition, considerable discussion will be found on the location of certain types of community service buildings, particularly schools and other educational institutions. In contrast almost no reference will be found to the problems of locating buildings for the health services. Town planning literature discusses in depth how the design of towns should attempt to cater for the needs of many types of buildings, but health buildings are rarely mentioned. The locational pattern of schools and other educational facilities has been used as a major parameter in planning many new towns and communities. Shopping or community recreational services have served as a focus for developing concepts of community life, and for grouping residential areas in nuclei related to social services. Strangely, health buildings seem never to have entered into the thinking of planners in this connection. The structure of the health service from the doctor up to the regional medical center should be considered a major element in the arrangements of cities.

As soon as possible some links should be established between studies concerned with the provision of health care to the community and studies of urban development. Research into town planning at the present moment is entering into an extremely exciting and fruitful stage. In the last few years workers have recognized that the problem of urban development requires study in a new way. Urban development is now generally seen as a field in which the forces of individual choice, acting through the market, interact with major interventions by local and national government. Local and national policies in development control, highway construction, investment of public funds and taxation policy substantially affect, but by no means wholly control, the development of cities. A substantial body of research into the interaction of the economic forces of the market, which bring about building and redevelopment, with the pattern of control and intervention by society is now underway in several countries, particularly in the United States and Great Britain.[16]

Among topics that have interested the research workers in this area, the role of institutions has recently come to the front. One way of looking at the development of cities has been to consider the institutions which go to make up that city. Thus, great businesses, public institutions such as universities, hospitals, national art collections, and so on, have an autonomous life and growth pattern which make a profound impact on the city in which the institution is placed. Studies in the life pattern of these insitutions and their impact in terms of expansion and demand for additional space on the urban situation are already in progress in Britain. Of the major institutions which go to make up a city, those for medical care are amongst the most important.

In many countries the present pattern of urban development is profoundly affecting the location of health buildings. The need for expansion of building volume for many central institutions has posed space problems insoluble within the boundaries of existing sites. Institutions are, therefore, often faced with the alternative of staying where they are, with the impossibility of expansion, or of removing themselves at great economic and social cost to a new location out side the present area of dense building in the city. In some European cities major medical institutions have had to leapfrog their way from the center of the city, outwards more than once. Such a displacement in the location of health buildings may or may not be desirable. In some cases this outward movement has been related to a movement of population, but in others it may have been quite inappropriate for the institution concerned. In any case, dictating the location of health buildings wholly by pressure of local land values is an undesirable situation. By their nature health services are unlikely to be able to bid in the open market in competition with businesses for high priced central sites. But, viewed in terms of the total economy of the city, maintaining at least some of the medical services to the community in central locations may be desirable, if all the economic factors are taken into account.

All over the world cities are undergoing cataclysmic change as a result of the population explosion. Urban population is increasing at twice the rate of world population as a whole. As a result the whole anatomy of towns is changing, historic centers are dying, shifting or expanding, new residential areas are springing up and new communication networks are changing the relationship of one place to another. Great new cities are being planned and built in many countries. In this fast-moving situation the locational needs of the health services must be properly taken into account. Urban land is a scarce resource, and if the health plant is the last arrival it will be the worst served. For very many reasons, studies of health plant location should be encouraged as vigorously as possible.

Some work is already going on. But present studies have mostly sprung from the pressing problems of major individual institutions, and little has yet been done on a regional or community basis. Examples of current studies include those undertaken in Birmingham, England[17] and Boston, Massachusetts.[18] All these, however, are primarily studies of one great medical institution in relation to a surrounding community.

What is now needed is research into plant location as an element in urban planning. The present location of all health buildings serving a community should be mapped and the historical pattern by which the present buildings have been located, very often for reasons which no longer apply today, should be studied. For example, locating psychiatric hospitals far from the community they serve resulted from attitudes to mental illness which no longer obtain. But, without a clear understanding of the present, and the forces which governed location in the past, the proper course of action for the future is uncertain. Next, the studies in location should be coupled with the general systems analysis of health services discussed earlier in this paper.

Cowan[19] has introduced some order of generality to these problems and has suggested the outlines of a model for hospital location, but the work is as yet undeveloped and this approach need not be pursued further.

Research in this area will need men trained in public health medicine, together with planners, geographers and economists. It will be most fruitfully carried on within, or in partnership with, a research unit engaged in urban studies at a university. One object of study might be to produce a mathematical model linking the location of health facilities with the expansion of a community.

COST STUDIES AND COST-BENEFIT ANALYSIS

Refence was made in the introduction to the inadequacy of most cost studies to date with regard to health building and equipment. Both the decisions involved in health care must, of course, depend on

266

the costs of alternative plans and programs, and the capital and running cost of plant is often an important component.

Some attempts have been made to consider building cost at a national or regional level. Titmuss and Abel-Smith[20] have discussed national investment policy for health plant in Great Britain. But, global figures for national or regional investment do not help decision making at the level of the individual institution or facility. For this purpose numerous attempts have been made to extract useful comparative data from hospital cost records. These attempts have often failed because of poor accountancy in the health services, but this is a difficulty which could be overcome. Studies in effective methods of cost comparison should be encouraged.

When alternative systems of providing health care to a community are compared, simple direct costs are not sufficient. Here a value has to be put on the loss to the community resulting from absence from work, for example.

An analogous problem has been met with in town planning. For example, decisions as to the spending of public funds on urban renewal, housing or highways require a study of economic costs and benefits going beyond normal accounting methods. Economists have recently begun to develop a research tool for this purpose, known as *cost-benefit analysis*. This method has been developed both in the United States and in Great Britain.[21] In Great Britain it was applied to the problem of whether a new major motorway would repay the national investment involved, and more recently to a proposed new subway through London.[22] Essentially, cost-benefit analysis attempts to consider benefits and costs of a kind not directly measurable in normal accountancy. In doing so it must, of course, make numerous, rather debatable assumptions. But these assumptions are explicit and can be considered and debated.

Many questions of investment in systems of health care could probably be studied by similar methods and the result would be valuable. Even if it did no more than bring out into the light many of the tacit, unchallenged assumptions which are used in decision making in health programs, this would be a valuable contribution.

Cost studies and cost-benefit analysis are not research topics on their own. They are tools which should be brought into use on a wide range of studies. To apply them economists or accountants will be needed who have become acquainted with the methods now being developed in relation to urban investment generally. Pilot studies will be needed to develop appropriate concepts and methods for applying the techniques to health facilities.

REFERENCES

[1] Llewelyn-Davies, Richard and Macauley, H. M. C., HOSPITAL PLANNING, Geneva, The World Health Organization, in press.

[2] Nuffield Provincial Hospitals Trust, Division for Architectural Studies, STUDIES IN THE FUNCTIONS AND DESIGN OF HOSPITALS, London, Oxford University Press, 1955.

[3] ————, A BALANCED TEACHING HOSPITAL, London, Oxford University Press, 1965.

[4] ————, THE DEMAND FOR MEDICAL CARE, London, Oxford University Press, 1960.

[5] Hopkinson, R. G. (Editor), HOSPITAL LIGHTING, Heinemann Publishing, London, 1964; ————, ARCHITECTURAL PHYSICS: LIGHTING, London, HMSO, 1963.

[6] Ittleson, W. H. and Kirkpatrick, F. P., Experiments in Perception, *Scientific American*, 185, 50–55, 1951.

[7] Abercrombie, M. L. J., PERCEPTUAL AND VISUAL MOTOR DISORDERS IN CEREBRAL PALSY: SURVEY OF THE LITERATURE, London, Heinemann Publishers, 1964, p. 136.

[8] Baker, A., Llewelyn-Davies, Richard and Sivadon, P., PSYCHIATRIC SERVICES AND ARCHITECTURE, Geneva, World Health Organization, Public Health Paper Number 1, 1959.

[9] Osmond, H., Functions as the Basis of Psychiatric Ward Design, *Mental Hospital*, 23–29.

[10] Nuffield Provincial Hospitals Trust, STUDIES IN THE FUNCTIONS AND DESIGN OF HOSPITALS, *loc. cit.*

[11] Nuffield Foundation, NUFFIELD HOUSE MUSGRAVE PARK HOSPITAL, BELFAST: CASE HISTORY OF A NEW HOSPITAL BUILDING, London, Nuffield Foundation, 1962.

[12] Henn, Walter, Burogrossraum und Architekt, *Baumeister*, 655–66, July, 1963.

[13] Cowan, P., Studies in the Growth, Change and Ageing of Buildings, *Transactions of the Bartlett Society*, 1, 1962–63.

[14] Bridgman, R. F., Les Banalisation des Services d'hospitalisation, *Techniques Hospitalieres*, 68–77, August-September, 1963.

[15] Cowan, P., Depreciation, Ageing and Obsolescence, *Architects' Journal*, 141, 1395–1401, June 16, 1965.

[16] Grigsby, W., HOUSING MARKETS AND PUBLIC POLICY, Philadelphia, University of Pennsylvania Press, 1963; Dyckman, J., CAPITAL REQUIREMENTS FOR URBAN DEVELOPMENT AND RENEWAL, New York, McGraw-Hill Book Company, 1961; Stone, P. A., Housing, Town Development and Costs, *Estates Gazette,* 1960.

[17] Nuffield Provincial Hospitals Trust, A BALANCED TEACHING HOSPITAL, *loc. cit.*

[18] Field, Hermann H., Application of Comprehensive Planning to the Urban Teaching Medical Center, Paper Presented for the Institute on Hospital Design and Construction, American Hospital Association, December, 1964; ———, Development of Tufts, New England Medical Center—A Preliminary Study, Planning Office, October, 1964; ———, Organizing the Planning Process, Paper presented at the Conference on Medical Schools and Teaching Hospitals, March, 1965.

[19] Cowan, P., Hospitals in Towns: Location and Siting, *Architectural Review,* 137, 417–421, June, 1965.

[20] Titmuss, R. and Abel Smith, B., COST OF NATIONAL HEALTH SERVICE New York, Cambridge University Press, 1958.

[21] Traffic in Towns, HMSO, London, 1963.

[22] Beesly, M. E. and Foster, C. D., Estimating the Social Benefit of an Underground Railway in London, *Journal of the Royal Statistical Society,* Series A, 1963.

[23] Central de Recherche et de Documentation sur le Consommation and Societe d'economie et de Mathematique Appliques.

DISCUSSION

Coordination of health facilities research. Much discussion is devoted to the problem of the fragmented environment in which research on health facilities is being conducted. Particularly stressed is the need to communicate research findings and to integrate conceptual and developmental research projects. The conceptual level of research, as distinguished from the descriptive and developmental levels, needs the most attention, for by combining seemingly unrelated and independent elements in a theoretical framework, it can provide the source of direction for the complex research on health facilities required in the future. The advance of such research and theory development appears to be particularly hindered by lack of communications and cross-fertilization, especially on the international scale. To eliminate duplication of effort, future research activities in facilities and equipment should be coordinated much more tightly in a network of program analysis on a global scale. Such a network of program analysis would specify the goals and purposes of the individual investigations and recognize the interrelationships of the individual research undertakings to the aggregate research efforts. An international health information system comparable to the Medlars project for medical literature was proposed by several speakers.

To further minimize research fragmentation, Dr. Llewelyn-Davies advocates increased circulation among people doing conceptual research—mostly found in universities—and those conducting developmental projects—usually located in operating health institutions and agencies. Neither the conceptual nor the developmental type of project could be conducted profitably by investigators working separately from each other. In his experience, developmental projects inevitably provide surprising feedback to basic theory and should not be regarded as a side branch of the mainstream of health facilities research.

The university teaching hospital and medical center, combining as it does academic with service excellence, may be the strategic institution for conducting comprehensive health facilities research. However, the development of the teaching hospital into a true interdisciplinary research center would require a rather basic change in attitudes on the part of administrators toward social scientists interested in studying facilities in depth. To further the integration of research and administration, as well as their own professional interests, hospital administrators should have the opportunity to leave their own environments sometime in mid-career and to take critical looks at what is going on.

Priorities in health facilities research. Llewelyn-Davies further emphasizes the importance of the time element in planning for support of health facilities research. In this research area, approximately ten years elapse from the time an idea crosses a man's mind to the practical impact of the study. The small-scale operational studies being conducted on an *ad hoc* basis—about individual patient care elements and design in relation to function—seem to be faring well. Leaders in health services research, however, now need to look ahead beyond this operational level, to determine the social and medical situation approximately ten to 15 years from now, and to analyze the kind of research that should be encouraged and supported at this time.

The two most important developments structuring the social and health scene in the future are the trend toward comprehensive regional and national planning and the population explosion and urban expansion. Both phenomena have received political attention and are embodied in legislation. Thus the future of the provision of health services, in terms of buildings and facilities, can no longer be looked at solely in terms of the health system, but must be related to other developments and regarded in terms of its social role and mode of action.

A whole series of questions concerning the placement of facilities require answers before the question of architecture and interior space could become a priority consideration. To determine how flexible facilities should be, not only changing technology but the art of forecasting population trends for small areas would have to be mastered. According to Llewelyn-Davies, studies of hospitals and other institutions affected by technological change are demonstrating that every institution must be seen as consisting of separate parts with different patterns of change and growth. Buildings like hospitals cannot be strictly tailored to a defined set of functions because the functions will change. The basic need is to discover what the different portions of the building are, to identify the differential change rates, and to

271

plan to leave these structures open-ended. An institution is like a tree: it requires room to grow. Flexibility entails uncommitted resources in terms of space. To meet the needs of the urban situation, a calculus must be developed that would permit certain parts or functions of the central institution to be detached. A good theoretical understanding, based on social sciences, of the actual patterns by which institutions develop and by which they can be studied would provide design criteria incorporating these differential changes.

Studies of demand for medical care, without a corresponding investigation of supply, cannot provide knowledge of how to integrate patient care functions, nor physical plant and personnel. Any change in the mix of services affects the demand of all the elements in the medical care process. Studies of demand for medical care can no more than reveal the deficiency in certain elements of medical care without indicating the alternatives. Effective demand in relation to the supply side of medical care is only beginning to be studied; for the purposes of planning research, the integrated study of the demand and supply sides should be particularly encouraged.

Applicability of cost-benefit analysis. Once the hard part of the task—the decision to build or to provide a particular service—has been set, cost-benefit analysis will not be required. Only the cost of doing the project one or another way would have to be estimated. Problems at the architectural level in general appear to be soluble through cost analysis alone. However, every alternative architectural design can be seen to embody not only its specific cost, but also its specific benefits in terms of social and psychological values. Whenever such special values are attached to projects, cost-benefit analysis is warranted, even at the architectural level. The more an undertaking is envisaged as a system and analyzed in relation to the population and to alternative arrangements for providing care, the less can benefits be specified precisely and the less can cost be regarded as the only variable to be considered. As the scope of planning expands, to include determination of an area's and a nation's requirements, the need for cost benefit analysis becomes more evident. Since mere summation of decisions made at lesser levels would fail to attain acceptable solutions, concepts and models geared to nation-wide health facilities planning appeared to be priority items.

HEALTH SERVICES RESEARCH II

THE POLITICAL INGREDIENT
OF PUBLIC HEALTH SERVICES
A NEGLECTED AREA OF RESEARCH

HERBERT KAUFMAN

Few things are more galling to most experts than the blocking or weakening by amateurs, laymen, or other relatively uninformed and unqualified persons, of a course of action clearly indicated by the prevailing doctrine of the expert's field. To most experts, few people are less qualified than politicians in technical fields, and few considerations are more irrelevant (if not downright hostile) to technical decisions than are political considerations.

Therefore, even experts whose careers will unfold in the public arena —that is, in government service or in areas closely associated with governmental programs—pay little attention to politics in the training of their successors and in the conduct of their own research. Politics is treated as an intrusion to be ignored at best, condemned at worst. No student of government can study his subject very long before discovering the familiar cries of the specialists: "Take education (or health or planning or a dozen other specialties) out of politics, and keep politics out of our specialties." "There is no Republican or Democratic way to fight a fire (or clean the streets or manage traffic, etc.)."

This state of affairs is distressing for three reasons. First, and least important, specialists believe everyone should know more about their specialties. (However, specialists confine their expertise to a limited group of initiates so that only a small number of people will know how the experts grope, stumble, bicker and err.)

Second, the penchant for neglecting or denouncing politics poses a threat to democratic government. This is an era of extraordinarily intensive specialization. Not only the occupations and trades now called "professional," but also those dubbed "skilled labor" have guilds controlling the training, qualification, entry, behavior and sometimes even the compensation of their practitioners. If every apprentice is trained to suspect and despise politics and to dedicate himself to remove his occupation from the political arena, an ever-increasing and more influential segment of the population may acquire a disrespect for the processes which are the core of a democratic policy. Moreover, if every specialty seeking exemption were in fact removed from the arena of partisan contention, the decision-making machinery of the society, deprived of an ultimate adjudicating authority mediating among the specialists, might grind to a stop. To be sure, these dangers are overstated here, but only to dramatize conflicts with the premises of democracy that are too significant to overlook even if they are not by themselves likely to be fatal to democracy.

Third, and most relevant to the topic of this paper, the neglect of political factors in the study of public health problems and programs omits a critical element in understanding, planning and executing public health services. For whether they like it or not, the practitioners of the public health disciplines are deeply immersed in a political environment. The ones who succeed are the ones who learn to understand it, adjust to it and turn it to their advantage. But few of them, in their formal training or in their professional research literature, receive any assistance in this vital aspect of their work. The purpose of professional education and research is to improve the level of performance on the job by placing at the disposal of each generation of practitioners the distilled experience of their predecessors and the latest knowledge relevant to their field. Therefore, expecting health officers to obtain insight into the political context of public health services through on-the-job training alone is a serious deficiency. If political science is not yet a science as rigorous and precise as epidemiology, nutrition or sanitation control, it can nevertheless help members of the public health professions prepare for the problems they will encounter when they move into the field. This is not to imply that schools of public health and public health journals should give themselves over chiefly to the study of politics, but political factors in public health services should not be entirely omitted from their curricula and their professional reports. Political scientists have also been remiss on their side in not devoting to public health services attention comparable to that given to other spheres of public policy, such as foreign policy, national security affairs, agriculture, natural resources and industrial regulation, among many others. At the same time, students and administrators of public health programs have the deeper and more enduring interest in the question, and the initial dialogue between the two disciplines must come from them if it is to come at all.[1]

THE CHARACTER OF THE POLITICAL INGREDIENT

The argument that the public health field is inescapably political in character does not mean that every technical decision is fraught with political overtones. This is not true. Nor does it mean public health programs and staff are dominated by political parties. They are not. But it would be an excessively narrow definition of politics that confined the term exclusively to nominations, elections and appointments, which are the principal concerns of parties. Politics also includes all efforts to influence public policy, which is to say the decisions and actions of public officers and employees. If politics is defined in this broader and more pervasive sense, then the field of public health is clearly as political as any other field of governmental activity.

The Creation and Jurisdictions of Public Agencies

For example, the decisions to establish a public agency and to invest it with particular powers are political choices of major magnitude. In the case of familiar agencies of long standing, with relatively stable spheres of responsibility, the political forces that brought them into being and shaped their activities are often forgotten and virtually taken for granted. If one recalls, however, the origins of many existing agencies, one realizes the political turmoil in which they were conceived and born. The Interstate Commerce Commission, for instance, was set up in an era of populist reform over strong opposition from the railroads. Later, the extension of its authority to pipelines and to trucks and busses was controversial, for it had come to be regarded as a captive of the railroads. The creation of a separate aviation agency, the Civil Aeronautics Board, to regulate air commerce represented in part a tacit recognition of its narrow orientation. The Tennessee Valley Authority was the product of two decades of bitter political battles (but advocates of similar agencies for the Columbia River and the Missouri River were defeated). The National Labor Relations Board was fought vehemently before, during and after its establishment, and new struggles raged over the modifications of its structure and its mandate when the Taft-Hartley Act was passed. The new Department of Housing and Urban Development had a stormy period of gestation and is likely to undergo severe trials until it carves a niche for itself. At the state and local levels, agencies to promote equality of opportunity in employment, housing and education had their determined opponents as well as their enthusiastic backers. Indeed, the list could be extended almost indefinitely; setting up or changing almost any administrative organization in government is a political issue for all who are served or regulated by it, for other agencies whose heads perceive it as a possible challenge to their own positions, for those who see career opportunities in it, and for those political leaders who must bear the onus of its potential failures though they may reap little direct benefit from its achievements.

Extensive studies of the history of many of these agencies have described their efforts to defend or expand their powers, and their strategies of survival. These have provided an understanding of the pressures exerted within and upon them in the present day as well as in earlier periods, the accidents of history that can make them prisoners of their own past, and the needs and the means for adjustment. Studies and inquiries can portray the larger setting in which the agencies operate, perceive the limits on their discretion and their resources, discern new opportunities for service and for growth. In short, analysis of the politics behind the creation and jurisdictions of public agencies provides explanations of the substance of their programs that no degree of technical expertise can supply by itself.

Yet few such studies exist in the field of public health services. Of course, formal chronologies of individual agencies abound, but these are a far cry from penetrating investigations of their political genesis and the political negotiations setting the boundaries of their jurisdictions.[2] The literature could be interpreted to show an almost complete consensus about what was to be done, how it was to be done and who was to do it. Considering, however, that public health agencies are powerful regulatory bodies, and that regulated interests commonly resist the introduction of controls affecting their freedom of operation and their margins of profit, the advocates of regulations could not have prevailed over the economic power confronting them had they not been adept at mobilizing their political resources and bringing them to bear on legislatures at all levels of government. Remembering also that expansions of governmental services invariably meet with objections from private interests which fear government competition, and that the medical profession has been particularly vehement on this point, the growth of even the most limited direct medical services by public agencies must have aroused contesting camps. Health officers have certainly been involved in contests over health fads, nostrums, food additives, birth control education and discouragement of smoking. Who the contestants were, what strategies they pursued, what compromises they made and the present stand of the contending forces of those days are seldom illuminated in available public health research reports.[8]

As another illustration of unanswered questions, legislatures have traditionally been reluctant to delegate authority to the executive branch of government. They have had to do so, of course, and with increasing frequency in the modern day, until more legislation pours forth from administrative bodies than from the legislatures themselves, and more adjudications are handled in administrative tribunals than in the courts. But they have not granted such power with alacrity, and have tried to maintain supervision of its exercise.

Consequently, the great scope of the discretion delegated to public health agencies, and the freedom with which they have been permitted to apply their powers, can by no means be regarded as routine legislative policy. In many ways, boards of health in state and local governments operate as unifunctional legislatures which promulgate codes having the force and effect of statutes. Although comparisons are difficult, not even in the field of education, where governing bodies are often popularly elected, do administrators enjoy equal autonomy, and in most fields administrative officers are still more tightly circumscribed. Thus, the resolution of differences, which in other governmental services are handled in legislative chambers and in executive mansions, are, in the case of health services, left in unusual degree to administrative disposition. The politics of public health has been removed from the broad governmental arena to a narrower and more specialized one in which health officials enjoy their greatest influence.

The high esteem in which the medical profession is held and the deep anxieties about the results of poor performance in protection of public health are doubtless important elements in the exceptional willingness of legislators to relinquish powers in this area which they refuse to surrender in other areas. But is public health so different from other governmental responsibilities? At the federal level, foreign relations and military security are argued to be too technical, and the consequences of error too costly, to permit politically minded laymen to interfere in such decisions. Yet members of Congress have not been notably eager to withdraw from them. At the state and local levels, police, fire, planning, highway and public works officers, among many others, have made similar claims, but rarely with the success of public health officials. In addition, public health officials often touch more politically sensitive spots in their regulatory functions (such as food and drug control and industrial hygiene) than do many of their brother officers in other fields. So the delegation of unusual authority to them is not fully explained by their expertise, the importance of their work or the allegedly apolitical character of their functions.

What, then, is the explanation? One finds little authoritative research that will help answer the question.

Nor is material available to explain the peculiar divisions of responsibility for public health administration at all levels of government in this country. In other fields, evidence indicates that administrative patterns are the result of political settlements among a variety of interests (including public officials, pressure groups, professional associations, legislative committees and many others) rather than of rational selection among alternative organizational structures solely on the basis of administrative efficiency or program effectiveness. For instance, the United States Forest Service was located in the Department of Agriculture instead of the Department of the Interior to reduce the influence of interests, strongly represented in the latter agency and in the interior committees of Congress, which were more concerned with quick exploitation of resources than in conservation. Evidence indicates that foreign aid programs were assigned to a new agency outside the State Department because many Congressmen did not want to give the Secretary of State the vast additional powers these programs would confer. Congress removed the Reconstruction Finance Corporation from the Department of Commerce because it was unwilling to let the Secretary, Henry A. Wallace, control its resources. The Atomic Energy Commission was given jurisdiction over fissionable materials because the non-military potentials of nuclear power might have been slighted had they been entrusted to the military. Little is known, however, about the organization of public health services.

Yet public health services are highly dispersed.[4] At the federal level, for example, the regulation of the food and drugs industries is lodged in the Food and Drug Administration, but most reports on proper nutrition and diet come from the Department of Agriculture. The Public Health Service has many direct operating and research responsibilities, administers grants to state and local health agencies, and disburses funds for research to universities and other nongovernmental organizations. But, the Bureau of Mines has its own program of research and service for improvement of health conditions in the mineral industries. The Federal Trade Commission's surveillance of advertising to prevent false and deceptive claims, which is a central feature of its program for discouraging unfair methods of competition, extends to drugs, cosmetics and curative devices. Conspiracies to fix the prices of these commodities and to make other agreements that illegally reduce competition, however, are under the jurisdiction of the Department of Justice. Some client-centered agencies, such as the Bureau of Indian Affairs and the Veterans Administration, furnish medical services to their charges, but the Children's Bureau does not.

In states and localities, mental health is often separated from other public health services and lodged in a separate agency. Similarly, programs of air and water pollution control are administered outside of the departments of health, although much of the responsibility for establishing and maintaining standards is placed on them. Sanitation and sewage control are likewise ordinarily excluded from the functions of public health agencies, and narcotics addiction is frequently treated as a penal rather than as a health problem. Health officers may move on such health hazards as trampoline concessions in amusement parks (where inexperienced customers often injure themselves), but few have taken on one of the major causes of death and injury in modern life— the automobile—which is left instead to the automobile industry and highway engineers, whose interests in public health are frequently subordinated to other considerations.

Sketching the fragmentation of health services among many agencies, is not to suggest that all these functions should be housed in one agency, or that a more symmetrical and logical arrangement is obviously preferable. Even if effecting such a reorganization were feasible, it would not necessarily be desirable. However, a great deal more about the character of public health services would be known if the political causes of the present administrative patterns were known.[6] For, in learning about these patterns, a great deal of knowledge comes to light about why some kinds of services are offered and others withheld, why some kinds of research are supported and others neglected, why some kinds of regulations are imposed and others not. What could be more relevant for public health services research?

Financing Public Agencies

No less political then the decisions to establish agencies and to define their jurisdictions are the decisions about their financing. Here again the expert is likely to feel frustrated over having to justify to laymen a budget that is technically competent and professionally obvious, and to depend on the judgments of the laymen for appropriations. But parliamentary assemblies won their place in democratic governments through the power of the purse, and through this power they exercise most of their influence in the processes of governmental policy formation. So long as representative institutions survive it will remain their most important and treasured authority.

Preparing budget estimates and justifications is not just a matter of accounting. It is a process of making concrete policy choices with regard to program, and a strategy for persuading budget officers, chief executives and legislative committees of the importance of supporting the courses of action proposed by an agency. A good deal has been written about budgeting, chiefly concerning rational methods of allocating scarce resources among more demands than can be met fully with what is available. Fiscal information about expenditures on public health is available, but largely in terms of what the money is spent on rather than how it came to be spent the way it is. Knowledge of the politics of public health financing is very thin.

A study of the political aspects of public health budgeting might illuminate the implicit political agreements represented tangibly in expenditure figures.[7] To what extent, for example, do public health officials design their programs and their budgets in anticipation of what they think will find favor with fiscal officers and legislators instead of on the basis of their own assessments of needs and priorities? How frequently are their financial plans thwarted or dictated by the mass media, by pressure groups, by other agencies? What programs considered valuable by public health leaders have failed to win support and why? Do grant-in-aid programs, shaped by pressures in Washington and the state capitals, induce local public health authorities to devote their limited funds and manpower to problems not vital to their communities, while more pressing needs are deferred or ignored? These

282

are certainly significant issues, yet little objective, systematic research been done to shed light on them.

Personnel Selection

The selection of personnel for government office and employment is a more familiar political issue, partly because it was dominated for a long while by political parties whose dominance civil service reformers succeeded in eliminating from many areas of government. In the electoral process, of course, parties are still the most influential participants, although even here they must now make concessions to other participants almost unknown two or three generations ago. In appointments, however, although they are by no means powerless, they no longer exercise hegemony. Specialists have displaced them.

At many levels of public service, the supplanting specialists are the public personnel administrators, who have multiplied prolifically with the expansion of "merit system" requirements. Most federal positions up to very high rungs on the classification ladder are covered by merit system safeguards. State and local personnel in agencies supported by federal funds are likewise covered. Most industrial states and large cities have civil service laws and regulations covering virtually all their officers and employees. Civil service examiners (instead of party leaders) now screen applicants for public positions, certify to employing organizations those they deem qualified, and protect those appointed against arbitrary dismissal.

The civil service reformers thought they were excluding politics from the appointing process. What they succeeded in doing was excluding the parties. This unquestionably eliminated most of the worst abuses of the spoils system, even in those jurisdictions that have to this day failed to adopt rigorous civil service laws and procedures. But the development of civil service bureaucracies generated new tensions in the public service. Administrators of the line agencies began to complain about civil service "red tape" as an impediment to effective program management. Intrabureaucratic friction replaced patronage problems. The politics of personnel selection shifted from the partisan to the bureaucratic arena.

Health officials have been among the most vehement critics of civil service procedures. They are not interested, they assert, in hiring party hacks in their agencies. They have an even greater concern for the competence and caliber of the people in their agencies than do the civil service commissions and their staffs. But the civil service bureaucrats, they argue, act as though health officers had no interest in life but political patronage, and the whole system is thus perceived by health officers as a design to ward off a nonexistent threat. Civil service, they charge, fails to procure the best personnel. The regulations actually make this more difficult, especially during a period of full employment in which highly qualified individuals are in short supply.

Is this really the case? Do rigidly enforced civil service laws in fact hamper public health agencies? If full discretion over appointments were restored to health administrators, would partisan influence reassert itself? Enough evidence to answer these questions exists, but research to gather and analyze the data is sparse.[8]

Little has been done, too, about studying the selection of the highest health officials. Their positions are deliberately exempted from civil service protections so that elected officers can appoint persons reflecting their own points of view and thus to execute the mandates they receive at the polls. In many fields, even when the law gives a chief executive full discretion to appoint and remove, hard reality places severe restrictions on him. The outcries of interested pressure groups, the reaction of the press, the criticisms of the opposition party and of factions within his own party, the advice and possible resistance of an agency's permanent bureaucracy to an appointee they find unacceptable, and the harmful public repercussions of inept performance by an appointee all combine to limit his freedom of choice. In addition, his discretion is often further circumscribed by statutory requirements of specific training and experience or by the practice (sometimes customary rather than legal, as in the case of judicial appointments in New York City) of confining his selections to a list of eligibles drawn up by a panel of presumably disinterested experts. Some officials are given fixed terms by law (as, for example, the Police Commissioner in New York City and the members of the great regulatory commissions) to prevent easy removal. So appointing officers make their choices under numerous constraints.

Many of the consequences of their restraints may be unanticipated and perhaps even undesired. For instance, if the commissioners and staff of a public utilities commission, charged with regulating the activities and rates of utilities companies, are chosen almost exclusively from the leadership of the companies because these are the men with the most knowledge about the industry to be supervised, are not their points of view and policy decisions likely to reflect their backgrounds and thus coincide more closely with the preferences of the companies than of the consumers? Furthermore, if they return to the industries after completing their tours of government service, are not their actions in office likely to be influenced by the expectation of resuming such employment? If they do return to the businesses they previously regulated, may not their associations with the commissioners and staff who remain afford them excellent access to the highest levels of the agency they left?

By the same token, if the high echelons of the permanent bureaucracy of an agency are held to be the best reservoir from which to select agency leaders, can one expect innovation, no matter how sorely it may be needed? Or will the officers who work their way to the top of an agency over time gradually acquire a commitment to the existing policies, personnel, organization and procedures that renders them unfriendly to change and exceptionally receptive to the claims of their subordinates and of the interest groups with which they are familiar and have long-standing relations?

Similarly, if restraints on the discretion of a chief executive limit his choices for the leadership of a particular agency to members of a single profession with a limited number of training institutions, all of which may have a common ideology, is this not likely to have a profound effect on what the agency does and how it does it? (Precisely this alleged state of affairs engendered many of the complaints about the Ivy League character of the United States Foreign Service, and was one of the reasons the selection and advancement practices of the service were so completely overhauled. Many a President or Secretary of State felt his policies were hindered by built-in hostility.)

If studying the characteristics of the appointment process provides understanding of the policies and practices of governmental agencies outside the field of public health, would not research in public health services also benefit from such inquiries? Perhaps the inquiries will merely confirm many of the beliefs about the present system now assumed to be true. If so, some solid evidence behind them would be advantageous. Perhaps, on the other hand, many of the assumptions about the public health community will turn out to be false. This, too, is important to know.

Agencies and their "Constituencies"

No matter where they come from or how they get their jobs, public health officers, like other public officials, can be sure of one thing: the day they assume office they will become the focal point of pressures from a variety of sources. Some will urge changes upon them, others will seek to veto proposed innovations. Some will be steadfast allies, others fair-weather friends, still others unremitting foes. Some will be in government, others outside, and those inside may be in other branches or in other agencies of the executive branch. How the leaders of public agencies manage these demands is a fascinating and illuminating subject for research. Analysis of these relationships in the public health field is sparse.

Yet almost all administrators deliberately cultivate allies who can be counted on to support the agencies in their efforts to increase their budgets or their authority, and who rise to the agencies' defense when hostile forces threaten. The administrators see that their supporters testify at hearings, that appropriate occupational associations and economic organizations adopt endorsing resolutions, that approving statements by influential persons reach the press and that the mass media are informed about the logic of the agencies' position on controversial questions. They try to get legislators to ask friendly questions at open proceedings. They seek to create a favorable public image. They may even curtail, or at least threaten to curtail, service on the grounds that they cannot fulfill their obligations unless their requests are satisfied, thus they often succeed in arousing a sense of alarm that buttresses their case. Seldom does an effective administrator enter the political arena without friends. Even more rarely does an administrator who neglects his political fences achieve all he wants.

On the other hand, the administrator may find himself a hostage of his allies. When they lend support, they also frequently establish themselves as moral creditors who may at some time ask favors in their turn, which are difficult for an administrator to ignore without risking the loss of future assistance. One may easily understand why an agency chief may defer or drop a program strongly opposed by members of his coalition, or undertake projects strongly recommended by some of his influential backers even though the projects would not otherwise be high on his list of priorities. Or why an energetic campaign by a prominent newspaper may persuade him to move in directions he might not prefer or may induce him to suspend actions he had planned. Or why he might take special pains to improve his services in the district of an especially powerful elected official even when the needs of other areas are greater. To cleave to abstract principle though all major supporters be alienated would in the long run do more damage to an

286

agency than strategic compromises and delays. An administrative leader dedicated to his program and loyal to his agency would do both a disservice if he were excessively rigid.

Management of relations with constituencies is especially complicated in the case of public health agencies because the constituencies are so diverse.[9] Public health services are not a homogeneous group of functions, but a most varied aggregate of related but distinct operations. They combine regulation, research, education and medical and hospital care. They are performed by physicians, dentists, nurses, engineers, biologists, chemists, dietitians, laboratory technicians and many other professional and subprofessional specialists. They affect processors and distributors of food and drugs, voluntary and proprietary hospitals, nursing homes, universities generally and medical schools in particular, voluntary health and welfare associations, as well as the general public. They impinge on many other public agencies, especially in welfare, education, sanitation, housing, water supply and land-use planning. Some of their duties, such as providing information about family planning, arouse the sensitivities of religious groups.

The pattern of public health services is an outcome of settlements and understandings, tacit and explicit, among all the groups and interests concerned.[10] Out of the rivalries, coalitions, common objectives and competing goals come the organizational structure, division of duties, procedural arrangements, and decisions about what to do, what not to do and where to locate public health facilities, that characterize the field. That political parties play a small part in this drama matters little. The drama is patently political all the same.

The Metropolitan Problem

Some observers may harbor reservations about designating agency-constituency relations as political; none would deny that setting governmental boundaries is a political problem.

Among the boundaries currently questioned in the United States (which include the lines of legislative districts and of school districts) are those of the urban units of government. However reasonable they may have been when first drawn, new developments in the technology of transportation and communication, and in housing, with the consequent redistribution of population, have rendered traditional arrangements obsolete. No longer, according to many commentators, are existing city lines appropriate. Urban difficulties can be solved only on a regional basis. Among the arguments for this position is the familiar slogan that health problems do not respect governmental jurisdictions.

If this is true, one might expect public health officials and their clienteles to be in the forefront of those struggling to create new units of government with regional jurisdictions. In fact, however, they are not much in evidence.[11] Is this because the allegations of present inadequacies are not true in the health field, or because the issue simply has not seemed salient to health authorities? Have public health agencies succeeded in overcoming, through reciprocal services and joint planning, the difficulties presented by the multiplicity of governmental jurisdictions in metropolitan areas, or do they acquiesce in this multiplicity because, like many other public officials, many of them fear their own programs, agencies and jobs would suffer if a new tier of government were established? Have they been comparatively silent because they are satisfied, because they fear retribution by opponents of metropolitan regionalism in their own communities, or because they consider participation in such debates inappropriate for health officers?

These questions are not raised to defend or criticize the proponents of metropolitan government; this is not the place to introduce that debate. But health administrators have been involved in the controversy whether they will it or not. If they believe governmental reorganization would make no difference in their field, then their silence has permitted one side in the controversy to involve their names and prestige without justification. Like American neutrality prior to World War II, disengagement helps one adversary and weakens the other. If they are of the opinion that health services would be improved or injured by metropolitan reorganization, then their public responsibilities may oblige them to take as firm and unequivocal a stand on this as on fluoridation of water supplies or the hazards of smoking. Indeed, the consequences may reach even further if proposed changes fail for lack of support or carry for lack of opposition. Remaining aloof does not take them out of politics; it only increases the chances of success of political decisions they consider wrong from a health point of view. Research on this phase of public health services is necessary to determine the existence of a consensus on the proper course of action among health officers, what they have done about it, why they have followed the paths they do, and how effective they have been.

Opportunities and Obstacles

This list of political issues pervading the field of public health, yet largely ignored by students of public health and politics alike, by no means exhausts the possible illustrations. Indeed, another commentator making the same point might assemble an altogether different series. For example, by whom and by what means are goals set for public health agencies and officers? To what extent are health problems created by political decisions in other program areas (such as urban renewal, public recreation, industrial location) in which public health professionals do not participate? Is not the blurred line between "public" health services and nonpublic services a fiction maintained for political purposes, among others? These issues, no less than those previously suggested, indicate the manner in which politics permeates the field of public health, and will not be separated from it. This list of examples represents the concerns of one political scientist, and was selected from subjects on which, in program areas other than health, substantial work has been done.

The comparative absence of research on the politics of such a political field as public health, while offering opportunities for fresh investigation, results from the difficulties of gaining access to the full facts. Some observers believe that the realities of politics are too sensitive for any "insider" to discuss frankly with an "outsider," even if the outsider presents credentials as a qualified, discreet, objective, responsible researcher. Indeed, so many of the negotiations and settlements are informal and unrecorded that even willing informants could not give an accurate and complete account of them. The "truth," therefore, is not accessible to the researcher, and his report is inevitably incomplete and distorted. Hence the dearth of sophisticated studies of politics in this field; those who are sophisticated enough to appreciate the complexities of the subject and the obstacles to the truth do not try to describe it.

The valid elements of this contention cannot be denied. The research advocated here is neither easy to do nor assured of success. But neither should it be regarded as hopeless. In many a sensitive area patient, diligent, discerning research has brought to light fuller, more balanced accounts of public policy formation than any single participant in the process could supply, and has both detected the unspoken customs and understandings involved in them and has analyzed the effect of these inarticulate premises of action (which are often unrecognized by those who submit to them) on the final outcome.[12] Moreover, incomplete or inaccurate presentations frequently elicit corrective commentaries, so the ultimate portrayal escapes the defects of the initial effort. If nothing more, at least the various versions of the truth can be collected. Experience shows that even those who think they know the full story gain new perspectives when skilled researchers assemble and order the views of all who take part.

A noncontroversial record of a policy decision may never exist. Certainly no record is likely to stand for all time as the only accurate one. But, a good deal more can be learned about the process of public policy-making than is now known if its political as well as its technical dimensions are acknowledged and explored. This has already been done in some fields.

THE UTILITY OF RESEARCH ON THE POLITICAL INGREDIENT

Even if one concedes that public health decisions are immersed in politics, inquiries into the kinds of questions raised here are not generally regarded as helpful to the health administrators and students of public health, who presumably read health research reports, as would be medical, chemical or similar studies.[18] To the contrary, however, such inquiries would be as valuable.

The press and urgency of daily problems almost always prevent any busy executive from keeping in perspective the larger environment of which he is a part. Three consequences flow from this: first, he tends to become a prisoner of the *status quo*. Second, he finds himself buffeted by forces over which he seems to have little influence, and that wear down his enthusiasm and energy. Third, he becomes an inadvertent party to agreements he never intended to make.

All social institutions sanctioned by time tend to take on an aura of sanctity removing them from contention. The longer they persist, the greater the likelihood that they will be taken for granted, and the stronger the commitment to them. Moreover, the greater their age, the higher the probability that the people familiar with them will have mastered their intricacies and will have established relationships that dispose these people to work to preserve the institution. The framework of policy is thus fixed within traditional limits.

Were this not true, the volatility of social organization might make life intolerable for everyone. A substantial measure of stability is essential for orderly development.

But if policy makers never lift themselves out of the traditional framework, the capacity of institutions to respond to new demands and unfamiliar challenges may fall short of what is required of them,

290

and the institutions may thereby be imperiled. A healthy skepticism is a prerequisite to social change.

The prevalence in the public health community of such skepticism about the *technical* aspects of their duties, cannot be doubted. Public health administration has made remarkable strides over the decades because its practitioners and researchers have not hesitated to question the technical orthodoxies of an era and to experiment with new methods and concepts.

About the political aspects of their field, they have been much more docile. They seldom do research that would lead them to take issue with the organization of the public health field, or with the finance decisions that determine the shape of their programs, or the pattern of staffing and its implications, or the influence of their many constituents, or the nature of the governmental units in which they find themselves. These they treat as "givens," as parameters with which they must submissively come to terms.

Administrators would be less inclined to accept unquestioningly the political decisions governing their activities if they were continually reminded that these *are* political decisions, and that what is handed down as the hallowed wisdom of an earlier generation is actually a product of negotiation, compromise and accommodation among the political interests of another day. This awareness could stimulate reexamination of a whole range of questions impinging on health services, but left to others to handle. The research generating this awareness could serve as a foundation on which to base judicious change. In short, such research might help to free public health administration from the fetters of which its students and practitioners are hardly aware.

Research of this kind could also make comprehensible and manageable political factors that thwart and discourage health administrators. As long as politics is treated by them as a forbidden realm, outsiders skilled in its mysteries can impose their will on the field. By the same token, every defeat of proposals that seem reasonable to health officers must seem like an infuriating, self-seeking, indefensible betrayal of the public interest rather than as an adjustment among a variety of competing claims. It thus becomes a disheartening, disillusioning experience, and no man can tolerate many of these.

Analysis of the political components of public health administration, in short, might sensitize practitioners to the opportunities afforded them by the political process instead of exposing them only to its obstacles. It might help them to develop quickly the tolerance and the patience to endure setbacks that every participant in government service encounters, and prepare them for the resistance evoked by every recommendation for change and for the strategies of the opponents. By allowing public health officers to share their political experiences with one another, such research might increase the effectiveness with which they all conduct their public business.

In addition, every study of the political process illustrates two basic axioms of public life: inaction is a decision, and decisions made in response to immediate pressures often have long-range consequences. Abstractly, everyone accepts these propositions. The value of research is that it turns abstractions into concrete events, and the many ways in which a seemingly noncommittal word or act can become an obligation or a commitment or a political instrument in someone else's hands are dramatically brought home.

Thus, public health administration is a political matter, and those who take the responsibility to know all that this implies are better off than those who undertake their task without knowledge of its political dimensions. For this reason, research in public health services hopefully will eventually embrace the political as well as the technical aspects of the function. The lion's share of the burden, if the burden is carried at all, will fall upon the schools and agencies in the health field.

REFERENCES

[1] To verify the impression that literature on public health devotes almost no attention to the political aspects of the field, some recent public health treatises and textbooks were examined for their comments on the subject. The impression was more than confirmed; it was intensified. Not a single volume included anything more than a passing reference to politics, and most of them did not contain even that. The books examined included: Anderson, O. E., Jr., THE HEALTH OF A NATION, Chicago, University of Chicago Press, 1958; Burn, J. L., RECENT ADVANCES IN PUBLIC HEALTH, London, Churchill, 1959; Davies, I. G., MODERN PUBLIC HEALTH FOR MEDICAL STUDENTS, London, Edward Arnold Publishers, 1963; Freeman, R. B., ADMINISTRATION OF PUBLIC HEALTH SERVICES, Philadelphia, W. B. Saunders Co., 1960; Rogers, E. S., HUMAN ECOLOGY AND HEALTH: AN INTRODUCTION FOR ADMINISTRATORS, New York, The Macmillan Company, 1960; Stevenson, G. S. (Editor), ADMINISTRATIVE MEDICINE, New York, The George Macy Companies, Inc., 1959; Turner, C. E., PERSONAL AND COMMUNITY HEALTH, St. Louis, The C. V. Mosby Co., 1959; Van Avery, P. (Editor), PUBLIC HEALTH, New York, H. W. Wilson Co., 1959.

Little research on the politics of public health was to be found in the last five years of the *American Journal of Public Health,* either. Fewer than ten articles in that period can be regarded even by liberal standards as dealing with the problems reviewed in this paper. Collectively, they total about 60 pages. They are cited at appropriate points in the text.

Political scientists are no less vulnerable to this allegation than are public health researchers. A search of a few recent textbooks and treatises, of some reputation and circulation, dealing with the politics of public policy formation in a number of program areas, discloses virtually no references to the politics of public programs. *See,* for example, Burns, J. M. and Peltason, J. W., GOVERN-MENT BY THE PEOPLE, Englewood Cliffs, New Jersey, Prentice-Hall Inc., 1962; Carr, R. K., *et al.,* AMERICAN DEMOCRACY IN THEORY AND PRACTICE, New York, Holt, Rinehart & Winston, Inc., 1961; Eliot, T. H., GOVERNING AMERICA, New York, Dodd, Mead & Co., 1964; Key, V. O., POLITICS, PARTIES AND PRESSURE GROUPS, New York, Thomas Y. Crowell Company, 1964; Lane, R. E., POLITICAL LIFE, Glencoe, Illinois, Free Press, 1959; Redford, E. S., *et al.,* POLITICS AND GOVERNMENT IN THE UNITED STATES, New York, Harcourt, Brace & World, Inc., 1965; Truman, D. B., THE GOVERNMENTAL PROCESS, New York, Alfred A. Knopf, Inc., 1951; Zeigler, H., INTEREST GROUPS IN AMERICAN SOCIETY, Englewood Cliffs, New Jersey, Prentice-Hall, Inc., 1964.

Even textbooks on state and local government, which often give extended treatments of state and local governmental programs, are notably thin on public health services. Moreover, even where they do address themselves to the subject, they usually confine themselves to short descriptions of existing health adminis-trative organizations and their activities, so that the politics of public health policy formation is no more apparent in these works than elsewhere. By way of illustration, *see* Adrian, C. R., STATE AND LOCAL GOVERNMENTS, New York, McGraw-Hill Book Company, 1960; ———, GOVERNING URBAN AMERICA, New York, McGraw-Hill Book Company, 1961; Anderson, W., *et al.,* GOVERN-MENT IN THE FIFTY STATES, New York, Holt, Rinehart & Winston, Inc., 1960; Babcock, R. S., STATE AND LOCAL GOVERNMENT AND POLITICS, New York, Random House, Inc., 1962; Banfield, E. C. and Wilson, J. Q., CITY POLITICS, Cambridge, Massachusetts, Harvard University Press, 1963; Blair, G. S., AMER-ICAN LOCAL GOVERNMENT, New York, Harper & Row, Publishers, 1964; Grant, D. R. and Nixon, H. C., STATE AND LOCAL GOVERNMENT IN AMERICA, Boston, Allyn & Bacon, Inc., 1963; Jacob, H. and Vines, K. N. (Editors), POLITICS IN THE AMERICAN STATES, Boston, Little, Brown and Company, 1965; Maddox, R. W. and Fuquay, R. F., STATE AND LOCAL GOVERNMENTS, Princeton, D. Van Nostrand Co., Inc., 1962; Snider, C. F., AMERICAN STATE AND LOCAL GOVERN-MENT, New York, Appleton-Century-Crofts, 1965.

For a notable exception to the general neglect of the political aspects of public health, *see* the fine study by Garceau, O., THE POLITICAL LIFE OF THE AMERICAN MEDICAL ASSOCIATION, Cambridge, Massachusetts, Harvard Univer-sity Press, 1941; Sayre, W. S. and Kaufman, H., GOVERNING NEW YORK CITY, New York, Russell Sage Foundation, 1960, pp. 272–273, 571–573; Mattison, B. F., Political Implications in Good Public Health Administration, *American Journal of Public Health,* 55, 183–199, February, 1965. Johnson, C. O., *et al.,* AMER-ICAN NATIONAL GOVERNMENT, New York, Thomas Y. Crowell Company, 1964; and Young, W. H., ESSENTIALS OF AMERICAN GOVERNMENT, New York, Apple-ton-Century-Crofts, 1964, each devote several pages to descriptions of the most obvious health agencies and programs. *See* also, notes 2 and 3 below.

2 Peltason, Jack W., Welfare, Health, and Housing, *in* Burns, J. M. and Peltason, J. W., FUNCTIONS AND POLICIES OF AMERICAN GOVERNMENT, Engle-wood Cliffs, New Jersey, Prentice-Hall, Inc., 1958. Peltason devotes a section to public health policy problems (pp. 354–68) and specifically discusses the creation of the Department of Health, Education and Welfare (pp. 366–68). Limited as this is, it is a strong indication of what systematic research might

contribute to understanding the politics of public health. *See* also, Crabtree, J. A., Plans For Tomorrow's Needs in Local Public Health Administration, *American Journal of Public Health*, 53, 1175–1182, August, 1963; and Wylie, C. M., Current Problems of Administrative Research in Public Health, *American Journal of Public Health*, 55, 698–702, May, 1965.

[3] The controversies over fluoridating water supplies, however, attracted considerable attention in the general press as well as in professional journals, and even generated several books. *See*, for example, Exner, F. B., *et al.*, THE AMERICAN FLUORIDATION EXPERIMENT, New York, The Devin-Adair Co., 1957; Israel, L. D., WATER FLUORIDATON: FACTS AND MYTHS, New York, Public Affairs Press, 1957; McNeil, O. R., THE FIGHT FOR FLUORIDATION, New York, Oxford University Press, Inc., 1957.

Apparently, the ability of a determined minority to block (temporarily, as it turned out) a measure enjoying almost unanimous expert support inspired widespread interest and curiosity in the event itself and in the nature of the political system that made it possible. The heuristic value of studies in the politics of public health, demonstrated in this instance, makes all the more disappointing the exiguousness of such studies in other areas of public health policy, especially since the fluoridation inquiries indicate many public health professionals were less adept politically than their adversaries.

[4] "Despite the various steps being taken," observed John B. Grant, an expert in the field of health service, "health care services in the United States, both public and private, continue to exhibit a greater lack of coordination than is found anywhere else in the world." *In* Seipp, C., HEALTH CARE FOR THE COMMUNITY: SELECTED PAPERS OF DR. JOHN B. GRANT, Baltimore, The Johns Hopkins Press, 1963, p. 174. "As of 1960, there were more than 1,500 local health units in the United States, as well as various state and federal health services." Suchman, E. A., SOCIOLOGY AND THE FIELD OF PUBLIC HEALTH, New York, Russell Sage Foundation, 1963, p. 36; see generally, pp. 34–42. "According to a study made by the United States Public Health Service in 1950, separate agencies of the state government alone participating in some form of health activity at that time totaled 60 in number." *Ibid.*, p. 102. "More than half of the departments and agencies of the Federal Government conduct medical or health activities, bringing their influence to bear by grants-in-aid and the offer of direct consultative services." *In* Leavell, H. R., and Clark, E. G., PREVENTIVE MEDICINE FOR THE DOCTOR IN HIS COMMUNITY, second edition, New York, McGraw-Hill Book Company, 1958, p. 310. Moutin, J. W. and Flook, E., GUIDE TO HEALTH ORGANIZATION IN THE UNITED STATES, United States Public Health Service Publication Number 196, 1953, list more than 50 federal agencies engaged in public health work.

[5] The international health programs in which the United States has been actively involved through its own agencies or through international organizations have not been included. *See* Suchman, *op. cit.*, pp. 37–38. Here, particularly, political factors are important.

[6] That the prevailing administrative patterns are the product of political factors is suggested by Leavell, H. R. and Clark, E. G., *loc. cit.*: "Whenever some group interested in some phase of health has become sufficiently influential, Congress has been persuaded to establish a program to deal with that particular problem." *See* also, Goodenough, E., Agency Structure as a Major Source of Human Problems in the Conduct of Public Health Programs, *American Journal of Public Health*, 55, 1067–1074, July, 1965, and Levine, S., Community Interorganizational Problems in Providing Medical Care and Social Services, *American Journal of Public Health*, 53, 1183–1195, August, 1963.

[7] *See* Wildavsky, A., THE POLITICS OF THE BUDGETARY PROCESS, Boston, Little, Brown and Company, 1964.

[8] But note Ames, F. B., The Manpower Predicament of the Health Department, *American Journal of Public Health*, 55, 1437–1443, September, 1965; and Wittman, M., Social Work Man-Power in the Health Services, *American Journal of Public Health*, 55, 393–399, March, 1965. *See* also, Stanley, D. T., PROFESSIONAL PERSONNEL FOR THE CITY OF NEW YORK, Washington, The Brookings Institution, 1963, especially pp. 34, 71–72, 126, 157.

[9] "Since World War II more than 100,000 national, regional, and local voluntary health and welfare agencies have come into being, with a total solicitation from the public of about one and a half billion dollars annually." Suchman, *op. cit.*, pp. 38–39.

[10] *See* notes 6 and 9 above.

[11] *See*, however, Terry, L. I., THE COMPLEX WORLD OF MODERN PUBLIC HEALTH, Washington, United States Public Health Service, 1963, p. 12. "City and state boundaries," according to this former Surgeon General, "are fictions. Problems of public health have become involved with economics, with politics, with public administration, with transportation, with every facet of modern life." *See* also, Schwartz, D. A., Integration of Hospital and Community Mental Health Services on a County and Regional Basis, *American Journal of Public Health*, 55, 873–878, June, 1965.

[12] The case studies produced by the Inter-University Case Program, and its predecessors, demonstrate the degree to which trained observers and analysts can succeed in unearthing, reporting and interpreting details of policy making that few actors in the decisions regarded as accessible. *See* Stein, H., CASES IN PUBLIC ADMINISTRATION AND POLICY DEVELOPMENT, New York, Harcourt, Brace & World, Inc., 1952; Inter-University Case Program, cases published by the Bobbs-Merrill Co., Inc.
For another example of a study that probes deep beneath the surface of a highly sensitive, much publicized, hotly contested political decision, *see* Wildavsky, A., DIXON-YATES, New Haven, Connecticut, Yale University Press, 1962.
This is not to imply that every policy decision will submit to this kind of treatment. The point is only that a great deal can be learned about public health policies if appropriately selected issues are examined from a political as well as a technical point of view.

[13] *See*, however, Rosen, G., Some Substantive Limiting Conditions in the Communication between Health Officers and Medical Practitioners, *in* Katz, A. H. and Felton, D. S., HEALTH AND THE COMMUNITY: READINGS IN THE PHILOSOPHY AND SCIENCE OF PUBLIC HEALTH, New York, Free Press of Glencoe, Inc., 1965, p. 597: "We need studies of the power relationships that exist in the community between the health officer, the organized medical profession, the political groups, and others that effect his actions. What constraints (financial, political, social, personal) lead the health officer to act as he does?" For an attempt to answer this question as regards forest officers, *see* Kaufman, H., THE FOREST RANGER: A STUDY IN ADMINISTRATIVE BEHAVIOR, Baltimore, The Johns Hopkins Press, 1960. *See* also note 11 above.

ACKNOWLEDGMENT

I wish to acknowledge with profound thanks the invaluable contribution of my research assistant, Bradford C. Snell.

295

DISCUSSION

The discussion following Kaufman's paper brought out widespread agreement on the significance of political processes to the understanding of health services. Discussants pointed out the unfortunate tendency to focus solely on public health issues such as fluoridation that have generated public controversy, while forgetting to study successful and "quiet" health activities which are fully as "political." Furthermore, community power studies were cited as showing how critical are informal processes of political decision-making in which many participate who are not ostensibly qualified by training, or empowered by election or appointment.

Comprehensive research has been handicapped by the dispersion of health activities and functions under a number of semantic hexes (including that of "public health") and a number of political and administrative jurisdictions. A program of research on the political implications of health services would be unrealistic if it did not take into account the relationships among public health services and the health professions, the economic forces of the local community, such quasi-political institutions as schools, and, of course, the public at large. For such research to take place, however, health officials must be willing to take investigators into their confidence, allow them to observe and raise questions about how things are done. Research will become even more pressing in the future when demand will seek higher levels of health, well-being and even beauty, well past the simple and traditional demand for curative services.

Other discussants emphasized the need for public health officials to be clear and definite about their own goals and, when they are important to the public health, to hold to them in spite of their political unpopularity. They would be helped in realizing their goals, however, if they could learn more of the principles of political science. To aid the official in seeing its value, political scientists should provide concrete examples of the way political theory can succeed in clarifying and systematizing what is usually taken to be an art by the practical public administrator.

SOME IMPLICATIONS OF ORGANIZATION THEORY FOR RESEARCH ON HEALTH SERVICES

W. RICHARD SCOTT

INTRODUCTION

Organization theory is not highly developed at this point, and a discussion of its implications for any specific type of organization may be premature. Enough progress has been made in recent years, however, to provide some indication of the more critical variables and problem areas and to suggest some of the data which might usefully be collected to improve the services of health organizations and contribute to the development of more adequate general theories. The lack of an overarching theory dictates a highly selective approach. Discussing a few promising areas of inquiry in some depth seems preferable to parading lists of variables or strings of hypotheses linked only by conjunctions. The paper will discuss in some detail four foci of research interest: organizational goals, tasks, control systems and status systems.

Just as the approach to the organization literature will be selective, so will the explicit attempts to apply these materials to the health field. The varieties and types of organizations implicated in some manner in the service of health are so diverse and numerous that only a few of them, particularly hospitals and clinics, can be discussed here. However, researchers and practitioners working in other types of medical settings should find at least some of the topics treated relevant to their own situations.

Before discussing specific topics the limits of the present paper should be disclosed. Attention here is focused exclusively on formal

297

organizations. *Organizations* are social units consisting of a network of relations which orients and regulates the behavior among a specific set of individuals in the pursuit of relatively specific goals. An organization is said to be *formal* to the extent that positions are identified and defined and relations with other positions specified irrespective of the characteristics of the individuals occupying the positions.[1] Formal organizations contain many idiosyncratic and "informal" elements, but so much stress has been put on the latter by other analysts that the present discussion will concentrate on the formal system. Although all organizations are subsystems of larger social units, such as communities and societies, this discussion will center on the internal structure of organizations rather than on their external relations.

ORGANIZATIONAL GOALS

Goals perform a variety of functions for an organization. They assist in the task of carving out a specified arena of activity and in mobilizing legitimacy and support from the environment; they frequently serve as a source of identification and motivation for participants. This paper, however, will focus on the way in which goals are established and on some of the problems met in assuring that the established goals are those which guide the behavior of participants.

Goal Setting

Debate continues over whether the term "organizational goal" is appropriate and accurate. Some insist that such a concept involves reification—that this concept should be forgotten. The behavior of participants could more accurately be termed goal-directed. However, the concept has meaning if carefully employed to refer to the desired ends toward which participants are expected to direct their behavior.

A much neglected question in organizational analysis is who sets the goals toward which participants are expected to direct their activities?[2] One answer to this question is the so-called *entrepreneurial* solution. The organization's goals are accepted as what the owners and/or the managers of the enterprise say they are. This view assumes that the managers actually succeed in managing and directing the performances of participants. While this state of affairs may prevail in some types of organizations, it describes few medical organizations, where administrators with such views are unlikely to retain their positions for extended periods. Another answer is that organizational goals

298

are those shared in common by all participants in the system—goals are assumed to be *consensually* defined.[3] If this view is taken, however, most medical organizations would appear to be in trouble, for little consensus exists among their members as to the primary organizational objectives. At least, this is what Wessen found when he asked 75 respondents in various positions within a general hospital to list the basic aims of the institution.[4]

Perhaps for the majority of medical organizations the most satisfactory answer to the question of who sets goals is that goals emerge from a continual *bargaining process* among shifting coalitions of the more powerful participants.[5] Coalitions are formed and reformed through the use of side-payments, one group backing another and, in turn, receiving support for its own demands. A group successful in getting its demands accepted as policy commitments contributes to goal setting just as does a group which succeeds in obtaining binding agreements as to the side-payments it will receive. Both involve the allocation of scarce resources which adds new goals and puts constraints upon the attainment of goals set by earlier agreements. Much theoretically significant and useful research on medical organizations could be conducted from this perspective. Careful descriptions are called for as well as attempts to specify the conditions under which various kinds of groups will coalesce and be more or less successful in promoting their demands.

Two recent papers analyzing medical situations are consistent with this bargaining perspective. Perrow's historical analysis of shifts in the goals of a general hospital as related to shifts in the relative power positions of trustees, physicians and administrators is a study of changes in the relative bargaining position of these three groups over a period of time.[6] Bucher and Strauss' depiction of the segmented medical specialties acting as "social movements" to defend and extend their position *vis-a-vis* other competing groups provides rich descriptive data of the sort necessary to carry forward this type of analysis.[7]

The fierceness with which coalitions bargain is clearly affected by the state of the organization as a whole. If times are good and the organization is fat with resources, the several groups can afford to be generous in the bargains they strike; competing and even conflicting goals may be simultaneously pursued. However, in those lean times when the organization is forced to struggle for its very survival, hard bargaining takes place with the result that the desires of weaker groups are sacrificed.[8]

Subgoal Formation

A vexing problem is faced by organizations insofar as they parcel general goals into subgoals and delegate these subgoals to particular individuals or departments. In such cases—and they are very frequent in most organizations—what is delegated as a goal or end to the department is for the organization only a means for attaining a more general objective.[9] For example, within a hospital, a goal for the radiology department—processing and interpreting x-rays—is only a means to attain a more general objective—arriving at a definitive diagnosis. Certain cognitive and motivational factors conduce participants to pursue their particular subgoals in ways which are not always consistent with the goal attainment efforts of related departments or of the organization as a whole. Thus, March and Simon note that a given participant assigned a subgoal will, because of the processes of selective perception and rationalization, focus exclusively on attaining this objective without regard to the possibly negative consequences for the larger system to which his actions are supposed to contribute. These individual tendencies are reinforced both by the content of ingroup communications and by the selective exposure of his department to stimuli from the larger organizational environment.[10] In addition to these cognitive processes, both Selznick and Dalton have emphasized the motivational factors supporting such actions, an individual being encouraged by self-interests, by identification with his work group or department,[11] or by his "commitment" to particular skills, arrangements or other vested interests generated in the course of action,[12] to pursue his own limited objectives even at the expense of interfering with the attainment of more general goals.

One characteristic of medical organizations encourages subgoal formation while another mitigates its negative consequences. The feature conducive to subgoal formation is the plethora of specialty groups brought together under a single organizational canopy. Such skilled occupational groups have a "trained incapacity"—to use Veblen's happily descriptive phrase—to see situations in which they are involved from any perspective other than their own. They tend to exaggerate the importance of their own endeavors and see their own skills and standards as applicable to virtually every circumstance encountered. In short, organizations staffed by specialty professional and technical workers are particularly vulnerable to the processes of subgoal formation. The organizational characteristic which helps to neutralize the negative consequences of subgoal formation is the type

300

of departmental specialization which tends to predominate in medical organizations: most departments exhibit "parallel" rather than "interdependent" specializations.[13] Parallel departments perform specialized but relatively independent functions; e.g., the departments of pediatrics and geriatrics. Interdependent departments perform specialized and interrelated functions; e.g., the departments of medicine and radiology or pathology. To the degree that departments are organized to function relatively autonomously of the rest of the organization, the negative effects of subgoal formation among departments (albeit not within departments) will be minimized. However, as medical technology becomes more complex and medical specialty groups more specialized, parallel departmental organization is giving way to a more interdependent structure. The more pronounced these changes, the more deleterious the consequences of subgoal formation for the achievement of general organizational goals.

Goal Specificity

Formal organizations are, fundamentally, instruments for attaining goals. How blunt or fine an instrument depends on many factors which are summarized by the concept "rationality" of structure. Rationality has in this context a specific and limited meaning, referring to the extent to which "a series of actions is organized in such a way that it leads to a previously defined goal."[14] Specific goals supply criteria by means of which the organization's structure may be rationally designed: they specify what tasks are to be performed, what kinds of personnel are to be hired, how resources are to be allocated among participants. Goals determine the basis for compensation of members—the degree to which each contributes to goal attainment—and stipulate the prerogatives of status and authority according to position. That virtually every organization theorist insists on the importance of specific goals as a defining criterion of organizations is not surprising.

Although organizations as a category define their goals more precisely than do other collectivities, organizations still vary greatly in the specificity of their objectives. The goals of a governmental bureau or a small private firm typically exhibit a relatively high degree of specificity, but the goals of most professional organizations, such as medical institutions or universities, are lamentably lacking in precision. Universities are supposedly geared to the production of educated men, but the definitions of precisely what constitutes an education vary widely both within and outside the academic community. Similarily, most medical institutions are concerned with promoting health and preventing illness, but who has yet satisfactorily defined these states? As Thompson and Bates point out, in universities and hospitals as compared with factories or commercial establishments, "the general goal of the organization specifies an area of activity instead of a specific activity and therefore is subject to wide differences in specific interpretations."[15] If the previous argument is correct, lack of specificity of objectives will reverberate throughout the structure as disagreements over choosing tasks to be performed, personnel to be hired, resources to be allocated, members to be compensated and status and authority to be distributed.

One solution to these problems, the "strong man" approach in which one individual or group decrees the organization's objectives, and forces conformity in accordance with this definition, is comparatively rare for medical organizations in this country. The extra-organizational power wielded by medical groups makes them impervious to the coercive pressures of administrators. Also, lack of agreement on goals and too few common interests hinder the medical staff as a body in arbitrarily specifying the objectives to pursue. The other solution for the problems created by lack of goal specificity is to decentralize the structure as much as possible, allowing considerable autonomy for individuals and groups to pursue self-defined objectives. In this approach the administrator's tasks are to represent the interests of the "organization as a whole" in those instances where such interests are involved and can be identified, serve as mediator when conflicts erupt between powerful departments, and plea the cause of weaker groups. In short, hospital administrators and medical managers have their work cut out for them, and committees, standing and *ad hoc*, will meet far into the night.

ORGANIZATIONAL TASKS

Goals are only conceptions of desired ends. If they are to have consequences for the behavior of organizational participants—and all professed goals do not have such consequences, as numerous investigators have noted—they must become operative: that is, they must be translated into specific tasks which are allocated to participants. A *task* is simply a set of activities performed to achieve some goal. The end product of performing a task is an *outcome*—the actual result

302

achieved by carrying out the activities. Of course, an outcome may or may not correspond closely with the original goal—the desired result.

Carrying out a set of task activities always entails overcoming some kind of "resistance." For example, the inertia of an object which is to be moved, the opposition of a competitor, or the complexity presented by a problem to be solved. For present purposes, the amount of resistance to be overcome is not so critical as its variability. Thus, two polar types of tasks may be distinguished. *Inert* tasks consist of those activities performed against resistance which is relatively constant across performances. *Active* tasks are those activities performed against resistance which is relatively variable across performances.[16] In the case of inert tasks, because resistance is constant, it is predictable; for active tasks, the amount of resistance to be encountered at any given time is less likely to be known.[17] These task characteristics have important implications both for designing efficient work arrangements and for evaluating and controlling task performances.

Nature of Task and Work Arrangements

Routine Task Activities. Inert tasks are more likely to call forth routine task activities. That is, when the resistance confronted is constant and known, the appropriate task activities to be performed may be specified in advance. In March and Simon's terms, "performance programs" can be devised.[18] Developing efficient work arrangements for inert tasks requires economy in centralizing decisions concerning appropriate task activities and assigning specific sequences of standard activities to individual, subordinate participants. Inert tasks lend themselves to subdivision and thereby permit the efficiencies associated with specialization: short training periods, replaceability of participants, increased skills through frequent repetition of activities, ease of control, etc. Costs are also associated with extreme specialization, including the fatigue associated with repetitive activities, lowered worker satisfaction and work group morale, and job insecurity. A large administrative staff is required to design the performance programs, recruit, train and supervise the work force, handle unusual problems, direct the flow of materials, and coordinate the contributions of the various participants. In short, bureaucratic[19] arrangements seem to be ideally suited for carrying out activities in the performance of inert tasks. Innumerable examples may be found of bureaucratic structures dealing with inert tasks. To name but a few, automobile production assembly lines, the Bureau of Internal Revenue, post offices, and housekeeping, cafeteria, and laboratory facilities in hospitals.

Of course, the bureaucratized arrangements just outlined may be used to process active tasks. In such cases organization participants must behave as if the resistance offered by the objects being processed were constant. This assumption can only be made at a cost. Because the standard prescribed activities may be inappropriate to meet the particular amount of resistance encountered at a given time, standard approaches to active tasks will entail a high proportion of errors or failures. Such a situation is exemplified, at least to a considerable degree, by the operation of public welfare agencies in this country. Here, over the protests of the professional social work community, a very diverse client group is "processed" in large measure by the performance of standardized sets of activities.[20]

Nonroutine Task Activities. The proportion of errors associated with performing active tasks can be reduced by allowing individual performers to assess the amount of resistance with which they are confronted at a given time and to adjust their activities accordingly. To the extent that individual workers are permitted to exercise discretion in handling tasks, the subdivision of such tasks is not feasible. A performer usually carries out the entire sequence of activities, making adjustments in later activities in accordance with the responses to his earlier efforts. The greater discretion permitted workers must usually be coupled with greater individual competence—requiring longer training periods—if the discretion granted them is to be effectively employed in guiding the selection and sequencing of task activities. A smaller administrative overhead usually results since less planning, supervision and coordination are required. But, generally speaking, processing task activities by large numbers of skilled practitioners is a more costly organizational arrangement than the one previously described.

Obviously, the arrangement just outlined, in which individual performers are delegated discretion over their own task performances, has many of the earmarks of a professional system. The most important missing element is one which is likely to develop in these circumstances; namely, the formation of coalitions among practitioners to establish and maintain performance standards and to prevent undue interference from "outsiders"—those not possessing similar skills.[21] As noted, professional arrangements are more expensive than bureaucratic ones. They do, however, facilitate the effective handling of active tasks. Hence, in situations where persons are concerned about the quality of outcomes—where they are unwilling to allow a high proportion of errors—these increased costs are accepted and borne. Such is the case for physicians' tasks in clinics and hospitals, for scientific tasks in research enterprises, and for scientific and, to a lesser degree, teaching tasks in most colleges and universities.

To summarize, tasks aimed at surmounting constant resistance can be effectively organized by means of bureaucratic arrangements. Tasks aimed at overcoming variable resistance are usually better organized in a "professional" manner since skilled, nonroutine responses are better calculated to meet unpredictable resistance with a minimum of errors. The nature of the resistance to be overcome in task performance is certainly not the only factor to be taken into account in developing appropriate organizational arrangements. It does, however, appear to be a factor of considerable consequence.[22]

Task Conceptions. Whether a given task is active or inert can usually be determined by empirical investigation. However, occupational groups tend to develop collective conceptions of the nature of the tasks they perform. For example, all tasks performed by professional persons, such as physicians, are not active in nature, but professionals often define them as such, demanding the right to exercise discretion, free from bureaucratic controls, with respect to all of their tasks. In short, task conceptions may in some circumstances reflect ideological claims rather than empirical realities as occupational groups seek justification to support preferred work arrangements.

Conceptions of tasks can have rather far-reaching implications for occupational groups. Nursing groups, for example, have never reached agreement as to the basic nature of their primary tasks. Some, such as the British advocates of the "Nightingale approach," see nurses performing largely routine tasks under the direction of physicians and the matron. Strict discipline and conformity are emphasized and apprenticeship to ward nurses is perferred as the principle training method over theoretical or didactic instruction. Others, such as the United States advocates of the "professional approach," believe that nurses should exercise discretion in meeting the nursing needs of individual patients and emphasize the importance of theoretical training.[28] Advocates of the professional approach in this country have been fairly successful in inculcating students with their views, but have been less successful in transforming hospital arrangements within which nurses must work, with the result that large numbers of professionally trained nurses refuse to work in a hospital setting.[24]

To conclude, the nature and the conceptions of the tasks to be performed are important determinants of organizational structures. The distinction which has been proposed between active and inert tasks is admittedly crude and will require much refinement. However, researchers must concern themselves with the actual work that is done by participants in organizations if they are to understand the structural arrangements which allocate and control this work. This distinction may be of some use in obtaining a preliminary focus on these matters.

Task Evaluations

Organizations attempt to structure the behavior of their participants in the pursuit of more or less specific goals. Evaluations of task performance play an important role in this structuring process. In the most rational case, task performances of participants are evaluated to determine the extent to which they contribute to goal attainment. Organizational sanctions—rewards and penalties—are distributed among participants on the basis of these evaluations. In relatively few organizations are performance evaluations allowed to completely determine the distribution of sanctions. On the other hand, relatively few organizations do not make at least some attempt to evaluate task contributions and to distribute sanctions, at least in part, in accordance with these evaluations. In any case, evaluation of task performance is clearly essential to the control of task performance, and an organization concerned with goal attainment requires, therefore, some system for evaluating the relative contributions of its participants.

The ease or difficulty, the accuracy or inaccuracy, the fairness or unfairness of evaluations made of task performances will depend on many factors, all of which are important topics of investigation. As already noted, ambiguities may appear in the definition of objectives— lack of goal specificity. Such a condition will clearly create problems for evaluating performance since, when goals are diffuse, the criteria of evaluation are likely to be either unclear or conflicting. In situations where goals are not clearly specified, those components of the task which are most easily measured are evaluated and those less readily assessed are ignored. Some participants, noting which aspects of their performances are and which are not evaluated, concentrate their energies on the subset of task components which will affect their evaluations and neglect other aspects. This tendency, which may be referred to as the "when I'm not near the goal I love, I love the goal I'm near" principle, results in a transformation of goals. Evaluated task components specify the new operative goals while the remaining task components are not pursued although they may continue to be professed. Such transformations are particularly prevalent among semi- or subprofessional employees because of their lesser commitment to the professed objectives.

Another factor having an important bearing on the evaluation of performance is the extent to which task performances are visible or observable.[25] Very often in medical contexts, visibility is impaired both by professional norms and fragmentation of contacts. Thus, the norms of physicians typically allow administrators little access to their medical performances, and, although colleague evaluations are supposed to substitute for such administrative control, contacts among physicians—even those working together in medical clinics—are often so limited or fragmented that no over-all impression of the quality of medical performances is gained.[26] Such norms among physicians are intended to protect the rights of each practitioner to make decisions for his own patients and to insure that non-medical criteria are not allowed to intrude into the decision-making process.

The distinction introduced earlier between inert and active tasks is also relevant to task evaluation. Evaluations of performance may be based either on an assessment of the characteristics of the task performance itself (the activities) or on an assessment of the characteristics of the task outcome resulting from the completed performance. For inert tasks, the nature of the outcome is a regular function of the quality of task performances. Because the resistance offered by the task object is constant across performances, the performances may be evaluated (compared) by evaluating (comparing) outcomes. On the other hand, the variability of the resistance in active tasks increases the difficulty of judging quality of performance of the task activities from the nature of the outcome achieved. Thus, the outcome of a good performance may not be success, but will sometimes be failure. To correctly infer the quality of performances, using outcomes from active tasks, the evaluator must either 1. know the amount of resistance met during a specific task performance, or 2. take a probability approach based on assumptions of the distribution of resistance over a succession of performances. Thus, the proportion of successful outcomes can be compared to a standard derived from other performances carried out under similar circumstances. For example, the death rate for all deliveries over a specified period provides a valid measure of obstetrical performance, assuming a random distribution of difficult cases among the physicians being evaluated.[27]

Active tasks are more effectively handled by professional workers, as noted above in the discussion of work arrangements. Given the problems of evaluation associated with the performance of active tasks, one of the primary functions a profession can perform for its individual practitioners is to protect them from inappropriate evaluations. The client, having a high personal investment in the success or failure of his case, tends to use this one outcome as a primary basis for evaluating his particular practitioner. Most administrators are accustomed to situations in which they direct the performance of subordinates and evaluate them on conformity to their assigned performance program. Professionals as a group attempt to wrest evaluation prerogatives from both clients and administrators and substitute mechanisms and procedures for in-group control over performance.

Physicians in hospitals and clinics, for example, attempt to restrict the right of evaluation to members of their own profession. In general, two kinds of evaluation are permitted within the professional group: 1. outcome evaluations, based on some probability model of the appropriate number of successes expected for a given type of patient load; and 2. indirect performance evaluations, based not on a direct inspection of an ongoing task performance—professionals resist such attempts because they are viewed as interfering with the free choice of task activities—but on attempts to "reconstruct" the performance after the fact. Friedson and Rhea have described how medical records are used for this purpose:[28]

> The medical record for each patient is, in its wealth of detailed information, a bureaucratic delight. But although the information is continuously recorded (in part because of the legal liabilities of the work) it is not scrutinized by anyone on a routine basis. The medical chart is a working tool rather than a supervisory device, becoming a supervisory device only when interest in the case has been triggered off by some event suggesting the necessity of investigation—a patient complaint, a law suit, an accidental observation, and the like. It is thus only latently supervisory, used after the fact to *reconstruct past performance* in damning or exonerating detail.

Generally speaking, the test applied by professional evaluators in the reconstruction of a task performance is: would a "good" medical practitioner faced with the same circumstances have come to similar decisions and have implemented them as skillfully as did the evaluatee? That is, relative rather than absolute criteria are used in the assessment of past performances.

These few comments on task evaluations and some of the types of problems with which they are beset, are not set forth as conclusions but as tentative hypotheses worthy of investigation. Evaluation is one of the central organizational processes and many of the disputes and conflicts which arise among participants can be traced to faulty evaluation techniques. This paper has attempted to indicate a close relationship between the type of work done, organizational arrangements for work allocation, and the sorts of evaluation procedures which will be acceptable to participants.

ORGANIZATIONAL CONTROL

Task evaluation, as discussed in the preceding section, is closely related to and is an important part of an organization's control system. But it is only a part of that system, not the whole of it. Control attempts are often, but not always prefaced by evaluations of past performances. Thus, the following discussion will draw on the preceding, but will not be limited by it.

The primary tasks carried on within medical organizations such as hospitals or clinics are diagnostic and therapeutic activities performed on specific patients. These activities are conducted or directed for the most part by individual professional practitioners, the most important group of whom are physicians. Physicians organize themselves into a medical staff to conduct and control these activities and to protect individual practitioners from "inappropriate" control attempts by nonpractitioners. Generally speaking, physicians have succeded in achieving a considerable measure of autonomy for their activities. The hospital or clinic is an autonomous professional organization for physicians.[29] This characterization, although generally accurate, is so oversimplified that it is misleading. The complicated relations which are summarized and distorted by such generalizations must now be discussed.

Professional Peer Group Controls

To begin, the amount of control exercised by groups of physicians over their own members is not clear. As a result of their study of a medical clinic, where opportunities for control should be optimal, Friedson and Rhea question whether physicians 1. have sufficient opportunity to evaluate their colleagues (this is the question of visibility of role performance discussed earlier); 2. possess the necessary competence, because of the high degree of specialization marking such groups, to confidently make such evaluations; or 3. have a sufficiently varied arsenal of effective sanctions at their disposal to back up their evaluations.[30] Such questions are too important to be settled by one empirical study of one medical clinic, and further studies along this line are called for. Nevertheless, this study does raise serious doubts as to the adequacy of the vaunted "professional peer group control system."

Probably, however, undue emphasis has been placed on the importance of peer group controls for professional workers. (Sociologists like to focus on characteristics which distinguish among groups rather than on those that groups hold in common.) In professional occupations, like most others, the seniority principle operates in such a way that one may speak of "differential peer control."[31] Etzioni points to three major ranks of professionals: professionals in training, pre-tenure professionals and professionals with tenure. In the case of professionals in training, such as interns and residents in hospitals, "it is obvious that their income, promotion, prestige, privileges, and facilities are controlled to a considerable degree by higher ranking professionals." "Pre-tenure staff have only limited control over each other, and very little control over superiors," while tenured professionals "control access to the administration and the allocation of major rewards and facilities in the organization. Mutual control among the highest-ranking members of the tenure staff is the only place in professional organizations where control approximates pure peer control."[32] These distinctions and assertions have the "ring of truth" although they appear to be based on a general knowledge of such structures rather than on specific empirical research. Such studies would seem to be in order and of high priority.

Professional and Administrative Controls

Even more important than such differential peer group controls in supplementing the pure colleague controls exercised by physicians, are the administrative control structures. Considering first just those medical administrative positions filled by physicians, such as the heads of the various medical departments, Etzioni suggests that "a large amount of control over professional performances has been transferred from the professional community to the professional organization."[33] In her description of control patterns among a group of hospital clinic physicians, Goss reported that physicians in the position of assistant clinic director exercised "authority"—issued directives to which compliance was expected—with respect to such administrative matters as the scheduling of patients, but only proffered "advice" in the area of patient care. Nevertheless, what is important to note in this situation is the extent to which surveillance duties had been concentrated in a few positions rather than distributed throughout the colleague group, so that physicians holding these positions were granted the "right" to routinely review all case records and to make suggestions to individual practitioners. In addition, as Goss notes, these rank-and-file physicians "considered it their duty to take supervisory suggestions about patient care into account, and in this sense they accepted supervision."[34] Of course, at this point the good organizational sociologist notes the time-honored distinction between control based on incumbency in a position (bureaucratic) and control based on technical competence (professional). While this is a theoretically important distinction, it is difficult to apply, particularly in professional organizations that often exhibit a very high correlation between technical competence and position in the hierarchy. Also, current styles of supervision are such that differentiating between a directive and a suggestion is often very difficult when both the "professional" suggestions and "administrative" directives emanate from the professional incumbent of an organizational position.

Turning now to the larger, overarching administrative structures in medical organizations, the fact has often been emphasized that physicians in most United States hospitals are not, strictly speaking, a part of the organization. While this official fiction can be overemphasized, it does point to the important problem that physicians can be and apparently often are very cavalier in their attitudes toward the organizational needs of their hosts.[35] Spending relatively little time within the structure and focusing almost exclusively on the particular needs of their own patients, physicians often create havoc for those personnel whose positions and responsibilities orient them to the needs of patient groups as a whole and to the maintenance of stable control relations. Thus, Bates and White found in their survey of 13 voluntary hospitals that while the authority exercised by administrators and nurses was perceived in generally favorable terms by participants, perceptions of the physicians' use of authority tended to be generally unfavorable.[36] This conflict is but an instance of the ever-recurring administrative dilemma between "rules," on the one hand, and "exceptions to the rules" on the other. What makes the hospital somewhat unique is the extent to which powerful groups are polarized around these foci. Administrators and other permanent groups defend the necessity for rules which will keep the larger structure intact, and physicians argue for the exceptions to meet the particular medical needs of the individual patients for whom they bear the brunt of responsibility. In these struggles, as Hall noted, the physician gains a tactical advantage over administrators and other personnel by his power to define virtually any problem as a medical emergency—as a unique (active) and critical situation calling for nonroutine, immediate measures.[37]

A structure in which the subordinate members are routinely subject to conflicting directives from powerful groups is not exactly an administrator's dream organization. Most commentators emphasize the detrimental consequences of such "multiple subordination" for the morale and performance of lower-level participants, although Hamilton has suggested the interesting (and unresearched) possibility that "the split in authority works to the benefit of the patients since it sets up a series of checks and balances."[38] In a general sense, Hamilton is no doubt correct; good total medical care is dependent on a structure which will provide enough stability that the routine aspects of care can be efficiently carried out, coupled with enough flexibility that special procedures can be readily instituted for handling nonroutine patient needs. Coordination is absolutely essential to achieve the first of these objectives. In their recent study of ten hospitals, Georgopoulos and Mann found that the more highly developed the apparatus of coordination, the higher the overall quality of patient care.[39] However, "nursing care" and "overall care" are primarily improved by greater coordination, not "medical care" in the more narrow sense as dispensed by physicians.

As coordination problems—both among physician specialty groups (a recent study reports higher levels of tension within hospitals between doctors and other doctors than between doctors and other major groups[40]) as well as between physicians and other professional and semiprofessional groups—become increasingly salient for the smooth operation of hospitals, administrators are gradually getting the upper hand over physicians in running the hospitals. Problems of coordina-

312

tion involving the conflicting interests of the many participating groups place the administrator in the powerful role of final arbiter.[41] If one is concerned with the quality of patient care, he cannot view with unmixed feelings the ascendancy of the administrators. No doubt, routine patient care needs, as well as those which depend on the coordination of numerous specialty groups, will be better served under a strong administrator. On the other hand, high quality patient care is also dependent upon physicians retaining sufficient power to prevent the routine processing of all patients, to allow for exceptional needs and situations. The optimal distribution of power between physicians and administrators is apparently one in which neither has full control over the other. A system of effective "checks and balances" is essential to the provision of high quality medical care. Precisely what mechanisms and structural arrangements will procure and maintain this delicate balance is a matter to be determined by practical experimentation and careful research.

Interprofessional Controls

The effective functioning of a complex medical organization is dependent on the cooperation of many types of specialists, working both as groups and as individuals. Far too little research attention has thus far been devoted to such collaborative activities among professional groups in medical institutions. Studies of scientific groups in industrial settings[42] can serve as the bases to identify two types of arrangements for organizing such groups. 1. "Specialist groups" (or "functional groups") are more-or-less permanent work groups organized along professional specialty or academic discipline lines, working alongside one another on similar individual problems or together on joint problems. Examples of such groups in medical settings are most department and specialty clinic groups. 2. "Task groups" (or "project groups" or "teams") are multidisciplinary groups mobilized to solve a particular problem. They are often disbanded when a solution is reached. In medical organizations task groups may be temporary (e.g., research collaboration among teams of specialists or medical groups temporarily mobilized around the care of a given patient) or they may operate on a more permanent basis (e.g., operating room teams, nursing teams, mental health teams, etc.). Kornhauser suggests that specialist groups tend to foster a narrowing of interests which interferes with the ability of the members of a given group to cooperate effectively with other specialist groups. On the other hand, although task groups are likely to be the more effective in problem-solving activities,[43] they are likely to be more unstable:[44]

> Since status is more secure and power relationships more stable in specialist groups, there is a tendency for task groups to become transformed into specialist groups and for new groups to be formed as specialist groups.

The one good study of professional relations within a health task group—mental health teams composed of psychiatrists, psychologists and social workers—demonstrated the instabilities generated by status and power problems.[45] Some evidence in this study indicates that relations between social workers and psychiatrists caused less strain than those between psychologists and psychiatrists. This was in part because the agreement between social workers and psychiatrists "upon the unique skills that they and the other profession can provide . . ." was greater than between psychologists and psychiatrists.[46] This in turn suggests the more general proposition that effective collaboration among members of specialty groups is more apt to occur when the groups involved are characterized by a relatively high degree of role differentiation. A related notion is that strong pressures are generated by task group organization toward the development of differentiated roles. In particular, subordinate members will be constrained to carve out a special niche for themselves in which they can operate relatively independently from control by other groups and which allows them some claim to superior status. Such a proposition could help to account for the emergence of the professionalization movement among nurses,[47] and also helps to account for the emergence of new medical specialities such as anesthesiology.[48]

ORGANIZATIONAL STATUS SYSTEMS

Organizations, in addition to being task and control systems, are status systems. Differential prestige is distributed among (or becomes attached to) the various organizational positions. Prestige is an important psychic reward and, insofar as the organization can control its allocation, status is one of the most important kinds of sanctions an organization has at its disposal. In the most rational case, status is distributed among participants in such a manner that it both reflects differences in past contributions to goal attainment (status as reward) and assists in future contributions (status as facility). The symbols of status also serve as important insignia, allowing persons to identify

314

others in terms of membership in one or another status class and to adjust their behavior accordingly.[49]

Generally speaking, organizations not only face the problem of how to allocate status prerogatives among individual participants (or positions) but also how to combat or accommodate status distinctions arising outside the organization, and which tend to accompany members as they enter the system.

Internal Stratification

All observers readily agree that medical organizations are relatively highly stratified systems. Participants in the systems are arranged into rigid status hierarchies, often identified by distinctive apparel. Medical sociologists have greatly emphasized the "blocked mobility" aspect of these structures. This means that personnel cannot be promoted from one level to another without acquiring further training of a sort not available on the job.[50] But this characteristic does not appear to differentiate medical organizations from others where great emphasis is placed on technical skills. As might be expected, participation and interaction reflect status groupings. Thus, in his case study of a voluntary hospital, Wessen found that the preponderance of interaction on the wards took place within status classes—doctors talking primarily to other doctors, nurses to other nurses, etc.[51] Caudill systematically tallied interaction in 63 administrative conferences involving staff members of a ward in a private psychiatric hospital and discovered that participation in such conferences was strongly and positively associated with status on the clinical team.[52] Such interaction regularities undoubtedly have important implications for other aspects of the organization's operation. For example, Wessen asserts, but does not empirically demonstrate, that the self-containment and rigidity of status classes within the hospital contribute to the marked differences in ideology he found among personnel as to the nature of the hospital and its basic aims.[53] Caudill shows that topics introduced by nurses and other lower status personnel at the ward conferences were more likely to end inconclusively with consequent frustration for the initiator than topics introduced by higher status personnel.[54] Given the dependence of higher status personnel, such as physicians, on lower status personnel, such as members of the nursing and house staff, for information relating to changes in the patient's condition, an even more critical problem associated with status hierarchies is the effect they have, not only on amount, but also on content of communications from subordinates to superiors. For example, in a study done in three industrial organizations, Read reported the tendency among lower status personnel to screen information passed up the hierarchy, particularly "when the information content is of a type which might reflect negatively upon the competence and thus, indirectly, upon the security or progress of members of the subordinate level."[55] Of course, superiors need to be kept apprised of precisely such mistakes and problems in the interests of effectiveness. Evidence indicates that hospitals and other medical organizations are not immune from such status-defensive processes.

One of the more interesting attempts to assess the effects of the internal stratification system on the behavior of medical personnel is the study by Seeman and Evans of hospital ward stratification and intern performance.[56] The results of this study are not so clear-cut as to be easily summarized (perhaps in part because the independent variable, degree of ward stratification, was not very successfully measured[57]), but some of the findings were that: 1. degree of ward stratification was related to type of task performed (surgical wards were more likely to exhibit high stratification than medical wards); 2. communication to and about patients was believed to be more clear and the teaching function was said by interns to be better performed on wards marked by low stratification than by those characterized by high; and 3. on medical wards, those with low stratification produced more than their share of the total number of medication errors. (Note the apparent relevance of these findings to the earlier discussion of inert and active tasks and the appropriate forms of organization for each.) Clearly, the Seeman and Evans study does no more than hint at the interesting possibilities for research on the determinants and consequences of status structures within medical organizations.

External Status Characteristics

For the purposes of many kinds of analysis, organizations must be treated not as self-contained isolated systems but as subsystems of larger community or societal systems, and this is the case with the analysis of status. Obviously, a person does not change his status characteristics when he enters an organization: status is among the most portable of all human baggage. An individual who is a Negro in his community will remain a Negro in his place of employment; a woman will continue to be a woman. Most of the research on such external status characteristics indicates that organizational status systems generally attempt to accommodate to the larger stratification systems: organizational status is allocated in such a way as to be consistent with community status.[58] For example, if Negroes occupy a low status in the community, they will tend to be assigned to low status positions in the organization.[59] In extreme cases, the allocation of status among participants of an organization is virtually determined by their position in some external system. Udy's data from a sample of production organizations in nonindustrial societies demonstrates[60] that the greater the degree of involvement of the organization's status structure with that of some external group unrelated to the purposes of the organization, the less rational the internal structure of the organization.

On the other hand, the more emphasis placed on goal-attainment, and the clearer the specification of goals, the more organizations will attempt to insulate themselves from their larger social environments and suppress or define as irrelevant external status characteristics. The tactics by which organizations "de-stratify" their recruits are many and varied, ranging from the use of uniforms to implanting universal norms.[61]

No organization can function completely autonomously of the communal and societal systems of which it is a part, but if it is to effectively pursue the goals for which it was established, it must be permitted to recruit, allocate and reward personnel on the basis of their ability to carry out the work that is to be done. No organization utilizes this criterion exclusively—and because they do not, organizations make important contributions to the stability of the stratification systems of the larger social order. But their success in doing so determines to a large degree their effectiveness as instruments to attain specific goals.[62]

CONCLUSION

A conclusion to a long paper should be brief. The selectivity of the coverage of the organizational literature should again be emphasized. Other equally, but hopefully not more, relevant topics could have been discussed. The materials which have been presented will not be equally applicable to all health organizations. Every organization is, in some respects, like all other organizations, like some other organizations, and like no other organization. Hence, any attempt to apply general propositions to particular organizations must be carefully wedded with detailed knowledge of that structure.

Hopefully, this paper has demonstrated that, although organization theory can provide no final answers to the problems that beset health organizations, it is beginning to frame, with a degree of clarity, some of the important questions to be asked and to provide some clues as to where the answers might be sought.

REFERENCES

[1] Important advantages, as well as some disadvantages, are associated with formalization from the standpoint of rationality of operation. *See* Scott, W. Richard, Theory of Organizations, *in* Faris, Robert E. (Editor), HANDBOOK OF MODERN SOCIOLOGY, Chicago, Rand McNally & Co., 1964, pp. 491–492.

[2] This question goes begging in part because one of the major approaches to organizations—the "rational instrument" view championed by Weber and his intellectual disciples—takes the goals as given.

[3] This solution is proposed by Barnard, who did, however, differentiate between the organizational purpose—agreements among participants as to the aims of the organization—and the personal motives of participants which lead them to contribute their efforts. *See* Barnard, Chester I., THE FUNCTIONS OF THE EXECUTIVE, Cambridge, Massachusetts, Harvard University Press, 1938, pp. 86–89.

[4] Wessen, Albert F., Hospital Ideology and Communication between Ward Personnel, *in* Jaco, E. Gartley (Editor), PATIENTS, PHYSICIANS AND ILLNESS, Glencoe, Illinois, Free Press, 1958, p. 459.

[5] Cyert, Richard M. and March, James G., A BEHAVIORAL THEORY OF THE FIRM, Englewood Cliffs, New Jersey, Prentice-Hall, Inc., 1963, pp. 26–32.

[6] Perrow, Charles, The Analysis of Goals in Complex Organizations, *American Sociological Review*, 26, 854–866, December, 1961.

[7] Bucher, Rue and Strauss, Anselm, Professions in Process, *American Journal of Sociology*, 66, 325–334, January, 1961.

[8] Cyert and March, *op. cit.*, pp. 36–38.

[9] Simon, Herbert A., ADMINISTRATIVE BEHAVIOR, (Second edition), New York, The Macmillan Company, 1957.

[10] March, James G. and Simon, Herbert A., ORGANIZATIONS, New York, John Wiley & Sons, Inc., 1958, pp. 151–154.

[11] Dalton, Melville, MEN WHO MANAGE, New York, John Wiley & Sons, Inc., 1959.

[12] Selznick, Philip, TVA AND THE GRASS ROOTS, Berkeley, University of California Press, 1949, pp. 253–259.

[13] Blau, Peter M. and Scott, W. Richard, FORMAL ORGANIZATIONS, San Francisco, Chandler Publishing Co., 1962, pp. 183–184.

[14] Mannheim, Karl, MAN AND SOCIETY IN AN AGE OF RECONSTRUCTION, New York, Harcourt, Brace & World, Inc., 1950, p. 53.

[15] Thompson, James D. and Bates, Frederick L., Technology, Organization, and Administration, *Administrative Science Quarterly*, 2, 329, December, 1957.

[16] Dornbusch, Sanford M., *et al.*, "Evaluation Processes and Authority Structures," paper presented at the annual meeting of the American Sociological Association, Chicago, September, 1965.

[17] It is possible to distinguish between active tasks in terms of whether or not the resistance encountered is patterned. If the resistance exhibits regularity, its strength is more likely to be predictable, and to the extent that it is, patterned active tasks may be organized in a manner comparable to inert tasks.

[18] March and Simon, *op. cit.*, pp. 141–150.

[19] A bureaucratic organization is characterized by the existence of particular structural features, the most critical of which is a specialized administrative staff. Also involved, in varying degrees, are elaborate procedural rules, an advanced division of labor, impersonal relations between hierarchical levels and an emphasis on technical criteria of recruitment and advancement. *See* Weber, Max, THE THEORY OF SOCIAL AND ECONOMIC ORGANIZATION, Glencoe, Illinois, Free Press, 1947, pp. 328–341. Since these several features do not necessarily exhibit concomitant variation, measures of the degree of bureaucratization exhibited by a given organization will vary depending on choice of indicator.

[20] *See* Scott, W. Richard, Professional Employees in a Bureaucratic Structure: A Case Study of a Public Welfare Agency, to appear in a forthcoming volume on the "semi-professions" edited by Amitai Etzioni.

[21] For a discussion of professional groups placing heavy emphasis on the organization of practitioners for self-regulation, *see* Goode, William J., Community within a Community: The Professions, *American Sociological Review*, 22, 194–200, April, 1957.

[22] For a related discussion of routine-nonroutine task activities and associated organizational arrangements, *see* Litwak, Eugene, Models of Bureaucracy which Permit Conflict, *American Journal of Sociology*, 67, 177–184, September, 1961.

[23] Glaser, William A., Nursing Leadership and Policy: Some Cross-national Comparisons, *in* Davis, Fred (Editor), THE NURSING PROFESSION: FIVE SOCIOLOGICAL ESSAYS, New York, John Wiley & Sons, Inc., 1966, pp. 4–30.

[24] Davis, Fred, Olesen, Virginia L. and Whittaker, Elvi W., Problems and Issues in Collegiate Nursing Education," *in* Davis, *op. cit.*, pp. 162–167.

[25] *See* Merton, Robert K., SOCIAL THEORY AND SOCIAL STRUCTURE, (Revised edition), Glencoe, Illinois, Free Press, 1957, pp. 319–322, 336–357, 374–377; and Coser, Rose L., Insulation from Observability and Types of Social Conformity, *American Sociological Review*, 26, 28–39, February, 1961.

[26] *See* Freidson, Eliot and Rhea, Buford, Processes of Control in a Company of Equals, *Social Problems*, 11, 119–131, Fall, 1963; and ———, Knowledge and Judgment in Professional Evaluations, *Administrative Science Quarterly*, 10, 107–124, June, 1965.

[27] Dornbusch, *et al., loc. cit.*

[28] Freidson and Rhea, *Social Problems, op. cit.*, p. 123. (Emphasis ours.)

[29] Scott, W. Richard, Reactions to Supervision in a Heteronomous Professional Organization, *Administrative Science Quarterly*, 10, 65–68, June, 1965.

[30] Freidson and Rhea, *Social Problems, op. cit.*

[31] Etzioni, Amitai, A COMPARATIVE ANALYSIS OF COMPLEX ORGANIZATIONS, New York, Free Press of Glencoe, 1961, p. 256.

[32] *Ibid.*, p. 257.

[33] *Ibid.*, p. 259.

[34] Goss, Mary E., Influence and Authority among Physicians in an Outpatient Clinic, *American Sociological Review*, 26, 44, February, 1961.

[35] Wilson, Robert N., The Physician's Changing Hospital Role, *Human Organization*, 18, 177–183, Winter, 1959–1960.

[36] Bates, Frederick L. and White, Rodney F., Differential Perceptions of Authority in Hospitals, *Journal of Health and Human Behavior*, 2, 262–267, Winter, 1961.

[37] Hall, Oswald, Some Problems in the Provision of Medical Services, *Canadian Journal of Economics and Political Science*, 20, 456–466, November, 1954.

[38] Hamilton, Edith Lentz, Hospital Administration—One of a Species, *Administrative Science Quarterly*, 1, 460, March, 1957.

[39] Georgopoulos, Basil S. and Mann, Floyd C., THE COMMUNITY GENERAL HOSPITAL, New York, The Macmillan Company, 1962, pp. 389–391.

[40] *Ibid.*, p. 315.

[41] *See ibid.*, pp. 566–575, and Perrow, *op. cit.*

[42] Kornhauser, William, SCIENTISTS IN INDUSTRY, Berkeley, University of California Press, 1962, pp. 50–56.

[43] *See* Shepard, Herbert A., Nine Dilemmas in Industrial Research, *Administrative Science Quarterly*, 1, 302, December, 1956.

[44] Kornhauser, *op. cit.*, p. 52.

[45] Zander, Alvin, Cohen, Arthur R. and Stotland, Ezra, Power and the Relations among the Professions, *in* Cartwright, Dorwin (Editor), STUDIES IN SOCIAL POWER, Ann Arbor, University of Michigan Press, 1959, pp. 15–34.

[46] *Ibid.*, p. 29.

[47] Glaser points out that early professional leaders "recommended that nurses specialize in distinctively nursing work and resist excessive delegations at the discretion of the doctors." Glaser, *op. cit.*, p. 13.

[48] *See* Lortie, Dan, Anesthesia: From Nurse's Work to Medical Specialty, *in* Jaco, *op. cit.*, pp. 405–412.

[49] The best general discussion of status systems in organizations is still Barnard's classic paper. *See* Barnard, Chester I., Functions and Pathologies of Status Systems in Formal Organizations, *in* Whyte, William F. (Editor), INDUSTRY AND SOCIETY, New York, McGraw-Hill Book Company, 1946, pp. 46–83.

[50] Smith, Harvey, Two Lines of Authority: The Hospital's Dilemma, *Modern Hospital*, 84, 59–64, March, 1955.

[51] Wessen, *op. cit.*, pp. 448–468.

[52] Caudill, William, THE PSYCHIATRIC HOSPITAL AS A SMALL SOCIETY, Cambridge, Massachusetts, Harvard University Press, 1958, pp. 231–265.

320

[53] Wessen, *op. cit.*, p. 459.

[54] Caudill, *op. cit.*, pp. 294–296.

[55] Read, William H., Upward Communication in Industrial Hierarchies, *Human Relations,* 15, 3, February, 1962.

[56] Seeman, Melvin and Evans, John W., Stratification and Hospital Care: I. The Performance of the Medical Interne; II. The Objective Criteria of Performance, *American Sociological Review,* 26, 67–80, February, and 193–204, April, 1961.

[57] Their measure of stratification is based on the judgment by nurses of the physician in charge of the ward with respect to power differences, social distance and prestige distinctions. Such a measure is questionable because 1. it is based on the reports of nurses rather than interns, 2. it is a measure of the behavior of a single physician rather than a measure of the status structure of the ward as a whole; and 3. it appears to be as much a measure of "leadership style" as of status behavior.

[58] This involves an over-simplification since organizational status systems also help to determine community status: they are, in short, mutually dependent.

[59] For a summary of this literature and an attempt to construct a general theory of "balanced" organizational status structures, *see* Zelditch, Morris, Jr., Berger, Joseph and Cohen, Barnard P., Stability of Organizational Status Structures, *in* Berger, Joseph, Zelditch, Morris, Jr. and Anderson, Bo (Editors), Socological Theories in Progress, volume 1, Boston, Houghton Mifflin Company, 1966.

[60] Udy, Stanley H., Jr., Administrative Rationality, Social Setting, and Organizational Development, *American Journal of Sociology,* 68, 299–308, November, 1962.

[61] *See* Dornbusch, Sanford M., The Military Academy as an Assimilating Institution, *Social Forces,* 33, 316–321, May, 1955; and Goffman, Irving, Asylums, New York, Doubleday & Company, Inc., 1961.

[62] For an extended discussion of organizational autonomy and its limits, *see* Scott, Theory of Organizations, *op. cit.*, pp. 522–525.

ACKNOWLEDGMENTS

Portions of the section on Organizational Tasks are based on work done in connection with a study of "Authority Structures and Evaluations" under a grant from the National Science Foundation (G 23990). My major collaborators in this research are Sanford M. Dornbusch, Bruce C. Busching and James D. Laing.

DISCUSSION

General appreciation was voiced of Scott's presentation as a review of the bearing of some of the literature on organizational theory on needed research in the health field. This appreciation was followed by a variety of comments about specific points of the paper, additional topics that might have been covered had time and space permitted and some practical and policy concerns of physicians and administrators in medical organizations.

Organizational goals. The first discussant began his comments by considering the utility of the concept of organizational goals. He noted that it is difficult, at times treacherous, to determine what are organizational goals. Nevertheless, we have little choice but to use the concept of goals in organizational analysis. Wherever order is found in the analysis of organizations, it is created by assuming some goal. One assumes that a system has some given end by which it is analyzed and evaluated. Virtually all studies in health services, including apparently objective and "hard" operations research studies, assume some organizational end or output. However, what is often overlooked is that the end assumed is an arbitrary entity and may reflect the point of view of only one out of a number of actual participants or observers.

"Goals, measured by data which are treated as desired outputs, then are arbitrarily chosen in studies that take them for granted," the discussant continued. "It must surely be necessary to understand how one goal is chosen and how its selection is enforced over the preferences of other people engaged in an enterprise. If we understand this, we can understand why it is that the goals of the system selected as 'the' goals (such as efficiency or humane patient care) by high level participants are not realized, and are not even considered to be the real goals by some members or students of the organization. Without attention to the problem, operational studies of health service systems and their translation into practice cannot fail to be irrelevant to real organizations."

Organizational goals and organizational structure. The second commentator stressed the need to be concerned both with goals that relate to the future of health services and with organizational forms that will best provide for the solution of problems of the future. He argued that the present organization of medicine not only may be poor in its attempt to meet current problems, but also is inadequate to meet the needs of the future. A tremendous instability and flexibility must be built into the organizational framework to meet future needs that are

322

unforeseeable at the moment. To this end the organization of medical care programs should very definitely provide for emphasis on research and innovation. The organizational framework must above all be one which prevents uniformity of operation; rather, the premium must be put on research and demonstration. Need is for an organizational framework which permits feedback from a demonstration area to flow into the total organizational program in a way that the entire program can be gradually reformed with a minimum of threat. Very little exists in the way of organizational models which will show how this can be done properly. Nevertheless, the discussant urged, organizations based on flexibility, research, demonstration and feedback must be erected.

Controversy developed around this discussant's emphasis on the need for flexibility in medical organizations. Some persons suggested that rationality is the essence of formal organization and is functional for the efficient performance of the tremendous amount of routine work that needs to be done in the medical field. Although a certain amount of flexibility might be useful, carried far it would prove dysfunctional to the achievement of the organization's goals. Useful research might be conducted on what happens to a medical organization that is dedicated to change.

Several discussants noted that Scott's paper focused primarily on formal organization. Had time permitted, discussion could have considered the degree to which the health organizations are dependent upon the community and other organizations within it. Additional research in this area would prove fruitful.

Although Scott emphasized the analysis of formal organizations, it was believed to have implications for other organizational aspects of medical care. He noted that "medical practice—even when it is private and 'solo'—is a functionally organized system that may be treated as if it were a formal organization." Solo practice is embedded in a natural organization linked by referrals, and many of the concepts appropriate to the analysis of formal organizations are quite applicable to such practice even though no formal administrative system of official positions surrounds the organization of solo practice. Scott's questions of goals, evaluation, control and stratification must all be raised to understand medical practice in general and must all be understood properly to be able to sensibly manipulate the medical care system in ways in which it is likely to work. Once solo practice is considered as an organized system itself, perhaps ways may be discovered in which the institution may be quite practical for some of the new technological

323

and qualitative aims of medical care reformers. Now, perhaps because it is a *formal* organization that makes sense as an organization, far too much unrealistic and uninformed emphasis has been placed upon the values of group practice over any other kind of practice.

The role of informal organization in medical care should have been explored both within the context of larger formal organizations and as a subject in its own right.

Organizational tasks. Scott's treatment of organizational tasks was regarded as a stimulating source of ideas for additional research on the nature of work in the field of medicine. One discussant noted that the time has come to think about the implications of the technology of a task for the way in which it can be organized. The purely technological distinction between inert and active tasks, and between patterned and unpatterned, seems a good beginning. But a mistake is made in assuming a real technolgical difference between everyday professional work and everyday nonprofessional work. This is particularly the case for medicine, which is far more advanced scientifically and mechanically than the other traditional practicing professions of law, teaching and preaching. The logical distinctions among tasks that Scott makes should be tried out carefully and critically. It is wiser to treat them as ideological claims about work that doctors can make stick and cab drivers cannot. These claims support resistance against socially "inappropriate" (though technically feasible) forms of evaluation. Scott, of course, recognizes this when he refers to "definitions" or "conceptions" of task. The careful study of such conceptions, when it comes to formulating realistic and functioning methods of evaluation, is the only way to avoid slipping them in in the guise of objective characteristics of the tasks.

Organizational control and evaluation of performance. One commentator noted that "Evaluation is of course an important thing to study because one wants to know how a given goal is being attained by the performance of a given task. Without knowing this, the whole point of an organization's existence is called into question. And without knowing this, an organization cannot be considered an organized and directed endeavor: without organizational control over tasks, a hospital, for example, can be called a building inhabited by a collection of people but certainly not an organization. The question of control is thus central to the question of organization."

"But as Dr. Scott points out, there are many ways in which control based on evaluation of task can operate, ways that become especially difficult to understand in the health services. The traditional model of control in American medicine is one that does not presuppose the need for an organization. It is a model that relies on *socialization* and assumes that neither evaluation nor organization controls are necessary—just a particular type of person. The claim of the profession generally is that its members are special kinds of people—kind, conscientious, skilled and ethical. In this sense, there is no need for an organization to control medical work—just a method of recruiting and training that creates the true professional man. Furthermore, the profession lays claim to a certain dignity that, quite apart from being the 'right' kind of man who went to a 'good school,' leads the profession to resist or reject organization itself and the evaluation and control processes it presupposes. Professionals are ideological individualists, and in a position of sufficient influence to be able to heavily resist and obscure the whole question of organizational control. This is a central problem in the study of health service organizations: it is a problem of the practicality of adopting certain administrative measures, but it is no less a problem of formulation. Organizational theory, and practical research even more, have, in the case of professional rather than nonprofessional workers, been prone to accept the premises and rationalizations of the people being studied, rather than question them, and have been too ready to believe the professional a special kind of person who does a special kind of work. Dr. Scott's review of this area raises questions about those premises that should be pressed very hard. Studying health organizations from the point of view of how participants are controlled (not solely differential happiness, morale, or communications), without built in untested assumptions that controls do operate, should go far toward allowing us to adopt a rational and realistic approach to health service organization. Dr. Scott's emphasis on evaluation and control should help push us towards such a study, particularly if we make as few assumptions as possible about the intrinsic character of professionals and their work."

The discussant also pointed out that "the question of the quality of care is one that bears on organizational goals, on evaluation and control, stratification and socialization. In short, the practical problem of learning how to measure and produce care of a certain quality is one that requires for both formulation and solution consideration of the full range of concepts discussed by Dr. Scott. Measuring the quality of care and formulating procedures to administer it is more a sociological and organizational problem than it is a biochemical and medical problem. To establish criteria for the quality of care is a social process of selecting goals, which can be studied empirically in and of itself. To collect information on performance is similarly a problem in social engineering, rather than a problem of mere technique."

THE CONTRIBUTION OF HEALTH SERVICES
TO THE AMERICAN ECONOMY

VICTOR R. FUCHS

INTRODUCTION

Good health is one of man's most precious assets. The desire to live, to be well, to maintain full command over one's faculties and to see one's loved ones free from disease, disability or premature death are among the most strongly rooted of all human desires. That is particularly true of Americans who, on the whole, eschew the fatalism or preoccupation with the hereafter that is characteristic of some other cultures.

These sentiments are widely held. Therefore, is not the question—what is "the contribution of health services to the United States economy?"—presumptuous? Who can place a value on a life saved, on a body spared from pain or on a mind restored to sanity? If not presumptuous, is not the question a foolish one, and likely to evoke an equally foolish answer?

When an economist enters an area such as health—so tinged with emotion, so enveloped in an esoteric technology and vocabulary—he runs a high risk of being either irrelevant or wrong. What, then, is the justification for such an inquiry? The principal one is the fact that the question of the contribution of health services is being asked and answered every day. It is being asked and answered implicitly every time consumers, hospitals, universities, business firms, foundations, government agencies and legislative bodies make decisions concerning the volume and composition of health services, present and future. If economists can help to rationalize and make more explicit

327

the decision-making process, can provide useful definitions, concepts and analytical tools, and can develop appropriate bodies of data and summary measures, they will be making their own contribution to health and to the economy.

Plan of the Paper

This paper has limited objectives. It does not pretend to offer a measure of the contribution of health services. Even partial completion of such a task would require a major effort by a research team over a period of several years. Statistics are presented, but for illustrative purposes only.

The primary purpose is to set out in nontechnical terms how the problem looks to an economist, to discuss definitions, concepts and methods of measurement, to indicate sources of information and to suggest promising research approaches. The paper offers a highly personal view of the problem rather than a synthesis of all points of view. Some discussion of relevant literature is included, but no attempt has been made to be exhaustive. Moreover, the paper is limited to the assigned topic and does not provide a general review of the health economics literature. An overall survey of the field, through 1964, is available in Klarman.[1] In addition, useful bibliographies may be found in Mushkin,[2] Wolf[3] and the proceedings of a 1962 conference on the economics of health and medical care.[4]

First this paper will consider the meaning of "contribution." Then it will go on to discuss the inputs to health services, the outputs of health services (with special emphasis on health) and the contribution of health to the economy. The paper concludes with a brief summary and suggestions for research.

THE CONCEPT OF CONTRIBUTION

One frequently reads discussions of the contribution of an industry couched in terms of the number of jobs the industry provides, the volume of capital investment of the industry, and the value of its purchases from suppliers. Such use of the term is ill-advised.

In economic terms the contribution of an industry to the economy should be measured in terms of its output (what does it provide for the economy?), not in terms of its input (what drains does it make on the available supply of resources?). The fundamental fact of economic life is that resources are scarce relative to human wants. De-

328

spite a great deal of loose talk about automation and cybernetics, the desires for goods and services in this country and the world exceed the available supplies. Indeed, if this were not the case, no reason could be found to study the economics of health or the economics of anything else. Additional resources would be devoted to health up to the point where no health want would be unmet. That this cannot be done at present is obvious. The reason should be equally obvious. To devote more resources to health services, the people must be willing to forego some other good or service. To the extent of the unused capacity in the economy, some increase could be obtained without diversion from other ends. The extent of this unused capacity, however, relative to the total economy, is very small at the present time.

What is the output of the health industry? No completely satisfactory answer is available. One possible way to think about the problem is to distinguish three different kinds of output that flow from health services. They are health, validation services and other consumer services.

Probably the most important of these, and certainly the one that has received the most attention, is the contribution of health services to health. However, to define the output of the health industry in terms of some ultimate utility, such as health rather than health services, runs counter to the general practice followed by economists in the study of other industries. For the most part, economists follow the dictum, "whatever Lola gets, Lola wants." They assume that consumers know what they want and know how to satisfy these wants. They further assume that goods and services produced under competitive conditions will be sold at a price which properly reflects (at the margin) the cost of production and the value to the consumer. The health industry, however, has certain characteristics, discussed by Arrow,[5] Klarman[6] and Mushkin,[7] which suggest that special treatment is required. In the present context, three important differences could be emphasized between the health industry and the "typical" or "average" industry.

Consumer ignorance. Although expenditures for health services account for more than six per cent of all personal consumption expenditures, consumers are, for the most part, terribly ignorant about what they are buying. Very few industries could be named where the consumer is so dependent upon the producer for information concerning the quality of the product. In the typical case he is even subject to the producer's recommendation concerning the quantity to be purchased. A recent report by the American Medical Association says flatly, "The 'quantity' of the hospital services consumed in 1962 was determined by physicians."[8]

The question is even more complicated, as indicated in the following statement by J. Douglas Colman, president of the New York Blue Cross:[9]

> We must remember that most elements of hospital and medical care costs are generated by or based on professional medical judgment. These judgments include the decision to admit and discharge patients, the decision to order the various diagnostic or therapeutic procedures for patients, and the larger decision as to the types of facilities and services needed by an institution for proper patient care. For the most part, these professional judgments are rendered outside of any organizational structure that fixes accountability for the economic consequences of these judgments.

One reason for consumer ignorance is the inherent uncertainty of the effect of the service on any individual. How can the lay person be expected to know the value of a particular procedure or treatment, when in many cases the medical profession itself is far from agreed? Also, many medical services are infrequently purchased. The average consumer will buy many more automobiles during a lifetime than he will major operations. Therefore, he cannot develop the necessary expertise. Furthermore, the consumer is often not in a good position to make a cool, rational judgment at the time of purchase because he is ill, or because a close member of his family is ill. Finally, the profession does little to inform the consumer; in fact, it frequently takes positive action to keep him uninformed. This leads to the second important difference.

Restrictions on competition. In some other industries where the possibilities for consumer ignorance are considerable, the consumer obtains protection through the competitive behavior of producers. If the producers are engaged in vigorous competition with one another, some of them, at least, will go out of their way to inform the consumer about the merits of their product and those of the competition. Also, middlemen, such as retailers, are usually involved, one of whose main functions is to provide information and dispel consumer ignorance. In the case of physicians' services (and this is the keystone to health services because of the dominant role of the physician in the industry) the reverse is true. In the first place, severe restrictions on entry are assured through the medical profession's control of medical schools, licensing requirements and hospital appointments. Advertising is forbidden and price competition is severely frowned upon. Critical comment concerning the output of other physicians is also regarded as unethical.

330

A good example of the conflict and confusion on this point can be found in the report previously cited. An extensive discussion of medical care in America is presented, and an attempt is made to identify it with the competitive free enterprise system. The report then goes on to say, "The Medical Care Industry has as its prime social goal the development and maintenance of optimum health levels."[10] The authors apparently fail to realize the inconsistency of this statement with their attempt to place the industry in the context of a market system. In such a system, industries do not have "social goals." The goal of the individual firm is maximum profit (or minimum loss); the achievement of social goals is a by-product of the profit-seeking activities of individual firms and industries.

Numerous arguments can be advanced in support of each of the restrictive practices followed by the medical profession. (Arrow's discussion of the role of uncertainty in health is particularly relevant.[5]) In the present context, these restrictive practices mean that an appraisal of the industry's ouput and performance by economists cannot be pursued using the same assumptions that would be appropriate in appraising the output of a more competitive industry.

The role of "need." Health services are one of a small group of services which many people believe should be distributed according to need rather than demand (i.e., willingness and ability to pay.) Other services in this category, such as education, police and fire protection, and sanitation are typically provided by government. For a time philanthropy and the generosity of physicians were relied upon to achieve this distribution for health services, but now increasing reliance is being placed on taxation or coverage in compulsory insurance schemes. If "need" is to be criterion, however, a closer examination of the role of health services in filling that need seems in order.

If a person "demands" an article of clothing or a haircut or some other good or service, in the sense of being willing and able to pay for it, usually no special cause for concern or inquiry arises on the part of anyone else regarding either the need underlying the demand or whether the purchase will satisfy the need. However, if a service, such as health, is to be provided to others on the basis of "need," then those paying for it would seem to have some right to inquire into the actual presence of "need," and an obligation to determine whether or how much the service actually satisfies the need. Because need is often the criterion for obtaining health services, much of the payment for these services is by a "third party." This means that the consumer has less incentive to make certain that the output (what he is getting) is truly worth the cost.

These characteristics of the health industry indicate why output cannot simply be equated with expenditures. However, that does not mean that economic analysis cannot be applied to this industry. On the contrary, precisely these special characteristics make the industry an interesting subject for economic analysis, both from the scientific and public policy points of view.

Total versus Marginal Contribution

In studying the contribution of health services to health the *total* contribution must be distinguished from the *marginal* contribution. The total contribution can be appraised by asking what would happen if no health services at all were available. The results would almost surely be disastrous in terms of health and life expectancy. A reasonably safe conclusion seems to be that the total contribution is enormous. A modern economy could not continue to function without some health services.

The marginal contribution, on the other hand, refers to the effects on health of a small increase or decrease in the amount of health services provided. To expect a small change in services to have a large effect on the level of health is, of course, out of the question. But that is not what is being measured. Rather, the question is, what is the relative effect on health of a small relative change in health services?

The reason this question is crucial is that changes are usually being made at the margin. Most decisions are not of the "all or nothing" variety, but involve "a little more or a little less." The goal of an economic system, in terms of maximum satisfaction, is to allocate resources in such a way that the last (marginal) inputs of resources used for each purpose make contributions that are proportionate to their costs.

HEALTH SERVICES

"Health services" can be defined as services rendered by:

1. Labor: personnel engaged in medical occupations, such as doctors, dentists and nurses, plus other personnel working directly under their supervision, such as practical nurses, orderlies and receptionists.

2. Physical capital: the plant and equipment used by this personnel, e.g., hospitals, x-ray machines.

3. Intermediate goods and services: i.e., drugs, bandages, purchased laundry services.

This definition corresponds roughly to what economists have in mind when they refer to the "health industry." Payment for this labor, capital and intermediate input is the basis for estimating "health expenditures."

This definition seems satisfactory for the purposes of this paper, but some classification problems are worth mentioning. First, some health-related resources might or might not be included in health services, such as the provision of a supply of sanitary water. A second problem arises because a portion of the personnel and facilities in hospitals is used to produce "hotel services" rather than health. This paper will not exclude such inputs from health services, but will try to allow for them by showing that part of the output consists of other consumer services (see Figure 1).

One of the greatest problems concerns the unpaid health services that people perform for themselves and for members of their families. According to present practice in national income accounting, this labor input is not included in health services. Therefore, this "home" production must be treated as part of the environmental factors that affect health.

Approximately two-thirds of the value of health services in the United States represents labor input. Somewhat less than one-sixth represents input of physical capital and the remainder represents goods and services purchased from other industries. These are all rough estimates. Information about the volume and composition of health services must be derived from a variety of official and unofficial sources. No census of the health industry compares to the census of manufacturing, trade or selected services. As the importance of the health industry grows, the government may wish to reconsider whether a periodic census of health should be undertaken.

Present sources of information are of two main types: those that give information about expenditures for health services, and those that report on one or more aspects of inputs of resources. A good example of the former is the material supplied by Reed and Rice.[11] A few problems arise when these data are used to measure inputs of health services. First, some of the items represent investment expenditures by the health industry rather than payment for current services. Expenditures for construction and medical research are the most important ones in this category. No particular economic justification may be found for treating these as inputs in the year that the investment takes place. On the other hand, current input of capital may be understated to the extent that hospital charges do not include an allowance for depreciation and interest.

The expenditures shown for drugs, eyeglasses, etc., do not all represent payment for intermediate goods purchased from other industries. A substantial portion (probably about one-half) represents the labor services of pharmacists, opticians and the like and the services of the plant and equipment used by this personnel.

The net cost of health insurance represents output of the insurance industry. It may be thought of as an intermediate service purchased and resold by the health industry.

A final point concerns the failure of expenditures data to reflect contributed labor. This results in an underestimate of labor input, especially in hospitals.

Other sources of information on expenditures for health services include: the Office of Business Economics,[12-14] detailed annual data on personal consumption expenditures for health service; the Social Security Administration,[15] special emphasis on government spending for health services; the Public Health Service,[16, 17] expenditures cross-classified with characteristics of the individual incurring the expense; the Health Information Foundation,[18] and Bureau of Labor Statistics.[19, 20]

The decennial population census[21] is an excellent source of information about labor inputs to health services. In addition to providing a complete enumeration of the number employed and their geographical location, numerous economic and demographic characteristics are described in considerable detail. With the aid of the 1/1000 sample of the 1960 census,[22] comparisons may be made within the health industry and between health and other industries on such matters as education, earnings, age, sex, race and hours of work. The labor input to health services may be defined as all persons employed in the health and hospital industry, plus those persons in medical occupations employed in other industries. Health employment, so defined, amounted to almost three million in 1960. This represented almost five per cent of total employment.

Another good source of data on labor input is provided by the Public Health Service.[23] This source is particularly useful for those interested in such characteristics as physicians' type of practice, specialization, medical school and location of practice.

Information on capital inputs to health services is more difficult to obtain. The annual guide book issue of *Hospitals* reports the book value of hospital plant and equipment.[24] This was given as 21.3 billion dollars in 1963. This figure is biased downward as a measure of present value, because of the rise in prices of construction in recent decades. It is biased upward to the extent that hospitals have failed to make deductions for depreciation. This same source also provides useful data on labor input by type and size of hospital.

Some information on the capital inputs associated with the labor input of physicians can be gleaned from the reports of the United States Internal Revenue Service.[25] According to these reports, 163,000 returns were filed for unincorporated businesses under the heading of "physicians, surgeons, and oculists" in 1962. These returns showed business receipts of six billion dollars. They showed net rent paid of 250 million dollars (most of this represents payment for capital services) as well as depreciation charges of 190 million dollars. Some information for other types of health services, such as those provided by dentists and dental surgeons, is also available from the same source.

One important source of information about inputs of equipment and intermediate goods that has not received much attention is the quinquennial CENSUS OF MANUFACTURER.[26] The latest one (1963) provides considerable data on shipments by manufacturers of drugs, ophthalmic goods, dental equipment and supplies, ambulances, hospital beds and many other health items.

Real versus Money Costs

One problem in measuring inputs that has already been alluded to in connection with volunteer labor is the need to distinguish between "real" and "money" costs. The person who is not an economist usually thinks of the cost of health services in money terms; when more money has to be spent, costs are said to be rising. This approach is readily understandable and for some purposes useful and proper. The analysis of many problems, however, requires a stripping away of the money veil and an examination of "real" costs. The real cost to society of providing health services, or any other good or service, consists of the labor and capital used in the industry, plus the cost of producing the intermediate goods and services. For instance, if the workers employed in a given hospital are unionized, and they nego-

335

tiate a large increase in wages, the money costs of that hospital clearly rise, other factors remaining unchanged. But the real cost of that hospital service has not changed at all.

In a perfectly competitive market economy, money costs usually provide a good measure of real costs. But in the health industry, with its curious mixture of philanthropy, government subsidies, imperfect labor markets and contributed labor time, concentration on money costs alone may frequently be misleading. Good decisions about the allocation of resources require information about the real costs involved.

One important element of real cost is often overlooked, namely, the time of the patient. When the patient is ill, the value of this time (measured by alternative opportunities) may be very low. But, in calculating the costs of periodic medical examinations and routine visits, omitting this cost would be a mistake.[27]

HEALTH

Any attempt to analyze the relationship between health services and health runs headlong into two very difficult problems. The first concerns the definition and measurement of levels of health, or at least changes in levels. The second involves an attempt to estimate what portion of changes in health can be attributed to health services, as distinct from the genetic and environmental factors that also affect health. This section discusses the question of definition and measurement of levels of health.

What is Health?

Definitions of health abound. Agreement is hard to find. The oft-quoted statement of the World Health Organization[28] is framed in positive (some would say Utopian) terms—"A state of complete physical and mental and social well-being." Others, e.g., Ffrangcon Roberts,[29] simply stress the absence of, or the ability to resist, disease and death.

A few points seem clear. First, health has many dimensions—anatomical, physiological, mental, and so on. Second, the relative importance of different disabilities varies considerably, depending upon the particular culture and the role of the particular individual in that culture. Third, most attempts at measurement take the negative approach. That is, they make inferences about health by measuring the degree of ill health, as indicated by mortality, morbidity, disability, etc. Finally, with respect to health, as in so many other cases, detecting changes in health is easier than defining or measuring absolute levels.

Indexes of Health

The most widely used indicators of health levels are those based on mortality rates, either age-specific or age-adjusted. The great virtues of death rates are that they are determined objectively, are readily available in considerable detail for most countries, and are reasonably comparable for intertemporal and interspatial comparisons.

Health experts rely heavily on mortality comparisons for making judgments about the relative health levels of whites and nonwhites in the United States, or of smokers versus nonsmokers, and for other problems. A recent survey of health in Israel, for example, concluded:[30]

> The success of the whole system of medicine in Israel is best judged, not by an individual inspection of buildings or asking the opinions of doctors and patients, but by an examination of the health statistics of the country. Infant mortality is about the same as in many European countries, and life expectancy is equal to, or better than, most.

The tendency in recent years has been to dismiss mortality as a useful indicator of health levels in developed countries because very little intranational or international variation occurs. These reports of the demise of mortality indexes are premature.

Differences within the United States are still considerable. The most important differential is race, but even considering rates for whites only, the age-adjusted death rate (average 1959–61) in the highest state is 33 per cent greater than in the lowest; the highest infant mortality rate is 55 per cent above the lowest; and the death rate for males 45–54 in the worst state is 60 per cent higher than in the state with the lowest rate.

Comparing the United States with other developed countries, the differences are even more striking, as shown in Table 1. For males 45–54, (a critical age group from the point of view of production), the United States has the highest rate of any country in the Organization for Economic Cooperation and Development (OECD), and has a rate which is almost double that of some of the other countries. Such gross differences surely present a sufficient challenge for scientific analysis and for public policy.

Another argument that seems to underly the objections to mortality

TABLE I. DEATH RATES IN OECD COUNTRIES RELATIVE TO THE UNITED STATES, AVERAGE 1959–61

Country	Age-Adjusted Death Rate*	Infant Mortality	Mortality Males 45–54	Mortality Females 45–54
United States	100	100	100	100
White	96	88	94	87
Nonwhite	138	164	155	220
Iceland	78	62**	62	81
Netherlands	82	63	57	65
Norway	82	74**	54	58
Sweden	86	63	52	69
Greece	86	155	56	64
Denmark	90	85**	59	78
Canada	92	107	76	79
Switzerland	94	83	67	75
France	96	105	89	83
Italy	98	166	74	77
Belgium	102	113	82	79
United Kingdom	103	87	76	85
Spain	104†	178	75†	84†
West Germany (excluding Berlin)	107	129	77	84
Luxembourg	107	122	96	89
Ireland	109	118	74	105
Austria	110	142	87	87
Japan	115	127**	83	102
Portugal	131	328	84	84

* Age-adjustment is by the "indirect" method. For each country, United States age-specific death rates were applied to the actual population distribution and the result was divided into the actual number of deaths to obtain the mortality ratio, i.e., the age-adjusted death rate in index number form.

† 1957–59 average.

** 1958–60 average.

Sources: Age-Adjusted Death Rate, Mortality Males 45–54 and Mortality Females 45–54: United States Deaths: United States Public Health Service, VITAL STATISTICS OF THE UNITED STATES, 1959, 1960, 1961. United States Population: United States Bureau of the Census, 1960 CENSUS OF POPULATION, Volume I, Characteristics of the Population, Part 1, United States Summary. OECD Countries: Population and Deaths: World Health Organization, ANNUAL EPIDEMIOLOGICAL AND VITAL STATISTICS, 1959, 1960, 1961. Data for Luxembourg from United Nations, DEMOGRAPHIC YEARBOOK, 1960, 1961.
Infant Mortality Rate: United Nations, DEMOGRAPHIC YEARBOOK, 1961, Table 17.

indexes is that age-adjusted death rates (and average life expectancy) have been relatively stable in the United States for the past decade. The real costs of health services have increased over this period, and medical science has certainly made some progress; therefore, one may assume that some improvement in health levels occurred that was not captured by the mortality indexes.

This type of reasoning begs the question. Possibly the increase in health services has not resulted in improved health levels and the scientific advances of recent years have not had much effect on health. An alternative explanation is that changes in environmental factors in these years have had, on balance, a negative effect on health, thus offsetting the favorable effects of increases in services and medical knowledge. The latter explanation seems to be a very real possibility. Health services do not operate in a vacuum, nor can they be regarded as being matched against a "health destroying nature" that remains constant over time. An apt aphorism attributed to Sigerist states that "Each civilization makes its own diseases."[31]

Most of the suggestions for new and better indexes of health involve combining morbidity and mortality information. An excellent discussion of some of the problems to be encountered, and possible solutions, may be found in Sullivan.[32] One particularly intriguing approach, suggested by Sanders,[33] consists of calculating years of "effective" life expectancy, based on mortality and morbidity rates. Such an index would measure the number of years that a person could expect to live and be well enough to fulfill the role appropriate to his sex and age. This approach could be modified to take account of the fact that illness or disability is a matter of degree. The years deducted from life expectancy because of disability should be adjusted by some percentage factor that represents the degree of disability. The determination of these percentage weights is one of the most challenging research problems to be faced in calculating a health index.

HEALTH SERVICES AND HEALTH

Writing this section would be more appropriate for a physician than for an economist since the relation between health services and health is a technical question best answered by those whose training is in that technology. All that is intended here is to record some impressions of an outsider who has reviewed a minute portion of the literature from a particular point of view.

The impact of health services on health depends upon two factors: 1. How effective are the best known techniques of diagnosis, therapy, etc.? 2. How wide is the gap between the best known techniques ("treatment of choice") and those actually used across the country? The latter question has been reviewed extensively in medical literature under the heading "quality of care";[34] it will not be discussed here. A useful introduction to the first question is provided in Terris.[35]

The belief that an important relationship exists between health services and health is of long standing. Reliable evidence to support this belief is of much more recent origin. For thousands of years sick people sought advice and treatment of physicians and surgeons, but many of the most popular remedies and courses of treatment of earlier centuries are now known to have been either harmful or irrelevant.

If this be true, how can one explain the demand for health services that existed in the past? Two possible explanations seem worth noting; they may even continue to have some relevance today. First, doctors probably received a great deal of credit that properly belonged to nature. The body itself has great healing powers, and most people who successfully consulted physicians would have recovered from or adjusted to their illness without medical intervention. Second, and probably more important, is the intensive need "to do something" that most people have when faced with pain and the possibility of death.

In more recent times, the value of health services for certain illnesses has been established with considerable certainty; but broad areas of doubt and controversy still remain. The following discussion considers a few examples of each type.

Infectious disease is an area where medical services are demonstrably effective. Although the decline of some infectious diseases (e.g., tuberculosis) should be credited in part to environmental changes such as improved sanitation, the important role played by improvements in medical science cannot be downgraded. For many infectious diseases the health service is preventive rather than curative and "one-shot" rather than continuous. Such preventive services do not occupy a large portion of total physician time, but the results should nevertheless be included in the output of the health industry.

Examples of the control of infectious disease through immunization are: diphtheria,[36] tetanus[37, 38] and poliomyelitis;[39] chemotherapy is effective in tuberculosis[40] and pneumonia.[41] The decline in mortality from these causes has been dramatic and some correlation can be observed between changes in the rate of decline and the adoption of specific medical advances. For example, during the 15-year period, 1935 to 1950, which spanned the introduction and wide use of sulfonamides and penicillin, the United States death rate from influenza and pneumonia fell at a rate of more than eight per cent per annum; the rate of decline was two per cent per annum from 1900 to 1935. In the case of tuberculosis, considerable progress was made throughout this century, but the relative rate of decline in the death rate accelerated appreciably after the adoption of penicillin, streptomycin and PAS (para-aminosalicylic acid) in the late 1940's, and of isoniazid in the early 1950's.

Even more dramatic examples are the death rate patterns of syphilis and poliomyelitis, where the introduction of new forms of treatment for the former and immunization for the latter were reflected very quickly in precipitous drops in mortality. To be sure, the diseases mentioned have not been eliminated. Partly for sociocultural reasons, the incidence of syphilis has actually increased in recent years. In other cases, modern treatments of choice are losing their effectiveness because of the development of resistant strains of microorganisms.

The situation with respect to the noninfectious diseases is more mixed. Some examples of demonstrable effectiveness are the following: replacement therapy has lessened the impact of diabetes,[42] dental caries in children are reduced by fluoridation[43] and medical care has become increasingly successful in treating trauma.[45] The diagnostic value of the Papanicolaou test for cervical cancer is established[46, 47] and the incidence of invasive cancer of this site has been reduced in the 1960's, presumably due to medical treatment during the pre-invasive stage disclosed by the test. Also effective is the treatment of skin cancer.[48]

Less heartening are the reports on other cancer sites. The five-year survival rate for breast cancer (the most common single organ site of malignancy in either sex) is typically about 50 per cent. Moreover, a review of the breast cancer literature found such striking uniformity of results, despite widely differing therapeutic techniques, that the author was prompted to speculate whether such end results record therapeutic triumphs or merely the natural history of the disease.[49] Some writers stress the importance of prompt treatment for cancer; others question whether elimination of delay would dramatically alter survival rates. The problem of delay itself is complex, and not simply attributable to ignorance or lack of access to health services: "Physicians with cancer are just as likely to delay as are laymen."[50]

Heart disease is another major cause of death where the contribution of health services to health leaves much to be desired. Despite the contributions of surgery in correcting congenital and rheumatic cardiac defects[51] and the decline in recurrence rates of rheumatic fever,[52] apparently no curative treatment has been found for rhematic fever.[53, 54] The treatment of coronary heart disease is only partially effective.[55] The value of antihypertensive drugs in preventing early death in case of malignant hypertension seems assured, but these drugs may be harmful in nonmalignant hypertension.[56] The value of anticoagulants in reducing complications and mortality with acute myocardial infarction has been questioned by recent reports.[57, 58]

Definitive therapy is still not available for widespread afflictions such as cerebral vascular disease[59] and rehabilitation results indicate that only the more severely ill may benefit from formal therapy (the others seem to recover spontaneously).[60] No cure is known for schizophrenia. The tranquilizing drugs and shock therapy have had a significant impact in shortening hospital stay, yet they do not seem to lower rehospitalization rates below those achieved with other methods.[61]

Health services have always been assumed to be very valuable in connection with pregnancy, but a recent study of prenatal care reveals little relation to prevention of pregnancy complications or prevention of early pregnancy termination, except in uncomplicated pregnancies of 30 weeks' gestation and over.[62] The latter cases do not clarify whether the medical care component of prenatal care, as distinct from nutritional and other components, is due the credit.

Innovations in health services are not limited to improvements in drugs, surgical techniques or other technological changes. Research concerning the effects on health of group practice,[63, 64] intensive care units[65, 66] and special arrangements for neonatal surgery,[67] has yielded encouraging results with respect to these organizational innovations. In other cases, results have been disappointing, e.g., multiple screening,[68] periodic medical examination of school children[69] and cancer control programs differing in duration, intensity and cost.[70]

This very brief review indicates that no simple generalization is possible about the effect of health services on health. Although many health services definitely improve health, in other cases even the best known techniques may have no effect. This problem of relating input to output is one of the most difficult ones facing economists who try to do research on the health industry. They must gain the support and advice of doctors and public health specialists if they are to make progress in this area.

Environmental Factors and Health

One of the factors contributing to the difficulty in reaching firm conclusions about the relationship between health services and health is the importance of environmental factors. Some environmental changes are biological, involving the appearance and disappearance of

342

bacteria, viruses and other sources of disease. Many environmental variables are related to economics in one way or another. Some are tied to the production process, e.g., the factors associated with occupation. Others are part of consumption, e.g., diet, recreation. Major attention has frequently been given to income, partly because many other environmental factors tend to be highly correlated with real income, both over time and cross-sectionally. Examples include housing, education, urbanization, drinking and the use of automobiles.

The prevailing assumption, in some cases with good evidence, has indicated that an increase in real per capita income has favorable implications for health, apart from the fact that it permits an increase in health services. This assumption for the United States at present, except for infant mortality, may reasonably be questioned. This country may have passed the peak with respect to the favorable impact of a rising level of living on health. This is not to say that some favorable elements are not still associated with a higher income, but the many unfavorable ones may outweigh them.

After a period of neglect of environmental factors by medical researchers, the tendency in recent years has been to overemphasize the favorable aspects of rising income levels. For example, the American Medical Association recently stated, "Medical science does not seek major credit for the improvements in the health levels during the past 25 years. Certainly, our standards of living and higher educational levels have contributed substantially to the betterment of the health level in the United States."[71] Although modesty is becoming, the Association provides no evidence to support this statement, and the chances are good that it is wrong.

Altenderfer[72] was able to show some slight negative association between age-adjusted death rates and income across cities in the United States in 1940, but the adjustment for the effect of color was crude, and no allowance was made for the correlation between health services and income. The question at issue here is the relation between income and health, not of the fact that higher income permits a higher rate of utilization of health services.

Some preliminary work suggests that education is indeed favorable to health, but by far the largest share of the credit for improvement in health levels over the past 25 years probably should go to what economists call improvements in technology—better drugs, better medical knowledge, better diagnostic techniques, etc. Cross-sectional regressions across states, for instance, reveal a positive relation between income and mortality for whites, except in the case of infant mortality.

Death rate patterns in countries where the level of income is far below that of the United States, should also cause one to question the level of living argument. In Table 2, death rates for five European countries in 1960 are compared with rates for the United States in 1960 and 1925. The latter date was included because, in 1960, these five countries were at a level of real per capita income roughly comparable to that of the United States in 1925.[73]

The table shows that the over-all age-adjusted death rates for the European countries are very similar to those for the United States, and far below the level of the United States in 1925. The European crude rates tend to be higher because of the larger proportion of older people in Europe. Despite this bias, the crude rates for tuberculosis and influenza and pneumonia (two causes where the rise in income levels has been alleged to be particularly important) are

TABLE 2. COMPARISON OF DEATH RATES OF UNITED STATES IN 1925 AND 1960 WITH EUROPEAN COUNTRIES 1960

	Age-Adjusted Death Rate All Causes*	Crude Death Rate All Causes	Crude Death Rate Tuberculosis (all forms)	Crude Death Rate Influenza and Pneumonia†
1925				
United States	1683.3	1170.0	84.8	121.7
1960				
United States	945.7	945.7	5.9	32.9
England and Wales	926.8	1150.2	7.5	70.1
France	926.8	1136.2	22.1	48.1
West Germany (excluding Berlin)	983.5	1136.8	16.2	43.8
Netherlands	766.0	762.1	2.8	26.6
Belgium	1002.4	1244.7	17.1	36.5

* Age-adjustment is by the "indirect" method. For each country the United States age-specific death rates in 1960 were applied to the actual population distribution and the result was divided into the actual number of deaths to obtain the age-adjusted death rate index. This was multiplied by the United States crude death rate in 1960, to obtain the age-adjusted death rate.

† 1959–61 average used instead of 1960 rates because of influenza epidemic in 1960.

Sources: United States in 1925: United States Bureau of the Census, HISTORICAL STATISTICS OF THE UNITED STATES series B114–128, B129–142, A22–33. European countries 1960 population distribution, influenza and pneumonia deaths 1959–61, total populations 1959–61, and total deaths 1960 in West Germany and Belgium: World Health Organization, ANNUAL EPIDEMIOLOGICAL AND VITAL STATISTICS, 1959, 1960, 1961, Table 4. Other crude death rates in 1960: United Nations, DEMOGRAPHIC YEARBOOK, 1961, Table 17. United States age-specific death rates in 1960: United States Department of Health, Education and Welfare, Public Health Service, National Vital Statistics Division, VITAL STATISTICS OF THE UNITED STATES, 1960, Vol. II, Part A, Table 1-C.

344

also much closer to the United States in 1960, than to the United States in 1925. One explanation worth investigating is that the European countries enjoy a medical technology that is similar to that of the United States in 1960, and that changes in medical technology have been the principal cause of the decrease in the United States death rate from 1925 to 1960.

One possible reason for the effect of income levels on health having been overestimated is that investigators often find a very high correlation between income and the health status of individuals. The tendency has been to assume that the latter was the result of the former, but some recent studies of schizophrenia[74] and bronchitis[75] suggest that the causal relationship may run the other way. Evidence shows that illness causes a deterioration in occupational status (from a skilled job to an unskilled job and from an unskilled job into unemployment.) The evidence relates to the decline in occupational status from father to son (where the latter is a victim of the disease) and also within the patient's own history.

Even though research on the relation between health services and health would seem to be primarily the responsibility of those with training in medicine and public health, the long experience that economists have had with the environmental variables, such as income, education and urbanization, suggests that a multidisciplinary approach would be most fruitful.

OTHER CONTRIBUTIONS OF HEALTH SERVICES

The effect of health services on health probably represents their most important contribution. However, two other types of output are worth noting—validation services and other consumer services.

Validation Services

One type of output that is not directly related to improvements in health can be traced to the fact that only a physician can provide judgments concerning a person's health status that will be widely accepted by third parties. This type of output is designated "validation services" in Figure 1. One familiar example is the life insurance examination. This examination may have some favorable impact on the health of the examinee, but it need not do so and is not undertaken primarily for that purpose. The insurance company simply wants to know about the health status of the person concerned. In

FIGURE I. SCHEMATIC OUTLINE OF THE PAPER.

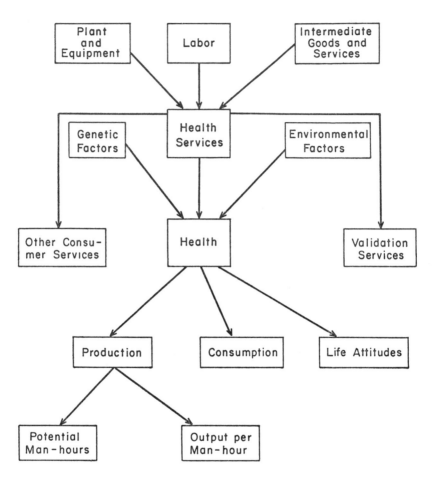

obtaining and providing that information, the physician is producing something of value, but it is not health.

Other examples include a physician's testifying in court, providing information in a workmen's compensation case, or executing a death certificate.

The validation role of physicians is probably much broader than in these sharply defined cases. Consider the following situation: a person feels ill; he has various aches, pains and other symptoms. He complains and looks for sympathy from family, friends, neighbors and co-workers. He may seek to be relieved from certain responsibilities or to be excused from certain tasks. Doubts may arise in the minds of persons around him. Questions may be asked. Is he really ill? Is he doing all that he can to get well? A visit, or a series of visits, to one or more doctors is indicated. The patient may not have the slightest hope that these visits will help his health, and, indeed, he may be correct. Nevertheless, the service rendered by the physician cannot be said to result in no output. The visit to the doctor is a socially or culturally necessary act. The examination, the diagnosis and the prognosis are desired by the patient to provide confirmation to those who have doubts about him. Only the professional judgment of a physician can still the doubts and answer the questions.

The validation service type of output should not be confused with another type of problem that arises in measuring the output of health services; namely, that advance knowledge about the effect of health services on health is sometimes difficult to obtain. This problem is similar to the "dry hole" situation in drilling for oil. That is not to say that the work done in drilling dry holes results in no output. Rather, when the drilling operation is viewed in its entirety, some successes will be noted as well as some failures. All those who participate in the drilling operation are considered to be sources of the output. Similarly, if a surgeon operates on ten people and only six are helped, one should not say that no output occurred in the other four cases, if one could not determine in advance which cases could be helped and which could not. The output consisted of improving the health of six people, but this output was the result of a production process which encompassed the ten operations.

Other Consumer Services

The outstanding example of other consumer services produced by the health industry is the so-called "hotel" services of hospitals. Those hospital activities that directly affect health are difficult to separate from those that are equivalent to hotel services, but the latter clearly are not insignificant. One way of getting some insight into this question would be to study the occupational distribution of health industry employment. A very significant fraction consists of cooks, chambermaids, porters and others who are probably producing "other consumer services."[11]

In mental hospitals and other hospitals providing long-term care a major proportion of all costs are probably associated with producing consumer services other than health. The fact that these other consumer services would have to be provided somehow, either publicly or privately, if the patients were not in the hospital, is often neglected in discussions of how total hospital costs are inflated by the presence of people who are not really ill. Possibly some of these consumer services are actually produced more inexpensively in a hospital than on the outside. This point comes to the fore in New York City, now grappling with the problem of housing and feeding patients who have been discharged from mental hospitals, not because they are cured, but because the new drugs mean they no longer need to be confined to an institution.

Some of the services rendered by nurses outside hospitals also bear little relation to health, but nevertheless they may have considerable value to consumers. This type of service is likely to grow in importance with the increase in the number of elderly people with income who are seeking companionship and help with their daily chores.

The failure of mortality indexes to decline with increased expenditures for health services in recent years has led some people to conclude that mortality no longer measures health levels properly. But if most of these increased expenditures have gone for health services that largely produce "other consumer services" rather than health, a great deal of the mystery is removed.

HEALTH AND THE ECONOMY

An increase in health has two potential values for individuals—consumption and production. Good health is clearly something consumers desire for itself. (That they do not put an overriding value on health is also abundantly clear from the figures on smoking, drinking, overeating, fast driving, etc.) To the extent that health services lead to better health, they make a contribution to the economy comparable to that of any industry producing a good or service wanted by consumers.

In addition, better health may contribute to the productive capacity of the economy. It may do this, first, by increasing the supply of potential man-hours through a reduction in mortality and decrease in time lost because of illness and disability. Second, better health may in-

348

crease production by improving productivity, that is, increasing output per man-hour.

Beyond its potential direct contribution to production and consumption, better health probably has important indirect effects on the economy. These indirect effects occur through the changes in life attitudes which may accompany changes in health. When the average life expectancy in a country is only 30 or 35 years, attitudes toward work and saving, for instance, may be different from those in countries where life expectancy is 50 or 75 years. When infant mortality rates are very high, attitudes toward birth control are likely to be different from those in countries where mortality rates are low. Indeed, the idea of progress itself may be intimately bound up with the health levels of the population and the rate of change of these levels.

Health and Production

A substantial literature is now available which attempts to measure the impact of changes of health levels on the productive capacity of the economy.[76] The principal approach is to ask how many more people are available for work as a result of a decrease in death rates, and what potential or actual production can be attributed to this in-increased supply of manpower. The capitalized value of the increase at a given point in time can be obtained by summing the value of future potential production represented by the lives saved. Current earnings patterns are usually used with or without adjustment for future increases in earnings per man, and with future earnings discounted at some appropriate interest rate.

The details of calculating the value of lives saved vary greatly from one investigator to another, but one result is common to all: the value of a man (in terms of future production potential) is very different at different ages. Table 3 shows some calculated values for United States males at three different discount rates based on average patterns of earnings and labor force participation rates in 1960.

The principal implication of the age-value profile is that the economic return (in production terms) from saving a life is not the same at all ages. Different kinds of health programs and different kinds of medical research are likely to affect various age groups differently; therefore, wise planning should give some consideration to these matters. For example, accidents accounted for only 6.6 per cent of all male deaths in the United States in 1960, but accounted for 12.8 per cent

TABLE 3. AGE-VALUE PROFILE OF UNITED STATES MALES IN 1960 ESTIMATED FROM DISCOUNTED FUTURE EARNINGS

	Discount Rate		
Age	4.0 Per Cent Per Annum (A)	7.2 Per Cent Per Annum (B)	10.0 Per Cent Per Annum (C)
0	$32,518	$14,680	$ 8,114
10	48,133	29,361	21,047
20	68,863	52,717	45,023
30	81,300	70,515	64,697
40	73,057	67,365	64,012
50	54,132	52,406	51,363
60	30,285	29,853	29,570
70	9,395	9,395	9,395
80	2,465	2,465	2,465
90	0	0	0

Note: The indicated discount rates were applied to the following earnings:

Age	Annual Earnings
0–14	$ 0
15–24	1,201
25–34	4,582
35–44	5,569
45–54	5,327
55–64	4,338
65–74	1,386
75–84	493
85 and over	0

No discounting was applied within ten-year age groups. No allowance was made for future increases in real earnings or for life expectancy.

No deduction was made for additional consumption attributable to decreased mortality. No earnings were imputed for males not in the labor force.

Source: United States Bureau of the Census, 1960 CENSUS OF POPULATION. Occupational Characteristics, Table 34.

of the economic cost of these deaths as measured by age-value profile B in Table 3. On the other hand, vascular lesions accounted for 9.5 per cent of all male deaths, but only 5.7 per cent of the economic cost of these deaths.

Table 4 shows how the age-value profile can be used to calculate the economic value (in production terms only) of the United States, using the 1960 death rate instead of the 1929 rate, or of lowering the United States rate in 1960 to the Swedish rate in 1960. In the former comparison, the greatest savings in number of lives were for infants and ages 75–84, but the greatest gain from a production point of view was from the reduction in the mortality rate for men 35–44. The United States-Swedish comparison highlights the current importance and potential of the 45–54 age group.

Most studies that attempt to place a value on a life saved (or on the cost of premature death) discuss the question of whether some deduction from discounted future earnings should be made for the future

1960 United States Rate Compared with 1929 United States Rate

Age	United States Male Population 1960 (Thousands)	Death Rate* 1929	Death Rate* 1960	Number of Deaths At 1929 Rate (Thousands)	Number of Deaths At 1960 Rate (Thousands)	Number of Lives Saved (Thousands)	Economic Value of Lives Saved (Millions)
Under 1	2,090	79.8	30.1	166.8	62.9	103.9	$1,525
1–4	8,240	6.5	1.2	53.6	9.9	43.7	834
5–14	18,029	2.0	.6	36.1	10.8	25.3	743
15–24	11,906	3.7	1.5	44.1	17.9	26.2	1,381
25–34	11,179	5.1	1.9	57.0	21.2	35.8	2,524
35–44	11,755	7.8	3.7	91.7	43.5	48.2	3,247
45–54	10,093	13.9	9.7	140.3	97.9	42.4	2,222
55–64	7,537	26.7	22.7	201.2	171.1	30.1	899
65–74	5,116	57.6	48.3	294.7	247.1	47.6	447
75–84	2,025	126.8	99.6	256.8	201.7	55.1	136
85 and over	362	256.0	208.4	92.7	75.4	17.3	0
Total	88,331	16.2	10.8	1,435.0	959.4	475.6	13,958

TABLE 4. (CONCLUDED)

Swedish Death Rate Compared with United States Death Rate

Age	Death Rate* Sweden 1960	Number of Deaths at Swedish Rate (Thousands)	Lives Saved If U.S. Rate Lowered to Swedish Rate (Thousands)	Economic Value of Lives Saved (Millions)
Under 1	19.1	39.9	23.6	$ 347
1–4	1.0	7.8	2.1	39
5–14	.5	9.0	1.8	53
15–24	1.0	11.9	5.9	314
25–34	1.2	13.4	7.8	552
35–44	2.0	23.5	19.9	1,346
45–54	5.1	51.5	46.4	2,433
55–64	14.1	106.3	65.6	1,958
65–74	38.2	195.4	51.2	481
75–84	98.2	198.9	4.5	11
85 and over	236.0	85.4	−9.3	0
Total	8.4	743.1	219.5	7,533

* Three-year average centered on year indicated.

Sources: United States Death Rates: 1929: United States Bureau of the Census, HISTORICAL STATISTICS OF THE UNITED STATES, series B123–154. 1960: United States Public Health Service, VITAL STATISTICS OF THE UNITED STATES, 1960, 1961, Table 1C. United States Population: United States Bureau of the Census, 1960 CENSUS OF POPULATION, United States Summary, General Characteristics, PC(1) 1B, Tables 45 and 46. Swedish death rates: ANNUAL EPIDEMIOLOGICAL AND VITAL STATISTICS, 1959, 1960 and 1961, Table 4.

consumption of the individuals whose lives are saved. The arguments for and against are usually framed in terms of whether the value being measured is the value to society including the individual or excluding him. A slightly different way of looking at this problem could be suggested. Consider someone contemplating whether a certain expenditure for health services is worthwhile for him in terms of its expected benefits. He is highly unlikely to think that his own future consumption must be subtracted to calculate the benefits. Many collective decisions might be listed concerning the allocation of resources to health in the same way. Who will be the beneficiary of these additional services is not known. Each person, therefore, will tend to evaluate the potential benefits in much the same way that he would a decision concerning his own expenditures for health; i.e., he will see no reason for deducting consumption, since he may be the one who will benefit from the expenditure. *Ex post* he may reason that saving someone else's life did not do him any good, but in advance of the event and in the absence of knowledge concerning who the beneficiary will be, the full value of the discounted earnings seems the appropriate basis for valuation.

Better health can increase the number of potential man-hours for production by reducing morbidity and disability, as well as by reducing mortality. Some estimate of the potential gains to the economy from this source can be obtained from data collected periodically as part of the National Health Survey. In 1964, approximately 5.5 workdays per person were lost for health reasons by those currently employed.[77] Additional loss was contributed by those persons who would have been employed except for reasons of health.

Health and Productivity

Common sense suggests that better health should result in more production per man, as well as more men available for work. Unfortunately, very little research has been done to provide a basis for estimating the magnitude of this effect. Company sponsored health programs would seem to offer an excellent opportunity for the study of this question, but not much has been done. In one investigation of what executives *thought* were the results of their company's health program, "less absenteeism" was mentioned by 55 per cent of the respondents, "improved employee health" was mentioned by 50 per cent, but "improved productivity on the job" was mentioned by only 12 per cent of the respondents.[78]

A number of studies have examined company health programs,[79-82] but their emphasis is on turnover rates, accident rates, absenteeism and Workmen's Compensation insurance premiums, rather than on output per man-hour. Whether this is because the latter effect is small, or because it is difficult to measure, is not clear. Many of the studies suffer from failure to consider other relevant variables along with the presence or absence of a company health program. Also, these studies do not clarify whether the benefits of company health programs should be attributed to improvements in health. For example, absenteeism and medical expenses may be lowered because of better controls rather than because of any change in health.

One special aspect of company health programs is the periodic health examination, much favored by those interested in preventive medicine. The basic notion is that if diseases or other injurious conditions are discovered early enough the chances for arrest or cure are greatly enhanced. An extensive literature exists on this subject, reviewed by Roberts,[83] but, unfortunately, the studies do not clearly establish the economic value of such examinations. Roberts lists several values served by such examinations but concludes that both public health service activities and personal health practices have much more effect on health than do periodic examinations.

A thorough economic analysis of the costs and benefits of company health programs and periodic health examinations is needed. Such an analysis should pay special attention to all the real costs of these programs including, for example, the time demanded of the examinees. It should attempt also to distinguish between those benefits which are realized through improvements in health and those which are unrelated to health.

Health and Consumption

In contrast to the substantial number of studies that look at the economic value of health in terms of production, very little information is available concerning its value as an end in itself (consumption). Klarman has suggested that one way of approaching the problem would be to observe the expenditures that people are willing to incur for the elimination of nondisabling diseases or the expenditures incurred by those not in the labor force.[84]

Many people in the public health field greatly overestimate the value that the consumer places on health. The health literature frequently seems to read as if no price is too great to pay for good health, but the behavior of consumers indicates that they are often unwilling to pay even a small price. For example, surveys have shown that many people do not brush their teeth regularly, even when they believe that brushing would significantly reduce tooth decay and gum trouble.[85,86] Smokers who acknowledge the harmful effects of smoking refuse to stop,[87] and a group of executives whose obesity was called to their attention by their physicians took no action to correct a condition which is acknowledged to be injurious to health.[88] Some cases (mostly communicable diseases) may be noted where the social consumption value of health is greater than the private consumption value because of important external effects. The examples cited, however, do not fall into this category.

One of the problems that should be squarely faced in framing a social policy for health services is that people differ in the relative value that they place on health, just as they differ in the relative value that they place on other goods and services. Any system which attempts to force all people to buy the same amount of health services is likely to result in a significant misallocation of resources.

Health and Life Attitudes

This is another area where one can do little more than say that research would be desirable. Many people have speculated about the effect of changes in health levels on attitudes toward work, saving, birth control and other aspects of behavior, but not much evidence has been accumulated. One interesting question concerns the ability of various populations to perceive changes in health levels. A study of low income Negroes in Chicago revealed very little awareness that a significant decline in infant mortality had actually occurred.[89] This suggests that changes in life attitudes, if they are related to changes in health levels, probably occur only after a lag.

CONCLUSION

The principal line of argument in this paper may be stated briefly: health services represent the combined inputs of labor, capital and intermediate goods and services used by the health industry. Their contribution to the economy must be measured by the output of this industry, which takes three forms: health, validation services and other consumer services. Of the three, health is probably the most important. The problem of measuring changes in health levels was examined and followed by a discussion of the relationship between health services and health. Measure of the latter is greatly complicated by the fact that health depends upon environmental factors as well as health services. Most of the studies treat rising income as favorable to health, but some reasons are presented for questioning the validity of this assumption for the United States at present. The economic importance of changes in health levels flows first, from the importance of health as a consumption goal in itself, and, second, from the effect of health on production. This effect can take two forms—changes in potential man-hours and changes in output per man-hour. Changes in life attitudes attributable to changes in health levels also may indirectly affect the economy.

Throughout the paper the need for additional research on each of these concepts and relationships has been stressed. Many of the studies cited have also dealt at length with the question of needed research. The best stimulus to good research is a good example; exhortation is a poor substitute. Nevertheless, this paper will conclude with a few comments on possible points of departure for research.

One promising line of inquiry would be to capitalize on the fact that health services in this country and abroad are produced and financed under a bewildering array of institutional arrangements. Important differences may be found with respect to the ownership and control of facilities, the organization of medical practice, the pricing of health services, the remuneration of health personnel and many other aspects of industrial organization. A basic question to be asked in each case is, "What are the implications of these differences for health and for the economy?"

Another potentially fruitful area of work concerns the advances in medical technology which are the principal source of productivity gain for this industry. The American Medical Association has compiled a list of "significant advances and technological developments" for the period 1936–62, by specialty, based on the response of knowledgeable physicians to a mail survey.[90] The same source presents a list of 30 important therapeutic agents now in use that have been introduced since 1934.[91] Both could provide a useful departure for research on the costs and benefits of medical research as well as for studies of innovation and diffusion similar to those that Mansfield[92] and Griliches[93] have developed for other parts of the economy.

The introduction to this paper argued that one of the principal reasons for wanting to know something about the contribution of health services to the economy is to be able to make better decisions concerning the allocation of resources to health. These decisions are increasingly made by government and are implemented in the form of subsidies for hospital construction, medical education and even medical care. This suggests that one line of fruitful research might be developed as follows:

1. First, the question of health versus other goals must be considered. Although lip service is often paid to the notion that health is a goal to be desired above all else, the most casual inspection of human behavior provides ample refutation of this proposition. Viewed as a source of consumer satisfaction, good health is often shunted aside in favor of the pleasure to be derived from other objects of expenditure and other patterns of behavior. Although the path to better health is frequently portrayed in terms of more hospitals, more doctors and more drugs, most people have the potential of improving their own health by their own actions. Ignorance may be cited to explain the failure of people to take these actions, but this is manifestly untrue in many cases (e.g., doctors continue to smoke). Furthermore, "ignorance" frequently means nothing more than that people have not taken the time or trouble to obtain readily available information about health.

Health also contributes to the economy through production, but alternative ways of increasing output are available. To cite two important ones, resources allocated to increasing health could be allocated to increasing the stock of physical capital, or to increasing the rate of technological change through research and development. Anyone arguing for greater investment in health to increase production should be prepared to show that the return to investment in health is greater than the return to alternative forms of investment.

2. Once a decision has been made regarding the allocation of resources for health relative to other consumer goals and alternative forms of investment, a second allocation decision is required to divide resources among health services and alternative routes to better health. For instance, expectant mothers may benefit from frequent visits to a board-certified obstetrician, but they may also benefit from a better diet, or from not having to work during the last months of pregnancy, or from having someone to help them with their other children.

One can think of health problems where the environmental factors are of negligible importance and health services can make the difference between life and death. However, many situations also exist where both the environment and health services have a role to play and, given a fixed amount of resources to be used for health purposes, knowing the relative contributions (at the margin) of each is important so that resources may be allocated efficiently.

3. The third and most detailed level of decision-making concerns the allocation of resources among various types of health services. More doctors, more nurses, more hospitals, more dentists—in short, more of everything—is needed. Given the decision about resources available for health and the allocation of these resources among health services and other health factors, however, one must have some notion about the contribution (again at the margin), of various types of health services. The absence of such knowledge probably means that public decisions concerning increases of these services can be made on only an arbitrary basis. The argument that the various health resources must be increased in fixed proportion is refuted by the evidence from other countries where health systems are successfully using doctors, nurses, hospital facilities and other health inputs in proportions that differ strikingly from those used in the United States, as well as differing among themselves.

One final note of caution seems to be in order. Whatever research approach is pursued, and whatever questions are attacked, economists must become familiar with health institutions and technology. The practice of medicine is still more an art than a science. The intimate nature of the relationship between patient and doctor, the vital character of the service rendered, and the heavy responsibilities assumed by medical personnel suggest the dangers inherent in reducing health care to matters of balance sheets, or supply and demand curves. Economics has something to contribute to health problems, but it should proceed as the servant of health, not its master.

REFERENCES

[1] Klarman, Herbert E., THE ECONOMICS OF HEALTH, New York, Columbia University Press, 1965.

[2] Mushkin, Selma J., Health as an Investment, *Journal of Political Economy,* Supplement, 70, 129–157, October, 1962.

[3] Wolf, Bernard M., The Economics of Medical Research and Medical Care —From the Point of View of Economic Growth, Washington, D.C., Public Health Service, Resources Analysis Branch, 1964 (manuscript).

[4] The University of Michigan Department of Economics and Bureau of Public Health Economics, THE ECONOMICS OF HEALTH AND MEDICAL CARE, Ann Arbor, The University of Michigan Press, 1964.

[5] Arrow, Kenneth J., Uncertainty and the Welfare Economics of Medical Care, *American Economic Review,* 53, 941–973, December, 1963.

[6] Klarman, *op. cit.*

[7] Mushkin, Selma J., Why Health Economics?, *in* THE ECONOMICS OF HEALTH AND MEDICAL CARE, *op. cit.,* pp. 3–13.

[8] American Medical Association, COMMISSION ON THE COST OF MEDICAL CARE REPORT, Chicago, The American Medical Association, 1963–64, Volume I, p. 19.

[9] Anonymous, An Interview with J. Douglas Colman, *Hospitals,* 39, 45–49, April 16, 1965.

[10] American Medical Association, *op. cit.,* p. 9.

[11] Reed, Louis S. and Rice, Dorothy P., National Health Expenditures: Object of Expenditures and Source of Funds, 1962, *Social Security Bulletin,* 27, 11–21, August, 1964.

[12] United States Department of Commerce, Office of Business Economics, NATIONAL INCOME, 1954 EDITION, A SUPPLEMENT TO THE SURVEY OF CURRENT BUSINESS, Washington, United States Government Printing Office, 1954.

[13] ————, SURVEY OF CURRENT BUSINESS, Washington, United States Government Printing Office, annual July issues.

[14] ————, U.S. INCOME AND OUTPUT, A SUPPLEMENT TO THE SURVEY OF CURRENT BUSINESS, Washington, United States Government Printing Office, 1958.

[15] Merriam, Ida C., Social and Welfare Expenditures, 1963–64, *Social Security Bulletin,* 27, 3–14, October, 1964.

[16] United States National Health Survey, PERSONAL HEALTH EXPENSES: DISTRIBUTION OF PERSONS BY AMOUNT AND TYPE OF EXPENSE, UNITED STATES JULY–DECEMBER 1962, Series 10, Washington, United States Government Printing Office, 1965.

[17] ————, MEASUREMENT OF PERSONAL HEALTH EXPENDITURES, Series 2, Washington, United States Government Printing Office, 1963.

[18] Anderson, Ronald and Anderson, Odin W., Trends in Personal Health Spending, *Progress in Health Services,* 14, November–December, 1965.

[19] United States Bureau of Labor Statistics, STUDY OF CONSUMER EXPENDITURES, INCOMES AND SAVINGS, Volume VIII, SUMMARY OF FAMILY EXPENDITURES FOR MEDICAL CARE AND PERSONAL CARE, Philadelphia, University of Pennsylvania Press, 1956.

[20] ————, STUDY OF CONSUMER EXPENDITURES, INCOMES AND SAVINGS, Volume XVIII, SUMMARY OF FAMILY INCOME, EXPENDITURES AND SAVINGS, ALL URBAN AREAS COMBINED, Philadelphia, University of Pennsylvania Press, 1957.

[21] United States Department of Commerce, Bureau of the Census, CENSUS OF POPULATION, Washington, United States Government Printing Office, decennial.

[22] United States Department of Commerce, Bureau of the Census, U.S. CENSUSES OF POPULATION AND HOUSING: 1960, 1/1000, 1/10,000: Two NATIONAL SAMPLES OF THE POPULATION OF THE UNITED STATES, Washington, United States Department of Commerce.

[23] United States Public Health Service, HEALTH MANPOWER SOURCE BOOK, Sections 1–19, Washington, United States Government Printing Office, 1952–64.

[24] American Hospital Association, HOSPITALS, Guide Issue, Part 2, 38, August 1, 1964 (annual).

[25] United States Treasury Department, Internal Revenue Service, STATISTICS OF INCOME . . . 1962: U.S. BUSINESS TAX RETURNS, Washington, United States Government Printing Office, 1965 (annual).

[26] United States Department of Commerce, Bureau of the Census, UNITED STATES CENSUS OF MANUFACTURERS, Washington, United States Government Printing Office, 1963 (currently every five years).

[27] Becker, Gary S., A Theory of the Allocation of Time, *The Economic Journal*, 75, 493–517, September, 1965.

[28] World Health Organization, Constitution of the World Health Organization, Annex I, *in* World Health Organization, THE FIRST TEN YEARS OF THE WORLD HEALTH ORGANIZATION, Geneva, The World Health Organization, 1958.

[29] Roberts, Ffrangcon, THE COST OF HEALTH, London, Turnstile Press, 1952.

[30] Johnson, R. H., The Health of Israel, *The Lancet*, 7417, 842–845, October 23, 1965.

[31] Morris, J. N., USES OF EPIDEMIOLOGY, Second Edition, Baltimore, The Williams & Wilkins Co., 1964, p. 14.

[32] Sullivan, D. F., Conceptual Problems in Developing an Index of Health, *in* VITAL AND HEALTH STATISTICS, DATA EVALUATION AND METHODS RESEARCH, Public Health Service Publication Number 1000, Series 2, Number 17, Washington, United States Government Printing Office, May, 1966.

[33] Sanders, B. S., Measuring Community Health Levels, *American Journal of Public Health*, 54, 1063–1070, July, 1964.

[34] Anderson, Alice L. and Altman, Isidore, Methodology in Evaluating the Quality of Medical Care, An Annotated Selected Bibliography 1955–61, Pittsburgh, University of Pittsburgh Press, 1962.

[35] Terris, Milton, The Relevance of Medical Care to the Public Health, paper delivered before American Public Health Association, November 13, 1963.

[36] Rosen, George, The Bacteriological, Immunologic and Chemotherapeutic Period 1875–1950, *Bulletin of the New York Academy of Medicine*, 40, 483–494, 1964.

[37] Long, A. P. and Sartwell, P. E., Tetanus in the U.S. Army in World War II, *Bulletin of the U.S. Army Medical Department*, 7, 371–385, April, 1947.

[38] Long, A. P., Immunization to Tetanus, *in* Army Medical Services Graduate School, RECENT ADVANCES IN MEDICINE AND SURGERY, Washington, Walter Reed Army Institute of Research, 1955, pp. 311–313.

359

[39] American Medical Association, *op. cit.*, Volume III, Chapter 4.

[40] ———, *op. cit.*, Volume III, Chapter 7.

[41] Lerner, Monroe and Anderson, Odin W., HEALTH PROGRESS IN THE UNITED STATES 1900–1960: A REPORT OF THE HEALTH INFORMATION FOUNDATION, Chicago, University of Chicago Press, 1963, p. 43.

[42] Marks, Herbert H., Longevity and Mortality of Diabetics, *American Journal of Public Health*, 55, 416–423, March, 1965.

[43] World Health Organization, EXPERT COMMITTEE ON WATER FLUORIDATION, FIRST REPORT, Technical Report Series, Number 146, Geneva, The World Health Organization, 1958.

[44] Schlesinger, E. R., Dietary Fluoride and Caries Prevention, *American Journal of Public Health*, 55, 1123–1129, August, 1965.

[45] Farmer, A. W. and Shandling, B. S., Review of Burn Admissions, 1956–1960—The Hospital for Sick Children, Toronto, *Journal of Trauma*, 3, 425–432, September, 1963.

[46] Kaiser, R. F., *et. al.*, Uterine Cytology, *Public Health Reports*, 75, 423–427, 1960.

[47] Dunn, John E., Jr., Cancer of the Cervix—End Results Report, *in* National Cancer Institute and American Cancer Society, FIFTH NATIONAL CANCER CONFERENCE PROCEEDINGS, Philadelphia, J. B. Lippincott Company, 1956, pp. 253–257.

[48] Krementz, Edward T., End Results in Skin Cancer, *in* National Cancer Institute and American Cancer Society, FOURTH NATIONAL CANCER CONFERENCE PROCEEDINGS, Philadelphia, J. B. Lippincott Co., 1961, pp. 629–637.

[49] Lewison, Edwin F., An Appraisal of Longterm Results in Surgical Treatment of Breast Cancer, *Journal of the American Medical Association*, 186, 975–978, December 14, 1963.

[50] Sutherland, Robert, CANCER: THE SIGNIFICANCE OF DELAY, London, Butterworth and Company (Publishers) Ltd., 1960, pp. 196–202.

[51] Stout, John, *et al.*, Status of Congenital Heart Disease Patients Ten to Fifteen Years After Surgery, *Public Health Reports*, 79, 377–382, May, 1964.

[52] Wilson, May G., *et al.*, The Decline of Rheumatic Fever—Recurrence Rates of Rheumatic Fever Among 782 Children for 21 Consecutive Calendar Years, *Journal of Chronic Diseases*, 7, 183–197, March, 1958.

[53] The Rheumatic Fever Working Party of the Medical Research Council of Great Britain and The Subcommittee of Principal Investigators of the American Council on Rheumatic Fever and Congenital Heart Disease, American Heart Association, Treatment of Acute Rheumatic Fever in Children: A Cooperative Clinical Trial of ACTH, Cortisone, and Aspirin, *British Medical Journal*, 1, 555–574, 1955.

[54] Kutner, Ann G., Current Status of Steroid Therapy in Rheumatic Fever, *American Heart Journal*, 70, 147–149, August, 1965.

[55] Brest, Albert N., Treatment of Coronary Occlusive Disease: Critical Review, *Diseases of the Chest*, 45, 40–45, January, 1964.

[56] Combined Staff Clinic, Recent Advances in Hypertension, *American Journal of Medicine,* 39, 634–638, October, 1965.

[57] Lindsay, Malcolm I., Jr. and Spiekerman, Ralph E., Re-evaluation of Therapy of Acute Myocardial Infarction, *American Heart Journal,* 67, 559–564, April, 1964.

[58] Lockwood, Howard J., *et al.,* Effects of Intensive Care on the Mortality Rate of Patients with Myocardial Infarctions, *Public Health Reports,* 78, 655–661, August, 1963.

[59] Cain, Harvey D., *et al.,* Current Therapy of Cardiovascular Disease, *Geriatrics,* 18, 507–518, July, 1963.

[60] Lowenthal, Milton, *et al.,* An Analysis of the Rehabilitation Needs and Prognoses of 232 Cases of Cerebral Vascular Accident, *Archives of Physical Medicine,* 40, 183–186, 1959.

[61] May, Philip R. A. and Tuma, A. Hussain, Schizophrenia—An Experimental Study of Five Treatment Methods, *British Journal of Psychiatry,* 111, 503–510, June, 1965.

[62] Schwartz, Samuel and Vinyard, John H., Prenatal Care and Prematurity, *Public Health Reports,* 80, 237–248, March, 1965.

[63] Shapiro, Sam, *et al.,* Comparisons of Prematurity and Prenatal Mortality in a General Population and in a Population of a Prepaid Group Practice, *American Journal of Public Health,* 48, 170–187, February, 1958.

[64] ———, Further Observations on Prematurity and Prenatal Mortality in a General Population and in the Population of a Prepaid Group Practice Medical Plan, *American Journal of Public Health,* 50, 1304–1317, September, 1960.

[65] Lockwood, *et al., op. cit.*

[66] United States Public Health Service, CORONARY CARE UNITS: SPECIALIZED INTENSIVE CARE UNITS FOR ACUTE MYOCARDIAL INFARCTION PATIENTS, Washington, United States Government Printing Office, October, 1964.

[67] Forshall, Isabella and Rickham, P. P., Experience of a Neonatal Surgical Unit—The First Six Years, *The Lancet,* 2, 751–754, October, 1960.

[68] Wylie, C. M., Participation in a Multiple Screening Clinic with Five Year Follow-Up, *Public Health Reports,* 76, 596–602, July, 1961.

[69] Yankauer, Alfred and Lawrence, Ruth A., A Study of Periodic School Medical Examinations, *American Journal of Public Health,* 45, 71–78, January, 1955.

[70] McKinnon, N. E., The Effects of Control Programs on Cancer Mortality, *Canadian Medical Association Journal,* 82, 1308–1312, June 25, 1960.

[71] American Medical Association, *op. cit.,* Volume III, p. ix.

[72] Altenderfer, Marion E., Relationship Between Per Capita Income and Mortality in the Cities of 100,000 or More Population, *Public Health Reports,* 62, 1681–1691, November 28, 1947.

[73] Denison, Edward F., Study of European Economic Growth, Washington, The Brookings Institution, unpublished.

[74] Morrison, S. L. and Goldberg, E. M., Schizophrenia and Social Class, *Journal of Mental Science*, 109, 785–802, 1963.

[75] Meadows Susan H., Social Class Migration and Chronic Bronchitis: A Study of Male Hospital Patients in the London Area, *British Journal of Preventive and Social Medicine*, 15, 171–175, 1961.

[76] Klarman, *op. cit.*, pp. 162–172.

[77] United States National Health Survey, DISABILITY DAYS: UNITED STATES JULY 1963–JUNE 1964, Series 10, Washington, United States Government Printing Office, 1965, p. 16.

[78] National Industrial Conference Board, COMPANY MEDICAL AND HEALTH PROGRAMS, Studies in Personnel Policy, Number 171, New York, National Industrial Conference Board, 1959, p. 12.

[79] Grant, Ellsworth S., The U.S. Concept of and Experience in Small-Plant Health Services, *in* PROCEEDINGS OF THIRTEENTH INTERNATIONAL CONGRESS ON OCCUPATIONAL HEALTH, New York City, 1960, pp. 118–120.

[80] National Health Forum, Are Occupational Health Programs Worthwhile?, *in* Maisel, Albert Q. (Editor), HEALTH OF PEOPLE WHO WORK, New York, National Health Council, 1960, pp. 11–28.

[81] Cipolla, J. A., The Occupational Health Experiences of Two American Hotels for 1955 and 1956, *in* PROCEEDINGS OF FOURTEENTH INTERNATIONAL CONGRESS ON OCCUPATIONAL HEALTH, Madrid, Spain, 1963, Volume II, pp. 290–291.

[82] Blankenship, Marilyn, Influenza Immunization and Industrial Absenteeism—A Seven Month Study, *in* PROCEEDINGS OF THE FOURTEENTH INTERNATIONAL CONGRESS ON OCCUPATIONAL HEALTH, *op. cit.*, pp. 294–295.

[83] Roberts, Norman J., The Values and Limitations of Periodic Health Examinations, *Journal of Chronic Diseases*, 9, 95–116, 1959.

[84] Klarman, *op. cit.*, p. 64.

[85] Kirscht, John P., A National Study of Health Beliefs, Ann Arbor, University of Michigan, 1965 (manuscript).

[86] Haefner, Don P., *et al.*, Preventive Actions Concerning Dental Disease, Tuberculosis and Cancer, paper delivered at the 22nd Annual Meeting of the Association of Teachers of Preventive Medicine, Chicago, October 17, 1965.

[87] Swinehart, James W. and Kirscht, John P., Smoking: A Panel Study of Beliefs and Behavior Following the PHS Report, paper delivered at the Annual Meeting of the American Psychological Association, Chicago, 1965.

[88] Wade, Leo, *et al.*, Are Periodic Health Examinations Worthwhile?, *Annals of Internal Medicine*, 56, 81–93, 1962.

[89] Bogue, Donald J., Inventory, Explanation, and Evaluation by Interview of Family Planning: Motives—Attitudes—Knowledge—Behavior: Fertility Measurement, document prepared for discussion at International Conference on Family Planning Programs, Geneva, Switzerland, August 23–27, 1965.

[90] American Medical Association, *op. cit.*, Volume III, pp. 4–12.

[91] ——, *op. cit.*, Volume III, pp. 13–14.

[92] Mansfield, Edwin, The Diffusion of Technological Change, National Science Foundation Reviews of Data on Research and Development, October, 1961.

[93] Griliches, Zvi, Hybrid Corn: An Exploration in the Economics of Technological Change, *Econometrica*, 25, 501–522, October, 1957.

ACKNOWLEDGMENTS

I am grateful to Deborah W. Sarachek for the preparation of the bibliography and tables and for numerous contributions to the text. I am also grateful to Dr. Richard H. Kessler for reading the section on medical care, and to Irving Leveson for several useful suggestions.

DISCUSSION

The discussion of Dr. Fuchs' paper falls naturally into two parts— comments made by economists and comments by physicians. The author's replies are incorporated where appropriate.

Comments by Economists

The discussants agreed with the author on the desirability of studying the effects of diverse medical care systems on the health of populations. Regional comparisons within a country would be just as useful as intercountry comparisons. One discussant attached extra importance to the study of the entrepreneurial (ownership and managerial) factor in the production of health services.

One discussant would pursue several additional questions:

Suppose that under defined circumstances a high-quality program of health services is attained. Can these results be extended to the mass of the population? Even if differences in mortality rates are still sizable, do they not overstate differences in health status? Several scholars have suggested that progress in the health services has entailed the trading of a reduction in mortality for an increase in morbidity.

Attention should be paid to the distributive aspects of health services—by social class or by income class. The poorer half of the

363

population stands to gain more from additional and improved health services than the richer half. If so, the public policy adopted would depend heavily on the social values that are espoused.

Given Fuchs' recognition of the variety of society's goals, would it not be desirable to develop cost-benefit analyses for alternative value systems, as well as for alternative service programs? How feasible is it to do this?

Another discussant noted the large number of unknowns cited in Fuchs' paper and the need for cooperative research among economists and physicians to reduce the area of ignorance. He attached particular weight to detailed studies of the health services industry. Such studies have traditionally fallen within the unique competence of economists.

In addition, he noted that the upward trend of costs and prices in the health services industry poses problems for the economy as a whole in its efforts to stablize consumer prices.

Still another discussant invited the attention of those participants who are not economists to Fuchs' emphasis on marginal changes in cost and in benefit. Public policy issues are not likely to take the form of all or nothing, but rather of more or less.

He noted that Fuchs employs income as a variable in two ways: 1. as an index of the standard of living and 2. as a measure of capability to maintain health resources. Correlations between health levels (whether measured by mortality rates or otherwise) and income must be examined after the effects of available health resources are removed, as well as before. Fuchs' group at the National Bureau of Economic Research is currently pursuing this line of inquiry.

Moreover, the negative correlation that Fuchs has found between the death rate and income derives from recent data. The inference that the rising standard of living has come to exert a negative effect on health status would gain in validity if the correlation between the same two variables 40 or 50 years ago were found to be positive. This would be an interesting question to pursue, if the necessary data were available.

In response to Fuchs' request for opinions on his three-fold classification of the output of the health services industry—health services, validation services and other consumer services—the suggestion was made that validation services may not be sufficiently distinguishable from health services. The concept of other consumer services is probably of greater value in long-term illness than in short-term illness.

364

Comments by Physicians

The focus here was on the section in the paper entitled Health Services and Health. The consensus was that the review of the literature was excellent, discriminating as well as complete.

On specific points certain questions were raised and disagreements expressed, some pertaining to the paper itself and some to the remarks made by other discussants.

Long-term trend data for certain diseases, such as rheumatic fever, scarlet fever, diphtheria, and tuberculosis, indicate that improvements in medical technology have not effected abrupt changes in the incidence of disease. If so, reason exists to doubt Fuchs' thesis that advances in medical technology must have been of sufficient import to offset the negative effects on health of the rise in the standard of living.

Along the same lines the point was made that differences in death rate among social classes have narrowed in England, but differences still exist, with the upper classes having the lower death rates. How these data should be interpreted in relation to Fuchs' thesis was not clear.

In his final remarks Fuchs pointed out that his views on the probable effects of the standard of living on health derive from correlation analysis of data for this country, from comparisons of data for this country and other countries, and from independent observation. Among the specific factors associated with the standard of living that may exert adverse effects on health are rich diet, alcohol consumption, motor vehicle accidents, the stress and tensions of urban life, etc.

The suggestion was made, and Fuchs agreed, that perhaps too much attention is paid to the effect of income on health and not enough to the effect of health on income. The latter is particularly important in long-term illness and may entail the transfer of deprivation from one generation to another.

In a broad look at the relationships that exist between the environment and health, biological and chemical factors must be included as well as socioeconomic factors. For example, the virulence of disease organisms may fluctuate over time.

Some controversy was voiced over the current status of treatment for cancer. One physician argued that no progress has been made in some time and that the several forms of therapy now in use yield substantially the same results in cure rates. Another physician cited recent, still unpublished data from California which indicated that substantial gains are being made in treating breast cancer by surgery.

RESEARCH INTO THE ORGANIZATION
OF MEDICAL PRACTICE

E. RICHARD WEINERMAN

Throughout recorded history the physician, or his primitive counterpart, has been the focal point of health protection in organized society. A constant thread linking the medical roles of shaman, priest, artisan, clinician and scientist has been that unique status awarded by society to those who undertake the prevention and treatment of disease. According to Sigerist:[1]

> The place that the physician holds in a given society is determined by a variety of factors of which the most important are the social and economic structure of that society, the valuation of health and disease by that society, the tasks it sets to its physicians, and finally the technology of medicine available to the doctors in such a period. These factors have changed a great deal in the course of time and so has, consequently, the position of the physician.

At this juncture of history, no less than in any previous or future time, the organization of medical practice reflects prevailing social, political and economic conditions in the various parts of the world on the one hand, and the stage of scientific and technological development in medicine on the other.[1-3]

A clear understanding of the role of the physician and the nature of the general medical care system in modern society requires, therefore, analysis of both the setting and the structure of medical practice. To the extent that serious research is directed to the socioeconomic and organizational aspects of medical practice, the prospects for an effective "fit" of health services to the needs of the community are enhanced.[4]

366

No understanding of the nature of medical practice is possible unless the specific role of the physician is placed in the context of the full fabric of contemporary medical care and unless this, in turn, is viewed as part of the total social milieu. Sigerist provides a basis for such a model of medical practice.[1,2] In this framework, the physician is seen as functioning in a complex web of relationships with patients, peers, assistants and consultants; conditioned by his own culture and class, and by the traditions of his training; responding to the pressures of market economics and lay expectations; adjusting with variable alacrity to the changing techniques of clinical practice; and affecting his own function with self-perceptions which resist and often ignore the rapid alterations in all of the other determinants of his professional role.

A model for the organization of medical practice must be constructed with two-way hinges and interchangeable parts to accommodate the continuing transformations and the puzzling inconsistencies. Medical practice in the western industrialized countries is essentially in transition. The parent society, itself in turmoil, is ambivalent with respect to the role of the physician as private entrepreneur or public servant. Health for the individual is the lure for the customers of billion-dollar industries, while the life-styles of an affluent society are increasingly pathogenic. Technological progress pushes independent medical artisans into imperfect institutional systems, and transforms solo practitioners into specialized cogs in largely unassembled wheels. In such a hurricane, the physician sees himself in a blur and at a distance.

The medical model, therefore, represents an economic market distorted by a hesitant public welare policy, a shifting mixture of efforts to serve social "need" and to effectively meet "demand," a combination luxury-necessity responding to the cultural as well as the physiological perceptions of consumers, and a professional structure rapidly assuming the triad of characteristics which may be identified as specialization, association and institutionalization.

Obviously, one brief review cannot assess the current state of knowledge in each of these complex areas of social concern. Other papers in this series do address themselves to the underlying sociological, economic and technical issues. Accepting the pattern of ecologic relationships presented above, this discussion will focus upon research into the organization of medical practice per se in the effort to identify the most useful contributions to the dynamics of the larger social system and to recognize the areas of fact and fiction which need further investigation.

FRAMES OF REFERENCE

The purpose of this report, therefore, is to consider recent research into the social settings and the organization patterns of medical practice. Although the importance of such research effort and the rich yield of applicable knowledge to be anticipated have long been exhorted,[5] the work done so far has barely passed the threshold of its own potential. Nonetheless, a vast literature has accumulated in recent years and the need is clear for some attempt to critically review the choice of subject matter, the methods used, the implications of the findings and the discernible needs for future research in this field.

Sharp limits have necessarily been imposed upon the content of this report. Five criteria have been adopted in the selection of available publications:

1. Reports of actual research, rather than narrative or conceptual writings.
2. Focus on the function of the physician, rather than on other types of health personnel.
3. Emphasis on the primary setting of the physician's practice, rather than his role in care of institutionalized patients.
4. Restriction to publications since 1950, available in English.
5. Selection of reports which illustrate the variety of work in this field, rather than exhaustive review of all pertinent literature.

In the few instances in which reference is made to publications which do not fit these exact criteria, the importance or relevance of the individual work has been the determining factor.

For purposes of this review, the material to be discussed has been somewhat arbitrarily divided into the following sections, although the demarcation lines are frequently crossed: 1. collection and analysis of basic information concerning various forms of medical practice; 2. studies of the social role of the physician; 3. evaluation of specific methods of medical practice; 4. methodology of research in these areas.

In general, attention is directed to the objectives and methods of the research reported, rather than to details of the findings. This emphasis is chosen as the necessary basis for identification of future needs and most promising methods for further research in this subject area.

FORMS OF MEDICAL PRACTICE

During the past two decades considerable effort has been expended, albeit somewhat unevenly, in basic survey and description of prevailing modes of medical practice. This has become technically possible with the development of modern methods of data gathering, statistical analysis and evaluation of performance. In each country major attention has, understandably, been given to the dominant form of contemporary practice. The overall pattern of active medical practice has yet to be completely described in any one area.

Studies of General Practice

The orientation of research in general practice has reflected the degree of stress and strain in the current status of the practitioner. Such studies have, in addition, been conditioned by the prevailing modes of medical and sociological research in the particular country. In Great Britain, Canada, Australia, New Zealand and Holland, for example, much of the assembled data derive from inventories of the vital statistics, the work load and the resources of the independent neighborhood practitioners. In the United States, by way of contrast, attention has been focussed on particular subject areas such as standards of clinical performance, new patterns of medical organization and sociological analyses of the doctor-patient relationship.

British studies of general practice. During the past 15 years or so, a number of critical surveys of British general practice have been conducted, both reflecting and contributing to the current "agonizing reappraisal" of the status of the family doctor under the National Health Service. The most frequently used methods have been those of direct observation by physician-surveyors and analysis of medical records.

Collings[6] undertook the first such investigation in 1948, with "participant-visits" to 104 general physicians in 55 practices in Great Britain. His appraisal was generally critical and suggested that the least commendable patterns of practice were to be found in urban England, particularly in comparison with his previous observations in New Zealand. Hadfield[7] reported a descriptive survey of a more representative sample of practitioners, conducted for the British

Medical Association in 1953, without attempting a qualitative appraisal. Taylor[8] adopted an avowedly positive approach in 1954, selecting 30 of the best practices identified in the previous surveys and seeking the elements of their success, using similar techniques of direct visitation and review of records. Cartwright and Marshall,[9] in 1963, interviewed a stratified and random sample of 157 general practices in behalf of the British College of General Practitioners, and added to the descriptive pattern a summary of the physicians' own reactions and recommendations. Most recently, in 1965, the Fry Committee of the College of General Practitioners[10] reviewed all available data as the basis for recommending new methods in general practice. Among these were the use of ancillary office personnel, joint health center practice, redesigned medical records and closer relationships with specialists and hospitals.

Although such direct observational surveys have been a characteristic of British research in this field, some investigators have applied analytical techniques to the mass of operational and diagnostic data regularly compiled under the National Health Service. Forsyth and Logan,[11-14] among many others, exemplify this approach, demonstrating the potential for insight into the conduct of medical practice which can be gained through interpretation of routinely available data.

An additional technique has been the analysis in some depth of an individual practice by the involved physician himself, analogous to the case study method in clinical medicine.[15,16] Such reports add substance to the patterns produced in the larger surveys, but do not significantly alter the now voluminously documented record of the strengths and weaknesses of general practice in the United Kingdom.

A final category of British studies in general practice is characterized by the view from the hospital rather than the neighborhood office. Analyses of patterns of referral to and utilization of hospital resources have been used as a basis for appraisal of the general practitioner system.[17-21] The overall pattern is one of somewhat uncritical use of a widely available resource. This research vantage point has contributed to the understanding of British medical practice, reinforcing rather than altering the overall picture presented by the field surveys.

American studies of general practice. Considerably less emphasis has been given to study of general practice in the United States. Those American studies which have focused on the "primary" physician have done so only in relation to special features of his work. Much of the literature on the subject of general practice is merely descriptive of individual experience or is essentially conceptual and exhortatory in content.

The classic American study is that of Peterson, *et al.*,[22] an imaginative survey and appraisal technique which has already inspired comparable efforts in other countries. Data collected in the course of observational visits to a stratified sample of 94 general practitioners in North Carolina were correlated with numerous indices of demographic, sociological and professional status. Although this project was designed primarily for purposes of appraisal of quality of performance, systematic information was gathered for the first time in this country on the office setting and work habits of the private general practitioner.

The American counterpart of the hospital view of general practice in Great Britain is found in the detailed studies of referral patterns, again conducted by a University of North Carolina research team.[23-26] Carefully drawn samples of local community practitioners (and their patients) were interviewed and relevant medical records were analyzed to identify the significant patterns and problems. The findings are strikingly similar to those of Acheson, *et al.*, in London[19, 20] with respect to the deficiencies of professional communication, the domination of patient influences and the inadequacy of medical follow-up. In a society apparently committed to the strategy of a huge backfield of specialists behind a rapidly thinning front line of generalists, such inefficiencies in the referral process are especially serious.

Both the sociologists and physicians in medical care research have investigated the degree to which individuals and families actually use general physicians on the local community level. Studies in an urban center,[27] a small town[28] and a rural area[29] indicate that a majority of lay respondents claim to "have"—although not always to "use"—a personal or family physician. Other studies suggest that important social and economic class differences lie behind the overall statistics.[30, 31] The extent of true *family practice*, as contrasted with individual relationship with a personal physician, is not always clear.

A further category of American research related to general practice is illustrated by the statistical surveys conducted periodically by the Public Health Service,[32] Health Information Foundation[33] and the journal *Medical Economics*.[34] Such summaries have provided an enumeration of active practitioners together with essential demographic and professional data, but have not approached the detailed content of the British field surveys. Relatively little has been done in analyzing patient

371

load and clinical services, although the work of Ciocco and Altman[35, 36] illustrates the value of the ore to be mined in these areas.

Overall, the United States pattern of general practice differs from the British in amount rather than in kind. The decline of the solo general practitioners in the United States relegates this professional group to minority status, to small town and rural location, and to older age brackets. Although the nature of office practice is not greatly dissimilar, the American general practitioner tends to function less often in the patient's home and more frequently in the community general hospital.

General practitioner studies in other countries. Less emphasis has been given in other countries to disciplined research into general practice (at least as far as is revealed in the English-language literature). Where studies have been conducted, they have revealed evidence of the influence of both the British emphasis on general practice and the American techniques of survey research.

Jungfer and Last[37] in Australia, and Clute[38] in Canada, have applied the Peterson method to description and appraisal of representative samples of general practitioners, with results quite similar to those in North Carolina. Such studies have not been based on national samples, as were the British surveys, but they have contributed significantly to the understanding of general medical practice in these countries. As is true of the North Carolina project, these studies were designed primarily for evaluation of standards of practice rather than for the gathering of representative and detailed "facts" per se.

The studies of Querido[39] in Amsterdam provide limited but perceptive views of Dutch general practice. In these modest research exercises, the content and conditions of urban practice are explored by means of interviews with both physicians and their patients. The research potential which exists in the context of routine public health administration is well illustrated.

Studies of Specialist Practice

A number of studies have documented the seemingly inexorable trend toward specialty medical practice in the United States. These have generally been based upon data gathered for official purposes by various agencies of state and federal government, and are published in regular series as part of the function of the Public Health Service.[32] Research into particular aspects of the specialization process has also been conducted under nongovernmental auspices. These studies may be categorized in relation to analyses of national trends, focus on individual specialties and characterization of office and hospital-based practice. In clear reflection of the specialist emphasis in this country, almost all of the published reports in these areas emanate from the United States.

Analysis of national trends. The reversal of generalist-specialist ratios in the past few decades has been well documented. Special analyses of records of training institutions and certification boards have identified the accelerating pace and the extent of atomization of medical practice which is inherent in this trend.[40–42] Huntley, White and their colleagues[25, 26] have shown some of the worrisome consequences of these developments in relation to the generic needs of patients. Others have documented the changing patterns of type and place of work of various categories of physicians in the United States.[43, 44] Such research is illustrative of the variety of studies of specialism in the American literature which have in common the methodology of statistical analysis of routinely collected data on physicians and their professional function.

Focus on individual specialties. Although much attention has been given to the general phenomenon of specialization, comparatively meager information has been collected about the conditions of practice within individual specialties. Questionnaire surveys of pediatricians,[45] internists[46] and surgeons[47] have shed needed light on the organization of practice in these basic specialist categories. Sociological investigation has also been made of surgeons[48] and psychiatrists[49] (by way of illustration), but little has been done to elucidate the organizational and work patterns of other specialties. Quite recently a household survey of the selection and use of all specialists in a small industrial town has been reported,[50] possibly heralding a widening scope of research interest in this subject area.

Aspects of hospital-based practice. A striking trend in modern American medical practice is the increasing association of specialists with hospitals for care of ambulatory as well as bed patients. One aspect of this is the appointment of salaried specialists to full-time hospital staffs, usually in association with educational, research or diagnostic service activities. Roemer[51] has used large-scale mailed questionnaire techniques in the effort to document the extent of these relationships, employing a varied set of indices of hospital standards to evaluate the significance of the pattern.

A more traditional system has been that of the hospital outpatient clinic, with staff including both community and resident physicians—

the former usually on a part-time and nonpaid basis. Only recently has this mode of medical practice been subject to serious study in this country.[52-54] Such studies have included direct observation of patient care, review of medical records, interviews with staff and patients and analysis of utilization patterns. The new clinic methods described are offered as antidotes to the persistent problems of fragmentation and depersonalization of the care of the ambulant patient.

In the interface of community and hospital, a parallel development has been that of locating physicians' offices within or adjacent to hospital facilities. Rorem[55] has illustrated this trend through appraisal of ten such arrangements in Philadelphia. A related pattern (although not necessarily in physical proximity to hospitals) is that of grouping physicians' offices in appropriately designed and centrally located "medical arts" buildings. A recent Washington, D.C. study[56] was based upon mailed questionnaire responses from 575 doctors in 15 such buildings (representing some 40 per cent of all practitioners in the city) and included comparisons with available data on other local physicians.

Studies of Medical Group Practice

Despite the fact that formal group practice is the primary method of professional work for a relatively small minority of American physicians, it does represent a rapidly accelerating trend in this country and has received (and probably deserves) a disproportionately large amount of attention in medical care research. The Public Health Service sponsored national surveys in 1946[57] and 1959,[58] as did the American Medical Association in 1957.[59] These were essentially based upon mailed questionnaires and analysis of generally available data. These studies show a relatively slow growth rate, a characteristic "profile" of specialty-oriented structure and function, and a self-contradictory spectrum of professional attitudes. A California survey in 1952,[60] using similar methods, included comparisons with the national pattern and undertook a limited appraisal of effectiveness of performance.

Analyses of individual group practice experiences have frequently been reported,[61, 62] although comparable study methods have not been developed in this area. General descriptive writings on group practice are also numerous.

Reports of more specific probing into particular features of the group practice method are beginning to appear. The "intrinsic" and "extrinsic" factors which affect the structure of prepaid group practice programs have been examined.[63,64] Sociological methods have been applied to studies of group interaction.[65,66] The nature of specialty practice in the group setting has been described.[67] The record remains, however, fragmentary and discontinuous.

The Health Care Team

With the increasing complexity of both disease patterns and medical care personnel, the advocacy of team structure involving medical, nursing, social service and related technical workers is remarkable only in its surprisingly recent demonstration on the American scene. Reports of experience in the Montefiore Health Maintenance Demonstration,[68] the Gouverneur Health Center[69] and various medical school projects[70] represent a still-underdeveloped frontier in "applied" medical care research.

In sum, the various studies in organization of medical practice reflect basic trends in the national patterns. In Great Britain, the obsolescence of the traditional form of general practice and its increasingly awkward isolation from hospital-specialist practice has been demonstrated. In the United States, the major trends revealed are those which have been summarized as specialization, association and institutionalization of medical practice.

SOCIAL ROLE OF THE PHYSICIAN

Although operational research and program demonstration have been a major focus of activity, sociologists and other behavioral scientists have turned their attention to diverse aspects of the role relationships of the physician in society. The American literature since 1950 is voluminous in this subject area, and has been unusually well indexed and annotated.[71-73] Primary concern has been with the status of the physician in the community, doctor-patient relationships, interprofessional association, cultural influences in medical practice and studies of individual attitudes and perceptions. A small sampling from the large number of published studies can illustrate these efforts.

Role of the Physician in Society

The works of Sigerist,[1,2] Stern[3] and Rosen[74] provide a firm historical foundation for the concept of cultural and socioeconomic determinants of the physician's role. Bloom[75] and King[76] have enriched this basic thesis in terms of contemporary American social theory. Specific documentation of the underlying sociological aspects has been provided by such studies as those of urban medical usage patterns,[27] of rural relationships[29] and of specialists' roles.[48-50] Nonetheless, the gaps in our understanding of cultural influences upon medical practice remain formidable.

Doctor-Patient Relationships

The bonds and stresses between doctor and patient, the conflicts between professionalism and the sick role, the clash of medical and lay expectations—all have been recently explored by social researchers. In addition to the studies cited above, this area has been investigated in the group practice situation,[65] in the setting of the hospital outpatient clinic,[77] in private practice relationships[78] and from the psychiatric viewpoint.[79] No less than 163 references are listed under the general heading of role relationships of the physician in a recent bibliography of medical behavioral science.[72] A major contribution of these studies has been to enrich the understanding of medical care utilization beyond the simplistic notions of rational response to medical "need" and purely economic determinants of consumer "demand."

Social Organization of Medical Practice

Most of the attention of social scientists in the medical field has been directed toward the social factors affecting health and of role relationships among medical personnel. Relatively few have considered medical practice as a social institution and explored its functional components in this frame of reference. Illustrative of useful current efforts in this direction are studies using the setting of ambulatory care clinics for analysis of organizational patterns. Underscored in these reports are the conflicts between professional autonomy and hierarchical authority,[80-82] between lay and professional referral systems[65] and between central and dispersed configurations of medical care.[52]

Attitude Studies

Modern techniques of opinion survey and recording of "perceptions" have frequently been applied to the subject of medical practice. Many sociologists have sampled lay attitudes regarding general or family practice, demonstrating in the process the presence of distinct social class variations.[27-29] Analyses of the reasons given by patients for choice or change of medical care plan throw needed light on the patients' perceptions of competing systems of organized medical care.[30, 39, 50, 52, 65, 77] A number of the medical practice surveys have included analyses of the attitudes of the physicians whose mode of practice is under scrutiny.[9, 22, 24, 37, 57, 83]

This brief overview of sociological studies is sharply limited by the author's own lack of professional competence in respect to social science and by the particular focus of this report on organizational aspects of medical practice. No clear appreciation of research efforts in the area of medical care can be gained, however, without reference to this body of investigative work. Other papers in this publication series deal more directly with the concepts and methods of research in the behavioral sciences.

EVALUATION OF MEDICAL PRACTICE

As indicated in previous sections of this report, many of the surveys of specific forms of medical practice have included some assessment of the effectiveness or quality of the professional performance. Almost all of these have had, however, the primary objective of information and description and have been limited in their efforts at evaluation by the lack of reliable indices and uniform criteria.[84] The purpose of this section will be to review some of the specific applications of these methods to appraisal studies of the organization of medical practice.

Evaluation of Independent Medical Practice

The major British studies of general practice have depended essentially upon the methods of expert observation and review of clinical records for evaluation of the traditional pattern of family medical care. Conclusions have, predictably, varied with the bias of the observer and such efforts have been handicapped by the inadequacy of private office records and by lack of accepted measuring devices.[85] Nonetheless, a generally consistent pattern of observations does emerge, stressing the positive values of continuity and personalization of the doctor-patient contact on the one hand, and the problems of inadequate resources and uneven clinical performance on the other. The deliberate attempt of Taylor[8] to discern the features which characterize "good" general practice, and of Cartwright and Marshall[9] to analyze the perceptions of the practitioners themselves, are examples of the more useful qualitative aspects of these studies.

More directly focussed on appraisal and evaluation have been the applications of Peterson's techniques to representative samples of general practice.[22, 37, 38] In these efforts the data collected during extended observation of actual medical work and abstracted from medical records were analyzed in relation to information gathered from training and professional sources, as the basis for the derivation of numerical scores and measures. In this way, the effectiveness of the practice could be objectively judged and compared, and tests of association could be constructed to identify the significant influencing factors. The findings raise many serious questions about the current levels of performance of community practitioners in at least three different countries. Of great interest are the conclusions that the important determinants of high standards in medical work are such factors as time elapsed since training status, specific content (rather than length) of hospital residency training, and isolation in clinical practice.

Other investigators have attempted to develop more direct measures of the effectiveness of medical practice. Wolfe[83] used the dichotomy of "constricted" and "comprehensive" practice to classify the 30 Canadian practices he observed. Price[86] applied modern computer techniques to the analysis of 200 separate factors affecting the quality of medical practice. The large number of studies of referral procedures on both sides of the Atlantic Ocean permit inference about the quality of practitioner performance on the basis of the appropriateness of the use of available diagnostic and consultation facilities.[17, 20, 24, 26] Evidence from these sources suggests that judgment, content and follow-up in such referrals are highly variable among general practitioners. Koplin[87] has reported an interesting experience with the appointment of so-called "managing physicians" in the effort to reduce excessive hospitalization among a group of mine workers and their dependents.

Another approach to the evaluation of standards of practice is based upon the analysis of work load among physicians. Although data of this kind are included in many of the general surveys cited above, some medical care analysts have utilized such indices as volume of patients' visits and population-physician ratios as the basis for specific evaluation of the effectiveness of service.[14, 25, 35, 46]

Those responsible for hospital clinics have quite recently begun to explore possible methods of evaluation and control of standards of outpatient care.[88, 89] Although various techniques of so-called "medical audit" have long been applied to inpatients, appraisal of records in ambulatory services is unusual. In either setting the primary device has been analysis of clinical records, using selected and arbitrary indices of performance.

Evaluation of Group Medical Practice

Just as many of the general surveys of independent practices have included some efforts to appraise their effectiveness, so the various inventories of American group practice have attempted some qualitative evaluation. These studies have been based upon interpretation of the "vital statistics" of group practice (resources, ancillary aides, workloads, etc.), upon assessment of specific indices of patient care (such as organized preventive service, quality audits and controls) and upon analysis of the attitudes and reactions of both staff and patients.[57-60] The findings suggest that most medical groups fall short of the full theoretical potential of teamwork practice, but do achieve levels of clinical performance that compare favorably with those in solo practice.[63]

A number of quite different studies have been designed specifically for the evaluation of the group practice method. Dickinson[90] has analyzed the reasons for discontinuing medical groups; Makover[91] and others have developed techniques for appraising clinical records; the author of this review[63, 64] has proposed standards of group organization against which to measure individual programs; Fox[92] has critically appraised a variety of American medical groups from the vantage point of an experienced British clinician and educator. Again, no common frame of reference has been established.

Comparative Evaluation of Different Forms of Practice

Few studies have been designed specifically for comparisons among the existing forms of medical practice, although certain inferences have been drawn from investigations conducted for other purposes. Most comparative data have to do with the evaluation of group versus solo practice.

An interesting project by a Canadian medical student[93] attempted to compare the performance of general practitioners in selected independent and group practices in Toronto. Observations were based upon visits to eight physicians, each over a five day period, with results similar to those of Freidson[65, 94] in that more personalized care is ascribed to the independent practitioners and better technical standards to the group physicians.

In some of the studies of general practice, sufficient numbers of practitioners were in medical groups to make possible limited comparisons with those in solo settings. The associated physicians generally received higher average ratings than did their independent counterparts.[8, 10, 22, 38]

A few studies have been concerned with differences in the organizational features of various modes of practice. Elinson[95] has used the device of recording the choices made by physicians in selecting their method of practice. Logan and Eimerl[13] and Abel-Smith[96] have assembled available data for comparison of patterns of practice in different countries. Btesh,[97] of the World Health Organization, has recently described the possibilities for fruitful international comparative research in medical organization. At this writing, a comprehensive study is underway to compare the utilization of medical care in three different countries (Great Britain, Yugoslavia and the United States), although reports of findings are not yet available.

In general, comparative studies of different forms of medical practice have been fragmentary. The meager evidence to date suggests that independent and general practice is more familiar and acceptable from the patient's point of view, while specialty and group practice provide an objectively more rational and efficient standard of professional service. More convincing evidence must await the development of reliable standards for comparison, if useful guides are to be developed for future planning.

RESEARCH METHODS

In general, the methods utilized for research into the organization of medical practice—indeed, the methods used for most forms of medical care investigation—are borrowed from sister disciplines and applied to the particular situations. Thus, case analysis is traditional in clinical medicine and social work; questionnaire-interview surveys are common to many types of behavioral science research; anthropological techniques are adapted to the observation of practitioners at work; study of referral patterns owes much to the market analysis methods used by economists. The unique methodologic contribution developed specifically in this field is the derivation of indices and measures of the quality of medical care, such as are illustrated in certain of the works cited above. Yet, in this latter area more than in any other, the need exists for appraisal instruments with far greater validity and reliability.

Research Objectives

This review of studies of medical practice suggests the possibility of a fairly simple classification of research objectives, seemingly reflecting the relatively unsophisticated and exploratory quality of these pioneering efforts. The proposed classification is five-fold:

1. *Information.* By far the most common studies have been those which set out straightforwardly to obtain descriptive information which had been hitherto incomplete or entirely lacking.[7, 21, 33, 42, 58] For the research to be accepted as generally useful, attention has had to be devoted to proper methods of data collection and analysis, but these baseline surveys have been primarily concerned with the gathering of needed facts. Sampling techniques, controls, correlation, analysis of variables and hypothesis-testing have been included either not at all or hesitantly and, often, unscientifically.

This type of investigation, however, whether based upon "new" observations or upon refinement of existing crude data, does provide the necessary basis for more critical studies. Until clearer and more complete information is on hand regarding the nature and content of the different forms of medical practice, developing and testing creative hypotheses and applying the measures of efficiency and quality is not possible. Much more, rather than less, of this basic type of study is needed.

2. *Explanation.* An objective of medical practice research which is closely related to that of "information," and yet is obviously more ambitious, is that which includes an effort to enlarge the understanding of the known facts. Certainly, few of the studies classified as informational have ignored the implications of the data collected. (Many, indeed, have drawn wholly unwarranted inferences from nonrepresentative samples and incomplete "findings.") Certain investigators, however, have attempted to answer definite questions or to elucidate specific aspects of medical practice.

While many of the previously cited studies have been generally interpretive, a few are characterized by the commendable self-discipline of seeking explanations for one phenomenon at a time. This comes closer to the standard of the classical experimental method—that of testing and refining explanatory hypotheses—an approach still rare in medical care research. Thus, a British practitioner sought to determine if, in fact, his "workload" had been increasing over the years (and discovered that it had not);[16] a team of epidemiologists looked for an explanation of the contrast between the esoteric content of medical school education and the predominant needs of patients;[26] a hospital-based research group attempted to explain the increasing use of emergency facilities for routine conditions;[31] and a sociologist sought understanding of physicians' authority system.[81] This more focused and defined study method, when properly conducted, represents a necessary transition from counting to explaining in medical care research.

An important grouping within the category of explanatory research is the work of those behavioral scientists who have ventured into the medical care field. Such investigators have been curious from the outset about motivation, function and interpretation. Indeed, the major attraction for these workers has been the challenge of *how* and *why*, rather than *what* in relation to the practice of medicine. In this vein, many sociologists have studied the doctor-patient relationship with regard to its selection and stability, others in relation to its interpersonal dynamics, and still others in terms of the relevant cultural influences.[27, 49, 65, 78]

Much of the nature of modern medical practice is understandable only in terms of prior experience and of the total "ecological" complex of environmental forces. The insights of the historian and political analyst have further enriched the understanding of the role and function of the physician in modern society.[1-3, 5, 74]

3. *Evaluation.* A measure of the coming of age of the medical care field has been its recognition of the importance of qualitative as well as quantitative indicators of adequacy. This represents a further step in the maturation of the medical care research process, beyond "information" and "explanation," toward the systematic and objective appraisal of efforts and results. Not unexpectedly, as the purpose of this research grows more complex and judgmental, the techniques themselves become more difficult and both the number and the competence of such projects decline.

That is presently the case with respect to medical care research in general and medical practice studies in particular. In the absence of reliable methods, the work to date has had to be exploratory, presumptive and highly subjective. The most useful efforts have been those which have attempted to design and test the needed techniques, even in the absence of definitive evaluation results.[12, 22, 39, 86, 91]

4. *Comparison.* Only when evaluation methods are adequately standardized can serious efforts at comparison among different forms

of medical practice be attempted. Since such refinement of appraisal techniques has by no means been acheived, this research potential remains largely unexploited. A few comparative efforts have been cited, but this category of research has not yet become operative in respect to the organization of medical practice.[93-98]

5. *Demonstration.* The final category is that of the pilot demonstration project with a "built-in" evaluation system. To the degree that the latter component is applied seriously, systematically and objectively, the research label can be properly applied. This does not include the large number of reports of operating programs that are subjectively described and assessed. A few demonstration projects have included provision for reasonably objective evaluation,[68, 70] but the more common pattern is that of subsidized pilot programs with empirical— and even intuitive—value judgments.

Research Methods

Much of this review has already dealt with the methodological aspects of the studies under discussion. For the purposes of overall appraisal of this particular field of research, the major techniques now available should be classified and examined separately.

Statistical analysis of available data. As systems of medical care have become more structured and formalized, the requirements for regular record-keeping and data-reporting have increased. This pool of operational information has only recently been tapped as a source of research material for studies in medical practice. Modern statistical techniques of processing and analyzing such data have now made possible more detailed and continuous appraisal of medical work than has previously been the case. A limiting feature of the earlier field surveys has been their relative lack of sophistication with respect to gathering and manipulating statistical information. In more recent times, however, biometrists collaborating in medical care studies have demonstrated the importance of representative sampling, proper controls, significance testing and caution in interpretation.[12, 22, 23, 40, 42]

Questionnaires. Newer techniques developed in opinion research and other sociological study centers have become basic tools for those seeking to gather details on large numbers of medical practices. Thus, mailed questionnaires have been utilized (primarily in this country) by those studying specialty function, group practice, site of practice, business aspects of practice and referral patterns. Although the percentage of returns has been surprisingly good (65–90 per cent), the problems of selective bias in response, inaccuracy, incomplete data, and the rapidly approaching saturation point on the part of doctors and medical care administrators all are seriously limiting factors. Nevertheless, the mailed questionnaire remains a basic technique for gathering preliminary data on large numbers of medical practices.[23, 45, 46, 51, 57]

Interviews. Also adopted from the opinion surveyors and behavioral scientists, the carefully designed interview is productive of more detailed and reliable data on medical practice than is the impersonal questionnaire. The open or *unstructured interview* technique is used when the subject matter is clearly defined, when the interviewer is skilled and experienced and when the respondent is cooperative and informed.[22, 23, 27, 77] On the other hand, the structured interview or *administered questionnaire* is appropriate in most large-scale surveys when data must be comparable, quantitative and specific.[9, 28, 83, 95] In medical care research the place of interview is important, and has been located both at the site of care and at the patient's home. Even with the carefully supervised and delineated interview-questionnaire technique, the limitations of respondent and observer bias, the inconsistency of interpretations and the arbitrariness of coding and classification are real and troublesome.

Direct observation. A much used method in studies of individual and group practice has been that of direct and extended observation of the physician at work by clinically competent and specially prepared professional researchers, both medical and sociological. The more common technique is that of personal inspection of the work of the practitioner, usually over a period of some days and generally by a physician familiar with the particular field of practice. This direct observational technique is also utilized by the sociologist, often extending over periods of time sufficiently prolonged to permit adequate understanding of complex interrelationships. The advantages of firsthand data gathering and the drawbacks of observor bias and inconsistency are obvious.[8, 38, 77, 81, 83]

A more complex and less frequently used method of direct observation is that of the *participating visit,* where the research physician actually takes part in the activities under study. This method has been used in surveys of general practitioners, in evaluation of family health care units and in assessment of medical organization. In this method both the rewards and the hazards (from the research point of view) are magnified.[6, 65, 93]

Analysis of records. Few of the studies in the organization of medical

384

practice have completely ignored the medical record as a source of data or as an instrument for quality appraisal. Some investigations have been based entirely upon record analysis, while many others have incorporated this method into more complex research schedules. Although the medical record is obviously a prime source of data concerning medical practice, it is a variably reliable mirror of actual clinicial performance, is frequently inaccurate and is usually incomplete. A still unresolved difficulty is the lack of uniform and valid indices of overall adequacy to be applied to the medical record.[9, 23, 37, 87, 91]

Case analysis of individual practices. The method of clinical case analysis has occasionally been used in medical care research to provide data in depth and over time with respect to a single practice. Such self-study has been reported in the British literature for general practice, and by a few American group practices, the latter considerably less objectively.[16, 61] A retrospective technique almost by definition, this method provides information which is at once consistent and nonreproducible. The more objective sociological case studies, such as those of large group practice by Freidson and associates,[65, 66] do add more acceptable data to the fund of information on the organization of medical practice.

Content of Research in Medical Practice

Utilizing these techniques of medical practice research, a surprisingly variegated array of subjects have been investigated. In appraisal of this field of research and its future potential, the various focal points of content in the recent work should be identified.

Census and cataloguing of physicians. The basic descriptive or informational studies have been those which set out to identify the number and kinds of physicians, the proportions and ratios involved, and the trends to be found in the various distributions. Thus, the changing proportions of general and special physicians are analyzed, as are the shifting ratios of population to practitioner in various age groups, economic strata, geographical locations and medical care programs. In this category are direct "field" surveys, mailed questionnaires and analysis of collected data. Whatever the methods, the focus of such studies has been essentially census-taking among medical practitioners.[7, 40, 41, 57]

Profile of the practitioner. A second focus of the survey type of medical practice research is gathering information about the practitioner himself. In these studies emphasis is placed upon personal characteristics (age, sex, marital status, residence, social class, etc.), and upon aspects related to his practice (years in practice, vacation patterns, leisure time habits, professional income, etc.). Against the backdrop of the larger statistical pattern, these studies have added the identifying colors and shadings.[9, 15, 33, 34, 46]

Office setting for medical practice. The working environment of the practitioner has been an additional subject of research attention, particularly with respect to the primary focus of practice—the medical office or clinic. Utilizing, for the most part, the same study methods (indeed, usually included in the same survey projects), these investigations have produced information about physical premises, supplies and equipment, records and assisting personnel. They have described the human and material resources with which the physician carries on his professional function.[6, 38, 43, 55, 56]

Use of available resources. In recognition of the obvious fact that medical practice is not confined to the setting of the physician's office, studies of medical practice have looked beyond these walls to some appraisal of other available resources and the physician's utilization of them. Included here have been analyses of the use of such resources as community health and welfare agencies, diagnostic laboratories, hospital facilities, specialists' offices, chronic care institutions and other kinds of professional and ancillary services. Studies of the organization of medical practice have been concerned with these kinds of relationships in a number of different ways. The "census" and "profile" surveys have frequently included observations on use of diagnostic and hospital facilities. The referral studies already described are, obviously, directly to this point. Most appraisal efforts among general practitioners give substantial attention to the proper use of available "outside" resources. The analyses of hospital clinics and group practices similarly emphasize the relationships between "community" and "staff" physicians. These data help to complete the picture of the "setting" of medical practice.[10, 14, 18, 19, 24, 31, 52, 60]

Professional function of the physician. The dynamics of practice have been another subject for research in this area, portrayed within the framework of the resources already described. Studies of this kind have been concerned with the scope and limitations of activity of the practitioner, his workday, his patterns of professional function, his participation in educational and research activities, his involvement with professional organizations and his decision-making processes.

Again, much of this kind of information is included in the comprehensive survey studies. Additionally, data on amount and kind of medical service provided, numbers of patients seen, procedures employed and the like have been derived from analysis of interview protocols and regular clinical records. Particular emphasis is given to these factors in the evaluation studies of standards in medical practice. How physicians arrive at medical practice decisions is investigated in some of the studies of clinic referral, hospital admission and professional "interaction." Overall, the techniques of both epidemiology and behavioral science have contributed to a fuller understanding of the process of medical practice.[7, 13, 15, 22, 35, 46, 48, 66, 87]

Administrative aspects of medical practice. A small but useful body of research has concerned itself with the managerial and financial factors in medical practice. This has involved consideration of organizational structure, administrative procedures, payment mechanisms and the like.[10, 54, 59, 81, 96] Acceptable standards are far from complete in this area, but the task has been somewhat easier than has been the case with reference to performance indices. In many studies the adequacy of the organizational structure is used as the major criterion for appraisal of the quality of the services provided in the particular framework.[51, 60, 63, 69]

Characteristics of patients. A productive approach to the study of medical practice has been via the study of the patients, their disorders and their utilization patterns. Such information adds perspective to the portrait of medical practice which emerges from focus upon the physician. Here again, some of the surveys of general practice include data on disease entities and usage rates; diagnostic distributions are analyzed in relation to patterns of practice; patient-care services are used as one index in the appraisal of clinical performance; and observations of patients' behavior patterns commonly serve as the basis of sociological research.[9, 26, 27, 30, 36, 68, 98]

Measures of quality in medical practice. Another emphasis in medical practice research is that which deals with the problems of measurement and appraisal of the standards of medical care. These have been summarized elsewhere in this series.[84] However, enough attention has been given to this specific subject in the various studies of organization of medical practice that separate identification seems warranted. Specific indices and evaluation criteria have been derived and tested in various of the appraisal studies reviewed above. In others, judgments concerning a specific type of practice are presented in terms of the personal assessment of the observer. All in all, a concern with quality of medical care is increasingly evident in research reports on medical practice.[22, 68, 86, 89, 91]

Attitudes and perceptions. A final category of subject matter in medical practice research is that relating to survey of opinions and reactions among those who participate in the medical care process. Tested behavioral science techniques have been applied to this field, both with respect to patients' perceptions of medical practice and to physicians' attitudes about their situations. Even though attitudes are important determinants of actual behavior in medical care, data based upon such surveys are more difficult to analyze and more subject to distortion. Nonetheless, both lay and professional expectations and satisfactions must be understood if the nature of medical practice is to be fully clarified. This category of research has well demonstrated its usefulness.[27, 57, 65, 76–82]

Methodological Problems

Much has been written in recent years on methods of research which are applicable to the study of organization of medical practice.[5, 12, 85, 97–100] Despite these thoughtful contributions and the array of work sampled in this report, the first requisite for further progress in medical care research is that of better methods and materials for study.

Colleagues in related disciplines continue to ease the task. Methods of cohort analysis, multivariate correlation, computer programing and many other highly sophisticated techniques of collecting and processing research data are under continuous refinement. Greater accuracy and control are being introduced into the questionnaire, interview and observational methods of the behavioral scientists. In many research-conscious centers, routine clinical and administrative records are being revised and standardized with an eye to their usefulness for operational research. As voluntary and governmental programs of medical care extend to involve almost all segments of national populations, data on disease distribution, receipt of health services, supply of health personnel and costs of medical care all become more extensive and increasingly available. In short, the raw material and the basic research tools are on hand for the investigation of many as yet unexplored aspects of the organization of medical care.

That which is sorely lacking, however, and that which is almost wholly the responsibility of the medical care expert to develop, are methods of evaluating the effectiveness of the services rendered. Despite the ingenuity and resourcefulness of the work of such as Peterson, Makover, Trussell, Slee, Rosenberg, Lembcke, Morehead and other pioneers in the effort to appraise the quality of medical care,[84] the need remains for better design, testing and refinement of indices of total performance, for weighted measures of scoring, for criteria of acceptability and for standards of quality which are at once specific, representative, valid, reliable, unbiased and feasible. All of this is, obviously, a tall order in a field as variegated and complex as is that of medical practice.

Technical problems in methodology. Experience to date indicates a number of other unresolved problems in the methodology of medical care research. Highly sophisticated statistical techniques (including computer processing) are incapable of producing useful information when the raw data are collected from operating program records which are designed to serve routine administrative and financial functions. Wholly new methods of recording clincial observations are needed. A more conscious application of standard epidemiological methods is indicated if studies of distributions of resources or patterns of utilization are to yield reliable insights. Perhaps the most difficult of all methodologic lessons to be learned is that medical care itself has an as yet unproven effect upon such common health indices as morbidity and mortality and that change in health status of patients is a questionable index for the evaluation of medical practice.

Need for freedom from medical dogma and introspection. The theoretical model of medical practice suggested earlier stresses the complex "ecology" of health service organization and denies the assumption of independence or of rationality in the current role of the physician. Much of the recent research orientation in medical care, however, distorts the picture of medical practice by single-minded focus on the physician. More subtly, the acceptance of traditional medical care dogmas—such as the value of teamwork or of early diagnosis or of periodic health examinations—has led to projects designed to demonstrate such standards, rather than to test them or, even better, to collect the basic data needed for an unbiased derivation of fresh formulations to meet observed needs.

The thesis of this report has been from the outset that the organization of medical service and the role of the physician are determined, in every epoch, by the nature of society and the state of advancement of medical science. The forward thrust of research in medical practice must, therefore, be continuously directed toward understanding the changing characteristics of contemporary society and science as they affect the patterns of disease and the provision of health services. Those who would study this interface of community and medicine must seek the collaboration of demographer, economist, political scientist, clinician, ecologist and others in the biological and social sciences if all of the pertinent factors and each of the useful methods are to be included. The view must be prospective, even when the technique is retrospective; the researcher in medical care must anticipate the major direction and form of change, if he is to retain any hope of influencing either.

Evaluation of Content of Medical Practice Research

Overall, the knowledge developed from contemporary medical care research is uneven and discontinuous. More is known of the marginal systems of group practice than of the central trends toward informal associated practice and institutional relationships. Workloads of physicians are calculated and the nature of the clientele is ignored. Concepts of economic and geographic accessibility omit the psychological and cultural factors affecting the use of physicians' services. Most significantly, the practitioner is studied apart from the community as a whole and from the larger network of health service organization.

Specific Subject Areas for new Research

Within these general criteria, a few of the areas needing further elucidation may be cited.

Effects of lay influence upon medical practice. The pervasive effects upon the physician of patients' preferences and prejudices have been of much interest to the behavioral scientists. That interest is reflected, for example, in the studies of lay and professional referral patterns in medical care. Much more needs to be learned, however, regarding the impact of patient influences on the style and substance of professional function. Cultural and educational factors, among many others, are incompletely understood—compounded by the process of their own rapid transformation in modern society. The techniques that have been well developed for research into the doctor-patient relationship could, with profit, be more intensively applied to this aspect of the interaction.

Impact of medical technology on patterns of practice. The principles and techniques of clinical medicine advance with astonishing rapidity and, despite the worrisome lag in general application, have ultimate effects upon medical practice which are crucial to understanding its structure and function. The modern emphasis on laboratory tests, complex diagnostic equipment, injectable drug therapy, ambulatory surgical procedures and the like has limited the use of house calls, increased the physician's reliance upon technical aides, and moved the focus of clinical practice closer to the hospital. These trends need investigation in a wide variety of relationships.

Informal organizational factors. Current organizational theory emphasizes the importance of status relationships, prestige and reward systems, class influences and a host of "informal" influences upon the structure of medical associations. The relevance of such factors is obvious for a professional group with powerful educational traditions and a complex system of role stratification. Much more needs to be known about the professional "way of life" of physicians (and other health workers) if the more visible aspects of organization in medical practice are to be understood.

The health care team. The paradox of modern medicine is undeniable: the single personal physician is both outmoded and indispensable. In an era of chronic disease and of specialized medical practice, the need for a central coordinator within a team structure is compelling. Beyond this easy generalization, the details are unclear. Research is required into the desired composition of the basic health care team, the needed supporting consultants and assistants. The process of team function, the nature of group records, the matter of optimum size, the design of joint facilities, the structure of administrative systems— all need clarification if the seemingly inevitable trend toward group organization is to lead to improvement in the effectiveness of medical care.

The primary physician. Within the context of the health team, the scope and content of work of the primary physician require some new attention. Further analyses of the current functions of generalists, internists, pediatricians and obstetricians can contribute to the ultimate portrait of the ideal core practitioner. In addition, more demonstrations of new methods of primary physician function within the health care team are needed to develop working models and systems. Closely related to such operational studies, the training requirements for the primary physician should be investigated further, including such elements as correlation of various educational components with later performance in practice. Attention should also be directed to the matter of selection of candidates for the basic physician role.

The non-medical practitioner. As the ratio of general physicians to population declines (at least in the United States), serious consideration will be given to the possibility of preparing specially trained community health aides or medically oriented public health nurses to fill the widening gap of front-line family medical care. Analysis is needed of current experience with such community aides in various isolated areas (i.e., Alaskan Native Health Service, naval medical corpsmen, Kentucky mountain nurses, etc.). Further experimentation is indicated with nurse-directed follow-up clinics for patients with chronic disease. Experimentation is also needed in the matter of upgrading of existing cadres of unskilled and nonprofessional health workers. Wholly new pilot demonstrations might explore the many ramifications of this first-rank problem in medical care.

Content of specialty practice. Adapting some of the models of British surveys in general practice and building upon the available studies of pediatricians and internists in the United States, future research in medical practice must expand the areas of information about all specialities and their interrelationship. Only with such studies can knowledge be acquired adequate for designing appropriate health care teams, regionalized specialty services or adjusted training programs.

The health center. Many lines of evolution of medical care patterns are converging in the concept of the community health service center. Medical team practice, neighborhood service design, integration of preventive and curative health care, regional coordination of medical facilities—all involve the model of the local health center as the nucleus of the orbit. Further research into the design, location, community relationships, population base and program content of such centers is necessary. The appropriate methods include those of the urban and regional planner, with further use of the pilot demonstration with predesigned evaluation systems.

Relation of office and hospital practice. Two different models have emerged—at least in the "western world"—regarding the role of the general physician in relation to the hospital. The basic European system

392

separates the local family doctor from the hospital-based specialist, while the usual arrangement in the United States is for every type of practicing physician to care for "his" patients in the hospital. Variations do occur within each pattern: many of the best British practitioners care for their patients in small "cottage" hospitals, while a not inconsiderable number of American generalists lack admitting privileges in any local hospital. As indicated in the studies cited above on office settings, recent trends in the American scene include locating private and group offices in or near hospitals, branch affiliation of neighborhood medical practice units with larger medical centers, and expanded roles for hospital outpatient departments.

All of these developments emphasize the need for greater understanding of the advantages and disadvantages of relating the office and hospital practice of primary and specializing physicians. The methods developed in the studies of the referral process and in the analyses of private office practice provide useful tools for such further research.

Prevention in medical practice. Lip service has always been given, in any discussion of standards of good medical care, to the importance of preventive medicine. The studies here reported of individual and group practice indicate the infrequency of any orderly arrangements for preventive care in the day-to-day activities of physicians—except, perhaps, the well-baby and prenatal routines established in the better practices. The recent demonstrations of so-called "family health maintenance" and the special efforts of a few medical groups have formed the basis for claims that significant results can be expected from organized programs of case-finding, health education, reinforcement of chronic disease treatment regimens, public health nursing, etc. More such experimentation is indicated, in various settings and extending over long periods of time, but a pressing need is for rigorous and objective appraisal of the effectiveness and specificity of preventive measures as applied in medical practice.

Value of continuity in medical care. Another often repeated tenet of "good" medical care has to do with the role of a central, coordinating physician in the spectrum of preventive, therapeutic and rehabilitative medical care. The dangers of fragmentation and discontinuity are well described. This concern has seldom led, however, to studies which compare the results and costs of organized and unorganized systems. Little is known about the specific effects of, for example, a change of attending physician in the course of patient care, multiple "personal" doctors for different members of the family, or separate medical staffs for ambulatory and institutional care. Although the bias of this reviewer is completely in support of the value of strong continuity of service, the entire subject needs validation.

Effects of payment methods in medical practice. Numerous studies of the utilization and cost of medical care have demonstrated the great variation that exists among the different systems of payment to the physician. In contrast, little emphasis has been given to the effect of various payment mechanisms upon the function and professional conduct of the physician. As new medical care systems are developed and various combinations of fee, capitation and salary reimbursement methods are contemplated, much of value could be found in objective measurement of the effects of each method.

Relation of training to quality of practice. The work of Peterson, White, Price and others has indicated that no complacency is warranted regarding the relevance to the needs of the practitioner of medical training as it is now conducted in universities and teaching hospitals. The known patterns of morbidity and the required functions of the future physician have not, apparently, had great influence upon the design of present medical curricula. Further study is badly needed in this area to extend the analyses of disease distributions under different forms of medical practice, to identify the skills and methods required in good patient care and to test the effectiveness of appropriate alterations in the medical training programs. Recognition must be given, of course, to the extensive current research in medical education, but the specific connection between training programs and proficiency in practice requires considerably more emphasis.

Effects of automation upon office practice. Despite increasing attention given to the powerful impact of computers, laboratory automation, systems engineering and the like on institutional medicine, little attention has been paid to the potential implications for the neighborhood medical unit. The local practitioner's office and the community health center have felt the impact of few of the new mechanical and electronic techniques, due both to economic and informational reasons. The possibilities are, however, enormous—for new methods of record-keeping, telecommunication, instrumentation, analysis of clinical data, etc.—and the methods of operational research need application to the ambulatory medical care setting.

Relation of research to change in medical practice. An earnestly resisted but persistent impression gained in the course of this review of research in medical practice has been that research rarely leads—in demonstrable ways, at least—to appropriate alteration in the existing pattern. Almost two generations of studies of British general practice have revealed problems which still characterize its form and function. Similarly, repetitive appraisals of the impact on holistic patient care of specialist trends in the United States have been reported without apparent influence upon the velocity or direction of the change. Recent national legislation relating both to chronic disease control and to medical care of the aged seems to ignore the findings of a long series of studies and demonstrations. The relationship between research documentation and consequent change in the actual structure of medical care has been tenuous at best. A fascinating subject for a new kind of interdisciplinary research would be this very phenomenon: the influence of studies of medical practice upon changing patterns of organization and professional function.

SUMMARY

This limited and selective review of research in medical practice in western society during the last two decades has revealed both the rich variety of scholarly effort in this field and the huge gaps in needed experimentation and knowledge.

Primary attention in this report has been given to British and American studies of the organization of practice, patterns of patient care, professional-lay role relationships, evaluation of effectiveness of medical work and methodology of research into these matters.

The general conclusion seems inescapable that much more needs to be known about existing patterns of practice, many new concepts in medical care need to be explored, far better research tools must be developed and careful attention has to be paid to the connection between academic study and social progress. Universities and research institutes must share with operating medical care agencies the responsibility for expanding these efforts, improving their scientific caliber and attaining a more useful social focus.

Many lessons are to be learned from review of the work accomplished to date in this area of research. These might be summarized to aid future efforts:

1. In a time of rapid change in the organization of medical practice, research must be at once more panoramic and more profound.

The full spectrum of medical activity in community, region and country requires delineation, as the framework for more searching appraisal of the specific aspects of the function of the physician.

2. Descriptive information continues to be the necessary prerequisite for formulating the guiding hypotheses for more sophisticated investigation in this field. Much of the history and present character of medical practice remains to be documented through the further application of the survey and analysis techniques which are now so well developed.

3. On the basis of such broadened understanding of present patterns of the practice of medicine, better methods can be devised for appraising the quality and effectiveness of both current and newly demonstrated forms.

4. Research in medical practice must anticipate the direction and velocity of the major trends in the social organization of health service, to concentrate the light of critical investigation upon those intersections of public and professional decision-making which are the most crucial for the future.

5. Neither gathering and analyzing "data" nor testing hypotheses exhausts the obligations of the researcher in medical care. Experimenting with new models and demonstrating the value of new services are equally compelling needs in a field of endeavor which ultimately is to be judged on the criterion of social utility.

6. The wisdom of the Sigerist tenet appears to be validated: that the role of the physician in his medical care function can be understood only through comprehension of the social relationships within which he works and the technical resources at his disposal.

7. Both form and content of medical practice, as reflected in the studies reported from the most affluent and advanced of "western" industrialized countries lag considerably behind today's social need and technical potential. The primary task of research in medical care at this stage of history is to hasten the closure of the science-service gap.

REFERENCES

[1] Sigerist, Henry E., The Place of the Physician in Modern Society, *Proceedings of the American Philosophical Society,* 90, 275–279, September, 1946; reproduced in Roemer, Milton I. (Editor), HENRY E. SIGERIST ON THE SOCIOLOGY OF MEDICINE, New York, M.D. Publications, 1960.

[2] ————, MEDICINE AND HUMAN WELFARE, New Haven, Yale University Press, 1941.

[3] Stern, Bernhard J., AMERICAN MEDICAL PRACTICE IN THE PERSPECTIVES OF A CENTURY, New York, The Commonwealth Fund, 1945.

[4] Weinerman, E. Richard, Anchor Points Underlying the Planning for Tomorrow's Health Care, *Bulletin New York Academy of Medicine,* 41, 1213–1226, December, 1965.

[5] Davis, Michael M., Social Medicine as a Field for Social Research, *American Journal of Sociology,* 34, 274–279, September, 1938.

[6] Collings, Joseph S., General Practice in England Today: A Reconnaissance, *Lancet,* 1, 555–585, March 25, 1950.

[7] Hadfield, Stephen J., Report of Committee on General Practice, British Medical Association, *British Medical Journal,* 2, 683–706, September 26, 1953.

[8] Taylor, Stephen, GOOD GENERAL PRACTICE: A REPORT OF A SURVEY, London, Oxford University Press, 1954.

[9] Cartwright, A. and Marshall, R., General Practice in 1963: Its Conditions, Contents and Satisfactions, *Medical Care,* 3, 69–87, April–June, 1965.

[10] College of General Practitioners, REPORTS FROM GENERAL PRACTICE: II. PRESENT STATE AND FUTURE NEEDS, London, The Council of The College (Fry Committee), July, 1965.

[11] Forsyth, G. and Logan, R. F. L., Medical Technology and the Needs of Chronic Disease: A Review of Some British Studies on the Organization of Medical Care Services, *Journal of Chronic Diseases,* 17, 789–802, September, 1964.

[12] ————, Studies in Medical Care: An Assessment of Some Methods, *in* TOWARD A MEASURE OF MEDICAL CARE: OPERATIONAL RESEARCH IN THE HEALTH SERVICE, London, Published for the Nuffield Provincial Hospitals Trust by the Oxford University Press, 1962.

[13] Logan, R. F. L. and Eimerl, T. S., Case Loads in Hospitals and General Practice in Several Countries, *in* Acheson, Roy M. (Editor), COMPARABILITY IN INTERNATIONAL EPIDEMIOLOGY, New York, Milbank Memorial Fund, 1965.

[14] Logan, R. F. L., Studies in the Spectrum of Medical Care, *in* McLachlan, Gordon (Editor), PROBLEMS AND PROGRESS IN MEDICAL CARE, London, published for the Nuffield Provincial Hospitals Trust by the Oxford University Press, 1964.

[15] Backett, E. M., Heady, J. A. and Evans, J. C. G., Studies of a General Practice, II. The Doctor's Job in an Urban Area, *British Medical Journal,* 1, 109–114, January 16, 1954.

[16] Fry, J. and Dillane, J. B., Views of General Practice; Too Much Work?

Proposals Based on a Review of Fifteen Years Work in Practice, *Lancet,* 2, 632–634, September 19, 1964.

[17] Hopkins, Philip, Referrals in General Practice, *British Medical Journal,* 2, 873–877, October 13, 1956.

[18] Morrison, S. L. and Riley, M. M., The Use of Hospital Diagnostic Facilities by General Practitioners, *Medical Care,* 1, 137–142, July–September, 1963.

[19] Acheson, R. M., Barker, D. J. P. and Butterfield, W. J. H., How General Practitioners Use Out-Patient Services in Two London Boroughs, *British Medical Journal,* 2, 1315–1317, November 17, 1962.

[20] Acheson, R. M., *et al.,* Factors Influencing Referrals to the Out-Patient Department of a London Teaching Hospital, *British Journal of Social and Preventive Medicine,* 17, 81–84, April, 1963.

[21] Oxford Regional Hospital Board, Operational Research Unit, HOSPITAL OUT-PATIENT SERVICES, No. 3, Oxford, Oxford Regional Hospital Board, 1963.

[22] Peterson, O. L., *et al.,* An Analytical Study of North Carolina General Practice, *Journal of Medical Education,* 31, Part 2, December, 1965.

[23] Andrews, L. P., *et al.,* A Study of Patterns of Medical Referrals to a Medical Clinic in a Rural State: Methodology, *American Journal of Public Health,* 49, 634–643, May, 1959.

[24] Williams, T. F., *et al.,* Patient Referral to a University Clinic, Patterns in a Rural State, *American Journal of Public Health,* 50, 1493–1507, October, 1960.

[25] Huntley, Robert R., Epidemiology of Family Practice, *Journal of American Medical Association,* 185, 175–178, July 20, 1963.

[26] White, K. L., Williams, T. F. and Greenberg, B. G., The Ecology of Medical Care, *New England Journal of Medicine,* 265, 885–893, November 2, 1961.

[27] Koos, Earl L., THE HEALTH OF REGIONVILLE, New York, Columbia University Press, 1954.

[28] Sheps, C. G., Sloss, J. H. and Cahill, E., Medical Care in Aluminum City—I. Families and Their "Regular Doctors," *Journal of Chronic Diseases,* 17, 815–826, September, 1964.

[29] Hassinger, E. and McNamara, R. L., RELATIONSHIPS OF THE PUBLIC TO PHYSICIANS IN A RURAL SETTING, Columbia, Missouri, Missouri Agricultural Experiment Station, Research Bulletin No. 653, 1958.

[30] Weinerman, E. Richard, Patients' Perceptions of Group Medical Care, *American Journal of Public Health,* 54, 880–889, June, 1964.

[31] Weinerman, E. R., *et al.,* Yale Studies in Ambulatory Medical Care: V. Determinants of Use of Hospital Emergency Services, *American Journal of Public Health,* 56, 1037–1056, July, 1966.

[32] United States Public Health Service, Division of Public Health Methods, HEALTH MANPOWER SOURCE BOOK: MANPOWER IN THE 1960's, Washington, United States Government Printing Office, 1964.

[33] Health Information Foundation, A View of Our Family Physicians, *Progress in Health Services,* 7, June, 1958.

[34] Anonymous, Physicians' Economic Health: Excellent, *Medical Economics,* December 13, 1965.

[35] Ciocco, A., Altman, I. and Truan, T. D., Patient Load and Volume of Medical Services, *Public Health Reports,* 67, 527–534, June, 1952.

[36] Ciocco, A., Hunt, G. H. and Altman, I., Statistics on Clinical Services to New Patients in Medical Groups, *Public Health Reports,* 65, 99–115, January 27, 1950.

[37] Jungfer, C. C. and Last, J. M., Clinical Performance in Australian General Practice, *Medical Care,* 2, 71–83, April–June, 1964.

[38] Clute, Kenneth F., THE GENERAL PRACTITIONER: A STUDY OF MEDICAL EDUCATION AND PRACTICE IN ONTARIO AND NOVA SCOTIA, Toronto, University of Toronto Press, 1963.

[39] Querido, A., THE EFFICIENCY OF MEDICAL CARE, Stenfert Kroese, N.V., Leiden, 1963.

[40] Weiskotten, H. G. and Altenderfer, M. E., Trends in Medical Practice, *Journal of Medical Education,* 27, Part 2, September, 1962.

[41] Terris, M. and Monk, M., Changes in Physicians' Careers: Relation of Time After Graduation to Specialization, *Journal of the American Medical Association,* 160, 653–655, February 25, 1956.

[42] Pennell, Maryland Y., Career Patterns in Medicine, *Public Health Reports,* 80, 155–162, February, 1965.

[43] Health Information Foundation, Where Physicians Work, *Progress in Health Services,* 13, May–June, 1964.

[44] Sheps, Cecil G., Problems, Pressures and Prospects, *in* MEDICAL EDUCATION AND MEDICAL CARE: INTERACTIONS AND PROSPECTS, Evanston, Illinois, Association of American Medical Colleges, 1961, pp. 3–20 (also published as Part 2 of the *Journal of Medical Education,* December, 1961).

[45] Jacobziner, H., Rich, H. and Merchant, R., Pediatric Care in Private Practice, *Journal of the American Medical Association,* 182, 986–993, December 8, 1962.

[46] Kroeger, Hilda H., *et al.,* The Office Practice of Internists: I. The Feasibility of Evaluating the Quality of Care, *Journal of the American Medical Association,* 193, 371–376, August 2, 1965; II. Patient Load, *Journal of the American Medical Association,* 193, 667–672, August 23, 1965; III. Characteristics of Patients, *Journal of the American Medical Association,* 193, 916–922, September 13, 1965; IV. Professional Activities Other Than Care of Private Patients, *Journal of the American Medical Association,* 194, 177–181, October 11, 1965; V. Background and Form of Practice of 500 Internists in New York State, *Journal of the American Medical Association,* 194, 533–538, November 1, 1965.

[47] Health Information Foundation, Physicians Who Perform Surgery, *Progress in Health Services,* 10, June, 1961.

[48] Kutner, Bernard, Surgeons and Their Patients: A Study in Social Perception, *in* Jaco, E. Gartly, (Editor), PATIENTS, PHYSICIANS AND ILLNESS, Glencoe, Illinois, Free Press, 1958, pp. 384–397.

[49] Hollingshead, A. B. and Redlich, F. C., SOCIAL CLASS AND MENTAL ILLNESS, New York, John Wiley & Sons, Inc., 1958.

[50] Sloss, J. H., Cahill, E. and Sheps, C. G., Medical Care in Aluminum City: II. The Selection and Use of Specialists, *Archives of Environmental Health,* 12, 56–62, January, 1966.

[51] Roemer, Milton, I., Contractual Physicians in General Hospitals: A National Survey, *American Journal of Public Health,* 52, 1453–1464, September, 1962.

[52] Solon, J. A., Sheps, C. G. and Lee, S. S., Patterns of Medical Care: A Hospital's Outpatients, *American Journal of Public Health,* 50, 1905–1913, December, 1960.

[53] Weinerman, E. Richard, Yale Studies in Ambulatory Medical Care: IV. Outpatient-Clinic Services in the Teaching Hospital, *New England Journal of Medicine,* 272, 947–954, May 6, 1965.

[54] Walker, J. E. C., Murawski and Thorn, G. W., An Experimental Program in Ambulatory Medical Care, *New England Journal of Medicine,* 271, 63–68, July 9, 1954.

[55] Rorem, C. Rufus, PHYSICIANS' PRIVATE OFFICES AT HOSPITALS, Hospital Monograph Series No. 5, Chicago, American Hospital Association, 1959.

[56] Katz, Gerald, The Organization and Location of Medical Practice in Medical Arts Buildings: Preliminary Report of a Pilot Study in the District of Columbia presented before the Medical Care Section, American Public Health Association, Chicago, October 21, 1965.

[57] Hunt, G. H. and Goldstein, M. S., MEDICAL GROUP PRACTICE IN THE UNITED STATES, Public Health Service Publication Number 77, Washington, United States Government Printing Office, 1951.

[58] Pomrinse, S. D. and Goldstein, M. S., The 1959 Survey of Group Practice, *American Journal of Public Health,* 51, 671–682, May, 1961.

[59] American Medical Association, Committee on Medical and Related Facilities, Survey of Group Practice, *Journal of American Medical Association,* 64, 1338–1348, July 20, 1957.

[60] Weinerman, E. R. and Goldstein, G. S., MEDICAL GROUP PRACTICE IN CALIFORNIA, Berkeley, School of Public Health, University of California, June, 1952.

[61] Rothenberg, R. R., Pickard, K. and Rothenberg, J. E., GROUP MEDICINE AND HEALTH INSURANCE IN ACTION, New York, Crown Publishers, Inc., 1949.

[62] Esselstyn, Caldwell B., Group Practice With Branch Centers in a Rural Country, *New England Journal of Medicine,* 248, 488–493, March 9, 1953.

[63] Weinerman, E. Richard, An Appraisal of Medical Care in Group Heatlh Centers, *American Journal of Public Health,* 46, 300–309, March, 1956.

[64] ———, Medical Care in Prepaid Group Practice, *Archives of Environmental Health,* 5, 561–573, December, 1962.

[65] Freidson, Eliot, PATIENTS' VIEWS OF MEDICAL PRACTICE, New York, Russell Sage Foundation, 1961.

[66] Freidson, E. and Rhea, B., Physicians in Large Medical Groups: A Preliminary Report, *Journal of Chronic Diseases,* 17, 827–836, September, 1964.

400

[67] Harper, Paul A., The Practice of Pediatrics in a Medical Group Setting, *Pediatrics,* 18, 814–827, November, 1956.

[68] Silver, George A., FAMILY MEDICAL CARE, Cambridge, Harvard University Press, 1963.

[69] Brown, H. J. and Alexander, R. S., The Gouverneur Ambulatory Care Unit: A New Approach to Ambulatory Care, *American Journal of Public Health,* 54, 1661–1665, October, 1964.

[70] Snoke, P. S. and Weinerman, E. R., Yale Studies in Ambulatory Medical Care: III. Comprehensive Care Programs in University Medical Centers, *Journal of Medical Education,* 40, 625–657, July, 1965.

[71] Simmons, Ozzie G., Social Research in Health and Medicine: A Bibliography, *in* Freeman, H. E., Levine, S. and Reeder, L. G. (Editors), HANDBOOK OF MEDICAL SOCIOLOGY, Englewood Cliffs, New Jersey, Prentice-Hall, Inc., 1963, pp. 493–581.

[72] Pearsall, Marion, MEDICAL BEHAVIORAL SCIENCE: A SELECTED BIBLIOGRAPHY OF CULTURAL ANTHROPOLOGY, SOCIAL PSYCHOLOGY, AND SOCIOLOGY IN MEDICINE, Lexington, University of Kentucky Press, 1963.

[73] Roemer, M. I. and Elling, R. H., Sociological Research on Medical Care, *Journal of Health & Human Behavior,* 4, 49–68, Spring, 1963.

[74] Rosen, George, The Impact of the Hospital on the Physician, the Patient and the Community, *Hospital Administration Quarterly,* 9, 15–33, Fall, 1964.

[75] Bloom, Samuel W., THE DOCTOR AND HIS PATIENT: A SOCIOLOGICAL INTERPRETATION, New York, Russell Sage Foundation, 1963.

[76] King, Stanley H., PERCEPTIONS OF ILLNESS AND MEDICAL PRACTICE, New York, Russell Sage Foundation, 1962.

[77] Zola, Irving N., Problems of Communication, Diagnosis, and Patient Care: The Interplay of Patient, Physician and Clinic Organization, *Journal of Medical Education,* 38, 829–838, October, 1963.

[78] Blum, Richard H., THE MANAGEMENT OF THE DOCTOR-PATIENT RELATIONSHIP, New York, McGraw-Hill Book Company, 1960.

[79] Balint, Michael, THE DOCTOR, HIS PATIENT AND THE ILLNESS, New York, International Universities Press, Inc., 1957.

[80] Freidson, E. and Rhea, B., Processes of Control in a Company of Equals, *Social Problems,* 11, 119–131, Fall, 1963.

[81] Goss, Mary E. W., Influence and Authority Among Physicians in an Out-Patient Setting, *American Sociological Review,* 26, 39–50, February, 1961.

[82] McElrath, David C., Perspective and Participation in Prepaid Group Practice, *American Sociological Review,* 26, 602–603, August, 1961.

[83] Wolfe, Samuel, Talking with Doctors in Urbanville: An Exploratory Study of Canadian General Practitioners, *American Journal of Public Health,* 53, 631–644, April, 1963.

[84] Donabedian, Avedis, Evaluating the Quality of Medical Care, *in* Mainland, Donald (Editor), HEALTH SERVICES RESEARCH I, New York, Milbank Memorial Fund, 1966.

401

[85] Fry, John, Operations Research in General Clinical Practice, *Journal of Chronic Diseases,* 17, 803–814, September, 1964.

[86] Price, P. B., *et al.,* Measurement of Physician Performance, *Journal of Medical Education,* 39, 203–211, February, 1964.

[87] Koplin, A. M., Hutchison, R. and Johnson, B. K., Influence of a Managing Physician on Multiple Hospital Admissions, *American Journal of Public Health,* 49, 1174–1180, September, 1959.

[88] Tucker, W. R., *et al.,* Implementing Improvements in an Outpatient Department, *Archives of Environmental Health,* 11, 22–27, July, 1965.

[89] Huntley, R. R., *et al.,* The Quality of Medical Care: Techniques and Investigation in the Outpatient Clinic, *Journal of Chronic Diseases,* 14, 630–642, December, 1961.

[90] Dickinson, F. G. and Bradley, C. E., DISCONTINUANCE OF MEDICAL GROUPS, 1940–49, Chicago, American Medical Association, 1952.

[91] Makover, Henry B., The Quality of Medical Care, *American Journal of Public Health,* 41, 824–832, July, 1951.

[92] Fox, T. F., The Personal Doctor and his Relation to the Hospital, *Lancet,* 1, 743–760, April 2, 1960.

[93] Sellers, E. M., The Influences of Group and Independent General Practice on Patient Care: A Comparative Study in Ontario, *Canadian Medical Association Journal,* 93, 147–157, July 24, 1965.

[94] Freidson, Eliot, Organization of Medical Practice, *in* Freeman, Levine and Reader, *op. cit.,* pp. 299–320.

[95] Elinson, Jack, The Physician's Dilemma in Puerto Rico, *Journal of Health & Human Behavior,* 3, 14–20, Spring, 1962.

[96] Abel-Smith, Brian, Paying the Family Doctor, *Medical Care,* 1, 27–35, January–March, 1963.

[97] Btesh, S., International Research in the Organization of Medical Care, *Medical Care,* 3, 41–46, January–March, 1965.

[98] Morris, J. N., THE USES OF EPIDEMIOLOGY, Edinburgh, E. S. Livingstone, Limited, 1957.

[99] Elinson, Jack, Methods of Sociomedical Research, *in* Freeman, Levine and Reader, *op. cit.*

[100] Freeman, R., *et al.,* Patient Care Research: Report of a Symposium, *American Journal of Public Health,* 53, 965–969, June, 1963.

ACKNOWLEDGMENT

This paper was prepared with the technical assistance of Anthony Robbins, Yale University School of Medicine.

402

DISCUSSION

Dr. Weinerman's thorough review of what he and others agreed was rather spotty knowledge of medical practice based on research might, in the opinion of some, have benefitted from presentation in the context of a formal conceptual framework. In the present state of knowledge a single model would probably not suffice for all investigators and all viewpoints.

One suggestion was that research into the organization of medical practice might be best discussed within the context of the medical care process. An inclusive model of the process of medical care should contain an inclusive consideration of medical practice. The former might include the full spectrum of behavior from the individual's perception of some disturbance in health, through self-treatment, discussion with family and friends to seeking quasi-medical, paramedical, and medical care and, on recovery, returning to a stable state. Within the medical practice system, research could focus on factors affecting initiation, use, effectiveness and efficiency of all forms of medical care including physicians' services and those of other health professionals, community hospitals, referral centers and consultants as well as post-hospital care, long-term care, rehabilitation and home care services. Problems of availability, accessibility, acceptability, differential use of alternative forms of care, of internal and external communication systems within and between elements of the system, of the competency of health personnel and their rational use, of adequacy of facilities and equipment, of the quality of care, of the financing and organization of practices, of methods of payment and compensation for services, of patients' and of health professionals' expectations could all be the object of research. The advantages of ordering research in medical practice in some such spectrum as that proposed would be to shed light on gaps in the knowledge and to highlight problems at the many interfaces between elements in the system.

A second suggestion for the study of medical practice was that it be studied primarily from the viewpoints of the consumers and the community. This ecological approach would examine health, disease and medical practice in the broad context of human organization and especially in the larger context of medical care organization and the health services system. Simultaneous studies of medical practice and of the population served are needed. Patients, nonpatients and ex-patients all merit simultaneous study. The investigation of interactions, both personal and impersonal, between the purveyors and the consumers of care was advocated as a strategy for research which would then lead to studies of the manner in which the former organized their efforts and the latter used them to solve their health problems. Much of research in the organization of medical practice has been focused on professional concern and therefore has been normatively oriented. Unchallenged assumptions have conditioned many approaches to research. For example, the assumption that the critical variable in determining utilization of care is the presence of any economic barrier, has conditioned much of the thinking in research about the economic basis of medical practice. It may be that geographic and psychological accessibility are more important than economic accessibility. Other professional assumptions include, for example, the notions that "group practice is better than solo practice," that "all diagnosable diseases should be identified and labeled," that "patients have diseases until proved otherwise." These and others need challenging from the viewpoint of the broader perspectives of human organization and social need. In summary, the suggestion was made that much more emphasis should be placed on studies of the community and the whole social environment as a focus for physicians' activities rather than as determinants of the structure and patterns of their organization for practice.

A third framework for research in medical practice suggested that it be studied as a way of life or as an occupation. Physicians and other health professionals are conditioned by processes of education and socialization to behave in accordance with established patterns. Professional prestige systems, educational practices, implicit and explicit controls and punishment patterns may all affect the nature and quality of care. Medical practice may be studied as a "job," or as a way of relating to people, or even as a way of fulfilling the physician's psychological and social, as well as his economic needs. For example, this approach would question the assumption that the goal of medical practice is the "curing of illness." It may be that, but it may also be a way of "making a living" or of "spending one's time." The assumption that medical practice is always, or even usually, purely altruistic would be replaced by many other kinds of assumptions and questions if this third model were adopted.

To some extent these three suggestions or strategies for research in medical practice were those of the clinicians, the epidemiologists, and the social psychologists, or perhaps their counterparts, the public health

404

workers, the demographers and the sociologists. Discussants generally agreed that all three models could be used as valid methods for ordering and organizing research into medical practice and that people in a variety of research disciplines should be encouraged to study the problems.

The discussion of research methods again documented the differences in viewpoints between the clinicians, the epidemiologists and the social scientists. The need, however, seemed to be less for the development of new methodological approaches than for the application of methods already known to the two latter disciplines. Many of these can be readily applied to the study of medical practice. Several additional specific needs were mentioned. Among these are: 1. Increased attention to the application of multivariate methods of statistical analysis to the complex set of variables which are involved in medical care research. 2. Further development of operational methods for measuring these variables. Special attention probably needs to be paid to the problem of utilizing data already collected for other purposes. Studying methods for linking data available on the same persons in more than one setting may be especially fruitful. 3. Studies which provide adequate epidemiological data and information on utilizing medical resources by a single population are badly needed. Similarly, data on the attitudes and perceptions of physicians and their patients concerning the same referents are also needed. Obtaining these kinds of data, of course, poses difficult field research problems.

With respect to additional substantive areas for research, many suggestions were advanced. Among them were: 1. More factual information on people's perceptions of illness, including sociocultural variations; 2. information on patients' views of the availability, accessibility and acceptability of physicians, in relation to social, economic and cultural variables; 3. tests of the impact of changes in availability patterns on utilization of physicians' services in various community settings; 4. descriptive studies of defects in communications between patients and physicians, between health professionals and health institutions particularly with respect to variation by sociocultural groups, age, medical setting, etc.; 5. tests of the impact of efforts at more effective communication between patients and professionals both on the level of communication actually achieved, and on the utilization of physicians' services; 6. health assessment of the individual by himself; 7. tests of the impact of more patient knowledge and greater participation by the individual in the care of his own health on utilization of other medical resources as well as on the health status of the individual; 8. studies of medical practice as a decision-making process; 9. studies of formal and informal organization; even solo practitioners participate in some kind of informal organization of medical practice through membership in medical societies, appointments to hospitals or referral patterns which can be observed and studied as elements in the larger health services system; 10. the history of medical care practice and medical care systems both in this country and in other countries could shed light on contemporary problems; 11. needs and opportunities are many for international comparative and collaborative studies of medical care systems and practices; 12. research is needed into physician substitutes and into the relative advantages and disadvantages of providing primary care through personal physicians versus hospital emergency rooms; 13. research is needed into the influence of various forms of "control," economic, monopolistic, administrative and organizational, on the utilization of health services, personnel and facilities.

With respect to the overall strategy of research, the need was emphasized for small studies which investigated elements or subsystems of the whole system rather than for global descriptive efforts. The latter might be useful in orienting research and in describing the terrain to be covered, but were apt to be less successful in providing deep insights into the system which might lead to improvements in medical practice.

The central problems which condition research in medical practice were agreed to be those surrounding the development of good criteria for its evaluation, and of methods for measuring performance. These problems are, however, much more substantive and theoretical than methodological. They are of great importance and, in fact, are probably among the greatest contemporary problems facing the administrative sciences, particularly as they concern themselves with the social and health services. For example: What is the nature of effectiveness and efficiency? How can we specify what is to be evaluated? In evaluating medical practice, the problem is not merely to develop methods of assessing performance, but also to determine what expectations concerning practice can legitimately be held in what situations. Is the measure of effective care to be whether or not the patient gets well? Or is it whether or not the practitioner does what his peers believe to be appropriate in a situation? Is the efficiency of a practice to be judged by the number of patients it serves for a unit of time-cost or by the satisfaction of the patients with the services they receive? Is the practice which stresses preventive medicine more effective than that which stresses curative medicine? Answers to these questions depend in large part upon what is known about the relations between means and ends, between action and outcome, in medicine.

In the final analysis, any evaluation necessarily affects the power and prestige of those whose actions are evaluated. Hence, the acceptability of an evaluation will depend largely upon its findings and their perceived validity, partly upon the relative status of the evaluators and the evaluated, and partly upon the salience of the values invoked by the evaluation and those who make decisions for the area under scrutiny. The extent to which any evaluation of human performance can be purely scientific in character may be severely limited. The plausibility of a "scientific evaluation" may ultimately rest upon the salience of science's value in a given situation. Thus, one may expect that powerful non-scientific influences may effect both the content of evaluative studies and their reception. The study of social influences depends upon knowledge about the social context of the practice situation. An adequate theory of medical practice will see it not merely as a function of determinant "social forces," but as an emergent outcome of a complex set of transactions in which medical personnel themselves play a leading role. Their aspirations, capabilities, expectations and cupidities are an integral part of the story.

RESEARCH INTO MANPOWER FOR HEALTH SERVICE

DALE L. HIESTAND

Manpower has often been said to be the key problem in the expansion of the health services, despite the fact that health manpower resources have expanded extremely rapidly (about four per cent per year in the 1950's, and 2.5 per cent per year so far in the 1960's). Yet, as in all services, manpower remains the crucial resource in health services. How rapidly and how well manpower is developed essentially determines how rapidly health services rise.

This paper provides an appraisal of the recent research into manpower for the health services, both to indicate its accomplishments and to suggest the main lines which should be pursued in the future.

The key question has always been: How can research on manpower contribute to the expansion and improvement of health services to the nation? Since the number of those who are engaged in health manpower research is quite limited, this paper has been written particularly with the potential, but inexperienced, researcher in this field in mind. The intent has been to make the key issues explicit, to indicate what has been emphasized to date and to point out open research areas where specific efforts are likely to yield significant contributions. At this stage, more rapid progress will be gained from solidly constructed, finely focused efforts rather than from grand designs.

THE CONTENT OF MANPOWER STUDIES

Research into manpower for the health services represents the juncture of many areas of interest. Both health and manpower economics have grown rapidly in the last decade, and have begun to take definite shape. Health economics, long the preoccupation of health professionals, is becoming a recognized field in economics itself. Manpower or human-resources economics is also relatively new.

Manpower studies are concerned with both the supply of and the demand for workers, including the various forces and institutions which affect the development of potential and actual workers in a field. These forces include the education, training, selection, hiring and assignment of workers. The manpower concept also includes the utilization of workers, i.e., the particular functions which workers in different occupations perform, and the way these functions change as a result of other changes in the economy, technology and society.

Manpower research deals with the economics of supply, demand and utilization, but also with nonmonetary factors, motives and institutional forces. Thus, manpower research borders on the fields of management, administration, education, training, psychology and sociology.

Research into health manpower is still in its infancy. The literature is already voluminous, but one is impressed more with what has not been learned than with what has. This paper is concerned with empirical research, rather than theoretical and *ad hoc* discussions of health manpower. The impact of the total educational system on the number and quality of workers in the health services is also not within the scope of this paper. Neither is the research bearing on the structure, functioning and financing of hospitals, governments and professional schools being examined, even though the amount and quality of manpower available for health services depends directly on the economics of the public and nonprofit sectors.[1]

The present paper is organized along six separate axes:

1. The availability of basic data on health manpower.
2. Shortages and future demands for workers in particular fields.
3. The inflow of workers into particular fields, including the development and training of personnel; the incentives, disincentives and opportunities to enter various fields; etc.
4. Losses from the health fields through retirement, leaving the labor force, transfer to other occupations, etc.
5. Current manpower utilization patterns and their changes over time.
6. The qualitative dimensions of manpower in the health services.

This rather structured approach is used because the field is so new that most manpower research has been of an *ad hoc* nature. Persons from different disciplines have investigated one or another problem relevant to their own work and, as a result, manpower problems in health services have usually been studied from relatively narrow points of view. By looking at topics rather than occupations one can appraise relative progress in different fields and indicate methods to deal with related problems of the different occupational groups.

TENDENCIES IN EXISTING RESEARCH

The most striking aspect of research into manpower for health services to date has been its concentration on a few groups and problems and its spotty nature otherwise. In 1960, as Table 1 shows, some 2.6 million persons were employed in the health services industry, and 291,000 were in selected health occupations in other industries. The central concern in health manpower research has been with physicians, who number only 230,000 (234,000 including osteopaths) or only eight per cent of the total. Indeed, most attention has been paid to physicians in private practice, who comprise perhaps six per cent of all health services manpower. Secondarily, attention has been centered on registered nurses, who comprise one-fifth of the total, and particularly on hospital nurses, who comprise less than one-seventh of the total. The other manpower groups employed in health services have received only sporadic attention. Of course, more up-to-date estimates may be found for some of these manpower groups, as is shown in Table 2. Although these data are not quite comparable, the central point remains.

The overriding attention given to physicians is clear in the literature and data on manpower discussed by Klarman[2] and Harris.[3] Of course, attention has centered on physicians and nurses for many reasons. These two occupations are the key manpower groups with specialized skills which are essential to the maintenance and improvement of health. Indeed, in a way unparalleled in any other industry, the physician controls and influences his field and all who venture near it. For many functions, no direct substitute for the physician exists. This has a great impact on the manpower problems of the health services industry.

However, other personnel groups may substitute directly and indirectly for physicians and nurses. Because nonprofessional nursing

410

TABLE I. OCCUPATIONAL DISTRIBUTION OF PERSONS EMPLOYED IN HEALTH OCCUPATIONS

	Hospital, Medical and other Health Services Industry	Health Occupations Outside Health Service Industry	Total in Health Occupations
Professional and technical	1,167,218		
Physicians and surgeons	218,301	11,370	229,671
Osteopaths	3,861	220	4,081
Nurses, professional	528,771	52,518	581,771
Nurses, student professional	57,746		57,746
Technicians, medical and dental	127,947	10,866	138,813
Dentists	85,263	1,624	86,887
Dietitians and nutritionists	18,190	8,280	26,470
Chiropractors	13,630	223	13,853
Optometrists	13,073	3,132	16,205
Pharmacists	6,504	85,729*	92,233
Veterinarians	382	14,823	15,205
Therapists and healers, n.e.c.	25,272	11,296	36,568
Other	68,278		
Service workers, except private household	799,887		
Attendants, hospital and other institutions	365,690	25,446	391,136
Midwives	896		896
Practical nurses	144,045	63,921	207,966
Other service workers	289,256		
Clerical	399,703		
Attendants, physician's and dentist's office	70,607	1,564	72,171
Other clerical	329,096		
Craftsmen, foremen	67,742		
Operatives and kindred workers	62,441		
Managers, officials and proprietors, except farm	50,092		
Laborers, except farm and mine	12,172		
Sales workers	1,838		
Occupation not reported	28,160		
Total	2,589,253		

* In addition, are 25,456 managers and proprietors of drug stores, an unknown number of whom work primarily as pharmacists.

Source: United States Census of Population, 1960, Occupation by Industries, pp. 132–136.

personnel and paramedical personnel in other than nursing service have received far too little attention, this paper calls attention wherever possible to them. Practically no research has been reported in connection with personnel who are necessary to the provision of health services, but who are not substantially identified with health fields per se. This would include cooks, clerical workers, housekeepers, mechanics and the like. As the health services industry grows, health specialties in such fields are being developed. Ward clerks, medical secretaries, hospital masons and so on are becoming a part of the health manpower complex. As they become a more integral part, the need for research on these groups is becoming pressing.

Basic Data

Whatever the reasons for inadequacies in health manpower studies, they cannot include lack of basic data with which to work. The decennial censuses of 1940, 1950 and 1960 contain a great deal of data about the occupational, educational, income, locational, demographic

TABLE 2. HEALTH SERVICE WORKERS, BY LEVEL OF TRAINING

Level of Training and Occupation:	Number of Persons
Total	2,417,000
Doctoral level	
Physicians (including osteopaths)*	288,000
Dentists*	93,000
Other	44,000
Total	425,000
Allied health professions	
Dental hygienists†	15,000
Medical record librarians**	10,000
Medical technologists††	32,000
Occupational therapists	8,000
Physical therapists	12,000
Professional nurses (BS)	70,000
Speech pathologists and audiologists	13,000
X-ray technologists***	70,000
Other	160,000
Total	390,000
Diploma nursing	522,000
Other 1–3 year post-high school	
Certified laboratory assist.	1,100
Cytotechnologists	3,000
Dental assistants	95,000
Dental laboratory technicians	27,000
Inhalation therapists	4,000
Practical nurses	265,000
Other	159,900
Tota	555,000
Short training	525,000

* Active.
† Licensed (some baccalaureate, primarily 2-year programs).
** Employed in hospitals.
†† Registered (both baccalaureate and less than baccalaureate).
*** Both baccalaureate and less than baccalaureate.
Estimates by Public Health Service on basis of available data from professional organizations.
Source: United States House of Representatives. *Report of the Committee on Interstate and Foreign Commerce on H.R. 13196* (Allied Health Professions Personnel Training Act of 1966). House Report No. 1628, 89th Congress, Second Session, 1966, p. 9.

and other characteristics of persons in the health service industry and health occupations. The various professional associations collect similar data from their members. A wealth of data on the personnel and operating characteristics of hospitals are collected and reported each year, and some data will be available on a monthly basis in the future. Indeed, annual occupational data are reported separately for practically every hospital in the country. The various educational and training institutions regularly report on their student bodies and their operations individually and through their associations. The relevant licensing agencies in the various states are also sources of valuable and detailed data, much of which is collected, classified and published by government or the various professional associations. Governmental agencies which employ, train, assist or in other ways deal with health manpower publish great quantities of relevant data. In addition, special surveys have been made from time to time by various governmental agencies and professional groups as a part of their continuing studies of one or another subject of interest.

In few other sectors of the economy are so much manpower data reported in comparable detail on a regular basis. In many cases, moreover, these data have been further processed to make them more useful to the researcher. The United States Public Health Service has published some 19 Health Manpower Source Books since 1952, providing data which have been partially processed but not analyzed to any significant degree.[4] Indeed, since the medical service industry is largely carried on under governmental and nonprofit auspices, new data are relatively easy to obtain. The only significant exceptions are independent practitioners, health workers employed in industry and the employees of privately owned hospitals. Even in these cases, responses to surveys have been good.

The development of research in health manpower has not been particularly impeded by a lack of data. Rather, vast amounts of information have not been well exploited. Some may question the quality of the data, but it is better than most manpower information in other sectors of the economy. New and better data can be relatively easily obtained if that appears advisable. But manpower researchers are exceedingly scarce, and priority ought to be given to analysis, rather than data collecting. That is particularly true for those newly entering health manpower research. As new concepts and relevant distinctions are developed, they can be fed into existing data collecting systems with relative ease.

Shortages

The preoccupation of manpower analysts in the health fields has been the estimation of shortages and the establishment of manpower goals for the future. One way in which shortages are measured is through the gap between minimum quantitative and qualitative standards and what exists in fact. For instance, in 1956, the American Psychiatric Association issued guide-lines on personnel-to-patient ratios for a variety of occupations and types of services in public mental hospitals. The number actually employed consistently fell short of the estimates of need based on these standards: by 55 per cent in the case of physicians, by 35 per cent in the case of psychologists, and so on.[5]

Another example of an estimate of shortage is the report of the Surgeon General's Consultant Group on Nursing. The Group based its estimate of a need for 850,000 nurses in 1970 largely on the finding of one study that in general hospitals "highest patient satisfaction was achieved when professional nurses gave at least 50 per cent of the direct care." This was in contrast to the existing proportion of 30 per cent. Realistically, considering the potential supply of students and the potential capacity of schools of nursing, the Group concluded that this total need could not be met by 1970. It then set a total of 680,000 professional nurses as a feasible goal for 1970.[6] Just prior to the time of the report, a total of only 582,000 nurses were employed in the United States.[7]

Another approach is the accumulation of data on budgeted vacancies. Hospitals, health departments and other units regularly provide data comparing actual employment with budgeted positions for various occupations and types of services. The vacancy rates thus computed vary greatly from one occupation to another and are lower for the higher administrative and other specialized nursing personnel than for general duty staff nurses.

Surprisingly, such estimates of shortages are received with little enthusiasm by many manpower analysts. The term shortage tends to be used in one way by non-economists and in a distinctly different way by economists. Non-economists use the term to describe a discrepancy between the situation which they view as necessary or desirable, and the situation which does in fact exist. That is, "shortage" often has meaning primarily in relation to the norms and value systems of those in the leadership of particular professions. Such professional leaders use a variety of terms: minimum standards, necessary levels of care, desirable staffing practices or optimum standards.

Whatever standard is employed, the usual judgment is that more services and resources are needed than can in fact be provided by the amount of funds which the community is spending either as individuals or through its public and private institutions. Economists point out that in a market economy the community indicates its own judgment as to what is necessary and desirable within the limits of the total resources available to it. It often decides to allocate its funds in ways which various groups in health, education and even business do not think wise or desirable.

From the economist's point of view, the difference between what some persons think the community should spend in a particular area and what it does spend is essentially irrelevant. For example, in 1957, the Joint Information Service of the American Psychiatric Association and the National Association for Mental Health stated that in staffing public mental hospitals, "no state even approaches the minimum standards."[8]

The public clearly differs with health leaders as to what is adequate or what is minimum. This point is difficult for the leaders of any field to accept. Complaints about deficiencies and inequities merely mask the fact that different standards of value exist in the community. Only as health proponents persuade the public at large to spend more for health services and manpower does the purported shortage become economically relevant. This is essentially a problem of value shaping and politics, not manpower research.

From the economist's point of view, a shortage indicates some discrepancy between the actual level of manpower supply and that which is possible, given the existing structure and level of demand for services and manpower in health and in all other fields. Any difference between what is possible and what actually exists can occur in two ways.

The first has to do with discrepancies which occur with a change in the conditions of supply or demand which have not had sufficient time for the essential resources to be re-allocated through the market place by way of the attraction and retention of personnel, the readjustment of demand and the like. This kind of shortage normally solves itself with time. A second kind of shortage is due to deficiencies or imperfections in the market system, such as artificial or institutional limitations to the flow of manpower because of monopoloid tendencies or ignorance.

Thus, every discussion of shortages is shot through with different opinions and confusion as to what is desirable and what is the result of supply and demand factors. The point can be made clearer by suggesting that if by some magic the supply of most kinds of health professionals were large enough to meet the stated minimum adequate needs, consumers would not increase their spending by nearly as much, many professionals would find themselves fully or partially unemployed and income levels would fall. Most governments and nonprofit institutions would not have the necessary funds to fill their reported vacancies and would reduce both the number of budgeted positions and salary levels. Many health professionals would flee to other occupations and enrollments in training programs would drop sharply.

But if the governmental and nonprofit agencies could somehow find the funds to absorb the minimum number considered to be adequate, one could be reasonably sure that the professional groups would soon announce new and higher minimum adequate standards. Such standards will almost always advance in front of what can exist in fact. In a progressive, increasingly affluent society, this is perfectly normal.

Estimates of manpower shortages based on conceptions of need rather than demand do have their uses. But most studies purporting to estimate present or prospective shortages of manpower are woefully inadequate. The primary problem is the lack of any way to evaluate such shortages or to appreciate their significance. Most estimates of shortages are based on some apparently arbitrary relations between the population and the various manpower groups. But the connection between the total population, its health needs and the precise needs for any particular manpower group are indeed tenuous. A complex of factors affects the health needs of a population. Among them are its age distribution, the natural, economic and technological environment within which it lives, and so forth. Public health practices change, and with them the frequency of various conditions. The skill and means for diagnosis and treatment change. Health treatment may become more institutionalized, as it has in the past, or a reverse trend may set in. The relative availability of different classes of personnel and the particular functions assigned to them also change. To be meaningful, estimates of needs will have to pin down the probable course and effect of each of these factors. Generalities do not suffice.

RESEARCH ON DEMAND FOR HEALTH MANPOWER

In addition to estimates of need, estimates of the demands for health manpower, that is, estimates of what will in fact occur, are necessary. Demands are subject, of course, to all the changes enumerated above. But, in addition, estimates would be needed of changes in incomes, insurance and public funds, as well as how much would be spent for various types of health care and personnel. Surprisingly, arbitrary ratios of health professionals to population have shown remarkably stable trends over the past several decades. Since 1938, every 100,000 persons in the population have been served by between 131 and 135 physicians. On the same population basis, the ratio has been eight or nine osteopaths since 1931, and 56 or 57 dentists since 1947. The number of active professional nurses per 100,000 population increased from 175 in 1930 to 280 in 1960, but the increase has been at a remarkably stable pace—a little more than 30 per 100,000 during each decade.

These stabilities are remarkable in view of the great changes which have occurred over these periods in the factors affecting the supply of and demand for health services and health manpower. Some of these changes have tended to increase and others to decrease the supply of and demand for professional health manpower, sometimes in conflicting ways. The steadiness of the trends has been, of course, the net result of these conflicting influences. Canadian experience shows the danger of assuming that conflicting forces will counterbalance in any regular way. There the ratio of physicians per 100,000 moved irregularly upward from 97 in 1931 to 117 in 1961; and that for dentists irregularly downward from 38 in 1931 to 30 in 1962. Both ratios are lower than in the United States. In contrast, the ratio for nurses increased from 181 in 1941 to 338 in 1961, more rapidly in the latter decade. It is now much higher than in the United States.[9]

Almost every writer on the needs and demands for health manpower denigrates the use of simple population ratios—and then proceeds to use them with little real qualification. If ratios are inadequate—and they are—considerably more research is needed to assess the relative effect of the diverse trends which have occurred in the past so that more useful methods can be found to estimate the impact of diverse future developments. The Bureau of Labor Statistics has a study underway on future employment in the health occupations, but a great deal of basic work will continue to be necessary.

Most discussions of demand have centered on physicians.

At the very least, alternative estimates ought to be made of the expected demand in the various secondary and tertiary occupations, given various estimates as to what will obtain in the key manpower groups. This involves an estimate of the consequences of shortages in terms of the availability and quality of health services as well as in terms of utilization practices. The various health manpower fields both complement and substitute for each other. A shortage of physicians could have two possible effects. If physicians are uniquely necessary, any shortage of them will be accompanied by a lack of demand for nurses and other paramedical personnel, while an increase in the number of physicians will be accompanied by a nearly equivalent increase in the employment of various auxiliary personnel. On the other hand, to the extent that nurses and other paramedical personnel are substitutes for physicians, a shortage of physicians will add to the demand for paramedical personnel, while an increased supply of physicians reduces the demand for paramedical personnel. Similar relationships exist between registered nurses and other nursing and non-nursing personnel, and wherever diverse groups of workers are combined directly or indirectly to provide a service. Some clues as to the nature of diverse relationships appear in the literature, but no research has been directed specifically at the degree to which complementarity and substitutability exist. This topic will be raised again in the discussion of utilization practices.

Besides national estimates of health manpower demands, an equally interesting question concerns the level of demand in the various states and communities. Every inventory of health manpower reveals the wide differences which exist among the states in terms of health manpower per capita. A number of analyses have shown a correlation between income levels or urbanization and the number of physicians and dentists.[10] The urbanized states tend to have higher per capita incomes, educational levels and hospital admission rates; they also have higher per capita expenditures for mental hospitals and more employees per patient in hospitals.[11] Health manpower also tends to be scarce where the population is widely dispersed.[12] Urbanization, income levels, population density and education are all highly correlated, and cause and effect cannot be traced. They are, however, far from a full explanation of the variations in the level of demand for health service personnel. The subject deserves considerably more investigation.

The few demand estimates which have been attempted suggest that both national and state studies of manpower demands can be more fruitfully undertaken if they are deaggregated as much as possible. That is, studies should be limited to specific areas of demand or particular types of institutions. A good example of this approach is that of Albee.[5] By concentrating on the problem of manpower demands for mental health, he was forced to keep in the forefront the very crucial questions of competition between that and other fields for manpower, as well as the functional relationships among the various professional and nonprofessional groups.

The various studies of dental health manpower also illustrate the value of constricting the scope of demand studies. These studies have made substantial progress in estimating trends in demand in the states, regions and nation. The earlier studies commented on expected changes in some of the factors affecting the demand for dentists, but finally resorted to manipulating conventional ratios of population per dentist. The later studies, however, include rather complex estimates of the increased demand for dental services based on trends in population, per capita expenditures for dental services and income levels, as well as an estimate of expected decreases in the incidence of caries through fluoridation. The resulting estimates of the demand for services were compared to estimates of the likely increase in the number of dentists, as well as to changes in their productivity through improved equipment, better office management, and the increased and improved use of auxiliary personnel.[13]

The dental manpower studies were perhaps fortunate in that a few key implicit assumptions about the methods of practice, the degree of specialization, the rate of increase in improved equipment and so forth could be made with some confidence. By restricting the scope of other studies, the usefulness and validity of other similar assumptions can be progressively explored. Other studies might be made of the demands for health manpower for, say, public health, general hospitals, rehabilitation service, services to the aged and research and development. Clearly, such studies would overlap and cause problems in reconciling them. But if the focus is kept on demand rather than hopes and goals, such studies can be of immense value.

Types of Shortages and Research Policy

As a summary judgment, the nature and extent of shortages in the health occupations vary greatly among different fields. In the case of physicians, the evidence overwhelmingly indicates a shortage in the senses mentioned earlier. The demand for physicians' services is increasing rapidly. Nearly all those trained as physicians work as physicians. The number of qualified applicants to medical schools substantially exceeds the number of openings available.

Very few medical students withdraw prior to graduation. Nearly 20 per cent of all new physicians' licenses issued each year go to graduates of medical schools outside the United States and Canada. Some are American citizens who were qualified, but were not accepted to enter domestic schools, and went abroad for training. Finally, the income levels of physicians have consistently exceeded those in other professional fields, even after considering the time and cost of education. On any grounds whatever, the shortage of physicians and, more importantly, of opportunities to enter medical school is evident.

On the other hand, in an economic sense, little or no evidence indicates a shortage of registered nurses. In the first place, nearly half of those who have been trained as nurses and a third of those who are currently registered as nurses are not employed. Since nearly all nurses are women and many have family responsibilities, the significance of these unemployed trained and licensed nurses is not unequivocal. But many are not working simply because the incentives are not great enough, or because hospitals and other employers are not willing to make the necessary adjustment in hours, part-time work, etc. In contrast, female physicians and dentists usually work at least part-time during all but a few months prior to and after delivery.[14]

Secondly, rather than having a surplus of qualified applicants, hospital schools of nursing typically operate at only 90 to 92 per cent of capacity.[15] Thirdly, as noted later, utilization practices with respect to registered nurses continue to be inconsistent with the purported fact that they are a scarce manpower resource. Finally, no evidence shows that salaries in nursing are unusually high or have advanced rapidly as normally occurs in a shortage. Rather the incomes of nurses are equal to or lower than women of similar educational level, whether or not one takes into account other factors which might affect income, such as race or regularity of employment. Yett reports that professional nurses' salaries increased by only about 50 per cent during the 1950's, compared to 70 per cent for teachers or all female professional and related workers.[16] From the point of view of the "need" for registered nurses in some abstract sense, shortages may well exist. But these needs are unsupported by private or public expenditures for them.

The situation in the nonprofessional nursing and other paramedical professions is somewhat less clear. In part that is because these fields are relatively new and rapidly growing. Evidence, one way or the other, is almost nonexistent either in terms of the number and quality of applicants, the experience of training programs, or employment patterns and income. The single most relevant fact is that the supply of personnel in nearly all nonprofessional nursing and paramedical fields is increasing rapidly and new occupations are appearing. This warrants the hypothesis that what shortages exist in these fields are primarily the result of imbalances of a rapidly increasing demand continuing to outdistance the supply. If so, achieving a better balance between supply and demand is more or less a matter of the market working out training programs, incentives, etc., making opportunities available and attractive, and attracting the necessary manpower into the fields.

The nature of the shortages in the different fields has significance for research into health manpower. Priority in research depends on an evaluation of what the important problems are and what the significant policy decisions are likely to be. With the excess of qualified applicants for positions in medical schools and as long as practically all persons trained as physicians continue to work as physicians, research into the characteristics and motives of those who enter medical school may prove interesting, but will make little contribution to policy, for it will not show how to increase the number of medical school opportunities. Rather, the significant research will lie in the area of predicting the demand for physicians' services to justify more medical schools, in studying such alternative sources of physicians as those trained abroad, and in learning how to improve the utilization of physicians for maximum benefit from these scarce resources. In the case of nurses, the principal questions would center on why purported shortages and poor utilization practices have not been rectified, and particularly on the incentives of nurses and their employers in these matters. In the case of paranursing and paramedical personnel, research into every aspect of manpower would be relevant: the determinants of demand, the recruitment and retention of personnel, the effects of different training mechanisms, their allocation among different types of health activities and their utilization on the job. The

421

goal would be both to help supply become more responsive to demand and to insure that wasteful efforts are not undertaken.

CHARACTERISTICS AND MOTIVES OF THOSE ENTERING HEALTH SERVICE

Who enters the various health fields? Considerable research has been done on the social, economic and intellectual characteristics and goals of medical, osteopathic and dental students. In part, this reflects the considerable concern during the last dozen years with the quality of medical school applicants.

In the early 1950's, the proportion of newly admitted medical students who had had an "A" average in their undergraduate education declined, with a corresponding increase among "B" students. During those same years, the number of applicants to medical schools decreased by over 40 per cent, and the proportion admitted increased from less than one-third to over one-half. This apparently was a temporary situation, perhaps related to the changes in the supply of students in connection with World War II, the Korean War and the low birth rates some two decades earlier. Since 1954, the quality of medical school students has been stabilized and quite high. Although some schools accept students who do not rate particularly high, this is more likely to occur at some state-owned schools which seem to accept local applicants rather than more highly qualified out-of-state applicants.[17] This point could be verified, but it has not.

Actually, a ratio of admissions to applicants of about one-half held throughout the 1930's, the early 1940's and since 1952. This ratio probably has no particular significance. Students and their advisors are aware of the standards of admission, and those not likely to be accepted do not apply. The standards of admission are generally considered somewhat less demanding in dental than in medical schools, but in both a ratio of one-half has held in recent years. This was true even when dental schools were willing to accept more students, but did not think those being rejected were qualified. In dentistry, no decline in quality of students occurred during the 1950's.[18]

The evidence of a decline in quality is not convincing on more basic grounds. Quite consistently, studies have found little relationship between undergraduate grades, aptitude test scores, or other criteria used in admitting students and subsequent performance in medical school. Even more important, almost no evidence relates quality as

422

conventionally gauged in student applicants and ultimate quality in medical practice.[19] The question of further research in this area will be examined later.

What are the motives for entering the health professions? The popular discussion and the analyses of economists suggest that income factors are of overriding importance. Medicine is the highest paying profession of all.

Primarily because of the long training period, the investment in actual expenditures and foregone income of the student and his family are also quite high. Friedman and Kuznets found that, considering both of these factors, the rate of return on this investment to both physicians and dentists was above that in other occupations.[20] In more recent analyses, Hansen concluded that the relative incentives to enter dentistry were adverse in 1939, quite attractive in 1949, but about balanced in 1956. In the case of physicians, he concluded that the relative incentives were about balanced in 1939, strongly in favor of medicine in 1949, and somewhat less strongly in favor of medicine in 1956. Hansen suggests that these shifts may be partially responsible for the reported decline in the quality of medical school applicants in the 1950's.[21] Serious difficulties cast doubt on the accuracy of income data, and whether Hansen's income data were increasingly influenced downward by the influx of foreign trained physicians during the 1950's is not clear. More importantly, one may question whether the manpower market in the medical or any other field operates so neatly and quickly. Complaints as to the quality of medical school applicants began to appear in 1951, just two years after the differential in favor of medicine was at its widest. No record exists of complaints on the quality of students in the late 1930's, when the incentives to enter medicine were apparently balanced.

Composite estimates of costs and returns are only a starting point. The length of the training period, the level of tuitions, the availability of loans and scholarships, the level and rate of growth in income during internship, residency and different forms of practice may each have somewhat different effects which may be relevant to manpower policy. Altenderfer and West made an exceptionally complete study of medical and osteopathic students and the types and levels of their money receipts and expenditures classified by the source of the funds and their marital status, number of children, living arrangements, geographical location, year in medical school and public versus private school,[22] but did not face the effect of these financial factors.

423

In varying forms, salary increases, changes in the amount and rate of increase in salaries over a career, lower tuition costs and greater availability of grants and loans have all been used in the several health fields and new proposals appear regularly. The effects of these alternative mechanisms in different occupations ought to be carefully appraised. More follow-up studies of the recipients of federal and other scholarship or traineeship grants are needed over longer periods of time. Particularly in the case of women, the results of investments in occupational training may not be clear for 20 years or so.

A careful appraisal of the various steps in the education and training process with a view to finding the extent to which it can be shortened might produce significant results. Various proposals have been made, for instance, to reduce the time in premedical and medical school, as well as to reduce or even eliminate internship. A shorter training period would add to the incentives to enter a program. It would also permit training more manpower with the same training resources of faculty and facilities. This all presupposes no essential qualitative changes in the training process due to a shorter period.

The non-monetary incentives to enter the health occupations have been speculated upon but have not received enough attention. The health professions have been characterized as fundamentally appealing to deep motives of service, the application rather than the development of science, and involving quite unique responsibilities in many cases along with a unique measure of independence.

More's survey of dental students is exceptional for a study of a health occupation in the extent to which he sought to compare them with other groups in ways which were relevant.[23] Davis has also distinguished medicine from nine other (generally broader) career interest fields in his large-scale study of college seniors and their occupational choices. In this way he was able to compare the aspiring medical student to others in socioeconomic terms, academic performance and expressed values.[24] In the health fields, as in many ubiquitous fields, one would expect to find a high proportion who are committed to a particular occupation very early. One would also expect many to be deeply interested in the health field, but with the final occupational choice slow to emerge, perhaps depending on circumstance. He will also find many who are seriously interested in a health occupation, but also in other fields. At some margin, occupations and fields compete for students, and the students compete for entry. The key points in these two processes should always be the central focus. This requires the knowledge of the fields with which health service competes at each level (doctoral, bachelor, diploma, associate, technician or even lower) and the factors which affect these decisions. So much work is going on with respect to the career patterns of highly qualified persons that better insights should appear regularly; the lesser level occupations have been neglected.

Alternative Career Paths

The professional associations are beginning to make rather extensive longitudinal studies of the career patterns of those entering their fields. The American Association of Medical Schools, for instance, is making a longitudinal study of the class of students which entered in 1957. The American Dental Association has data on the class which started in 1958, and may follow them up. The National League for Nursing Education is following up the class which entered and graduated from the various types of nursing programs in 1962. Longitudinal studies covering the entire occupational spectrum are also under way under several auspices. Such longitudinal studies cannot fail to be interesting, but they will be slow to produce data. They ought to be supplemented by studies following up the students of earlier years as well as surveys of the educational and work histories of those now in various types of practice and responsibility. The rapid growth of continuing education suggests that it be periodically examined for its effect on skills, mobility, utilization patterns and the like.

One of the major sources of medical manpower which has not received the attention it deserves consists of persons trained in other countries. Between 1950 and 1959, the proportion of all new medical licenses issued to persons trained outside the United States increased from 5.1 to 19.7 per cent, and it has remained at or near the latter level since. Foreign-trained physicians include both the citizens of other countries and Americans who studied abroad, usually after being rejected by a medical school in the United States. The increased number of alien physicians is directly related to the increase in the number of physicians who are members of hospital house staffs, i.e., interns and residents. Between 1951 and 1963, the total number in approved programs at hospitals increased by nearly 60 per cent. Aliens accounted for about half of this increase and they comprised about one-fourth of both residents and interns in the latter year.[25]

The role of middle-aged women as source of manpower for the health professions has been noted but perhaps not explored as adequately as it might. Yett estimated that the return of women past age 35 accounted for at least one-third of the increased employment of registered nurses between 1948 and 1962.[26] Just how important they have been among practical nurses, nurses' aides and the like ought to be ascertained. Several other questions might be raised in each of these fields having to do with just where middle-aged women have gone to work, why they went to work and the extent to which they obtained training of one sort or another after or in preparation for their return.

Very little has been done to portray with any accuracy the various routes by which technical assistants and other paramedical personnel enter their occupations. Most of the literature in the field describes the few programs which are in operation and the formal systems of certification which are developing. Many changes are occurring here, particularly as junior college programs are expanding and special programs have been instituted under the Manpower Development and Training Act and through the Poverty Program. Research into the education and training, the actual functions performed and the deficiencies of those now employed as technicians and in other paramedical jobs might point up possible approaches to improve their quality through various training mechanisms.

Upgrading: An Unexplored Area

A crucial area which needs research is the opportunities and problems in connection with the transfer of persons from one level of practice to another. In most non-medical fields, recruitment from the next lower level on the basis of experience, with such additional education and formal training as is warranted in the individual case, is often as important as the prescribed formal route of entry into the field. Semi-skilled workers are the major source of craftsmen,[27] persons without college degrees are a major source of engineers,[28] and so on.

Alternative routes into the various health fields have often been foreclosed by tight control of training requirements for licensure, or have been obscured or denigrated by leaders of various occupational groups. One-third of the degree candidates in nursing already have an R. N., but the leaders of the nursing profession assert that this is an unusual situation which will disappear with time.[29] Special degree programs for registered nurses are being closed out in favor of basic nursing programs. However, this tends to increase the length of time in school, with the predictable results that the number entering and graduating after an R. N. has declined and the total number of graduations at the bachelor's level has failed to grow significantly for several years.

Research, including experimental programs, should investigate ways to encourage upgrading and transfers among the health occupations. The need for such mobility is likely to increase as a greater degree of differentiation occurs in nursing and other health occupations. Research would probably disclose that advancement by stages is a sensible course for those with limited means and uncertain ambitions and opportunities; that is, that it reflects some very normal exigencies of life. Research also ought to further illuminate the effects current practices in upgrading of health personnel are having on recruitment and retention of personnel.

More specifically, research needs to be done on the qualities of nursing, technical and paramedical personnel at each level to see whether new sources of manpower for the next higher level might be found. Can ways be found to elevate experienced nurse's aides to the practical nurse level, short of having them take the entire practical nurse program? Can experienced practical nurses be similarly upgraded to the associate or diploma nurse level? How can associate and diploma school graduates be most effectively upgraded to the bachelor nurse level? How can laboratory helpers be upgraded to technicians, and technicians to technologists? Research might indicate ways in which new occupations in patient care and diagnosis might develop between the physician and the bachelor-level nurses and technologists.

Crucial policy questions are involved here. The practice is so common in other fields, however, that upgrading might become a major source of manpower in each of the various levels of nursing, technical and paramedical service. In a similar vein, Kissick points to the need to explore the opportunities for lateral transfer among the various paramedical occupations. He also suggests the need for experiments in core courses in the various health occupations, not only to conserve educational resources, but also to encourage both vertical and lateral mobility.

Losses of Health Manpower

A number of earlier comments about the effectiveness of various training devices in terms of the extent to which trained personnel remain in their fields is only part of the larger problem of the retention of personnel. A number of illuminating hospital turnover studies have been made in recent years. A major shortcoming of these studies is that they usually fail to distinguish between losses of people who immediately go to work elsewhere in health services and losses which reduce the total health manpower supply through retirement, leaving the labor force or entering some other occupation.

The evidence is that physicians rarely leave medical functions short of retiring, and that dentists are almost as persistent. On the other hand, about five per cent of all nurses are said to leave the field each year, primarily due to marriage or pregnancy.[30] This is somewhat lower than the annual loss rate of seven to eight per cent among school teachers, which contrasts sharply with the finding that job turnover rates for nursing personnel are about three times as great as among public school teachers.[31] Of course, high losses among young women are to some extent counterbalanced by their return at a later date when their family responsibilities have been reduced. Data on loss rates among other health service occupations do not seem to have been published.

Physicians in independent practice face no problem of compulsory retirement. One observer notes that physicians tend to be retired as their practices shrivel, in part due to competition from younger physicians.[32] Dentists start to reduce the number of weeks they work per year in their forties, and the number of hours per week in their fifties.[33] Salaried employees may face the prospect of compulsory retirement, although pension plans may not be so prevalent in nonprofit institutions. The process of retirement in the various health fields, however it occurs, deserves investigation to determine its effect on the manpower supply.

The spate of hospital turnover rate studies in recent years has undoubtedly given hospital administrators valuable tools to improve personnel practices, lower turnover and thus lower their costs. In the process, too, they have probably reduced losses from the health manpower field. About 20 to 25 per cent of the losses in one study, and about 75 per cent in another were considered avoidable.[34]

Levine has studied turnover of nursing employees in general hospitals in the midwest and northeast relating it to length of employment, size and ownership of hospitals, particular nursing occupations and whether or not the hospital had a school. Turnover of nursing personnel in these hospitals was higher than for female factory workers; among aides, orderlies and attendants it was twice as high.[35]

Turnover can be quite costly. One study in a Minneapolis hospital found that direct costs amounted to three per cent of the payroll. The study noted but did not measure the costs that would have to be incurred to reduce this turnover or would result from lower turnover. The simple reduction in turnover drives up salary costs because of the longer tenure of employees. Again, higher salaries might discourage turnover, but would lead to higher salaries to other employees, not just those who would otherwise leave. Other costs might be incurred to improve other personnel functions to reduce turnover.[36] Of course, some efforts might lead to reduced costs in other directions. For instance, expenditures to improve on-the-job training, supervision, the definition of responsibilities or communications might lead to reduced turnover while improving the effectiveness of the enterprise as a whole. These tradeoffs between costs and benefits have not been carefully studied, however.

THE UTILIZATION OF HEALTH SERVICE MANPOWER

As has become evident, utilization of manpower in the health fields is an extremely complex and crucial issue. Changes in utilization practices can make key professional workers, and thus the health enterprise, more efficient. Changes in utilization practices may partially convert the demand for manpower from occupations which are in short supply to those in which manpower can be more easily obtained. Utilization practices are crucially determined by the character of training that health workers have received. On the other hand, utilization practices are highly relevant to the character of the training health workers ought to receive. Utilization practices directly affect the incentives to enter and stay in different fields. Moreover, to the extent that improved utilization practices affect the efficiency of an organization and the economy, the quantity and quality of services may be raised, and expenditures to help increase and improve staffs may be made.

Most of the knowledge about actual utilization practices is really confined to assertions, rather than being determined by research. The assertion has been made that, because of shortages, physicians have become less accessible, less communicative and busier; that they keep longer hours, have reduced night and home calls, rely more on telephone consultations and schedule office visits more closely; and that they have reduced their role as family counselors.[37] Presumably, therefore, variations in the extent of these practices in different communities

429

at the present time would be related to the size of local complements of physicians versus the local population, income levels, etc. This has not been investigated.

National surveys of utilization practices appear to have only limited value. Utilization practices must be judged against the costs and returns of alternative possibilities, and these can only be judged in the specific instance. By looking at the amount of time various kinds of workers spend at various tasks, one may identify time which is wasted and tasks which could be more economically performed by others. Tasks which can be more efficiently performed by more highly skilled persons should be shifted to them, provided such personnel are available at a lesser cost for the same amount and quality of work. If not, the task should remain with the workers performing it, but they may require additional training to improve their skill. Tasks which can be more efficiently performed by less skilled, lower paid workers should be shifted downward. Such workers can usually be more easily obtained, but the requirement of reducing costs while maintaining the amount and quality of service always holds.

The question of the relative availability, cost and productivity of different personnel groups can only be answered in the context of a local situation. What can large-scale research contribute to this process? This is certainly not just an academic question. Research showing utilization patterns, that is, the tasks performed by various personnel groups and the costs involved, can serve as norms to guide individuals and administrators. Gathering the data for comparative utilization studies can be directly useful to administrators, for they immediately indicate some situations which can be altered for the better on the spot. Utilization studies can call attention to persistent and generic problems, leading to concerted efforts to better understand and rectify them. Moreover, studying changes in utilization patterns over time can illuminate the conditions under which practices are likely to change, the types of changes which occur and the problems which are likely to accompany them. But studies showing the amount of time nurses or any other group spend on one task or another are not, per se, evidence of good or bad utilization.

Almost no aspect of health services can be overlooked in its effect on utilization patterns. Careful examination of the interaction between each of the several professional and nonprofessional groups may reveal ways to more effective utilization of the available manpower resources. The assertion that registered nurses have been delegated many functions once performed only by physicians has never been investigated. Are the functions of nurses different in different geographical areas? To what extent are differences in utilization practices among communities a reflection of different availabilities of manpower? How is this related to relative wage and income levels for nurses and other types of personnel?

Levine and others have been analyzing utilization and staffing patterns of hospitals according to their size and other characteristics. Great variation has been found from hospital to hospital in terms of the hours of nursing service available per patient. To some extent, this is related to the size of the hospital, in that the smaller the hospital, the more hours of nursing service available per patient.[38] This may be interpreted to mean either that in small hospitals patients receive better care or that nursing personnel are being utilized inefficiently. No clues are given as to exactly what tasks were being performed by registered or practical nurses and aides.

Although the number of nursing hours per patient is steadily increasing in each smaller size class of hospital, the pattern is more complex for both registered nurses and nurses' aides. These data provide some clues on the extent to which aides are substitutes for nurses. In general, however, one is impressed with the great unexplained variations in nursing staff patterns among hospitals of the same type and in the same general location. Other variables could easily be introduced into these and similar analyses which would provide insight into the question of whether nursing and other salaries, local supplies of nurses and relatively unskilled women, local income levels and similar variables have anything to do with these variations in staffing patterns.

Also, hospital design, including the layout and size of each unit, clearly affects the extent to which scarce nursing personnel must be relied upon and the extent to which auxiliary nursing and clerical personnel may be used.[39] The larger the unit, the more options that become available, although the maximum could probably be reached, depending on the precise situation, types of patients, etc. This topic deserves research in connection with hospital architecture.

In recent years, a rapid increase in the number of detailed management analyses of work performance in nursing service and in the other departments of hospitals has revealed innumerable half-concealed and inadequately understood problems. Such management research at the working level is ultimately the responsibility of local administrators. From a larger point of view, some better insight into the utilization

431

problem might be gained by examination of the administrative process itself. What explains the great variations in utilization practices from hospital to hospital? Which hospitals are making internal surveys, which are not, and why do they not? To what extent have surveys led to the introduction of new practices? What difficulties arose in making changes? What apparently poor utilization practices turned out to be not so inefficient after all? Studies which would illuminate this aspect of the management process might be of considerably greater value than the examination of global ratios and percentages.[40]

One reads the material on the utilization of nursing personnel with the feeling that the major problem is inadequate organization and supervision. Another apparently pervasive problem is the mismatch between training and function. Registered nurses seem to be trained for patient care, but are primarily engaged in supervisory and administrative tasks, including paper work, while the nurse's aides and orderlies, who actually spend most of their time in patient care, are essentially untrained. Most people involved seem to be unhappy with this situation. This is especially true for nurses, in part because they were motivated to enter their fields by ideals of patient service, which motives may be accentuated by the training program itself. If nursing function studies were more concerned with what actually is occurring or is likely to occur on the job, rather than with what ought to occur, they might provide a better guide to what ought to occur in training programs. Moreover, studies are needed on the question of whether training programs which are closely aligned to the actual functions workers subsequently perform on the job are related to better work performance, improved recruitment and improved retention.

Innumerable examples could be cited of specific cases where utilization practices were changed and new health occupations developed, leading to lower total costs for salaries and training, the tapping of new labor supplies and improvement in the quality of service. The health services industry is ubiquitous, and essentially the same conditions are faced by a great many institutions across the country. Because of the fragmented nature of the American health service system, individual administrators under pressure can relatively easily resort to unconventional tactics in the assignment of function and in the types of personnel utilized. Some of these tactics turn out to be feasible, and the result is new occupations, new utilization patterns and so forth.

Sometimes, however, fragmentation and lack of funds inhibit creative experimentation with new utilization patterns or new occupations.

Legal limitations which surround the performance of many functions in the health field also inhibit change. Special institutes or other type of institution may be needed which could establish experimental units for carrying on research in different personnel patterns. In addition, considerable research should be carried out on utilization practices in the armed services and in foreign countries to see what could be translated into American civilian practice.

One problem which ought to be studied is how utilization practices have changed over time in local areas in relation to other variables. Much data on employment in the various health occupations generally and in hospitals and health departments are available over time and for geographical areas at the regional, state and even county level. These data ought to be more fully explored to see how a geographical health complex grows, or even declines. How are changes in the number of physicians, nurses and other health personnel related? How has change in the health fields in new and rapidly growing areas differed from that in depressed or slowly growing areas? What is happening in the city and in the suburbs? Do areas where active campaigns have been carried out to solve health manpower problems have any greatly different experience from other areas?

The increasing degree of specialization of health manpower, either within a health occupation or in the form of new health occupations, is the direct result of improvements in utilization practices. In the literature on physicians, however, specialization often is looked upon with some disfavor. This theme was popular a generation ago, as it is now, despite the fact that specialization has steadily increased for over a century.[41]

Specialization is often said to flow from increased scientific knowledge, forcing a practitioner to limit himself to a smaller and smaller part of the whole. From economics, however, one learns that specialization is a function of the scale of the enterprise or market. As the population became more concentrated, as transportation improved for both patient and physician, and as patients were concentrated in hospitals, increasing numbers of physicians could occupy themselves fully while restricting their types of patients. With a limited practice, they gained increased skill and productivity through deeper explorations into particular disease entities and medical techniques. Specialization is the source of increased knowledge, not the result. More importantly, it leads to higher quality and an increased supply of services, since the specialist can usually handle a given problem

433

better and in less time than a less skilled practitioner. The relative size of the medical and dental professions may, therefore, be the major reason why less than half of all physicians, but practically all dentists, are in general practice.

Considerable difficulty has been encountered with the integration of specialists' services under a system of independent private practice. Not enough is known about just how referrals are handled at the present time. A particular effort ought to be made to ascertain both the incentives and the inadequacies of the existing system, as seen by specialists, general practitioners and patients.

Many physicians utilize specialists less than they might, either because they want to avoid extra expenses to their patients, because they fear a loss of face or because they really do not know how to use the skills and services of the various specialities. Many physicians seem to be reluctant to call in paramedical people, such as social workers, visiting nurses or occupational therapists. Some even seem to be ignorant of the resources available to them, or how to call them into action.[42] Studies might well be made of the extent to which different physicians utilize the services of the wide range of personnel. That could yield some clues as to how to utilize them more efficiently. Although some might object that these are matters for the professional person to determine for himself, these decisions could hardly be compromised if the individual physician had some useful information as to what is being done by others.

Quality

Leaders in the health occupations have been increasingly concerned with the low quality of many entering or in their fields. In some cases, the leaders may have despaired of obtaining significantly greater numbers into particular fields and have turned to quality and skill as the only way to obtain an effective increase in the quantity and quality of health services. At a number of earlier points, research questions bearing on the quality of health manpower resources have been noted.

Certain difficulties arise in dealing with the concept of quality, however. Quality and quantity often go together, and the ability to attract a better quality of applicants is usually equivalent to the ability to obtain larger numbers of applicants in general. An increase in number of applicants means that educators, administrators and others can be more selective, raising the quality of the personnel

434

actually entering training or employment in a field. Research to find ways to increase the flow of applicants to any field is thus directly relevant.

In the second place, a key route toward expanding the quantity and quality of health services has been the addition of lower quality manpower, for the employment of paramedical and paranursing workers has expanded much faster than that of physicians and nurses. Bringing in more persons of lesser skills to perform less demanding functions has released the time of the more highly qualified professional, making him more productive. The result has been the growth of various technical specialties and paramedical groups. Wherever research can illuminate ways to use persons of lesser quality, it makes a great contribution because high quality is always in short supply.

For reasons which are not entirely clear, those who make decisions in the health service industry often seem to choose quantity over quality. The rapid growth in auxiliary nursing personnel in recent years suggests that hospital and nursing administrators have systematically been saying in effect that they can get more nursing service from three nurses' aides than from two registered nurses. Otherwise, they would have competed in the market for registered nurses, bidding up salary levels, and ultimately attracting more students into nursing and inducing more nurses to re-enter employment. A really careful research effort is needed into the productivity of the different kinds of nursing personnel and the incentives to which administrators are responding in their staffing policies.

Quality has often been equated with training and skill, and rightfully so. But improved quality has often been equated with longer training programs. Since the length of a training program is a crucial incentive, attempts to improve quality through longer training programs tend to be self-defeating, adding to the difficulty in recruiting more and better applicants.

Research which indicates ways in which training in the various fields can be improved with no increase in training time, or even with a decrease in training time, might be most productive in terms of raising both the quality and quantity of manpower in the several fields. Research into the qualities, functions and backgrounds of workers in the various paramedical occupations, with a view to devising appropriate upgrading opportunities, on-the-job training programs and supervisory structures which encourage training, also appears to be a promising route to follow.

In a broader sense, research bearing on quality in health manpower may not proceed fruitfully until the concept, criteria and measurement of quality are more fully explored. That is true whether one is concerned with the quality of persons entering a field, the quality of their education and training, the quality of their school performance, or utlimately the quality of their service. These aspects of quality are arousing great interest, not only in manpower, but also in education, economics and many other disciplines. With the service sector of the economy growing in importance, quantitative measures of output no longer suffice as they have with goods, and economists are faced with the question of how to measure intangibles. Conceptually, this is akin to the measurement of such intangibles as intelligence, aptitude and performance. The inadequacies of aptitude tests or school grades as predictors of later performance suggest how difficult is the problem of measuring quality. The point is that the assessment of quality is a major problem, and research on it will have to be of a quite fundamental nature.

CONCLUSION

This paper has been concerned to clarify priorities in research into health manpower. That is quite diffierent from priorities in manpower policy. As noted earlier, manpower is the crucial resource for health services. Manpower research can help indicate how the attraction, retention and utilization of manpower might be improved. But manpower research cannot solve manpower problems. Only manpower policy can do that.

The most striking things to one who has been preoccupied with manpower studies in many fields, and not health manpower studies alone, are: 1. the rapid growth in employment and training in most occupations in health service; 2. the continued complaints about shortages of health manpower; and 3. the continuation of essentially the same problems with respect to utilization, high losses, turnover and the like over a long period of time. Given these conditions, the collection of more data of essentially the same nature as in the past does not seem to be particularly promising. The question must finally be raised as to why, when so much has been changing, the issues seem to remain the same.

An easy answer is that policies have been wrong. But this begs the question as to what the public and private policies have really been designed to accomplish. For this reason, the difference must be clarified between the goals of leaders in the health fields and the goals of those who make public and private policy as indicated by their spending and employment policies. The determinants of demand for health manpower must be clarified if realistic planning is to be accomplished. Apology for, but continued reliance on, simple population ratios must be called into question.

A considerable redirection of the occupational orientation of research seems particularly necessary. For researchers to continue their preoccupation with physicians and nurses is anomalous while the paramedical and paranursing occupations proliferate and expand so much more rapidly. The social, economic and technological reasons for these developments need to be explored in depth and the functional relationships between the various groups clarified. Whether this is a temporary response to shortages or a more fundamental change in the technology of producing medical services, akin to the shift from handicraft to mass methods of manufacture of goods, deserves exploration. The problems of management, work organization, selection, training and placement take on entirely new meanings as the work force becomes increasingly differentiated in function and skill level.

Studies of career choice and motivation are improving, but more is needed in the way of comparisons which are relevant to the choices people make. In particular, studies are needed which explore the effectiveness of various financial and other incentives as means to increase the manpower in particular fields. Greater attention needs to be given to the irregular sources of manpower, particularly the import of manpower and the entry of nonprofessionals into health service. The highest priority should be given to research and experiments on upgrading personnel from one level of health service to the next through experience and training. New routes for the development of skilled manpower could be a powerful recruitment device.

Finally, one must ask why utilization patterns which distress health leaders continue to prevail. Global surveys have shown great differences in utilization patterns from one situation to the next, and these data could be used to determine whether utilization patterns are related to the relative availability of health manpower, pay rates or to other factors. Even more important are surveys of utilization patterns which seek to identify the role played by cost factors and the desires of the people concerned. Research is needed into the process of effecting

437

change in utilization patterns to find out why and how greater rationalization occurs in some situations than others.

The emphasis on what exists rather than what might be may appear to be retrogressive. However, a careful examination of why goals have not been achieved—or when they have been achieved, how and why—ought to illuminate the goals themselves. Impossible goals can stultify progress which could be made; attaining realistic goals can be a stimulus to further progress.

Even so, the growth of employment in most of the health occupations has been quite extraordinary by the standards of other industries. If the demand for health services continues to grow rapidly, as it may for the foreseeable future, one must ask the question of whether employment in the industry should also grow as rapidly. The health services are now becoming major consumers of the nation's manpower. In the past, rapidly growing industries, faced with mounting manpower problems in numbers and costs, have often turned to technology as a way out. At some point, capital equipment and relatively smaller numbers of highly trained manpower become cheaper and produce a better product than the utilization of gross aggregates of people. This shift has occurred throughout the goods producing sector, and it has occurred or is occurring in many parts of the service sector: in communications, in entertainment and in information processing. Indications are that in various aspects of laboratory analysis, medical information systems and so forth, the substitution of capital for manpower may be imminent. It is also occurring in many of the non-medical and non-nursing functions of hospitals, as in housekeeping, food services, inventory control, etc. The expanding manpower costs of health care provide increasing incentives to search out places for economizing on manpower. Where this will occur is difficult to see, but the possibility must always be kept in mind. As it does, entirely new perspectives on manpower for the health services will surely emerge.

438

REFERENCES

[1] For one attempt to clarify this subject, *see* Ginzberg, Eli, Hiestand, Dale L. and Reubens, Beatrice, THE PLURALISTIC ECONOMY, New York, McGraw-Hill Book Company, 1965.

[2] Klarman, Herbert E., THE ECONOMICS OF HEALTH, New York, Columbia University Press, 1965, Chapter 4.

[3] Harris, Seymour E., THE ECONOMICS OF AMERICAN MEDICINE, New York, The Macmillan Company, 1964, Chapters 5–9, 23.

[4] United States Department of Health, Education and Welfare, Public Health Service, HEALTH MANPOWER SOURCE BOOK, Sections 1–19, Washington, 1952–1965.

[5] Albee, George W., MENTAL HEALTH MANPOWER TRENDS, New York, Basic Books, Inc., Publishers, 1959, Tables 17–22.

[6] Surgeon General's Consultant Group on Nursing, TOWARD QUALITY IN NURSING: NEEDS AND GOALS, Washington, United States Department of Health, Education and Welfare, 1963, pp. 15, 20.

[7] American Nurses' Association, FACTS ABOUT NURSING, 1965 Edition, New York, pp. 10, 13.

[8] Albee, *op. cit.*, p. 41.

[9] Based on data in Royal Commission on Health Services, REPORT, Volume I, Ottawa, Roger Duhamel, 1964, pp. 238, 258, 266.

[10] Friedman, Milton and Kuznets, Simon, INCOME FROM INDEPENDENT PROFESSIONAL PRACTICE, New York, National Bureau of Economic Research, 1945, pp. 161–199; Judek, Stanislaw, MEDICAL MANPOWER IN CANADA, Ottawa, Roger Duhamel, 1964, p. 139.

[11] Albee, *op. cit.*, p. 60–61.

[12] National Manpower Council, GOVERNMENT AND MANPOWER, New York, Columbia University Press, 1964, pp. 123, 126–136.

[13] American Council on Education, THE SURVEY OF DENTISTRY, Washington, 1961, Chapter I and Appendix A; New England Board of Higher Education, DENTAL MANPOWER NEEDS IN NEW ENGLAND, Winchester, Massachusetts, 1958, Chapters II, III; United States Department of Health, Education and Welfare, Public Health Service, Division of Dental Resources, A STUDY OF DENTAL MANPOWER REQUIREMENTS IN THE WEST, Boulder, Colorado, Western Interstate Commission for Higher Education, 1956, Chapter IV; ———, A STUDY OF OKLAHOMA'S DENTAL MANPOWER NEEDS, Washington, 1954.

[14] American Council on Education, *op. cit.*, pp. 544–545.

[15] Yett, Donald, The Supply of Nurses: An Economist's View, *Hospital Progress*, 96, February, 1965.

[16] *Ibid.*, p. 97.

[17] National Manpower Council, A POLICY FOR SCIENTIFIC AND PROFESSIONAL MANPOWER, New York, Columbia University Press, 1953, p. 239.

[18] American Council on Education, *op. cit.*, p. 282.

[19] Gough, Harrison G., Hall, Wallace B. and Harris, Robert E., Admissions Procedures as Forecasters of Performance in Medical Training, *The Journal of Medical Education,* 38, 983–998, December, 1963.

[20] Friedman and Kuznets, *op. cit.,* pp. 291–295.

[21] Hansen, W. Lee, "Shortages" and Investment in Health Manpower, *in* University of Michigan, Bureau of Public Health Economics and Department of Economics, THE ECONOMICS OF HEALTH AND MEDICAL CARE, Ann Arbor, Michigan, 1964, pp. 75–90.

[22] Altenderfer, Marion E. and West, Margaret C., How MEDICAL STUDENTS FINANCE THEIR EDUCATION, Washington, United States Department of Health, Education and Welfare, 1965.

[23] More, Douglas M., The Dental Student, *Journal of the American College of Dentists,* 41, March, 1961.

[24] Davis, James A., UNDERGRADUATE CAREER DECISIONS, Chicago, Aldine Publishing Co., 1965, pp. 165–180.

[25] Datagrams, *The Journal of Medical Education,* 39, 1056–1057, November, 1964.

[26] Yett, *loc cit.,* p. 95.

[27] National Manpower Council, A POLICY FOR SKILLED MANPOWER, New York, Columbia University Press, 1954, p. 212.

[28] Blank, David M. and Stigler, George J., THE DEMAND AND SUPPLY OF SCIENTIFIC PERSONNEL, New York, National Bureau of Economic Research, Inc., 1957, pp. 86–92.

[29] Council of Member Agencies, Department of Baccalaureate and Higher Degree Programs, National League for Nursing, Statement of Beliefs and Recommendations Regarding Baccalaureate Nursing Programs Admitting Registered Nurse Students, *Nursing Outlook,* 57–58, June, 1964.

[30] Albee, *op. cit.,* p. xvii.

[31] Surgeon General's Consultant Group on Nursing, *op. cit.,* p. 47.

[32] Hall, Oswald, The Stages of a Medical Career, *American Journal of Sociology,* 53, 332, March, 1948.

[33] American Council on Education, *op. cit.,* pp. 492–493.

[34] United States Department of Health, Education and Welfare, Division of Hospital and Medical Facilities, HOSPITAL PERSONNEL, Public Health Service Publication No. 930-C-9, October, 1964, pp. 3–12; Christopher, W. I., Jr., Personnel Management, Planned and Controlled, *Hospital Progress,* 77, September, 1963.

[35] Levine, Eugene, Turnover Among Nursing Personnel in General Hospitals, *Hospitals,* 31, 51–53, 138, 140, September 1, 1957.

[36] A Study of Turnover and Its Costs, *Hospitals,* 29, 59–62, May, 1955.

[37] Means, James Howard, Homo Medicus Americanus, *Daedalus,* 712–713, Fall, 1963.

[38] Levine, Eugene, Some Answers to the "Nurse Shortage," *Nursing Outlook,* 30–34, March, 1964.

440

[39] For some discussion of this point *see* the comments by Tonkin, Thomas E., Planning the Nursing Unit, *Hospitals,* 39, 95–98, February 1, 1965.

[40] For an example of one management analysis, *see* HOSPITAL PERSONNEL, *op. cit.*

[41] Klarman, *op. cit.,* p. 82–88.

[42] Means, *op. cit.,* p. 716–717.

ACKNOWLEDGMENTS

My thanks go to William L. Kissick, M.D., Deputy Chief, Division of Public Health Methods, Office of the Surgeon General, United States Public Health Service; Stanislaw Judek, Ph.D., Professor of Economics, University of Ottawa, and other members of the Health Services Research Conference.

DISCUSSION

The vigorous and lengthy discussion of Hiestand's paper reflected the heightened national concern with medical manpower. The dynamic quality of the issues and the unusual opportunities which now exist for analyzing key problems in manpower were emphasized. The task of drawing up an agenda for research in health manpower was viewed not as an intellectual challenge or exercise, but rather as an ineffective means of focusing the interest of present and potential researchers on major problems. Clearly, now is a time when results of such research can significantly influence national policy decisions.

The concept that research into health manpower involves many related fields was emphasized by specifying that it is of necessity interdisciplinary, requiring the partnership of social scientists, administrators, social workers, statisticians and medical, dental, nursing and allied professionals. No serious questions were raised with respect to the author's choice of categories of health manpower research, although several alternative classifications were referred to or suggested. The impact of the educational system on the number and qualifications of health manpower personnel, and the structure, functioning and

441

financing of hospitals and professional schools, although specifically excluded in the paper, were considered equal in importance with the problems cited by the author. For example, the more efficient utilization of the existing educational resources for producing manpower, and the efficient design, operation and utilization of health care facilities were described as key elements in the overall effort to improve the delivery of health services. Educational engineering was thought to be especially pertinent to the problem of first attracting and directing the career interests of professional workers to those fields in greatest need of additional manpower. Discussants were in full accord with the author's view that numbers of health care personnel alone will not solve the problems of health services. The development of a taxonomy of professional functions was considered an essential preliminary step to the much-needed reallocation of specific tasks, comprising the medical care process, to those individuals qualified to perform the tasks by virtue of minimal training. This was considered the more logical course rather than the present reliance upon progressively longer periods of training as a guarantee of qualification to perform professional functions in a satisfactory manner.

The author's basic premise that a wealth of data lies fallow for lack of much needed exploitation was challenged as perhaps being applicable only to the United States. The Royal Commission on Health Services in Canada, had found a clear cut need for much more data even of the crude enumerative type.

Perhaps the sharpest questioning was directed to the author's discussion of techniques currently used for estimating shortages. In his paper he cites the inadequacies of conventional ways of denoting need which are based on professional value judgments. He stated that the approach of the economist would not substantiate widely prevalent estimates of shortages. However, discussants were quick to point out that the author had then proceeded to discuss manpower research with the apparently implicit assumption that serious shortages do, in fact, exist in almost all categories. Examples of techniques for estimating shortages which attempt to avoid the extremes of over- and under-estimate were drawn from the work of the Royal Commission on Health Services.

The fact that health manpower research is in the formative stages was amusingly illustrated by the diametrically opposed views regarding the influence of current salary scales for nurses on the availability of nursing personnel in the health care system. The views that salaries for nurses are and are not commensurate with their level of education and professional training were both attacked and defended with vigor, and the issue was not resolved. Discussants agreed that those institutions which offer the higher salaries enjoy a lower turnover rate than those institutions offering lower salaries.

Special note was made of the contrast which exists between the so-called health services industry and almost all other industrial organizations: both lateral and vertical mobility is sharply restricted in the former. The view was strongly endorsed by discussants that top priority should be devoted to the promotion of alternate career paths for health care personnel. This would require identification and acceptance of educational and experience equivalents, provision of core curricula and lessening of the rigid controls on certification now exerted by organized professional bodies. Such steps could significantly increase the number of health manpower personnel in the critically short higher levels of administration and service.

Strong agreement was expressed with the author's view that health manpower research has been over-concerned with the physician and the nurse. Someone asked to what extent the leadership role played by the physician affects the number of people who are willing to play the other roles in the health industry, namely, the paramedical roles. This train of discussion was halted when someone asked whether "You can really put on the play 'Hamlet' without the prince."

Little discussion centered on losses of health manpower and on utilization patterns other than to endorse their importance.

In contrast, lengthy discussion was devoted to the fact that the quality of health manpower personnel is currently equated with the length of training periods. Continuing education and provision of career incentives are not sufficiently understood or utilized in the health fields generally. The thought was expressed that the separate professional organizations, in legitimately exercising their responsibility to control quality, have, in fact, contributed to the anomalous situation which now exists: significant shortages are interfering with the delivery of quality health services to all segments of the population. The time has come for the universities, professional organizations, hospitals and other organized sectors affecting the supply and demand and utilization of health manpower personnel to engage in cooperative ventures directed to breaking the logjam of jurisidictional disputes which currently interfere with the free flow and fuller supply of health manpower.

RESEARCH PROBLEMS IN EVALUATION
OF HEALTH SERVICE DEMONSTRATIONS

EDGAR F. BORGATTA

Research problems in evaluative research are not unique to the health services or health service demonstration programs; rather, they recur in the many circumstances where programs operate manifestly to improve existing conditions, or where efforts are being made to prevent or stop deterioration of existing conditions.

In society many things are done with the intention of bringing about changes, and some of these are relatively simple to evaluate. That is, success may be relatively clear and agreed upon, and the methods utilized for bringing about the change may be accepted by all concerned. An implicit utility theory says that things that work will be retained in society. Stated somewhat backwards: just how some discoveries occurred and came into play is sometimes difficult to understand, because they appear to be so wise in their structure and so effective in their consequences. This, as a retrospective judgment, is sometimes called the "wisdom" of the system.

When a new program is initiated, lack of success may also at times be clear. That, of course, is most obvious not only when no change occurs in the direction intended, but when some worsening of the situation occurs. Where a program may have been initiated in response to a felt need, and the need was clear and obvious, lack of improvement may be equally obvious.

Between the clear successes and the clear failures lie many degrees of ambiguity as to what the results are. Whether something is or is not maintained as a service, then, may be a matter of values other

444

than those that are ostensibly related to the goal to be achieved. If success may be the case, for example, but doubt remains, the possible positive value may be worth keeping if the cost is not considered excessive. The value of life, for example, may itself he held as precious, depending on the circumstances.

Care must be taken, however, not to assume that matters of utility as measured by cost in money—or some other form of relative value— are always the bases for maintaining ways of behaving in societies. Even a peripheral contact with the comparative study of cultures will indicate that accepted ways of doing things do not necessarily exist because of some "rational" basis or because they are effective for particular purposes. Maintaining ways of behaving must often be described as an end in itself, which is to say that no rational way of explaining the behavior is uncovered. Expressed another way, people accept "things" with which they are familiar and, in fact, value what is familiar to them and has previously been accepted by them.

The references to normative forms of behavior in society have been relatively abstract to this point, but the relevance here must be obvious. Professions have norms that may not have a rational basis. How these arise is not at issue here, but many mechanisms may exist to generate forms of behavior of this type. For example, people have within themselves a tendency to rationalize from their own experience, and this, of course, is a fine art in some professions. If the case is sufficiently well dramatized, its relevance and importance may not be seriously questioned. Similarly, with tendencies that are called bureaucratization, institutionalization and so forth, processes once established tend to be maintained by the authority systems in which they reside. Thus, many things may exist where success or failure of the intended actions is not at all clear, yet authority, convention and other forces may tend to keep them as they are.

Concern with evaluation is not new, and presumably concern with effectiveness is something that has existed as long as people have tried to change situations or otherwise find out what were the fruits of their efforts. Scientific concern with program evaluation may be of more recent vintage, as general programs of amelioration of health and other social conditions appear to be associated with the greater value on human life and welfare that is identifiable with recent generations. But, in general, programs for amelioration have existed for a long time, and essentially when conditions are bad enough and social conscience is brought into play, both the need and the potential for improvement may lead to the development of a program designed to be corrective. Most programs that receive systematic attention for evaluation occur in the context of correcting an existing situation. Preventive programs are even of a more recent vintage and, essentially, to exist they require more general theories of cause and effect than do corrective programs.

WHAT IS TO BE EVALUATED

Evaluation research requires a clear statement of what is to be evaluated. In the health services, such a clear statement may be available and often contrasts with many other areas which have more implicit values of what is good. In theory at least, some medical disorder is undesirable, and eliminating or diminishing the problem in society is appropriate. Thus, for example, most persons may agree that to reduce the amount of tuberculosis in the community, to eradicate a particular communicable disease, or to reduce suffering from some disorder is important. However, developing programs for these purposes is not a simple matter, even with reasonable agreement as to what the appropriate condition in society should be. For example, although the community may agree that a concerted effort should be made to eliminate tuberculosis, the question of cost to produce a really effective program may become a serious issue.

Certainly, an effective method of controlling tuberculosis is to have all persons undergo appropriate medical diagnostic tests on a regular basis. How can that be done, however, in a society in which compulsion for such matters is found objectionable? Compulsion may be possible in certain circumstances, as, for example, when chest x-rays are required of all teachers in a state, with the rationale that these persons have contact with children and young adults and could conceivably infect them. The rationale may be extended to food and other services, but the segment of the population that becomes involved may be relatively limited.

With groups where compulsion is possible, evaluation may have a peculiar meaning. For example, what is to be evaluated under such circumstances? Whether or not people conform? Whether the tests are effective in detecting existing cases of tuberculosis? Whether the children and young adults in schools are appropriately protected? Under such circumstances evaluation research may not be at all appropriate, except in examining the intent of the program and its correspondence in fact. If no cases of tuberculosis are uncovered by the routine tests, the justification for the tests would be difficult to make. On the other hand, if a few cases are located, this may be sufficient in the value system of those who are concerned to warrant perpetuation of the system. In other words, under circumstances of compulsion and presumed 100 per cent participation, questions of evaluation may concern merely the appropriateness of assumptions relative to the medical diagnostic procedures involved. If the effectiveness of the program is being tested in a medical sense, questioning the validity of the procedure would be difficult unless ultimately more accurate diagnostic tests are carried out with segments of the population which allow additional case finding.

With no compulsion or less compulsion programs of evaluation may have different meanings. For example, regarding tuberculosis, questions may be raised about the extent of coverage of the relevant group and the possible selective factors that may arise. In the total population, for example, something is known about the groups most likely to have tuberculosis. Questions may be phrased around whether or not these groups are involved in the program, and if so to what degree. Effectiveness of a program may be stated not in how well the disease is uncovered among those who arrive for chest x-rays, but in the extent to which the project includes the relevant groups in the population. Depending upon rational persuasion rather than compulsion, such projects may often actually involve just those segments of the population that least need to be pursued. Those who are more educated and those who are most concerned with their health, possibly, are most likely to cooperate with such programs on a voluntary basis. On the other hand, those who are relatively ignorant of their limitations, particularly with regard to health, may not cooperate at all. Such groups may believe, for example, that if one is ill, one would know about it, and only then would a chest x-ray be appropriate. Thus, programs may be devised specifically to involve such segments of the population which are most difficult to reach. An evaluation of health services in such cases deals very little with the medical aspects of the problem, but rather emphasizes the effectiveness of the program as a piece of social engineering.

What is to be evaluated is not always clear. If a new program is being initiated, grandiose, general values may be stated initially. The implementation, however, may be a homely set of procedures. When testing for the effectiveness of the program, which of the values involved is to be examined? The broadly stated ones or specific ones that may not correspond very clearly to the broad program? What is the criterion of success? The problem in attempting to answer this is that the relationship of the goals involved in a program to what is considered success may be very complex. Evaluation of the situation by those who are conducting the program may involve many factors other than the intended changes. For example, if the staff derives satisfaction (not to mention income) from the program, that may influence their view of it. Even though the program may not effectively treat the disorder, the attention may appease those who are suffering. And, if it does not appease them, it may appease their relatives.

OBJECTIVITY IN SCIENCE

All science requires objectivity, but this goal may be achieved more easily in some circumstances than in others. Particularly in evaluative research, many factors may exist which will work against the actual application of evaluative research on the one hand, and may also provide rationalizations before and after the fact as to why evaluative research may neither be applicable nor useful. In other words, many values in the system may deny the feasibility of evaluative research on the one hand, and, on the other hand, if carried out and negative results are encountered, reasons are provided for discounting the negative findings.[1]

A few of the rationalizations that may occur could be mentioned to set the stage:

1. The effects of the program are long-range, thus the consequences cannot be measured in the immediate future.
2. The effects are general rather than specific, thus no single criterion can be utilized to evaluate the program, and, indeed, even using many measures would not really get at complex general consequences intended.
3. The effects are small, but important, thus cannot be measured effectively because instruments are not sufficiently sensitive.
4. The effects are subtle, and circumstances may not be ordered appropriately to get at the qualities that are being changed. The measurement would disturb the processes involved.
5. Experimental manipulation cannot be carried out because to withhold treatment from some persons would not be fair.

448

These rationalizations, of course, are relatively difficult to apply if medical criteria of success and failure in a discrete disorder are utilized. However, most evaluation research with demonstration programs in the health services is concerned with the impact on the community rather than with controlled experimentation under laboratory conditions, and these kinds of advance rationalizations may be feasible.

The fact that in health service demonstration programs medical diagnostic or treatment procedures are involved becomes a major rationalization for not becoming seriously involved in evaluation research. After all, the diagnostic utility of the x-ray, the pill, the innoculation and so forth is demonstrated. What is the point of evaluating a demonstration program that uses such dependable medical procedures?

Rationalization of negative findings after the fact, assuming an adequate research design, are possibly even more plentiful. A few of these are listed here:

1. The effectiveness of the program cannot really be judged because those who could most use the services did not participate.

2. Some of the persons who received the services improved greatly. Clearly, some of the persons who recovered could not have done so if they had not received attention.

3. Some of the persons who most needed the program were actually in the control group.

4. The fact that no difference was found between the persons receiving services and those not receiving services clearly indicates that the program was not sufficiently intensive. More of the services are obviously required.

5. Persons in the control group received other kinds of attention.

Of course, the previous list of rationalizations "before the fact" also applies in retrospect. Many other rationalizations are provided, of course, including indicating that the particular agency or program used was not really the best or the most modern or the most something else.

In this connection, response to evaluation research sometimes is peculiar. For example, scientists ordinarily do not define what the programs will be, although they may consult on design of programs. In evaluation research, the concern of the scientist should be with whether or not the program brings into effect the consequences intended. However, in circumstances where the evaluation research leads to negative findings, the scientist very often is placed in a position of apologizing about the lack of positive findings. The failure of the program is associated with the inability of the evaluation research to demonstrate the change.

CONFLICTING GOALS

Although certain circumstances render the goals of a program clear and well-defined, some goals within the program will conflict, and the goals of the program may well conflict with those of groups to which the program is directed. The problem of goals and values may be discussed more generally to show how they complicate evaluation.

In the minds of the social engineers who devise a program, the intentions and the definition of expected good may be relatively clear. They may be less clear, and indeed denied by others. For example, if a program designed to improve the social welfare and health of families involves contraceptive information, segments of the population may be aligned directly in opposition to the values of the program.

A program of dissemination of birth control information is a viable type within society, but some approaches to health and family planning are totally rejected and in fact are illegal. In Japan, abortion has been legalized, and for the lower classes has been the means for family planning and control. Medically speaking, the operation has become highly routine and under the best conditions involves little danger. The use of abortion has been relatively effective, and at this stage a transition is being noted in Japan such that preventive contraceptive procedures are becoming effective substitutes for the corrective abortions. That is, family planning and control have become possible and meaningful through legalized abortions and the value of these has been translated into preventive procedures. Thus, a short-term goal of family planning moves directly into a longer-term goal of family planning. No conflict of values manifestly exists between these goals in Japan. However, in the United States, abortion is illegal, and in many instances programs of contraception and information dissemination are opposed vehemently. The goal of an agency or program, thus, may be at variance with the goals of the population or a significant segment of the population they are supposed to serve, not because of disagreement on certain overriding general values, such as family planning, but because the effective implementation of the goal conflicts with other values.

450

As noted, conflict can occur between long-term and short-term goals. General community goals may conflict with goals that are appropriate for some families, and what may be good for families may not be good for particular types of individuals. Different subgroups may have different goals. Goals may be explicit and salient in one case and implicit, but equally salient in another case. The intended services may be directed to a set of values associated with a class of people, and thus may be incomprehensible and irrelevant to those of another class.

Science cannot determine the wisdom of any particular goal unless the goal is stated as a means to another goal. An intended program may be inappropriate to realize a particular goal, but scientific analysis or research may uncover the misdirection. Thus, science is directed toward increasing knowledge about the correspondence between intended goals and actual consequences of types of action. Science asks such questions as: By undertaking such and such a program, does the health of the population improve? In the long run, by taking a given course of action, do certain conditions of the poor improve?

Programs are initiated for many different reasons, other than those manifestly given as goals, as already implied when agencies and programs were said to have many different goals. The fact that some agreement can be found on the undesirability of a particular condition does not necessarily mean that it can be resolved. Evaluative research is not designed to solve a problem, but merely to examine whether a procedure which is being utilized to solve it actually works. In this circumstance, recognition must be given to the notion that many things are not done with a clear expectation that they will lead to positive results. When looking at the condition of the poor, the deprived or the unhealthy, the inclination of many is to say, "We must do something now." That does not mean that in fact something can be done within the ken of the relevant sciences. Or, as with the case of legalizing abortions in this country, obvious and viable solutions may be excluded.

EXPERIMENTAL DESIGNS AND EVALUATIVE RESEARCH

Whether one is dealing with health service demonstration programs or any other program of change, inferences about effectiveness can be made only to the extent that appropriate control group design is implied in the study. The classic design involves an experimental group and a control group, and a comparison of these after the program has been applied. In theory, if the assumption can be made that the groups were initially equivalent, no "before" measures are necessary, and the simple "after" comparison, will suffice. Variation in the experimental design can go in two directions. Either loosening the design to make it more applicable, but with greater dependence on assumptions about equivalence of the experimental group and the control group; or making it more rigorous if equivalence must be demonstrated before the program has been put into effect. These differences in experimental designs will be examined with reference to demonstration programs.[2]

Rigorous Designs

If the design utilized is the simple one of comparing experimental and control groups only after the program has been carried out, the most that can be indicated is that some difference does exist between the experimental group and the control group. But any of a number of alternatives may lead to the condition of the difference. For example, the difference may occur because the experimental group has improved faster than the control group, which also improved. The difference may be that the control group deteriorated, while the experimental group did not. Or, the difference might be that the control group deteriorated faster than the experimental group. In such a design, the relative advantage associated with the program (and the experimental group) cannot be judged unless some specific knowledge is available about the "before" condition of the two groups. Of course, still other factors may lead to the result. Although experimental and control groups were supposedly selected to be exactly equivalent in the "before" condition, they were not.

To be exactly equivalent in the "before" condition ordinarily requires some notion of random selection. If random selection is applied, in theory the experimental group and control group are both drawn from the same population. Selection of persons for the two groups is carried out in such a way that each person, and each combination of persons, has the same probability of being selected. As science becomes more rigorous, equivalence must be demonstrated rather than assumed. Demonstration usually consists of comparing the experimental and the control groups before the experiment on those variables considered to be relevant to the criterion that will be used to measure the change. Thus, the utilization of measurement before the experiment serves two purposes. First, it permits demonstration that the

452

experimental and the control groups are equivalent to begin with, and second, it provides the reference point for change.

In the actual design of experiments many other factors become involved, and these may require introduction of additional control groups. For example, perhaps the program could be judged more effective after the classical design of before and after measurement, using an experimental and control group, and the assessment could be fallacious. Interaction may occur between the program and the "before" testing in such a way that the combination leads to improvement, while in the absence of the "before" measurements, it might not. For example, utilizing the "before" measurements might make the persons receiving the program aware of matters to which they should attend and conscious of a need to change which becomes even more evident as they participate in the program. Thus, the experimental design may be made more complicated by adding two additional groups not to receive the "before" test, selected on the same bases as the two groups that will be given the "before" test. Examination of the four groups after the program has been applied should indicate that those who received the program are different from those who did not, whether a "before" test was given or not. If results indicate a difference in improvement for the two groups which received the program, this may indicate something more about how the program should be carried out. As indicated in the example, developing salience for the program through "before" testing may have some additional effect on the program itself.

When designing a program under circumstances where costs are a serious problem, the cost factors may alter the pattern of experimental design in allocating sample sizes. For example, if the method of assessing the relevant criterion is relatively cheap, control groups of larger size than the experimental groups may be used, although selection must be maintained on the random basis required of any experiment. However, if, as is often the case, the sampling procedures are relatively expensive, then the most efficient design is probably one in which the experimental and control groups are of the same size.

What is meant by random selection? Random selection means that a person has the same probability as every other person of being selected, and every combination of persons has the same probability of being selected. That means, of course, that an experimental group and control group must be chosen at the same stage. An experimental group, for example, cannot be chosen from those who arrive requesting services if a control group is to be selected from the population at large. These two groups would differ radically in the sense that one is seeking attention and the other is not. Thus, equivalence relative to the program could not under any circumstances be judged as existing. Random selection, in this case, would occur only if the experimental and control groups were both chosen from persons requesting services, or from the general population (and then some procedures would be implied for bringing those selected as the experimental group in for the services).

Additional comments may apply on the question of sampling. If particular variables are relevant to the response of the program, the sample may be stratified on these variables, essentially matching the two samples on these variables and doing random assignment within each of the cells involved in the stratification. However, selection must be from the same population. For example, stratifying on I.Q., but selecting the experimental sample from middle and upper class children in a test of "ability to absorb additional instruction" might lead to fallacious results. If I.Q. test performance bears some relationship to class differences, possibly persons in the lower classes are being selected who have more "native" intelligence than the middle or upper class group, thus the design would be contaminated. If large sample sizes are utilized, control for equivalence through stratification may be less necessary. The sensitivity with which matching is carried out must be related to the nature of the program that is being tested.

The problem of *post hoc* matching of persons in groups that have not been selected at random from the population may be illustrated easily. For example, suppose that the effects of a program on the poor is to be examined. Two communities are selected, one that is almost entirely Negro and one that is almost entirely white. Now, the question is one of how the effectiveness of a program could be tested if it were carried out in one of these communities and not in the other, say under circumstances where a special program directed to the improvement of conditions for Negroes is initiated, and where the white community is going to be used as a "control." Matching persons on the characteristic of being poor to have equivalent groups will raise thorny questions. The poor whites, for example, may have incomes of 3000 dollars per year per family. In the population at large, these may be the most deprived whites. By contrast, in the Negro community families at that economic level may not be relatively the most deprived. Thus, the first question is: Does matching on income mean matching on poorness?

454

Additional problems, of course, are encountered at the same time. For example, although Negroes of an income level may be reasonably prosperous relative to other Negroes, educationally they may still be inferior to the whites of equivalent income, who are relatively poor among the whites. Clearly, when such problems may be anticipated by attempting to compare groups that are quite different in what appears to be a cultural sense, all sorts of difficulties may be encountered if one is made the control for the other, even with *post hoc* matching. Thus, controls, groups or comparison groups should be chosen to be equivalent or similar on general grounds, and matching *post hoc* will not be satisfactory unless this is the case. Although statistical techniques can account for initial differences of groups in part, the cultural differences cannot be taken into account by the analysis of covariance or any other statistical maneuvering.

The idea that a control group is randomly selected by employing two groups, such as two neighborhoods, using one as an experimental group and the other as a control group, is only as good as the initial matching of the neighborhoods. Since people ordinarily select neighborhoods to live in, selective factors may be involved that are of great importance. If one compares different groups, and they are selected as groups initially, the sample size for the experiment may not be the number of persons in each group, but instead may be one (1) for the experimental group and one (1) for the comparison group.

Assuming that technical and cost factors are not a problem, in theory the most refined experiment will involve matching each person in each experimental group with each person in each control group, but the selection of the matched persons would be at random, with regard to which group they are assigned. Thus, even under the condition of maximum stratification, the requirement of random selection for experimental groups and control groups persists. Maximum stratification and matching is desirable if one is concerned that two groups may not be equivalent, even though they have similar marginal distributions of relevant characteristics. For example, two groups having approximately the same distribution in age and sex may actually differ; one group may have more older females and the other group more older males. Thus differences in the average and other statistical characteristics of samples may be eliminated without actually developing exactly equivalent experimental and control groups.

Some limitations involved in the research designs should be pointed out that may have little to do with the formal structuring of experimental designs as indicated thus far. Some of these will be relatively simple, but in fact may be forgotten in establishing demonstration programs in the health services, as they often are in other areas. For example, samples must be selected in such a way that they have a potential for change. In some types of services that are provided, of course, clients are brought to the attention of the organization when they are in an acute condition, possibly as bad as they can be and still be ambulatory. Under these circumstances, of course, considerable latitude for improvement, and thus an appropriate circumstance for applying a program, may exist. On the other hand, because people are arriving in an acute condition, most would improve, and the effect of a program may be difficult to demonstrate on the grounds that the spontaneous remission rate, or improvement by contact with ordinary aspects of society, may be as large as that under a planned program. Under such circumstances concern with "regression effects" is most important.[3] By contrast, some difficulty could arise if one is dealing with a preventative program under circumstances when most persons are in good health. The health habits of this population would be sufficient to maintain good health, and further improvement in the maintenance of good health may be difficult to demonstrate. Some thought must be given, explicitly, to outlining exactly what kind of improvement the demonstration program should make, and the feasibility with the selected population must be well established.

Before moving on to a discussion of some looser designs in evaluation research, the importance of defining what the program is that is being evaluated should be emphasized, particularly through the specification of the control group. For example, if the health service involved is a sheltered workshop for the rehabilitation of tuberculosis patients, the program may involve immediate location of the individuals when discharged from the hospital, introduction into the workshop program, medical, psychiatric and social work attention, removal of the client from his family for ten or more hours a day, support financially at a given level, etc. The control group might be selected at the same time, at the point of entry for the experimental group, and the control group might receive no attention directly. Then, the finding, if positive effects are demonstrated, would be that the program is better than no attention or such attention as might incidentally be found in the open community. This leaves totally unanswered many additional questions, such as what would have been the result if only the financial support had been provided for the experimental group. Would the experimental group have done as well merely with this support as with the entire program? Would the experimental group have done as well with only the medical attention provided? Obviously, such questions cannot be answered without devising an experiment in which many subgroups of attention are defined, in which case one is not only testing the effectiveness of a program, but its component parts. A program may turn out to be effective only when all its parts are involved, but it may also turn out that only a few of the parts contribute to the improvement of the clients, or that only one of the parts might be effective in this sense. Thus, the medical, psychiatric and social work attention given could conceivably be irrelevant, and merely the enforced routine of work and rest could be the important aspect of the program. Even if that were the finding it does not mean that the medical, psychiatric and social work aspects of a program would be eliminated. It might emphasize the fact that only one aspect of the program had been evaluated, mainly what was being done for the rehabilitation of the clients. Other aspects, such as the feeling that the program is worthwhile among the donors and benefactors of the program, was not tested. Their opinions of the effectiveness of the program could well be raised if medical, psychiatric, and social work help is given, independently of whether it does any good for the patients.

Looser Designs

To this point, the development of experimental design under conditions of considerable rigor has been emphasized. Implicitly, limitations to interpretation when the designs are not carried out have been emphasized. A few directions in which the designs may be loosened or relaxed should now be indicated on the assumption that rough measures may be sufficient and that judging equivalence is feasible. The main relaxation that is carried out is the utilization of the group that receives the health service demonstration program as its own control. The assumption is that the sample, group or community to which the program is directed is operating at a known level. Then, when the program is introduced, if it does have a significant change, it will be of sufficient magnitude that the contrast between the condition after the program and that before the program will be easily visible.

In medical practice such designs are frequent. Drugs are introduced and rates of disease or disorder are examined to see if significant changes have occurred. Serious problems often arise, of course, with this design. The program may not be what caused the change in rates, but

457

the change could be associated with other historical changes occurring at the same time. Sanitary conditions, control of pollution or other major circumstances may be changing at the same time that the drugs are being introduced. Or diagnostic procedures are becoming more accurate, and may show that conditions normally associated with the disorder are attributable to some other condition. The existence of a program in a community may cause other self-conscious interests with matters of health. But, additional factors may be involved that are associated with change in time. For example, resistance and immunities may be developing in the population, the population characteristics may be changing, either through migration or maturation, etc.

When less than full controls in experimental design are utilized, the key to drawing appropriate conclusions centers on raising questions about alternative explanations for changes that are observed. Systematically, alternative hypotheses must be raised, and, for the original hypothesis to be maintained, the alternatives must be adequately answered and eliminated.

Under the concept of demonstration programs, whether they be in the health services or in welfare, emphasis is placed on the exemplary application of a service that is assumed already to be effective. In theory, the demonstration indicates feasibility and resolves technical and administrative problems in such a way as to indicate how appropriate services may be provided. Under such conditions the use of controlled experiments is relatively unlikely, and effectiveness is more likely to be judged on some intuitive basis. Demonstration programs, thus, frequently are not initiated in a way in which they can be evaluated in any scientific sense. But, to be evaluated some analogy to controlled experimentation must be made.

That, of course, leads to one alternative to experimentation; that is, the systematic study of communities to find situations which are analogous with regard to important social characteristics of population, and where programs do or do not exist. Great care must be used in such comparative research, but if the unit of study is taken as the community rather than the individuals within it, a considerable amount of information could be garnered. This is particularly the case if a substantial number of alternatives exist, and if enthusiasm of communities and of staff may be expected for each of the alternatives. However, even here, care must be used in interpreting what is an effective program and what is not. Each, in its own way, may be providing some relevant services for the community.

458

Evaluation in other fields is no less difficult than with health services. For example, graduate school departments are constantly re-examining their criteria for a program of study leading to the Ph.D. Such a revision was recently made in the sociology department at Wisconsin, which is composed of a substantial number of younger staff members. Before proceeding with the discussion of the proposed new program each of the younger staff members was asked to describe the program under which he was trained. After the many reports were given the chairman concluded that by witness of the presence of all these young men, obviously quite different programs could produce excellent Ph.D's.

THE PROGRAM AS EXPERIMENTAL MANIPULATION

If attention is now given to the type of demonstration program being utilized, additional cautions arise as to how results of an evaluation study are to be interpreted. First, a prime difficulty that is encountered is in detaching the program, in its technical or professional specification, from other effects or circumstances. For example, often a program is introduced into a community at the request of some segment of the community. Thus, receptivity for the program may be established before the program is introduced, and for all practical purposes the community may have oriented itself to making a success of the program, independently of what the program involves in terms of technical or professional manipulations. Certainly, the success of the program could not be contributed to its specified procedures, and then be expected to work in another community where such local response is not a precursor.

Equally important, very often programs are initiated by individuals who have great confidence in them. In this case, professionals and non-professionals working together may develop such a level of enthusiasm that they, with charisma, may carry the program independently of what it is. This is sometimes called the pioneering effect, and a program that has been successful with such staffing will not necessarily be equally successful when introduced into other locations by staff who view the program more phlegmatically and with less enthusiasm.

The above comments suggest that either enthusiasm of the staff or the receptivity of the community may make a program successful, when its procedures may not be effective as such. Further, both these factors may lead to a favorable evaluation of the program, independently of whether it has been effective or not. Under such circumstances, each program must be viewed as a single case. Viewed comparatively, health service demonstration programs that are judged successful may well be those in which program directors and staff are enthusiastic and devoted and where the communities have been oriented in a receptive and equally enthusiastic way. What, then, would be the way of making inferences about the program itself? The question must be raised about the relevance of the program itself if the application of programs is to occur under less ideal conditions.

Aspects of evaluation under such circumstances often stimulate researchers to raise questions in such a way that they have policy or other implications. Having some knowledge of the areas involved, scientists may suggest that appropriate measures are not being taken. For example, if one is interested in control of veneral disease, the question of appropriateness of a program designed to cure when symptoms are already visible may be questionable. What is the rational basis for the program in terms of what is known about control of the disease? The public health service may be interested in controlling the disease, but in the willingness to actually bring it under control the community at large may not cooperate in procedures that would have higher likelihood of success. Is the community willing to have realistic sex education in the schools, common availability of prophylactic devices in all public locations and so forth? At this stage the answer is usually no. Bringing into effect these more direct and possibly more efficient procedures conflicts with other values in this society.

Here again the question of conflict of values returns. Health service demonstration programs ordinarily are concerned with attempts at providing services, and the evaluation of the medical aspects of the services may not be in question. What may be central to the program is the social engineering that brings the medical services to the proper clients. But values may apply in the situation that appears to be "irrational," and the procedures may be ineffective for various reasons as previously noted. Appropriate procedures may not be possible and ostensibly appropriate procedures may be thwarted. The process of providing the program may have a higher net survival value in the community than value measured in terms of intended consequences.

With regard to the evaluation of demonstration programs, the tendency is to move out of the arena of direct evaluation unless the program itself is designed as an experimental procedure. Questions of evaluation ask whether the program is an appropriate one for the population, and answers have to be given on bases other than those which involve scientific knowledge. Dependence increases on what is called analysis, which in fact boils down to opinion on the part of experts, some of whom may actually be quite wise. They may raise questions, for example, about the appropriateness of a program for a given population, assuming considerable knowledge of the cultural aspects of the population and its limitations. Further, a fair amount of experience may suggest the limitations of generalization of programs in communities other than the ones where the health service demonstration was carried out. Such experience, for example, may militate for the development of very simple programs and procedures that require little involvement on the part of the population to which they are directed, and where the effects are reasonably easily demonstrable. Appropriateness of a program may depend entirely on its ability to operate under the worst conditions rather than under the optimal conditions usually defined in demonstration programs. Of course, these comments are relevant whether or not a control group design or a historical descriptive case analysis is carried out.

REFERENCES

[1] For another consideration of such factors in the area of psychotherapy see, Borgatta, Edgar F., Research, Pure and Applied, *Group Psychotherapy*, 8, 263–277, 1955. In the area of criminology, another such list was prepared. *See,* Cressey, Donald R., The Nature and Effectiveness of Correctional Techniques, *Law and Contemporary Problems*, 23, 754–771, 1958.

[2] In the area of educational research, considerable attention has been given recently to questions of experimental designs in terms of the array of both "true" experiments and "quasi" experiments. Although designed for another area of concern, persons interested in evaluation research will profit from reading the following. Campbell, Donald T. and Stanley, Julian C., Experimental and Quasi-Experimental Designs for Research on Teaching, *in* Gage, N. L. (Editor), HANDBOOK OF RESEARCH ON TEACHING, Chicago, Rand McNally & Co., 1963, pp. 171–246.

³ The problem of "regression effects" in research that is less than experimental in design is enormous and presents itself in many ways. One brief but dramatic exercise shows how strong such effects are when a program is directed toward cases arriving in an acute condition, with a before and after design, but with no control group. *See,* Borgatta, Edgar F., Demonstration of Genuine Placebo Change, *Psychological Reports,* 64, 645–646, 1964. The problem of improvement when apparently irrelevant attention is given is frequently encountered in the literature under the consideration of "placebo reactors." That is a misnomer, for if persons are indeed reacting to the placebo, then it should be viewed as a (or another) change agent; it is not irrelevant. The reader may be interested in examining the kinds of statement that can be made in the absence of demonstrated effectiveness of a program, or, in fact, in the absence of even the test of effectiveness. *See,* Borgatta, Edgar F., The New Principle of Psychotherapy, *Journal of Clinical Psychology,* 15, 330–334, 1959.

DISCUSSION

The importance of evaluation of both special demonstration programs and regular health programs was emphasized. The increasing Federal support of new programs for the attainment of social objectives, important ones of which are improved health for several large groups of children and adults, and at the same time the practical recognition of limited resources, will require efforts to judge on some basis whether the benefits justify the costs. Judgments will be made and methods should be improved for assisting in sound judgments.

The discussion emphasized some of the practical difficulties of evaluation and made suggestions for dealing with some of them. Evaluation of demonstrations cannot by its nature be as rigorously and strictly scientific as laboratory experiments. Control groups are difficult to establish and a true experimental design is in the nature of things impossible. Evaluation is nevertheless necessary and possible if clear objectives are established and appropriate measures are chosen. The danger of evaluation appearing to threaten program staffs was pointed out. Program people should be prepared in advance for alternative results and when the evaluation results are disclosed a means should be available for feeding them back to the program people. In this way, when properly arranged before, during and afterwards, the evaluation process can be a morale builder rather than a threat.

Although to be completely objective in evaluations may not be possible, an open-minded approach must be maintained and any presentation of a persuasive view toward a specific result must be avoided.

462

Evaluation, as does most research, involves some oversimplification of both objectives and method. Attempts to deal with multiple objectives simultaneously can be self-defeating. Attempts to use too sophisticated methods may also be self-defeating because of costs and political problems. Even so, each year more is expected of evaluation efforts and methods are becoming more sophisticated. Discussion also centered on "quick and dirty" methods and their usefulness in some circumstances to identify both gross accomplishments and gross negative findings before undertaking more refined procedures.

At the very least and even without clear results, evaluation has the merit of raising questions and developing a more critical point of view toward apparent results. Differentiation between effectiveness and efficiency was considered to be important; effectiveness dealing only with attainment of a specific objective and efficiency dealing with the cost in resources to accomplish the effect.

In summary, the discussion indicated a favorable view of Borgatta's paper as a contribution toward improving evaluation methods in health service demonstration.

THE CONCEPT OF NEED FOR HEALTH SERVICES

KENNETH E. BOULDING

The concept of need is often looked upon rather unfavorably by economists, in contrast with the concept of demand. Both, however, have their own strengths and weaknesses. The need concept is criticized as being too mechanical, as denying the autonomy and individuality of the human person, and as implying that the human being is a machine which "needs" fuel in the shape of food, engine dope in the shape of medicine, and spare parts provided by the surgeon. Even if the need concept is expanded to include psychological and emotional needs, the end result would seem to be a wire run into the pleasure center of the brain which could provide a life of unlimited and meaningless ecstasy. Demand, by contrast, implies autonomy of the individual, choice, and a tailoring of inputs of all kinds to individual preferences. Only the slave has needs; the free man has demands.

In spite of the economist's uneasiness about it, a considerable demand exists for the concept of need. As even the most liberal of economists cannot deny the right of a demand to call forth a supply, the development and elaboration of concepts of need can hardly be denied. The demand, however, may be for a number of different concepts, and a single concept will not serve the purpose. The demands for this concept are quite varied, and the supply must be correspondingly differentiated. No single concept of need exists, and especially no single concept of need for health services.

One demand for a concept of need arises because the concept of demand itself has serious weaknesses and limitations. It assumes away,

464

for instance, a serious epistemological problem. The very idea of autonomous choice implies first that the chooser knows the real alternatives which are open to him, and second that he makes the choice according to value criteria or a utility function which he will not later regret. Both the image of the field of choice and the utility function have a learning problem which, by and large, economists have neglected. This problem is particularly acute in the case of medical care, where the demander is usually a layman faced with professional suppliers who know very much more than he does. The demand for medical care, indeed, is primarily a demand for knowledge or at least the results of knowledge. In the case of ordinary commodities the knowledge that is required is fairly easily available and the market itself is a learning process. If one buys something he does not like he will not buy it again. In the case of medical care, however, as in the case of certain other commodities such as automobiles, the learning process can easily be fatal, in which case it is not a learning process at all. In any case the experience of the market cannot teach people what they have to know in regard to the choices they have to make, or even what preference functions they should use in evaluating these choices.

The concept of need which emerges from the criticism of demand is that of professional choice. It is implied to some extent in the very idea of the patient or the client, and it is expressed in the aphorism that doctor (or father, or lawyer, or preacher, or president) knows best. One's demand for medical care is what he wants; his need for medical care is what the doctor thinks he ought to have. The demand for medical care leads to the proliferation of drug stores, patent medicines, osteopaths, chiropractors and faith healers.

That is the market for medical care and it is a large one. It spills over into the medical profession itself, in private practice and the reputation of particular doctors and surgeons, in the prestige of Harley Street and its equivalents in many cities, and it includes both the medicine cabinet in the bathroom and the psychiatrist's couch. It can be thought of as an "industry" or segment of the economy; it is subject to the general principles of the price system, in the sense that wherever a demand is sufficient to make a supply profitable it will arise, even though this principle has to be limited also by the power of the ingenious supplier to create his own demand.

In contrast with the market in medical care, an increasingly professionalized, socialized, organized structure satisfies what the professional conceives of as needs. The periodic medical examinations in

465

corporations and universities, the veterans' hospitals, the school doctor, public health, the professional public provision of clean water and sewage disposal—all this represents a professionalized sector of the economy, characterized by professions which set their own standards of what they ought to do and which are financed by taxation or near-taxation. Among these are Blue Cross and other health insurance plans, Medicare, or even private clinics supported by monthly assessments. Here the activity originates from the profession rather than from the client, from the supplier rather than from the demander. In its extreme form it takes on the flavor of, "What you need is what I as your professional advisor have to give you; what you want is quite irrelevant."

The idea of professional need always rests on some definition of homeostasis or state maintenance of the client, his property or his environment. The professional defines a certain state of his client and his related systems as a state of "health" which he has a professional interest in maintaining. The course of operations of any system, however, involves consumption. That is, the state of the client and his environment changes in some way and become "worse," or diverge in a downward direction from the ideal. The ideal in this case is the professional's ideal, that is, his impression of what state should be maintained. The maintenance of a state, however, requires certain inputs to replace what has been lost by consumption. It may also require the professional handling of certain outputs, such as excreta, which must be removed and disposed of if the organism or organization is to continue to maintain its state of activity. A very fundamental principle in nature implies that any state of activity can only be maintained by a throughput involving both inputs and outputs. In part that may be because inputs come in packages in practice, only part of which can be utilized, and what is not utilized must therefore be excreted as output. Even more fundamental reasons, however, dictate the presence of output in the form of excreta, whether gases from automobile exhaust, carbon dioxide given off in breathing or waste products of the digestive process. The transformation of chemical into mechanical energy, on which all organization seems to depend almost universally, seems to require an input of oxygen and an output of an oxide.

This suggests that certain minimum mechanical, chemical, biological, physiological, even economic and sociological requirements exist for the functioning of any organism or organization. That in turn sug-

466

gests that the concept of professional need can be broken down into two further problems; one the problem of what might be called homeostatic need. That is, what is actually required to maintain a given system in operation. The other is the problem of perception or knowledge of homeostatic need. That is, can the system itself be trusted to maintain the inputs and outputs necessary to satisfy homeostatic need, or is a professional required with a wider body of knowledge who can perceive and prescribe the homeostatic needs? Homeostatic needs can be divided into two categories, those which can be taken care of by the organism itself and those which require a professional decision.

These categories can be illustrated by pointing to certain undignified analogies between the human being as an organization and an item of material capital such as an automobile. Both require inputs of air if they are to function, and the air must be reasonably pure, though usually only automobiles are provided with air filters. Each of them pollute the air they breathe with the byproducts of combustion, and unless fresh air can be constantly supplied continued operation will become impossible. Both the man and the automobile require food; carbohydrates, proteins and fats in the case of the human, gasoline and oil in the case of the automobile. A certain parallel can even be drawn between the vitamins of the human and the various additives of gasoline. The parallel is particularly striking in Scandinavian countries where automobiles are "buttered," not greased. Food input is usually administered on a fairly nonprofessional basis. The automobile owner buys gas for his car in very much the same way as he buys food for himself, with a certain amount of professional advice but not much professional interference. In the course of operation of the system, internal stocks of food are used up fairly continuously and they have to be replaced at intervals. The automobile takes its dinner at the gas station, which is a kind of automobile restaurant.

The input of food and of fuel and the output of its waste products are not, however, sufficient. In the course of operation, both of the automobile and of the human, wear and tear occur. Consequently, not only are gas stations, restaurants and food stores needed, but also garages and hospitals. At this level need becomes professionalized. The greasing every thousand miles or the annual physical examination may be fairly routine, though at this point one begins to think of medical care for either automobile or man rather than simple fueling and feeding. The professional need is most apparent in breakdown, that is, when the subject simply refuses to function even when fueled and fed. Then the car goes to the garage, where mechanics perform operations on it, and the human goes to the hospital where surgeons perform operations on him. The atmosphere of the garage, indeed, is curiously like that of the hospital. The garage is permeated by the same air of professional importance, the same feeling that the customer is rather in the way, the same rather offhand bedside manner, the same assumption that the customer or the patient is, professionally speaking, an ignoramus, if not a fool. In fact, the principal difference between the garage and the hospital seems to be that the hospital is cleaner and more expensive. The concept of professional need appears in the helplessness of the customer. All he knows is that he hears a funny noise in the gear box or has a pain in his stomach. Once he puts himself into the hands of the professional, demand disappears and no substitute exists for trust in the professional's concept of need.

The difficulty with homeostasis as the basis for a concept of need is that homeostasis is never really successful. No matter what occurs in the way of inputs, virtually all known organisms and organizations exhibit the phenomenon of aging, which is closely related to the phenomenon of growth. Aging is common both to machines and to biological organisms, and it might almost be defined as that adverse change in state of the organism which no known input can remedy. In biological organisms, growth is actually rather similar. It can be thought of, indeed, as a kind of negative aging. The inputs of the growing child have to be sufficient not only to provide for replacement, but also to provide for growth. Growth, however, is almost as unpreventable as aging. Mechanical organizations such as the automobile are not generally subject to growth. They are more like the moth or the butterfly in that they emerge fully grown from the chrysalis of the factory, and henceforth are subject only to aging. Up to now very little is known about aging, at least in the case of the biological organism. It can perhaps be hastened by certain inputs or outputs or by certain deficiencies in input, which is also true of the automobile. In both cases, a life of hard work and poor nutrition results in premature aging. Up to now, at any rate, any inputs which would postpone the aging process beyond the allotted span have not been discovered. If they are, as seems not impossible, at least in the next 100 years, the human race will probably be faced with the greatest crisis of its history, for no existing human institution would

468

survive in its present form the extension of active human life even to 200 years.[1]

Aging introduces a very tricky problem into the concept of need for maintenance, which is difficult enough even in the case of the machine, more difficult in the case of the horse, and a problem of excruciating delicacy in the case of the human being. The problem with the machine is at what point in its history it should be scrapped. The formal answer to this is fairly easy: a machine should be scrapped when its present value as a functioning apparatus, derived by discounting the future costs and benefits to be allocated to it, has fallen just below the net value of a possible replacement. The net value is defined as the present discounted value of future benefits less that of all future and installment costs of the replacement plus the scrap value of the machine which is replaced. With no technical progress and if the machine is replaced by one exactly like it when new, the main factor determining the age at which it will be replaced is the increase in the maintenance cost and perhaps a decrease in its output as it gets older. Where technical change occurs a machine may be scrapped because of obsolescence, that is, because of a rise in the net value of what might replace it.

A machine is generally regarded as having no value in itself, that is, its value is purely instrumental; hence the owner feels no qualms about scrapping it if he feels such action is necessary. Even horses, however, when they can no longer fulfill their economic function, are sometimes put out to pasture in honorable retirement at some cost to their owners. In the case of the human being, the problem of the person himself becomes very acute, because persons cannot be regarded as purely instrumental. That is, they are not merely good for something else, they are good in themselves. They are, in other words, something *for which* other things are good. Whereas the death of a machine is determined mainly by economic forces, this principle as quite inapplicable to persons, where, in theory at any rate, the person supposedly possesses a positive value even up to the moment of death, and death, therefore, is always regarded as a loss. When death occurred mainly in childhood or middle life, this principle could evoke no criticism. As medical science, however, has successively eliminated the causes of early death, the fiction that death is always an "act of God" is increasingly difficult to maintain.

At this point the concept of professional need for medical care becomes most difficult. Should the medical profession devote a relatively large proportion of its resources, as it does now, in keeping miserable and senile elderly people alive, when their capital value even to themselves has become negative? Men, even physicians, have a reasonable aversion to playing God and to introducing a nonrandom element in what has hitherto been sanctified as random. The only solution may be to substitute an artificially random process for the natural randomness by which death came in the past. If death could be arranged by drawing a random number, perhaps by hiding one euthanasia pill in the nursing home diet each week, the Godlike power of the medical man might be laid on the shoulders of Chance, and death might be restored to its former dignity.

A proposal such as the above will seem deeply shocking to many people, and indeed, is put forward only in the form of a most tentative question, intended merely to illustrate a problem which is likely to be more and more prevalent. One principle in the spirit of the Hippocratic Oath to be argued for very strongly is that the person himself must decide at what point death or the chance of death is preferred to life, and no one else should have the right to make this decision for him. At this point, surely, demand must take precedence of need, and the autonomy of the patient be reasserted. Even at the moment of making this assertion, however, and nailing it to the masthead, realistic doubts arise. At what point, for instance, do people become incapable of making decisions for themselves? That is a question of immediate practical importance for the medical profession, for even if they do not have the power at the moment of consigning people to eternity, they do have the power of consigning them to what is often the living death of the mental hospital, and the moral problems of the latter are surely of the same order of magnitude as those of the former. Nevertheless, people do become incompetent and incapable of managing their own affairs. Society has decided that mental hospitals must exist, and along with them the machinery for committing people to them. Who is better able to estimate that professional need than the medical profession, especially when its decisions are mediated through the apparatus of the law? One sobering thought, however, is that a person virtually ceases to be a legal person when he ceases to have demands and has only needs.

Some of the above problems may well reflect a lag in society in the development of a professional sense of what the needs of the incompetent and the aged in fact ought to be. A marked shift has taken place in the care of the aged, from the family into hospitals and nursing homes. Even two generations ago most people died in their own beds in the bosom of their families, amid the consolations of religion and the ministrations of a beloved family physician. Such, at least, is the idyllic picture; the reality was probably more disagreeable. Nevertheless, of the people who die of old age today, most die in nursing homes, old people's homes, and hospitals, away from the comforts of the familiar and the ministrations of kin. No great deal of thought has been devoted to the needs of the departing, and none at all to the need for death. Death, however, is a medical matter. It is certainly part of the need for medical care, if such exists, and it deserves to receive a great deal more care and attention than it has in the past. That is not to suggest that the medical profession should abandon its concern for the needs of the incompetent, the aged and the dying; rather that more attention be given to this problem, both in medical research, so that vigor and physical well-being can be prolonged until the end, and in social and moral research that can devise economic, financial, architectural and social institutions which will give dignity and serenity to the last years of life and will not deprive its end of the majesty which is due it.

At the other end of human life, the increasing control, which the biological sciences seem to be opening up in genetics, presents even more difficult problems in regard to the need for medical activity. If the rights of the living and the dying are hard to determine, the rights of the unborn are an even more difficult problem. The whole problem of population control, in fact, in regard to both quantity and quality, is moving more and more onto the shoulders of the health sciences, and it is a problem for which they cannot escape responsibility. In the last 15 years, the spectacular decline in infant mortality which followed the introduction of malaria control in the tropics has created social problems which seem to be virtually insoluble in the next 15 to 20 years.

One must think here in terms of the homeostasis, not merely of the individual, but of a whole society. When, as a result of the introduction of certain public health measures, a society which previously was in approximate demographic equilibrium, with high birth rates and high death rates, suddenly finds the death rates drastically reduced while the birth rates continue high, an enormous long-run social disequilibrium is created which may have quite unforeseen consequences, both for good and for ill. Many societies in the tropics are now increasing in population at unprecedented rates—between three and four per cent per annum—and this in itself places an enormous burden on the poor society which is anxious for development. When the population doubles every 20 years a whole new country must be built, and the whole physical apparatus of a society doubled in a relatively short space of time, even if per capita capital is not to decline. If the country is already fairly thickly populated, with no unused land areas of any magnitude, the sheer problem of doubling the food supply in 20 years is almost insoluble, and a slow and deadly reduction in nutritive levels can easily follow.

Add to this gloomy picture the fact that in these countries most of the working force was born before the great decline in infant mortality and hence is small. That small working force has to support an enormous number of children and young people—in many of these countries more than half the population is now under the age of 18. Furthermore, very large teenage generations now exist which cannot be absorbed in the traditional structure, especially of the village society, and are forced to migrate to the towns. The towns, because of the phenomenon of what has been called the "rural push," are growing much faster than the population itself, some of them as much as 15 per cent annually which means doubling every five years. Under these circumstances providing housing and municipal services is impossible, and enormous slums and shack towns spread over the landscape like a blight. These circumstances dictate an extremely pessimistic forecast for the next 25 years for many of these countries. On the other hand, if a massive campaign for birth reduction takes place now, so that birth rates could be halved in five or ten years, then the next generation will be a large labor force able to cope with the smaller numbers of children and that will be the moment when these countries may be able to make the leap into the modern world. In the absence of substantial reduction in birth rates, however, the outlook is bleak indeed. Enormous famines, disastrous internal strife and even total civil breakdown may be expected. All this may well be the result of the World Health Organization's malaria eradiction campaign in the years around 1950.

On the other side of the picture, without a substantial increase in the expectation of life, and particularly without the elimination of mortality in the productive years, economic development is also very difficult. An essential step toward the modern world is the introduction of modern medicine and the elimination of the appalling waste of human knowledge and human capital which occurs in

472

countries where human life expectancy is little more than 30 years. The ideal situation would be a sharp reduction in the death rate and an equally sharp reduction in the birth rate, so that the demographic equilibrium was not unduly disturbed. Even if this happy result were unobtainable, a certain disturbance of the demographic equilibrium is entirely desirable in the interest of development, and a public health campaign is at least a start in disturbing the low-level equilibrium of a traditional society.

These problems present great difficulties, even for social scientists, and up to now at any rate the medical sciences have been extraordinarily lax in attending to them. Medicine has considered health mainly in terms of inputs to an individual, not to a society. The possibility of an acute conflict between the health of the individual and that of his society is a problem that has received scandalously little attention. Now the tables have been turning, and birth control has become fashionable and respectable, almost to the point of being advocated as a panacea for all developmental difficulties. Quantitative population control, however, is only a part of the general problem of what might be called societal health, which is not the same thing, incidentally, as public health. Public health concerns itself primarily with the environmental factors affecting the health of the individual. Societal health deals with the factors that determine the health of the whole society, and societies can be sick even when the individuals in them are medically well.

The problem of qualitative population control is beginning to rise seriously onto the human agenda. The eugenics movements of the nineteenth century were premature, and based on wholly inadequate genetic concepts. With the enormous advance in genetics in this century, however, the problems of the genetic composition of future populations are no longer as random as they used to be. Indeed, a recurrent nightmare is that all the medical advances will eventually prove ineffective simply because the improved techniques of individual survival will enable more and more adverse genetic strains to penetrate the population. In his argument against that position, Medawar says that if a genetic adaptation to medical knowledge produces more people who have to be kept alive by "artificial" means, nothing is particularly wrong with that, because genetics always adapts itself to the environment and medical knowledge is part of the environment of man.[2] The argument, however, is not wholly satisfactory, simply because of the cost of medical care for those whose genetic constitution requires it. If the existence of medical care produces a population of the genetic composition which requires it, the whole system seems to be self-defeating. Whatever level of medical care is established, no matter how high and how elaborate, one can argue that in the long run the genetic composition of the population will deteriorate to the point where the established level of medical care becomes necessary. In this case the level of medical care creates its own need. No objective need exists which determines the level of medical care.

Looking to the rather long run, therefore, one would expect to find large payoffs in research devoted to altering the genetic composition of the population in directions which would minimize the cost of medical care. Conceivably, genetic control might eliminate medical care almost entirely, except for accidents; for some genetic constitutions are extraordinarily resistant to disease, and if these could be propagated in the population, the need for medical care would correspondingly decline.

In the next few decades, the possibility of changing genetic constitutions even after birth is not wholly off the agenda, although it certainly seems to be difficult. Even without that, however, the possibility of genetic control at the moment of conception opens up an enormous and rather frightening horizon to the human race, even though this would also open up enormous possibilities for good. Certainly the elimination of the more obvious genetic-related diseases or conditions would be a great gain. The ethical problems involved at this end of the scale, however, are just as severe as those at the other end relating to death. At what point, for instance, in the life history of a person does he have any rights? Opinion seems to have shifted in this regard toward the moment of birth as the point at which human rights are acquired. The increasingly favorable public opinion in regard to abortion would seem to imply that the embryo has no rights, whereas the infant does, as infanticide is still severely censored. If, however, the process of conception can be controlled and, for instance, selective gene structures implanted in the egg, the question of the human rights even of the fertilized egg becomes acute. That again is a problem because the ethical standards and ideas of the human race have been adapted to processes of birth and death which in the past have been essentially random, and substituting nonrandom for random processes always produces an acute moral crisis. Perhaps some consensus might be salvaged with elimination of certain obviously maladaptive genetic traits, for instance mongoloidism and obvious feeblemindedness. Even considering the elimination of haemophilia, enough distinguished people have had this disability to suggest that something might be lost by eliminating it. The ethical problems become even more acute with the proposal to alter genetic structures positively. The production of a race of supermen who would supersede the present generation might not be regarded favorably by ordinary mortals.

Underlying all this discussion is a seldom-discussed specter regarding the idea of health itself. Even assuming the very simple position that need involves merely the maintenance of homeostasis, the question as to what state of the organism is to be maintained still has to be answered. That is like the problem of at what temperature the thermostat should be set. Every homeostatic mechanism implies an ideal, and the question of the critique of the ideal itself, therefore, cannot be brushed aside. In particular, the conclusion cannot be avoided that within limits which may be quite broad, health is a matter of social definition. Societies and cultures do exist in which what is now defined here as ill health is somewhat admired. One recalls W. S. Gilbert's pale young curate, whose tubercular charms in the eyes of the village maidens even outweighed those of gilded dukes and belted earls. In some societies, epilepsy is regarded as a sign of divine favor. The limits of what is socially defined as physical health are so narrow that not much of a problem arises.

With mental health and human behavior in society, however, the limits seem to be broader, and the matter of social definition more important. For instance, should the problem of homosexuality be considered a problem in mental health, to be "cured," even if no cure seems to be currently available, or should it be regarded as a legitimate variation of human behavior, to be accepted and regulated by custom and law? A rather similar problem involving the acceptance of deviant subcultures has descended upon society with the development of the psychedelic drugs such as mescaline and LSD. Some claim that these are legitimate avenues to the expansion of human consciousness and others claim that these are dangerous drugs the use of which should be prohibited by law, except under medical supervision, and that unauthorized users should be punished as criminals. A similar conflict of voices is raised on behalf of marijuana, some people claiming that it affords a legitimate expansion of human consciousness and is no more dangerous than alcohol. The prevailing sentiment, however, is to lash out at the use of these drugs with all the ferocity of criminal law.

The failure to deal with alcohol, which has been with the human race for a long time and is certainly the earliest of the psychedelic drugs, is not an optimistic indication that society will be able to deal with a succession of new chemical and perhaps electrical devices, such as the "pleasure wire," which produce various types of euphoria. One remembers with a slight shudder the use of soma as a social tranquilizer in Brave New World. Even in the medical field, not very much is known about the impact on society of the enormous use of the tranquilizing drugs both in medical practice and in private life in the past few years. The frightening possibility of a society steeped in agreeable chemical illusions to the point where it becomes quite incapable either of recognizing or solving its real problems is by no means a matter only for science fiction.

Different societies have given very different answers to these questions, and they constitute merely one aspect of a much larger question as to the boundary between health, morality and law. In many fields the problem is defining the point at which behavior which is in some sense disapproved or regarded as below normal is defined as sickness or is defined as turpitude. In this society a long-term movement has attempted to push this boundary to define fewer things as turpitude and more things as sickness. Nevertheless, no golden rule dictates where this line should be drawn. In Samuel Butler's Erewhon, crime was treated by doctors and illness by policemen, and one has an uneasy suspicion that this might work too. The problem of the overall effects upon society of its system of punishment is very little understood, and the line between the need for medical care and the need for criminal prosecution is really quite hard to draw.

A question which is even more fundamental and still more difficult to answer, but which should not remain unasked, is whether the concept of ill health can be applied to moral and political ideas themselves. For instance, do diseases of the moral judgment exist, and if so, are they subject to epidemics? How are these epidemics spread? The rise of National Socialism in Germany and McCarthyism in the United States, of witch-hunting, war moods and irrational hatreds in innumerable societies, indicates that the concept of disease in the moral and political judgment is worth taking seriously, even though it is very hard to define. One may be able to define something like mass infections of unrealistic images of the world, if only one could be sure what is realistic. Whether these phenomena fall under the purview of the medical profession is, of course, a debatable point. The medical profession has long been required in forensic medicine to

476

advise on the medical status of a possible criminal act. Perhaps, one day it may be called in to determine the medical status of a political act or even of a moral exhortation. The difficulty here, and it is a real one, is that, up to now at any rate, a clear physical correlate of mental, moral and political ill health does not exist. The idea is not wholly far-fetched, however, to suppose such physical correlates do exist and that the discovery will be made one day of a drug against malevolence or another that increases good will. Even if the physical correlates are hard to find, the status of psychoanalysis as a medical speciality suggests possible extensions into therapeutic communication in moral, political and social systems.

Society is so accustomed to thinking of the problem of the interrelations of government, science and medicine in terms of the impact of government on science and medicine that people are at a loss when asked to consider the impact of science and medicine on government. Nevertheless, that may well become one of the major questions in advanced societies in the next generation or two. Political decisions are still made largely in the light of what might be called folk knowledge or at best literary knowledge. The scientist is supposedly to serve the values and interests of the folk but he is not to insert any values and interests of his own. He is supposedly an instrument of the state or at least of the people and not an autonomous creator of values and needs. That is the point of view of the famous aphorism that the scientist in government should be on tap but not on top, and that he should be a humble servant of folk and national values. That, however, is a most unrealistic estimate of the present situation. Science is not a passive servant of existing values. It has its own culture, it creates its own values, and because of its enormous impact on the world, it compels a re-examination of values everywhere.

The role of the social sciences in this respect is even more striking than that of the physical and biological sciences. The physical or biological scientist operates in a different field from that of the politician. The special skills of the scientist in, say, physics or physiology give him very little comparative advantage in attempting to answer a question in social systems. In respect to the economic system or the international system, the physicist or biologist has as much right to be heard as any intelligent citizen, but no more. The social scientist, however, occupies the same field as the politician and is in direct competition with him. The possibility of severe conflict between the folk culture and the scientific culture is thus present at this level. Up to now the conflict has been muted only because it has hardly begun; because the social sciences are only barely at the point where they can begin to challenge the folk wisdom of the politician. Economics already has a kind of establishment of "Lords Spiritual" in the Council of Economic Advisors and in the Joint Economic Committee in Congress. The impact of this establishment is already noticeable in economic policy, and the United States is by no means the most advanced country in this regard. The other social sciences, and least of all what might be called the sociomedical sciences of clinical psychology and psychiatry, still seem to be a long way from any such status. The possibility, however, that one of the needs for medical care may be defined in the future as political mental health, though it may sound absurd at the moment, should not be taken lightly. Society is already beginning to see that the automobile is a problem in public health; to regard the Department of Defense as a similar problem is a simple logical extension of this position, for the present international system is almost certainly more dangerous to health than the automobile and far more dangerous than most communicable diseases.

Even at this point, the ambiguity can be maintained between demand as defined by the consumer and need as defined by the professional. All fields of life seem to feel the necessity for working out an uneasy compromise between these two concepts. Undiluted consumer sovereignty, whether in economics or politics, where it takes the form of the absolute sovereignty of the voter and the sovereignty of the nation, is ultimately intolerable and leads to corruption and disaster. On the other hand, total professionalization, in the case of the doctor, the economist, the sociologist or the political scientist, is likewise intolerable, if only for the reason that having that much father-image is intolerable; and the revolt against paternalism, no matter how benign, is an essential aspect of the human identity. Somewhere between the proposition that the customer is always right and the proposition that the public be damned must be an uneasy Aristotelian mean, and toward this the concept of professional need for medical care or for anything else uneasily steers itself.

The word need has a number of meanings, and the idea of homeostatic need or professional need which we have been discussing does not exhaust it. Another very important connotation of the word is that implied in the word "needy." One's need in this sense is not merely what some wise professional person thinks one ought to have, but what one cannot afford because he is poor. In this sense also, need is thought of as something which stands in contrast with demand, and the need for a concept of need arises because of certain deficiencies in demand as a principle of allocation. The concept of need as a criticism of demand here refers to the fact that effective demand is closely related to income and to the distribution of income. Need is an equalitarian concept. It recalls the famous communist slogan, "From each according to his ability, to each according to his need."

Demand, perhaps because of its very stress on autonomy and freedom, is libertarian rather than equalitarian, and liberty is seldom equally divided. If medical care is distributed according to demand, the rich will get most of it and the poor very little. One of the main concerns of society for the need for medical care, therefore, is the fact that a sizeable proportion of the population is "medically indigent" in the sense that its income is not large enough to provide a demand for the minimum medical care which a society, or a profession, identifies as need. That may be a part of the general problem of the social minimum. At present nearly all societies have a deliberate policy to establish a minimum standard life below which citizens are not supposed to fall. Whether the policy is in fact successful is another matter, for in almost all cases some people do fall below the minimum, and all the machinery of society is not powerful enough to elevate them. Nevertheless, the principle of a social minimum has been established for a long time and today is almost universally accepted.

Even the acceptance of a social minimum, however, does not necessarily resolve the conflict between need and demand. Some argue that insofar as the problem is one of poverty, the only solution to this is to make the poor richer, either by giving them money, by improving their skills or by integrating them more fully into the culture around them. Once the poor have been made richer, the problem of the need for medical care resolves itself essentially into the problem discussed earlier of a consumer's demand versus professional need, between which poles some uneasy compromise must be reached.

In the case of medical indigency, however, the temptation is to deny consumers sovereignty as the price of the relief of indigency, and to say that the poor must have what the professionals think is good for them whether they want it or not. This is part of a very old and still unresolved question as to whether the grants economy should content itself with grants of money, leaving the recipient to spend it as he will, or should consist essentially of grants in kind supplying needs as defined by the professionals. Those who are somewhat liberal are inclined to emphasize demand even in the case of the indigent, and to give them at least some freedom to reject medical care if they prefer a short life and a merry one, though the liberty to preach against such behavior should also be preserved.

One of the great problems of the grants economy—which appears in the relief of medical indigency just as it does elsewhere—is that it can easily result in quite unintended administrative distortions of the price structure which in turn can cause social loss and quite unnecessary individual misery. If, for instance, a grant system bases a grant on a cost of service which is wrongly estimated, it can severely discourage the services which are undervalued and unnecessary and encourage the services which are overvalued. For example, certain casual administrative regulations in the social security system have stimulated a profitable practice of keeping indigent patients in nursing homes in bed, simply because the nursing homes are paid an extra amount for keeping people in bed. Hence nursing homes make more money on bed patients than on ambulatory ones. As a result of the strong financial pressure patients are kept in bed, in spite of the fact that this may be quite unwarranted medically and may contribute to the already bad enough miseries of old age and incompetence.

Generally any system which sets out to administer a price structure will get it wrong so that some things will be underpriced and some overpriced. The same problem may be seen in the universities, where teaching is underpriced relative to research, or where good administration is underpriced and bad administration overpriced. Under these circumstances a kind of universal Gresham's Law operates: the overpriced bad always drives out the underpriced good. No proposition as far as is known says that this problem is insoluble. Unless it is solved, however, socialized and administrative medicine will operate under some handicaps. The uneasy compromise between need and demand takes the form that if needs are to be well satisfied, demand, if it is not to be free, must at least be simulated. If administrative terms of trade are established in the system, it must also have an apparatus that can get feedback from their consequences and review them and adjust them rapidly in the way that the market does.

The last question of this discussion relates to the problem of the effectiveness of medical activity and research. Probably only in the last 100 years has the medical profession done more good than harm in promoting health. Now, although the direction of the effect is not in doubt, a certain amount of doubt remains about its magnitude. Certainly the most spectacular productivity of human activity in the production of health is only indirectly related to the medical profession as such. That is the kind of activity involved, for instance, in antimalaria campaigns, in cleaning up water supplies, in improving nutrition and even in teaching more desirable habits of child-rearing. This fact should not be surprising, nor does it redound to any discredit to the medical profession. Nothing is wrong with the assumption that the business of the doctor is sickness rather than health, just as the business of the garage mechanic is the repair of automobiles, not their production, or the provision of roads on which they may safely be driven. The medical profession is only a single input in the enormous network of social inputs which together determine the general level of health of the population. No one wishes the medical profession to lose its interest in sickness, for that is when a doctor is most needed. On the other hand, one also likes to see a strong interest in preventive medicine and in public health and in what might be called the larger environment of the health sciences. The need is also strong for the development of a social science of health, not only in economics but also in sociology and psychology. Considerable strides have been made toward this, but not in many centers in the world—to bring even one to mind is difficult is the social science of health studied and taught as a whole.

One would like to see a research operation of at least the magnitude of the Rand Corporation, the object of which would be to study health in all its aspects, social, biological and physical, in a manner permitting a good deal of interchange among specialists. Such a study would clearly reveal that the need for medical services will depend on a very large number of other variables, economic, sociological, biological, and on the whole system of this planet. That answer may not satisfy those who are seeking quick results to solve administrative dilemmas, and the importance of administrative shortcuts cannot be denied. Nevertheless, in the long run, a very substantial intellectual endeavor still awaits mankind in the study of this problem, and at the moment its solution is not near.[3]

The Rand Corporation is used merely as a symbol of the magnitude of the research effort in the social science of health which would probably be profitable. Whether the effort should be concentrated in a single institution or scattered around the academic community is a matter of research strategy on which may rest very valid differences of opinion. Something is to be said for the theory of the "critical mass," especially in interdisciplinary research; and the extraordinary fruitfulness of the Center for Advanced Study in the Behavioral Sciences at Stanford, indicates that a critical mass of this kind may actually be quite small under some circumstances. On the other hand, a research strategy should certainly not be confined to any particular institution, and should envisage the whole intellectual community as its field. Research strategies which are too specific can easily do more harm than good, and even the concept of the need for research needs to be looked at with a slightly quizzical eye. The growth of knowledge is much more like an evolutionary than it is like a mechanical process, and this means that it is fundamentally unpredictable. This can be seen very clearly by asking the question, can anyone predict what will be known 25 years from now? The answer is obviously no, or it would be known now. If the results of a research program are known in advance, the point in doing it has been lost. Hence the growth of knowledge must always contain what is called fundamental surprise, and any research strategy must be built around the capacity to expect and react creatively to surprise.

If any research strategy emerges out of these considerations, it is that one should be extremely suspicious of research devoted specifically to finding out the need for medical care. Too much of such research has already been done, all of which has outlined "needs" which are absurdly inflated, and which, if allowed to be fulfilled, would justify themselves with the greatest of ease. A research program which concentrated solely on quantitative estimates of need would inevitably neglect the problem of demand and the problem of the price structure. A great deal in research depends on how questions are framed. If the question is asked, how does one use a combination of the grants economy and the price structure in producing a system of medical care that compromises between needs and demands, a much richer and more satisfactory answer will likely result than if one simply asks, what is the need for medical care? Almost everyone who has raised children has heard the anguished cry, "But I need—" and soon learns to interpret this as meaning, "I want something badly but I am not prepared to pay the price for it." This cautionary note seems a suitable place to end what is mainly an appeal to move gingerly into an inevitably uncertain future, without forgetting that the movement must be made.

REFERENCES

[1] Boulding, K. E., The Menace of Methuselah, *Journal of the Washington Academy of Sciences,* 55, 171–179, October, 1965.

[2] Medawar, P. B., THE FUTURE OF MAN, New York, Basic Books, Inc., Publishers, 1960.

[3] *See* Ginzberg, Eli, The Political Economy of Health, *Bulletin of the New York Academy of Medicine,* 41, 1015–1036, October, 1965.

DISCUSSION

If the concept of need for health services is to be made useful for research, it might better be restated or placed in a wider context, that of need in the health "system." Then the proper starting point becomes those factors that serve as the basis for a health system. The health services are only one of the several influences on health and a minor one at that, the others including environment, inheritance and behavior.

The goal of the system must be health, even if only understood as the absence of disease. The point is we do have a choice of goals. In effect, disagreement was being expressed with discussants of previous papers who had observed that meeting health service need is also a way of life for those who so serve and therefore must be counted among the goals of the system. However, by clinging to health as the goal of the system one can most clearly decide to what these services are to be directed. In fact, should they be directed to the kinds of economic incentives that have been allowed, even encouraged, to come into the health service system?

In respect to health services, if the goal is the ever-expanding potential for favorably influencing health through medical advance, problems currently deemed hopeless can be investigated, among them the plight of the aged sick. Evidence of progress is even here. In Oxford, under imaginative leadership, medical and social care of the elderly is at a standard well above that found in the nursing home situation of the United States.

As noted by the author, the concept of need cannot be considered without examining the rival concept of demand. The weaknesses in both concepts led to audience critique of the meaning and use of these terms. The author's denial of a single concept of need, especially in the case of need for health services, was not disputed. This being the case, objections could be raised against those who fault the concept of need as seeming to imply the single notion of want without limit.

The concept of medical need, as defined by Lee and Jones in their study, *The Fundamentals of Medical Care*, abstracting from ability to pay and representing professional judgment alone, since it was independent of personal awareness, was introduced for the purpose of discussion. One difficulty in applying this type of concept, aside from the author's contention that problems of demand and the price structure should not be ignored, arises in the doctor-patient relationship. What the professional perceives as need in his client may be in part a function of whether professional or client is in control of the relationship between them. The solo practitioner, being more dependent for his livelihood on the patient, is more apt to be responsive to the patient's wishes than is the physician in an institutional setting. The latter is more apt to appraise need by criteria within his span of initiative since he is in a position to be less sensitive to his patients' wishes. The concepts of need and demand must also be seen respectively as having social and political dimensions as well as individual and economic ones. The relativity of needs over time was also noted, with needs seen as constantly advancing in front of demand. In many situations the continuing compromise required between a capacity to cite needs and the capacity to satisfy them was seen in the view of one observer as having the nature of a hoax when compared with the reality situation. Although granting abuse in use of the concept, defense was noted, especially by physicians, for the validity for a concept of need aside from the separate question of how it was perceived or how it was expressed in terms of economic demand. In the view of the author, a certain tension exists between need and demand and this must also be represented in any research consideration of the need for health services.

On the question of whether the author's paper was likely to serve as a stimulus to research in the area under discussion, one commentator replied in the negative. He had expected that new vistas on need for health services would be explored, among them such matters as what effect do the economic arrangements under which the health services are available have on the need for health service? A second line of development that could have been employed concerns the social policies that might emanate from or be affected by research utilizing the concept of need for health services. Another area of interest would be to hear in what ways systematic reorganization of presently available data might lead to further research. Something on the questions and methods

484

that require investigation was seen as another alternative approach. Although the paper does contain imaginative and thoughtful ideas, even these had not been transformed into researchable areas by the development of a research strategy.

In defense of his paper, the author responded that his purpose was to ask questions and to urge everyone to think intelligently about research and this was stimulus enough. His questions involved issues, matters that are and will continue to be of common concern to investigators for many years ahead. Some of these are ethical questions, and a major problem is the evaluation of value systems. The greater the power acquired in science and medicine, or in any other walk of life, the more imposing these ethical problems become. When one has power, he has to start worrying about wanting the wrong things. Ethics is the study of why people want the wrong things.

In effect the author's paper, beyond serving as a critique of the concept of need for health services, must also be seen as a plea for study of certain related social phenomena and their dynamics, for example, study of the perception of need as more promising than the concept of need itself. Basic to such study would be examination of those matters which create saliency for perception within a social system. Perception depends on that, and behavior depends on perception. Even the behavior of organizations, among them those ranked as the most rational, are much influenced by salient events.

Such points as these only underscore the need to think about the information process as a totality in the social system, and research is only one part of this. The trend for research to separate increasingly from other information processes does not appear desirable and is leading to the development of a research subculture, a quasi-religion, an area thoroughly isolated from the rest of society. In other words, we need take a hard look at the problem, not of research, but of knowledge. How does one really come to know anything?

COMMENTS ON THE HEALTH SERVICES RESEARCH PAPERS CONFERENCES

EVELINE M. BURNS

The notable characteristic of these two conferences is that they have brought together professionals actively engaged in the organization, operation or rendering of health services, and social scientists from a variety of disciplines such as economics, sociology and political science among others.

When two such groups converge upon an area of human activity, such as the complex referred to as "the health services," they inevitably bring different perspectives. The social scientist in particular can seemingly adopt one of two attitudes. The first might be termed the scientifically selfish approach. The health services are viewed as yet another area in which the social scientist can test the appropriateness and universality of concepts he has forged or in which he can test the validity and applicability of his hypotheses of relationships. The second attitude is the professionally helpful approach. The social scientist can apply himself to the problems with which the health professions are struggling and put his knowledge and research skills to use in solving them. Such help might take the form of pointing to the applicability of certain techniques or ideas which would be useful in grappling with the professional's problem or of drawing attention to certain social considerations or relationships over and above the purely medical, which must be taken into account if the problem faced by the professional is to be solved.

Both approaches have been in evidence at these conferences. One result has been the production of an enormous array of research

486

topics; of list after list of "needed research." All of them are undoubtedly intrinsically interesting, but the total is out of proportion to our available health research manpower which is in short supply by any criterion. Therefore, the most effective use must be made of such manpower as is available and that means making decisions as to research priorities. Perhaps the last paper at the conference should not have been one on "The Concept of Need for Health Services" but rather one entitled "The Concept of Need for Research."

In this particular stage in history in which the likelihood is that the rest of this century will see a period of revolutionary change in the financing and organization of the health services, the priorities seem clear. For instance, much more knowledge is needed about the effect on availability, quality and continuity of care and on costs both financial and in terms of resource utilization, of different systems of financing health services, of different ways of remunerating professional personnel and of deploying the limited manpower resources, and of different methods of structuring and organizing the health services. Also needed is much more knowledge about motivation—how to motivate professionals to subordinate narrow professional interests to the wider public interest and how to motivate the public to make responsible use of the health services.

Research in these and similar problem areas requires the cooperation of social scientists and members of the health professions. But the imperative need of today is that the focus of their joint efforts be on the problems now facing the health services, not on the health services as a research resource, a rich mine of data, for testing social science theories and generalizations.

APPENDIX

Health Services Research in Scandinavia

Scandinavian Study Group

DUNCAN W. CLARK

RAYMOND HOFSTRA

HERBERT E. KLARMAN

ROBERT M. THORNER

ROBERT J. HAGGERTY, *Chairman*

489

HEALTH SERVICES RESEARCH IN SCANDINAVIA

INTRODUCTION

INTRODUCTION

This study of health services research in Scandinavia grew out of the Health Services Research Study Section's concern with its mandate to stimulate research in the field of health services, as well as its traditional function to evaluate grant requests. The purpose of this study is to identify individuals and agencies in Scandinavia engaged in research in the delivery of health services, to describe techniques being used, especially with defined populations, and to evaluate their potential for the scientific community in the United States. Scandinavia was selected for the study because the four countries of Denmark, Finland, Norway and Sweden all have a long tradition of innovation in health services and all were known to be conducting some research in the field.

The present study was organized as a supplement to the commissioned reviews of Health Services Research which are reported in this issue and the previous one of the *Milbank Memorial Fund Quarterly*. A study team comprising three members of the Study Section and two staff members of the Public Health Service spent four weeks in on-the-spot visits with individuals and agencies in the four Scandinavian countries in June, 1966.

After a briefing by the staff of the European Regional Office of The World Health Organization in Copenhagen, the study group visited persons in Copenhagen, Denmark; Lund, Sweden; Oslo, Norway; Stockholm, Linköping and Uppsala, Sweden; Helsinki, Pornainen and Tampere, Finland.

Several disclaimers must be made. First, the study group is well aware of the difficulties in defining research. As will be clear, a very broad definition has been used that includes demonstration, evaluation and planning, as well as more traditional research activities.

Second, this report is not balanced, in that it deals only with what was seen and heard and omits what was not encountered. The stay was too brief to encompass everything and could not be planned to cover a representative sample of the whole body of research in the health services. Some workers were away at the time of the visit. Moreover, references listed in the readily accessible literature are deliberately few to concentrate more on research currently in progress. The report draws more on what was heard than on what could have been read. Despite the patience and best efforts of the hosts, the visitors' unfamiliarity with the Scandinavian languages precluded the intensive study of many worthwhile documents.

Finally, to grasp research in the health services the functioning of these services must be understood. Space limitations preclude a full description of these services, which are already well presented in other publications.[1-9] However, where necessary to explain a research project, a brief description of the institutional setting is given.

Such a report could be organized in many ways for presentation. The findings here are presented under the three major headings of population studies, studies of facilities and manpower, and tools and techniques for research. A listing of places and people visited and subjects discussed is also available from the chairman.

POPULATION STUDIES

These may be classed by categorical groups: 1. Mothers and Children, 2. The Handicapped, 3. The Aged, 4. Migrants, and 5. Health of Workers.

Mothers and Children

Free health services for maternity and child care are available in health centers in all the Scandinavian countries. The vast majority of the population in all of these countries avail themselves of these services; and the usual indices of success, such as maternal and infant mortality, are among the lowest in the world. Logically, most of the studies are directed at special groups, such as handicapped children, or unsolved problems, such as perinatal mortality, rather than at the entire maternal or child population. Below are a few selected examples of such research.

Early pregnancy losses are a difficult problem to study, because criminal abortions are detected only when complications arise; and many early spontaneous abortions occur before prenatal care begins. Folke-Pettersson, in Uppsala, Sweden, is conducting a study[10] to determine the frequency and types of early pregnancy loss in one county in Sweden where, in spite of a liberal law regarding therapeutic abortion, ten to 20 per cent of pregnancies are allegedly terminated by criminal abortion. Among several methods being used to identify women who have criminal abortions is one unique case-finding method. In Sweden women may send a urine specimen directly to a laboratory for a pregnancy test without a physician's request. Folke-Pettersson was able to trace 1236 of 1286 women who sent in such urine specimens in Uppsala in one year, and in addition carried out retrospective study by interviews of women in family planning clinics and in hospitals after delivery. His study, not yet completed, appears to show a very low frequency of criminal abortions.

Unmarried mothers are also the subject of a sociomedical study in the Department of Social Medicine at Uppsala, where all such women delivered at the University Hospital (some 12 per cent of maternity patients) are to be interviewed and followed to determine factors associated with outcome.

Mothers with young children work outside the home in large numbers in each of the Scandinavian countries. The Danish National Institute of Social Research in Copenhagen, has engaged in an extended household interview survey[11] to determine the frequency of working mothers, describe and analyze factors of importance to the participation of married women in the labor market and the consequences of a married woman's employment to herself and her family.

The bridge between obstetrics and pediatrics is clearest in studies of the perinatal period. In Finland a nationwide study of perinatal mortality from midwife records has been completed.[12] Significant correlations were documented between several maternal factors and perinatal mortality that have application to the selection of high-risk pregnant women for appropriate obstetrical care. Factors that facilitated this study were: 1. 97 per cent of all pregnant women in Finland are seen in maternal health centers by midwives, physicians or both, allowing easy access to nearly all pregnant women for such studies; and 2. control patients (in this instance the next live birth surviving 14 days) were also easily identified from midwife records, and comparable data obtained.

Infant mortality has long been accepted as a valuable index of the quality of maternal and child care. Sweden, with an infant mortality of 15 per 1000 or lower, has one of the world's lowest rates. Many factors associated with infant mortality, such as civil status of the mother, parental age and education, are well known to affect this rate. Berfenstam is conducting a study to discover other more subtle factors that may be associated with infant mortality when such low rates are achieved.[13] He is using the death certificates to identify all infant deaths in Sweden for one year (about 1500) and obtaining a double control population, matched for parental age and certain social factors, of the nearest birth before and after the propositus in each parish.

Ascertaining the sociomedical characteristics of children with chronic disease is of obvious importance if gaps in current health services are to be identified. The group in Uppsala have completed or are conducting several studies of children and adults with osteogenesis imperfecta,[14] epilepsy,[15] asthma[16] and ulcerative colitis. These careful studies have been performed by physicians from clinical departments of the medical school, working with Berfenstam in the Department of Social Medicine. Such close collaboration between departments is a particularly fruitful model for sociomedical research. In addition, each study has benefited enormously from the ability to identify all or nearly all of the population of patients with each disease from official records, and especially from the availability of the national population register. These registers allow the investigator to obtain follow-up data on all patients by identifying his current address and by yielding a really adequate control population. The importance of these tools to health services research is discussed further in a later section of this report.

In Lund, Sweden, Lindquist and Köhler[17] have selected the entire population of four-year-old children in this community (about 600 such children) to determine the prevalence of handicapping conditions. They are identifying these children from the local population register and will use a "fine screen" method to identify all handicapped children. By defining even "minor" handicaps they hope, by long-term follow-up, to determine the significance of these minor findings. In addition, they plan to compare results from this method with another

494

approach to identifying children with handicaps, namely the follow-up of children from high risk pregnancies. In Britain, where the high risk pregnancy register has been used, 20 per cent of children are said to be so identified, and in Czechoslovakia, using a method similar to that in Lund, 15 per cent are found to be handicapped.

In Finland, another approach to registering handicapped children is going on with a study of all children (about 7000) born in 1956, upon their entry to school in 1964.[18] Utilizing a medical record that follows the child from infant welfare centers (where nearly all children are cared for) to the school, the study is seeking to determine the prevalence of chronic conditions recorded, the ability of this health record to identify them and the adequacy of the follow-up care of such children. The organization of the research unit as an arm of the National Board of Health will help insure that findings are translated into needed changes in the record system and follow-up care arrangements.

Another valuable resource for identifying handicapped children in Finland is the registry of such children with the Ministry of Social Affairs, if their parents wish to qualify for a cash allowance to pay for the added cost of their care at home.

Studies of the effectiveness of new programs for the mentally retarded and the physically handicapped are being initiated by the departments of social medicine and sociology in Uppsala, Sweden, with support from the Ministry of Labor and voluntary societies.

In the Fall of 1966, the European Office of the World Health Organization will hold a working group meeting on the "Early Detection and Treatment of Handicapping Defects in Children." One of the special points for discussion will be the need and advisability of "high-risk" registers of handicapped children. This issue is of great current interest in all countries, for on the one hand is a need to identify such children and insure that care is being given, but on the other hand one cannot assume that every register is beneficial. Identifying children at birth who are at "high-risk" gives rise to the serious concern that if they turn out to be normal, their parents will never be able to treat them as such. In the zeal to establish registers, adverse effects should also be investigated.

Problems in children are often difficult to categorize as medical or social or mixtures of both. The Danish National Institute of Social Research, in a series of studies aimed at this problem, first undertook, in 1963, studies of the number of children in the country who should be under supervision of the local communal child welfare committees.[19] As a result of the finding that a considerable number of children in need "slipped out," a law was passed which requires that these child welfare committees offer family guidance to any who need it rather than limiting the service to specific categories (such as foster children) as previously.

The Institute then undertook a new study of how best to define families in need of such guidance. They assumed a family in need was any family with a problem child and that the school is one place where society's demands are first placed on children and where problems would be likely to appear and to be identified.

A random sample of 350 classrooms was selected. The teachers in these classes were asked to identify children between the ages of nine and 12 and who had "problems" of various types (out of a total of about 7000). Interviews with these children and a random sample of control children from the same classes and interviews with 600 control and 600 problem families have been completed. Analysis and write up are now in progress. One major finding is the high frequency of problem families. From this finding the hope is that the stigma of such problems will be mitigated, earlier identification achieved, and the types of service needed will be developed.

Studies in childhood accidents have long interested Berfenstam in Uppsala, Sweden. He has published several studies and is currently engaged in a morbidity survey of all accidents in Stockholm county.[20] The unique aspect that makes this type of morbidity study feasible is that 95 per cent of accident victims requiring a physician's care go to hospitals. Thus, hospital records can be used for reliable morbidity studies.

Currently the Uppsala group are also cooperating in a World Health Organization-sponsored six-country study of fatal home accidents. In Sweden, all of the death certificates for such accidents (some 2500 per year) have been identified and data from police, physician and hospital records then obtained. All six countries are using the same protocol, and a conference will be held at a later date to share results. Remarkable cooperation has been achieved in obtaining data from all of these official sources.

A most interesting natural experiment was recognized by the Norwegian Tuberculosis Register group and led them to an important analysis of age-specific trends in tuberculosis in three Scandinavian countries, each of which administers BCG to most of the population but at quite different ages, and the United States with no mass BCG vaccination. A more favorable incidence trend was noted in each Scandinavian country in the age group following the one that receives initial vaccination,[21] a finding that adds weight to the evidence for the effectiveness of BCG vaccination.

The Handicapped

In Norway, a new law providing rehabilitation services for the disabled was passed in 1960, and expanded in 1964. A major effort at registration of all handicapped persons followed and nationwide estimates of the prevalence of handicapping conditions may shortly be forthcoming.

The inclusion of rehabilitative training in this new law was seen as a propitious time for studying decision-making by officials responsible for implementing a new public care program.[22] All of the county public health officers were interviewed, as were others concerned with the review of applications. The large numbers involved contributed to the task of review of applications. Decision-making could be categorized into one of the following classes: moralistic ("morally, an undeserving person"); judicial (i.e., rejectable on legalistic grounds); need oriented ("the law does not provide enough for the needy person"); temporally oriented (influenced by the size of the current backlog of cases); or determined by chance ("you made the last decision, so I will make this one"). From the results, the Ministry of Social Affairs is better informed on the quite different system and size of case load that may prevail, depending on whether health insurance personnel or physicians are given final authority to decide eligibility for benefits. The former are more prone to legalistic decisions and the latter to moralistic or need-oriented decisions. The same findings are also being used in training programs to help individuals and boards to recognize their dominant personal or group tendency.

In Sweden, a study of the prevalence of long-term disability is in progress with the aim of estimating the potential need and focus for rehabilitative services.[23] The source of data is the national sickness benefit insurance program which covers the population aged 16 to 67, including all working persons with annual earnings of more than $500. Housewives are automatically insured. Almost all of the adult population, save the aged, are included. The disability rate for all claims was 43 per 1000 and the average duration per insured person

497

was 16 days per year. A follow-up study of the patients with a disability of 90 days or more was completed to determine where rehabilitative measures could be more effectively begun.

The visitors had very limited contact with those responsible for the organization and for research in the health services for the mentally ill. Those interested in a review of the subject may consult Furman.[24]

The Aged

Survey research in social gerontology was represented in each of the countries visited. The study best known in the United States is a coordinated cross-national study on old age involving Friis of Denmark, Townsend of England, and Shanas of the United States. The aim of the survey is to provide a basis for comparing the living conditions and attitudes of people aged 65 and over in three countries that differ in their economic, social and cultural patterns. The investigators hope to be able to delineate the influence of external factors on the lives of the elderly and so distinguish the factors related to aging as such. National probability samples of the non-institutionalized aged have been drawn. Preliminary findings reveal no marked difference in the experience of the three countries in the use of health services by the aged.[25] The elderly in the United States were less likely than those in Denmark or Britain to be housebound and restricted in their mobility or to report incapacity in functioning. Whether the differences are "real" could not be ascertained. The final report is in the process of completion.

This study is of interest as well because of the large amount of planning effort exerted to anticipate the usual problems of cross-national studies. The same questionnaire and method are now being applied to a study of the aged in Poland and Israel.

A survey of the aged in Uppsala, Sweden, with emphasis on nutritional status, confirmed the usual findings of an excess of dietary carbohydrate and a deficiency of protein in elderly males residing alone.[26] These and related findings were transmitted to the County Council of Uppsala for their use in review of the need for constructing homes for the chronically ill aged. Sweden, like other countries, is faced with an unresolved problem of where public responsibility is best placed for the care of the aged, especially those who have personal medical and social problems. In the limited period of visitation no research or demonstration efforts were encountered that directly attacked the problem of the most suitable personal arrangements for the aged, or the most suitable division of labor between central and local government or between health and social welfare authorities when ill health and social problems co-exist. At the higher levels of government policy, the trend seems to be to bring health and welfare into closer alignment, generally under a Ministry of Social Affairs.

Migrants

In Norway, an epidemiologic study of Norwegian migrants to the United States and the United Kingdom is in an early phase.[27] Malignant disease is not the only interest, for attention is also devoted to the occurrence of cadiovascular and chronic pulmonary diseases.

In Sweden, gypsies are seen as a social problem group and have been a source of public concern completely out of proportion to their numbers. In a two-year search a staff member of the department of preventive and social medicine at Uppsala was able to establish contact with 95 per cent of the 1000 gypsies in Sweden. As a result, all of the younger gypsy children are now at school and work has been found for many of the adults. This project was financed by the Swedish Department of Labor, but at the instigation of the university. This population was also the object of biological research.[28]

No research was uncovered on the health needs or circumstances of groups migrating into certain Scandinavian countries as a result of recent labor shortages there.

Health of Workers

Of all the occupational dermatoses, contact dermatitis of the hand is by far the most common, accounting for about 85 per cent of all cases. Agrup of the department of dermatology of the University of Lund recently completed a questionnaire survey of the population of Malmo (population 130,000), which revealed that two per cent of the population acknowledged having or having had such lesions.[29] This group was invited to come for examination and 65 per cent (1600) appeared. Of these, half had allergic type lesions.

A community study of the capacity of older people for work is of interest even though published in 1958.[30] This involved an effort to study all people aged 65 and 70 on the Danish island of Bornholm, with particular attention to the condition of the limbs. In one-fourth of those aged 65, diseases of the extremities was the chief reason for reduction in working capacity.

A major resource for the study of occupational health problems may be found in Helsinki at the Institute of Occupational Health. It is believed to be one of the largest such units in the world and it incorporates under one roof and one administration virtually the whole range of occupational health. The annual reports of its director, Leo Noro, list all publications, scientific and popular. Some of the research is supported by the National Institutes of Health.[31]

FACILITIES AND MANPOWER

The Scandinavian countries rank high among the nations of the world in the ratio of general hospital beds to population—5.9 beds per 1000 population in Denmark in 1961, 4.2 in Finland, 5.7 in Norway, and 9.4 in Sweden. Considerable construction is under way in Sweden and Finland, particularly at central and regional hospitals.[32] (In Sweden a regional hospital is large, has the most medical specialties, and serves a designated region; in Finland the same is called a central hospital. The next, or intermediate, hospital, with fewer beds and specialties, is called central in Sweden and regional in Finland.)

Hospital Planning by Architects

The visitors witnessed considerable activity in hospital planning, ranging from the concern of architects with layout and function to the organization of a regional network of hospital care. Although some of the planning activity is conducted at the level of the central government, most of it is performed by local government—commune, county, region or federation of municipalities.

Architects reviewed the plans at the university hospitals in Copenhagen, Lund, Linköping (designated to be a university hospital) and Uppsala; and the study group visited the university hospital at Helsinki, and the central hospital at Tampere, Finland. In each instance, zoning, site, size and range of hospital functions, especially of the outpatient department, posed particular problems that had to be resolved in the best possible way, which is not always ideal. Recommended are a recent review article on the current status of hospital architecture in Scandinavia,[33] and Pesonen's illustrated book.[34]

In every instance one was impressed by the thoughtfulness of the planning, the length of time devoted to it, and by the high quality of materials and equipment used. The spaciousness, lighting and decor

500

of waiting rooms are noteworthy, as is the use of paintings and frescoes inside the hospital and of sculpture and fountains outside.

An American visitor is struck by the following:

1. In some hospitals the tendency persists for each clinic (department) to be self-contained, even to the point of having its own intensive care unit.

2. Intensive care units are being introduced at a rapid rate. These may be quite small (eight to 12 beds), but are usually slated to expand when new construction is undertaken.

3. Admitting or emergency ward bed units are being established for keeping patients overnight or even over the weekend, when staffing is low.

4. Ward (nursing) units are built in a group for combined staffing evenings or at night.

5. Large differences persist among the four countries in the space allotted to the outpatient departments of hospitals.

Hospital Planning by Central Government

In each of the Scandinavian countries the central government plays a role in planning for hospital care. The bases of authority vary, however, as do the specific activities.

In Denmark, local authorities are obligated under an ordinance of 1806 to provide an adequate number of hospital beds. This sets a minimum, but the localities are said to compete with one another to do more. The National Board of Health may advise, but has no authority to decide on hospital construction. However, an official permit is required in Denmark to undertake any type of construction, including hospitals.

Norway has no statute concerning governmental responsibility for building and operating hospitals. By tradition the provinces have built the general hospitals. The central government reviews hospital building plans and approves or disapproves them in accordance with their technical appropriateness for serving the particular population.

In Sweden, a central hospital planning board (CSB) passes on and must approve all plans for hospital construction for architectural adequacy and for conformity to a set of bed-to-population ratios by specialty that was promulgated some years ago. The Board's decision may be appealed to the King's Council (government).

In Finland, the communes are autonomous in building and operating hospitals. However, the central government subsidizes hospital construction to the extent of 25 to 67 per cent of expenditures (two-thirds for central hospitals, one-half for intermediate hospitals, and one-fourth to one-half for local hospitals), and it may refuse to assist a particular project.

The central government may conduct research and disseminate the results, as through CSB. Sjura, the Swedish Commission for the rational operation of hospitals, receives money from the county councils and the state and sponsors long-range research in the application of technical avances in hospital operation.[35]

State commissions established to investigate a specific problem and to recommend solutions may sponsor research. Such commissions have dealt with many problems in the health field. In Finland, 20 *ad hoc* commissions have been appointed since 1945.

Hospital Planning by Local Government

Construction, operation, and residual financial responsibility for hospitals rest at the local level. In Sweden, the mental hospitals will be transferred from the state to the 25 counties in 1967. In Finland, general hospitals were transferred to the local government only a decade ago.

The same organizations usually assume the task of planning and, with it, the associated task of research. In some instances the amount of money allocated to these purposes is sizable—20 million Swedish Crowns (four million dollars at the official rate of exchange) in Stockholm County over a period of eight to ten years. In Finland, the League of Finnish Hospital Federations devotes one-third of its budget to research.

In Sweden, the several regional hospital councils seem to specialize in certain aspects of research for planning while developing the plans for, and operating, their own hospitals. In Stockholm County, the emphasis to date has been on staffing the ward unit; in Linköping, on facilities for outpatients; and in Uppsala, on the operating suite. Some details on research in the first two locales follow.

In 1963, the KOD Committee of Stockholm County began to investigate the organization and staffing of the ward (nursing) unit. Different patterns of staffing were attempted and evaluated. Today four ward units at Danderyds Hospital are staffed according to the KOD recommendations; in 1967, 16 units will be so staffed. Savings

502

in nurses are achieved by means of: 1. "floating" personnel at the disposal of the chief nurse for assignment in accordance with variations in patient load; 2. wards combined for staffing evenings and nights; 3. centralization of certain functions, such as cleaning of rooms and washing dishes; and 4. relieving nurses of clerical duties and transportation outside the ward.[36]

At Linköping, four county councils cooperate in the regional hospital board. The Linköping County Council pays the bill for the regional hospital and is reimbursed by the others in accordance with its use by their residents.

The visitors were presented with the fifth edition of the Linköping plan for outpatient care.[37] Estimates of requirements for examining rooms and offices in 1970 and 1975 are made as follows. The base line is the hospital's own utilization data in 1963. The assumption is made that the volume of visits will continue to rise at an annual rate of seven per cent, as estimated by a Swedish State Commission. Physicians in each specialty were asked the length of time they required per patient visit, on the average. The number of physicians who will be working in each clinic—and will require space—was determined on the assumption of a six-hour work day.

In Helsinki, the Municipal Hospital Board maintains a planning and research unit, which has completed several studies applied in the city's ten-year plan for hospital construction, as follows.[38]

An inventory of patients in all institutions in Helsinki, carried out in two days in 1963, revealed some faulty distribution of patients by type of facility, as determined by the physician responsible for the patient. This was particularly true of mental patients.

A study of 6000 persons on 30 waiting lists showed that, for the most part, waiting intervals were not excessive. The major deficiency was failure to afford the applicant adequate advance notice of his admission date.

Another study of waiting pertained to wasted time within the hospital. The worst bottlenecks proved to be the x-ray department, the operating room and the rehabilitation department.

Budgetary controls are being attempted through the development of criteria by type of diagnosis for optimum duration of stay and volumes of laboratory tests and x-ray tests.

Research in Hospital Utilization

Of special interest to the visitors was the research associated with planning for hospital care. Certain basic studies of utilization are being conducted that may influence planning in the future. Several examples follow.

One study just completed is that of general hospital utilization in Finland in 1960.[39] The basic material was collected by the National Board of Health by having every general hospital submit a card for all patients discharged that year.

Another study, more analytical, was far enough along to permit the investigators to prepare a special report for the visitors.[40] This study is an epidemiological investigation into the utilization of general hospital care in the region of Kuopio in central Finland, based on the same 1960 data as the preceding one. The information on admissions, duration of stay, diagnosis, age, sex and residence was supplemented by a determination of the "urgency" of admission.

Several findings in this report are noteworthy.

1. In Finland, where communities use beds jointly, ownership of hospital beds by a community does not affect the volume of care used by its residents.

2. Communities with low use of general hospital care do not offset this with high use of nursing homes.

3. Of all patients, 27.5 per cent require admission urgently. So classified are all maternity cases and terminal cases, among others. Beds should be reserved for urgent cases.

4. The concept of a "saturation limit" is introduced—a level at which hospital use by a diagnostic or age group does not rise when the supply of beds increases. For certain population groups the investigators report the existence of such saturation limits. This finding appears to reopen the perennial question of the effect of the supply of beds on hospital use.

Two other hospital regions in Finland have performed such studies and the other 18 regions intend to do so.

A study of general hospital use is under way in the Uppsala region in Sweden. The following information has been collected: age, sex, residence, type of admission (home, other hospitals, other departments of the same hospital), type of discharge (home, other hospital, dead, autopsy), duration of stay, main diagnosis, operations and birth weight. The data are for 180,000 discharges in one year, 1964. The findings for this study are not yet available. Parallel studies are being conducted in other countries, including Osler Peterson's study in the United States.

A dissertation at the University of Copenhagen deals with the problem of gynecological bed requirements in Copenhagen.[41] The study was occasioned by the sharp increase in waiting lists for hospital admission between 1956 and 1958. It was facilitated by the presence of the Municipal Central Bureau for the Allocation of Hospital Services, which refers all patients to municipal hospitals. The principal tool of analysis is the distinction between emergency cases and waiting list cases. Much emphasis is placed on the role of the outpatient department in the referral process.

In Finland, a study of the utilization of tuberculosis hospitals has been completed.[42] It is based on samples of hospital discharge records for the years 1957–64. The variables analyzed are sex, age, occupation, severity of illness, first or subsequent admission, work capacity at discharge, chronicity, duration of hospital stay and interruption of treatment against medical advice.

A study of the utilization of psychiatric facilities in Finland will be completed shortly.

Research in the Utilization of Various Health Services

Hospital use is also covered in broader studies of health services utilization. Three are described below.

At Uppsala, a study of health services utilization is being conducted through a houschold survey and through the linking of existing administrative records.

The household survey of 16,000 persons drew a systematic stratified sample of the population of the entire country. The questions pertain to morbidity and utilization, but not to attitudes. Public health nurses served as interviewers.

The household survey has yielded data not obtainable from official records. Included are the utilization of dental services, non-prescribed drugs (one-fourth of all drug expenditures), visits to physicians free of charge, out-of-pocket expenditures by consumers and private insurance enrollment.

Reports on dental care and on drugs were prepared at the behest of State commissions and have been published in Swedish in the commissions' reports.[43] Certain recommendations on the provision of dental prostheses are said to have been implemented.

This phase of the study is parallel to two studies conducted simultaneously in the United States and the United Kingdom. Frequent contact is maintained among the three sets of investigators, but complete comparability is not likely to be achieved, owing to technical differences in the definition of terms, differences in social and political institutions among the countries, and the possibilities of substituting among health services.

The population sample for the record linkage study consists of all persons 16 years old and over who were born on February 15. The objective is to ascertain morbidity and utilization of services in 1963.

A major source of information for the demographic and socio-economic characteristics of the sample are the local registers of the National Health Insurance Plan.

Another important source of information is the special register maintained by the Central Bureau of Statistics of persons born on the 15th of every month. This register, which is up-dated annually, includes occupation, taxable income, income of spouse, number of children under 16, number of cars, education, etc.

Data on disability and hospital admissions were obtained from the National Health Insurance Plan. The disability data are practically complete in the working-age groups, but incomplete for teen-agers and aged persons.

For physician visits the receipts submitted by patients seeking reimbursement, which are kept in administrative files at the local offices, were sorted and sent to Uppsala. The volume of visits may be underestimated by 20 per cent, for these reasons: well-baby and maternity care and tuberculosis care are free of charge; the large university clinics do not charge outpatients; visits to industrial or occupational health services are not represented; and some persons may fail to claim reimbursement.

For prescription drugs the national association of pharmacists was persuaded to enlist the cooperation of the 500 pharmacies in Sweden to send their receipts for filled prescriptions to Uppsala. Each receipt contains the patient's name and birthdate, which were entered in the prescription by the physician. Again, a loss of about 20 per cent is estimated.

Results are not yet available from this phase of the study. Clearly this attempt at record linkage is important, because it is made under very able and energetic university auspices, enjoying the cooperation of all agencies.

In Finland, the National Pension Institute conducted a nationwide survey of 6400 representative households in the Spring of 1964, with data on utilization sought from January 1. Public health nurses served as interviewers and obtained a response rate of more than 90 per cent. The objective is to obtain a base-line on morbidity and the utilization of services prior to the application of the Sickness Insurance Act in 1964.[44] Factorial analysis is employed to reduce the number of independent variables, and multiple regression (correlation) analysis to measure the relative importance of each representative variable.

The Research and Training Center in Public Health of the National Board of Health of Finland has also undertaken a survey of morbidity and utilization of health services before and after the advent of sickness insurance. The method is different, however, in that the respondents are the communal health officers in 39 districts in the south and 18 districts in the north, each with an aggregate population of 142,000. Private practitioners are excluded from this study. To reduce the burden on the responding physicians, each reports only for one age class in five.[45]

Research in Manpower

Several studies of general practice came to our attention.

All Scandinavian countries, as does the United States, give the impression of having a shortage of general practitioners and other first contact physicians. All these countries are asking questions such as: What work does the general practitioner do? What is his proper role? Should he practice in groups? Should he be based in hospital or community? Who will provide first contact medical care if he does not? How many of such personnel are needed? Clearly, no one has answered these questions, but several studies in Scandinavia are addressed to these points.

Because of a marked difference in the role of the general practitioner in the four Scandinavian countries, studies of the work the general practitioner is now doing under these several systems is of great interest. In Denmark, the general practitioner is present in more adequate numbers and better distribution than in any other Scandinavian country. In small communities in the other Scandinavian countries an appointed community or district medical officer is responsible for public health, maternal and infant welfare clinics and to do fee-for-service general practice as well. In cities, hospitals provide first contact care.

Two studies of general practice in Denmark have been published. The first was sponsored by the Danish Medical Association to determine the number and type of patients seen throughout the country.[46] Over half of all general practices in Denmark were studied for a period of one year, 1958–59, with a record kept for each patient seen. In 1962, Dahlerup documented in more detail the work in his own general practice.[47]

In Norway, a similar detailed study of one physician's own general practice has been carried out.[48] One additional aspect of this study was the documentation of the utilization of health services by all 5000 people in his county, whether or not they were his patients. This is another example of a study made possible by the general population register.

The Finnish Medical Society, the Institute of Sociology of Helsinki University and the National Board of Health jointly sponsored a questionnaire study of all 3002 physicians in the country in 1962. Eventually 93 per cent replied, resulting in a rather complete picture of medical practice in Finland.[49] This study, like those in most other parts of the world, documents the decline in the number of doctors doing general practice and the increase in specialists. In 1962, 39 per cent of the graduates of the class of 1917 were specialists, and, of the class of 1948, 64 per cent were specialists. Perhaps most important for the future was the finding of a strong desire among general practitioners to become specialists, indicating some dissatisfaction with their current role.

A second study in Finland is concerned with the work of the communal medical officer.[50] Seven medical officers in six rural communes recorded information on daily activities for a two-month period in February and March, 1962, for a total of 6602 patient contacts plus 637 maternal or child health center contacts. At the same time, a one in ten random sample of the population in these communes was interviewed to determine their morbidity and utilization of medical care. Among the interesting findings was the fact that the percentage distribution of the doctor's time remained very much the same whether he had access to laboratory facilities, consultants or assistants, all of these resources being currently encouraged in Finland to spare the doctor's time.

In Sweden, where hospital-based specialists have been most fully developed of all the Scandinavian countries, only one study of general practice was known and it was not available. However, two Swedish medical schools—Lund and Uppsala—plan to establish community field research units with a defined population. Both seek to develop a health center staffed with general practitioners, nurses and other personnel, plus a research staff, to study how best to provide primary medical care to a known population, to provide a base for epidemiologic studies and to provide a training site for medical students and for postgraduate medical education.

These projects should prove extremely important to research on the role of the general practitioner. Factors that appear favorable to their development in both of these schools include multiple department participation with considerable unanimity of goals, well-defined geo-political units near each school with a mixture of suburban and rural population, and a current lack of medical care personnel in the area.

Studies of the supply of physicians were made in connection with the work of State commissions in Sweden and in Finland.

The Swedish Commission on the Future Need for Doctors projected requirements for physicians ten and 20 years ahead. Strong emphasis was placed on expanding facilities and staff for the care of the chronically ill.

The Commission's report introduced the concept of the medical care consumption unit. In effect, this is an index number for each age class and for each type of health service, related to average use or expenditures by the entire population.[51]

In Finland, the Review Committee on the Need for Physicians and Training Facilities reported in 1965.[52] Estimates of need in 1970, 1980 and 1990 were systematically prepared for each sector that uses physicians, as follows: general hospitals (on the basis of a physician-to-bed ratio), mental hospitals and facilities for mental defectives, tuberculosis hospitals, industry and business, "open" care (medical care outside the hospital), laboratories, teaching and research, government and insurance offices and the military. Needs for training facilities were estimated accordingly.

The Committee projected a need of 10,800 physicians in 1990. A strong dissenting statement calculated a need for 13,800. The major difference was in the estimate for general hospital staffing—5600 versus 8200. The difference is explained by the following factors: 1. a difference of 1/1000 each in the requirement for general hospital and chronic care beds; 2. application in the dissent of the same staffing ratio to chronic and general care beds.

In Norway, a study based on physician-to-population ratios recommended opening at least one more medical school in addition to expanding the two existing ones.[53] Enlarged medical school capacity is required to bring home a majority of the Norwegian medical students studying abroad, as well as to raise the physician-to-population ratio from 12 per 10,000 in 1962, to 18 per 10,000 by 1980.

TOOLS AND TECHNIQUES

Special tools and techniques in research that were observed included: methods and programs of presymptomatic disease detection, use of population and disease registers and record linkage systems, and economic analyses and operations research.

Research, Development and Demonstration Projects in Disease Detection

Interest in health maintenance and the problems associated with it varied considerably in the countries visited. In almost all of the countries preventive health services for pregnant women, infants and children are well established and covered by systems of free or insured clinic care.

The need for preventive services for adults, the first stage of which is presymptomatic disease detection, has been recognized and is being approached by a variety of projects that may be classified as follows: 1. reliance on the general practitioners or other primary contact physicians, 2. individual disease detection programs, and 3. multiple screening.

In Denmark, where the services of general practitioners are readily available to the public, the approach to adult health protection has been to rely on the general practitioner to provide this service. No formal programs of periodic health examinations or multiple or single disease detection programs were found, with the exception of the traditional x-ray screening for tuberculosis and some experimental work in cancer detection.

Experimentation with a more formal program of health maintenance based on the commune medical officer or general practitioner has been undertaken in Finland.[54] The Research and Training Center of the National Board of Health, in collaboration with the Institute of Hygiene of the University of Helsinki, has, since February, 1966, sponsored a project in Pornainen, a town of 2500 persons, to demonstrate how multiple screening can be conducted in a rural area.

All adults in the community will be asked to participate in a pre-symptomatic examination that includes a 12-hour urine and feces specimen, completion and review of the Cornell Medical Index, several chemical tests on blood and urine, spirometry, a miniature chest film, vaginal cytology, an electrocardiogram if indicated and a half-hour physical examination by the general practitioner (Communal Medical Officer). Methods for the detection of cancer of the stomach, a special problem in Finland, are also being evaluated in a long-term follow-up study. Participation has been about 90 per cent of those invited.

The second approach to health protection, i.e., individual disease detection programs, has been more widely used throughout the countries visited, and has been the object of more formal research. All countries have operated x-ray case-finding programs for the detection of tuberculosis. In Norway, the mass x-ray program is being subjected to epidemiological study and cost-benefit analysis to achieve maximum results.[55] In Denmark, the Danish Tuberculosis Index was created as a research office in conjunction with the initiation of a mass detection campaign in 1950–52. The Index has as its main purpose long-range, nationwide studies of the epidemiology of tuberculosis, and was given technical responsibility for the mass detection program to insure that the records, procedures, tuberculin testing, etc., would be accurate and uniform.[56] The Index also studied the characteristics of participants and non-participants in the campaign.[57]

A more controversial field of specific disease detection is the detection of cancer. Mass cancer detection programs are not extensive in Norway, Sweden and Denmark. Finland has a detection program operated by the cancer society. Much of the research revolves around the question of whether or not such activities should be undertaken and the methods to be used if undertaken. Examples of these studies follow.

In Denmark, a study was undertaken to evaluate the cytopipette, a method by which women can take samples of their vaginal secreta for cancer detection, mailing the self-gathered specimen to a central laboratory.[58] In Norway, an experimental program for the detection of gynecological cancer was introduced for evaluation in 1959. A sample of 45,000 women aged 35 to 60 years was drawn from the population register. These women are being given repeated examinations. The first examination yielded five *in situ* and 1.2 invasive cases per 1000 examined. The response rates were 80 per cent in married women and 50 per cent in the unmarried. On the repeat examination, 75 per cent of the women responded, but the yield dropped to one-third of the first screening. To date, the incidence of invasive cancer in the population has not dropped. Analysis of data from the register indicates that most of the invasive cases in the sample population are among nonrespondents to the screening. A comparison of the characteristics of the responders and nonresponders indicates that the nonresponders are a lower socioeconomic group. This finding raises questions about the efficacy of mass screening programs unless all of the population can be surveyed.[59]

In Sweden, a pilot study of cancer detection was undertaken in Eskilstuna in 1954, to demonstrate and evaluate methods for the detection of gynecological cancer.[60]

An experimental breast and gynecological cancer detection program in Malmö, Sweden, is now being evaluated. A sample of women born between 1899 and 1950 was invited for examination. With an initial invitation and a follow-up invitation, a response rate of 89 per cent was achieved. Cancer of the cervix was found in one per cent. Seven per cent of the participants were classified as suspects for cancer of the breast. Three per cent had persistent tumors, but only one of 3700 examined was found to be malignant upon biopsy.[61]

In Finland, a sizable program of examination of cervical cytology is being evaluated by comparison of rates with a control area in Turku.[62]

A considerable amount of investigation on the techniques for detecting specific diseases in large screening programs is being carried out at the medical school at Lund, Sweden. One of the most promising projects is the work of Scherstén and Fritz on the detection of urinary tract infections. These investigators observed that a low level or lack of detectable glucose in urine specimens obtained in the fasting state is indicative of urinary tract infection when a highly sensitive detection technique is used. In early results, the method appears to have a sensitivity of 95 per cent and a specificity of 98 per cent, with a cutoff level of two milligrams of glucose per 100 milliliters of urine. The method may provide a biochemical method for the detection of bacteria, and may thus eliminate problems of contamination and storage inherent in the current bacterial culture methods.[63]

Three projects in diabetes detection were also being carried out in Lund. Engelson described a program of screening for juvenile diabetes in which 8000 children were tested. One diabetic per 700 children was found. Nordén described a program of diabetes detection in conjunction with a tuberculosis screening campaign. Eighty-two per cent participation was achieved with a yield of 0.37 per cent new cases. Scherstén described a study of glucose tolerance in a normal population, which indicated a need for different standards for the diagnosis of diabetes by age.

The Lund group felt that screening should be confined to specific disease entities that are highly prevalent and for which effective screening and treatment methods are available.

The third approach to health maintenance, multiple screening, also received a great deal of attention in Sweden. One of the earliest projects in multiple screening was the pilot study in Värmland, begun in the autumn of 1962 under the sponsorship of the National Board of Health.[64] The purpose of that study was to test the feasibility of the concept of "Chemical Health Screening" developed by Gunnar and Ingmar Jungner.[65] In this procedure, heavy reliance is placed on a wide battery of blood and urine chemical tests to identify disease suspects for later diagnostic work-up. Little use is made of questionnaires or the physical examination during the screening stage. This type of screening was believed practical because of the advances in automation of biochemical tests, and the aim of the study was to demonstrate and evaluate this technique.

Final evaluation of the results of this screening program is currently being prepared for the Board of Health and a decision regarding a major program of this type is expected on the basis of the report. Preliminary data have been published.[64]

One important outcome of this project has been the development by the Jungner brothers of a sophisticated automated laboratory system, with computer read-out of results and transmission of data to remote stations. The basic analytical unit in this system is the Auto Chemist. This machine has 24 analytic channels in which such factors as temperature and duration of treatment are fixed. Samples are fed into the machine at a rate of 130 to 150 samples per hour from each of two transport belts. Identification of samples is made directly to the computer, and results of tests are read directly from photometers. At present a PDP8 computer is used for processing the results at the installation in the Roslagstulls Hospital in Stockholm.[66]

A different approach to multiple screening is being studied by Hall at the Karolinska Institute. He is seeking to establish a hospital-based program of preventive medicine with continuing health screening. One of the interesting features of this program is the computer handling of data, particularly the medical questionnaire. The questionnaire is viewed as the major tool of the examination. At present 750 questions are used and the results machine analyzed. Further refinement and reduction of the number of questions is now in progress. Also included in this examination are a chest x-ray, electrocardiogram, blood pressure measurement, height, weight and analyses of blood and urine. Present plans are to evaluate this technique in a controlled five-year study in which the use of medical care by the examined and control groups will be compared.

Still another approach to multiple screening is the Auto Clinics[67] recently inaugurated in Finland under the sponsorship of the National Pension Institute. Health examination clinics have been outfitted in trucks and are used in rural areas. Procedures include a questionnaire, chest x-ray, blood and urine analyses, electrocardiogram and a glucose determination one hour after ingestion of glucose. Biochemical tests are done by the State Serum Institute. Response to the examination is generally 80–90 per cent of the invited population.

Despite the different approaches to disease detection, two findings stand out in these Scandinavian studies. First, is a uniformly high proportion of patient participation (usually near 90 per cent), and second, notwithstanding, investigators display a considerable interest in, and are able to develop information about, the small but important segment of the population who are nonresponders.

Population and Disease Registers

One of the most important research tools available to investigators in the Scandinavian countries is the population register. All of these countries require local registration of each individual residing in a commune. In almost all cases, sex, address and date of birth are available to the investigator as a minimum. In all countries an identification number is, or will shortly be, added. In some communes, data are available only as rosters or card files, while in others they are on punch cards.

All countries are now working toward a system of computer-based national population registers. In Denmark, a network of regional centers has been established which maintains a complete index of the local population including removals by migration and death; and a national computer-based register will begin operation in April, 1967.[68]

Sweden has county registers with a national one in the Central Statistical Bureau in Stockholm. In Norway, the records in Oslo have been put on computers, but most other communes maintain their registers on punch cards. In Finland, local offices of the National Pensions Institute have a register of all persons from birth.

The personal registration number contains nine to 11 digits. In Norway, Denmark and Sweden, six digits are assigned to indicate the month, day and year of birth. Three digits are then assigned as a serial number. In Denmark, this number is divided into an over- and under-500 series to separate those born in the last century from those in the current. Blocks of hundreds are then assigned to regions, the serial number thereby giving an indication of the area of birth. In Denmark and Norway, two additional digits are added as a mathematical check; and Sweden plans to add such a check digit.

Other records that will bear this number in various countries include tax, school, military, hospital, health insurance, social security, disease registers and vital records.

Even in their most primitive forms as county rosters, the registers have proved invaluable as research tools. In several studies, they constituted an up-to-date sampling frame of the population and an accurate base upon which rates could be computed. They have also been used as a tool for follow-up of patients,[15,16] to identify nonrespondents,[57] and for record linkage studies, a potential which is just now beginning to be realized. A pioneering effort is the record linkage study by Smedby in Uppsala, previously described.[43] (Additional studies of this type will probably follow the establishment of central automated registers in the other countries.)

Special disease registers. Tuberculosis registers originated as local activities for case control and continue to be operated in most jurisdictions for this purpose. In addition, national registers have been established for epidemiological research and operational studies.

Oldest of these registers is the Danish Tuberculosis Index established in 1950 (national reporting dates from 1921).[69] A wide variety of epidemiological and methods studies have been produced by this organization, many in cooperation with United States investigators.

National Tuberculosis Registers in Norway and Finland are of more recent origin, and Sweden does not presently have a register but plans to begin one soon. Despite the recent establishment of the register, Norway has already produced operational studies concerned with the evaluation of BCG vaccination and with the costs and benefits of a tuberculosis program.[70]

National Cancer Registers are operated in all four countries. The Swedish Register was established in 1958 as a subsection of the Statistical Division of the National Board of Health; the Danish Register began operation in 1942, under sponsorship of the National Cancer League, assisted by the National Health Service; the Cancer Registry of Norway began operation in 1952, under the sponsorship of the Norwegian Cancer Society (the register is now government supported); and the Finnish Cancer Register began operation in 1953, and is sponsored by the Cancer Society.

All of these registers are used primarily for research[71] rather than case-control purposes. Chief uses are inter-Scandinavian comparisons of incidence for various sites and evaluation of end results. Close liaison is maintained with the National Cancer Institute and investigators in the United States.

In several countries, case registers are maintained for other categorical diseases or disabling conditions; or information and populations for study are available as a result of disability insurance or benefit programs. Examples of this type are a register of chronic psychoses and a disability register in Norway; schizophrenia, sarcoid and multiple sclerosis registers in Denmark; and registers of handicapped children in Finland.

Economic and Operations Research Studies

Several studies of the utilization of health services have been noted which apply multiple regression analysis, a tool frequently employed by economists. Other studies in economics were brought out, of which two examples follow.

On study reports on the economic costs and benefits of the BCG program in Norway, which has achieved 80 per cent protection. The benefits, estimated approximately, are of the order of 13 to 26 million dollars, compared with a cost of 1.8 million. The paper also states the formal criteria for the optimum allocation of resources and offers an example of how to achieve maximum coverage for a given budget.[70]

A study of hospital costs in Finland was made for the year 1963. Operating costs are divided among inpatients, outpatients and trading activities (employees' room and board, entered at the level of receipts).[72] Capital costs were excluded in this, the first, study.

In addition to the findings on unit cost and sources of income, certain technical features of this study may be noted.

1. The category of trading activities is unusual.
2. Patient days are defined to include both the day of admission and the day of discharge. Average duration of stay is therefore overstated, compared with the United States.
3. Duration of stay is calculated by averaging the number of admissions and discharges in the denominator. This method is similar to that employed by the United States Army in World War II, when the patient load was increasing rapidly.

Sjura has commissioned cost and benefit studies at the College of Commerce, Stockholm. The investigator, Eric Rheaman, was on vacation at the time of the visit.

Interest in operations research was evident. The Finnish Foundation for Education in Hospital Administration is sponsoring a manual on operations research in hospitals, to be published in the Fall of 1966.[73] Its author will be conducting operations research studies at the Central Hospital, Tampere, Finland.

At the Children's Hospital of the University of Helsinki, a computer simulation of a clinical laboratory is being performed. A preliminary draft of a paper was prepared for the visitors.[74]

At the Glostrup Hospital, County of Copenhagen, a project is under way to obtain hospital statistics by electronic computer. In comments on some preliminary tables,[75] the following points were made: 1. Complicated medical treatments are difficult to record. 2. Despite great effort, some medical records are lost. 3. Record keeping through the computer is likely to lend itself better to special studies than to routine data collection.

DISCUSSION

The outside observer of health services research in Scandinavia is impressed with differences between these countries and the United States in recruitment of research workers and support and sponsorship of health services research. At the risk of overgeneralization, the following impressions are valid.

Scandinavia has relatively few health services research workers, and recruitment into the field is not formally stimulated by training programs, special rewards or status. Notwithstanding, those engaged in health services research receive considerable visibility. Although this is in part due to the small size of these countries, it is also frequently due to the quick translation of this type of research into public policy. Examples include the Tuberculosis Registry in Norway, which was able to alter BCG and mass x-ray screening programs for the country on the basis of findings in its own studies; and the Institute of Social Research in Denmark, whose findings were recently translated into new laws within a short period. An interesting feature in two instances was the allocation of a certain percentage of the funds of operating agencies to research (the Sickness Insurance Fund of Finland has, by law, two per cent of all contributions to the Fund available for prevention and rehabilitation, including research). In other instances, research is supported by the back door through the use of educational or health services funds—an interesting contrast to the United States pattern. Neither pattern of financing research was considered ideal, for the first often carried the threat of directed research and the latter suffered from anemia—lack of funds and low status for the investigators.

Research carried out at universities sometimes showed a remarkable variety in sources of support and balance in types of project. One diversified program was presented by the Department of Social Medicine at Uppsala. Nine different sources of support were noted; The University, the national Medical Research Council fund (which in Scandinavia has rarely supported health services research), a city, the county, the employment service, the National Board of Health, the National Health Insurance Fund, the Ministry of Social Affairs, and voluntary sources (in this instance Boy Scouts collected money at polling booths at election time). In addition, certain collaborative studies with the United States were supported in part by the National Institutes of Health. Under these multiple sources of support, the department was able to study a variety of problems, some of immediate concern, others of more basic nature, some with direct implications to public policy changes (i.e., in a study of gypsies each person studied was helped to obtain more appropriate employment and after a study of dental care changes in dental services were introduced), others with no immediate implications for program or policy.

Several departments in two universities (Lund and Uppsala) were using the same defined populations with remarkable effectiveness. In both universities close connections were maintained between some of

518

the workers and government policy makers. Here the closest approach to balance was achieved. A large enough mass of workers had been assembled to be productive and to recruit new researchers; some were working with, and some were independent of government; and financial support seemed adequate.

CONCLUSIONS

The study group returns with several general impressions. These have been adequately documented in the text, but should be given added emphasis.

The first is the extreme importance of population and disease registers for facilitating health services research.

Next the group was impressed with the large sample size in household surveys and the extraordinarily high percentage of compliance of the population in Scandinavia with surveys, health examinations and follow-up studies.

A great deal of work was noted in early detection of presymptomatic disease by a variety of methods, especially using advanced technology—autoanalyzers for multiple blood tests and computer history-taking equipment.

Also impressive was the differences in emphasis toward hospital-based ambulatory services in the four Scandinavian countries. Denmark relies on the family physician, while the other three increasingly are developing hospital based programs to meet patients' needs for ambulatory services of all types.

The amount of local autonomy and responsibility for hospital and health services planning is surprising. Indeed, this emphasis is being strengthened. The cooperation achieved in health services research among different departments of some of the medical schools and among medical school personnel, public health authorities, independent institutes and political bodies is impressive. Such joint work may well be easier in smaller countries with more uniform population and culture. But the fruits of such collaboration seemed so valuable that every effort to achieve it seems worthwhile. In a very high proportion of research programs visited, the results had been translated into public policy and did not merely grace the pages of scientific journals or fill library shelves. In the final analysis, the purpose of research in health services is to affect health.

REFERENCES

[1] Schleimann, Robert, HEALTH AND HOSPITAL SERVICES, Copenhagen, Press and Information Department, Ministry of Foreign Affairs, 1964.

[2] Jacobsen, Charles, The Danish Health Insurance System, *Danish Medical Bulletin*, 9, 214–220, 1962.

[3] Albinsson, Gillis, PUBLIC HEALTH SERVICES IN SWEDEN, Halmstead, Swedish Hospital Association, Meijels Bokindustri, 1963.

[4] Biörck, Gunnar, Trends in the Development of Medical Care in Sweden, *Medical Care*, 2, 156–161, 1964.

[5] Evang, Karl, Prepaid Medical Care in Norway, in MEDICAL CARE AND FAMILY SECURITY—NORWAY, ENGLAND AND U.S.A., Englewood, New Jersey, Prentice-Hall, Inc., 1963, pp. 3–82.

[6] Evang, Karl, HEALTH SERVICES IN NORWAY, Oslo, E.K.B. Boktrykkeri, 1960.

[7] PUBLIC HEALTH, MEDICAL CARE AND THE MEDICAL PROFESSION IN FINLAND, Helsinki, Finnish Medical Association, 1964.

[8] Pesonen, Niilo, Odganization of Medical Care and Public Health Services in Finland, *World Hospitals*, 2, 92–96, 1966.

[9] HEALTH SERVICES IN EUROPE, Copenhagen, Regional Office for Europe, World Health Organization, 1965.

[10] Folke-Pettersson, Early Pregnancy Loss Study, in progress.

[11] Friis, Henning, *et al.*, Study of Married Women Working Outside the Home, in progress.

[12] Bardy, Anja and Kauttu, Kyllikki, Factors Connected with Perinatal Mortality, in press.

[13] Berfenstam, Ragnar, Swedish Infant Mortality Study, in progress.

[14] Smaars, Gunnar, OSTEOGENESIS IMPERFECTA IN SWEDEN, CLINICAL, GENETIC, EPIDEMIOLOGICAL, AND SOCIAL-MEDICAL ASPECTS, Stockholm, Svenska, Bokforlager, 1961.

[15] Berfenstam, Ragnar, *et al.*, Socio-Medical Studies of Epilepsy, in progress.

[16] Irnell, Lars, A Study of Bronchial Asthma With Special Reference to its Long-Term Consequences for Respiratory and Circulatory Function and Socio-Medical Condition, *Acta Medica Scandinavica*, 176, 1964.

[17] Köhler, L. and Lindquist, B., Handicap-Preventing Health Control of Four-Year-Old Children, in progress.

[18] Valanne, Kirsti, Child Health Study on School Entry, in progress.

[19] Jordahn, Bodil, *et al.*, The Child Welfare Committee's Administration of the Supervisory Systems in Denmark, Publication 10 of the Danish National Institute of Social Research, Copenhagen, Teknisk Forlag, 1963 (Danish), English Summary: Mimeographed Form E 74, January, 1966.

[20] Berfenstam, Ragnar, Accident Morbidity Survey, Stockholm County, in progress.

21 Bjartveit, Kjell and Waaler, Hans, Some Evidence of the Efficacy of Mass B.C.G. Vaccination, *Bulletin of the World Health Organization,* 3, 289–319, 1965.

22 Marthinsen, Arne and Löchen, Yngvar, Personal Communication.

23 Bergendal, T., A Study of Long-Term Illness in a Population, Preliminary Communication.

24 Furman, Sylvan S., Community Mental Health Services in Northern Europe (Great Britain, Netherlands, Denmark and Sweden), Public Health Service Publication number 1409, Washington, United States Department of Health, Education and Welfare, 1965.

25 Friis, Henning, Danish National Institute of Social Research, Preliminary Communication.

26 Berfenstam, Ragnar, Personal Communication.

27 Pedersen, Einar, Personal Communication.

28 Beckman, L. and Tochman, J., On the Anthropology of a Gypsy Population, *Hereditas,* 53, 272, 1965.

29 Agrup, G., Health Survey Regarding Hand Eczema in a Population, Preliminary Communication.

30 Felbo, Mogens, OLD AGE AND WORK, Copenhagen, Ejnar Munksgaard, Ltd., 1958.

31 Noro, Leo, Annual Reports, The Occupational Medical Foundation and Institute of Occupational Health, Helsinki, Finland.

32 World Health Organization, ANNUAL EPIDEMIOLOGICAL AND VITAL STATISTICS, 1961, Geneva, 1964; and DEMOGRAPHIC YEARBOOK, 1962, New York, United Nations, 1962.

33 Tengbom, Anders, Recent Developments in the Design of Hospitals in Scandinavia, *World Hospitals,* 2, 1–4, January, 1966.

34 Pesonen, Niilo, HOSPITALS OF FINLAND, Helsinki, 1964.

35 Sjura, The Council for Hospital Operation Rationalization, Information Sheet, Stockholm, June 10, 1965 (processed); and Biörck, Gunnar, Introduction to a Symposium on Data Processing of Medical Records in Clinical Practice, Stockholm, October, 1965, pp. 2–3 (processed).

36 KOD-Kommittén, Description of the Arrangement of Wards, Danderyds Hospital, 1963–66, Danderyd, Sweden, 1966 (processed; in Swedish).

37 Linköping Regional Hospital, Local Program for Floors Two and Three, Fifth Draft, Linköping, 1966 (processed; in Swedish).

38 Vauraste, Inkeri, Lecture on Hospital Planning by Municipal Hospital Board, City of Helsinki, 1966 (processed).

39 Natonal Board of Health, UTILIZATION OF GENERAL HOSPITAL SERVICES IN FINLAND, 1960, Helsinki, 1966 (English headings; English summary).

40 Härö, A. S., *et al.,* Objects and Methods of Research into Hospital Utilization in a Regional Hospital System, 1966 (processed).

[41] Jörgensen, Erik, Problems in Connection with the Allocation of Hospital Services and the Demand for Hospital Care, Dissertation for M.D. degree, University of Copenhagen, 1966 (English summary).

[42] Härö, A. S., The Patient Material in Finnish Tuberculosis Sanatoria During 1957–1964, *Journal of Social Medicine*, Supplement 1, 1A, 1966.

[43] Smedby, Björn, Habits in Dental Care and Costs of Dental Care, Reprint from Report of Commission on Health Insurance, Stockholm, 1965 (in Swedish); citation for drug study not yet available.

[44] National Pension Institute, Eighteenth Annual Report, 1965, Helsinki, 1966, pp. 16–17 (processed).

[45] Research and Training Center in Public Health, Morbidity Statistics from a Communal Medical Officer's Practice, Helsinki, 1966 (processed).

[46] Fuglsang, Robert, PRAKSISSTATISTIK, 1958–59, Danish with English Summary, Copenhagen, Danish Medical Association.

[47] Dahlerup, Jens, Study of General Practice, M.D. Thesis, available from P. Bonnevie, Department of Hygiene, Copenhagen University.

[48] Bentzen, Study of a General Practice in Norway, to be submitted as M.D. Thesis; may be contacted through Dr. Arne Marthinsen, Department of Social Medicine, University Hospital, Oslo.

[49] Haavio-Mannila, Elina, The Structure of the Medical Profession in Finland, *in* PUBLIC HEALTH, MEDICAL CARE AND THE MEDICAL PROFESSION IN FINLAND, Helsinki, Finnish Medical Association, 1964, pp. 28–29.

[50] Munter, Jussi and Kautti, Kyllikki, THE WORK OF THE COMMUNAL MEDICAL OFFICER IN FINLAND, Helsinki, Lääkintöhallituksen Julkaisusarja A. Kansanterveystyon Tutkimuskeskus, 1964, (with English summary).

[51] ABOUT THE NEED FOR PHYSICIANS AND THE NUMBER OF MEDICAL GRADUATES, Stockholm, Swedish Commission on the Future Need for Doctors, 1961, p. 74 (in Swedish).

[52] Review Committee on the Need for Physicians and Training Facilities, Part Two of Report, Helsinki, 1965.

[53] Strom, Axel, Medical Education in Norway, *Journal of the Norwegian Medical Association*, 799–803, May 15, 1964, (English summary, p. 825).

[54] Multiple Screening Project in a Finnish Rural Commune, Research and Training Center in Public Health, National Board of Health, Helsinki (mimeographed).

[55] Waaler, Hans T., Selective Case Finding by a Mass Radiography Service, *Tubercle, The Journal of the British Tuberculosis Association*, 46, 85–90, March, 1965.

[56] Horowitz, Ole and Palmer, Carroll E., Epidemiological Basis of Tuberculosis Eradication, 2. Dynamics of Tuberculosis Morbidity and Mortality, *Bulletin of the World Health Organization*, 30, 609–621, 1964.

[57] Horowitz, Ole and Knudsen, Jørgen, Comparison Between Attenders and Non-attenders at the Danish Mass Tuberculosis Campaign, 1950–52, *Bulletin of the World Health Organization*, 23, 669–681, 1960.

[58] Clemmesen, Johannes, Personal Communication.

[59] Pedersen, Einar, Personal Communication.

[60] Brante, G., *et al.,* Health Survey Studies by the Use of Among Other Methods Some Forty Laboratory Analyses, Technicon Scandinavian Symposium on Automated Analytical Chemistry, Copenhagen, 1965.

[61] Bjerre, B., Personal Communication.

[62] Voipio, Niilo, Personal Communication.

[63] Scherstén, B. and Fritz, H., Subnormal Levels of Glucose in Urine as a Sign of Urinary Tract Infection, Preliminary Communication, Department of Clinical Chemistry and Department of Medical Microbiology, University Hospital, Lund, Sweden (processed).

[64] Jungner, Gunnar and Jungner, Ingmar, The Health Screening Project in Värmland, Presented at the Symposium on Data Processing of Medical Records in Clinical Practice, Stockholm, 1965.

[65] ————, Chemical Health Screening, Department of Clinical Chemistry, University of Gothenberg, Gothenberg, Sweden (mimeographed).

[66] Jungner, Gunnar, Data Processing in the Clinical Laboratory, Presented at the International Conference on Automated Data Processing in Hospitals, Elsinore, Denmark, April 20–23, 1966 (mimeographed).

[67] XXVII ANNUAL REPORT, National Pension Institute, Finland, 1965.

[68] Dessau, E., Personal Communication.

[69] Horwitz, Ole, The Danish Tuberculosis Index, May, 1964 (Mimeographed).

[70] Waaler, Hans, Some Aspects of Cost of Tuberculosis, Proceedings of 18th Conference of International Union Against Tuberculosis, forthcoming (processed).

[71] Clemmesen, Johannes, Statistical Studies in Malignant Neoplasms, *Acta Pathologica et Microbiologica Scandinavica,* Supplement 174, 1965.

[72] Vaughkonen, Onni, FACILITIES, SERVICES AND COSTS OF HOSPITALS IN FINLAND, Summary for 1963, Helsinki, The Foundation for Education in Hospital Administration, 1965.

[73] Haimi, Olavi, Statistical Methods of Hospital Research, Helsinki, the Foundation for Education in Hospital Administration, 1966 (forthcoming).

[74] Väänänen, Ilkka, *et al.,* Computer Simulation of the Operation of a Clinical Laboratory, June 16, 1966 (processed).

[75] Bartles, Hospital Statistics by Electronic Computer, Copenhagen, Glostrup, 1966 (processed).

PARTICIPANTS AT THE CONFERENCES ON HEALTH SERVICES RESEARCH

Chairman, DONALD MAINLAND, M.D., D.SC.

Professor of Medical Statistics
New York University Medical Center

ANDERSON, ODIN W., PH.D.
Research Director
Health Information Foundation
University of Chicago
Chicago, Illinois

BADGLEY, ROBIN F., PH.D.
Senior Member, Technical Staff
Milbank Memorial Fund
New York, New York

BARNHART, GILBERT, M.D.
Chief
Office of Research Grants
Bureau of State Services
Department of Health, Education
and Welfare
Washington, D.C.

BLUM, HENRIK L., M.D.
Health Officer
Health Department
Contra Costa County
Martinez, California

BLUMENKRANZ, JOSEPH
Architect and Hospital Consultant
Joseph Blumenkranz & Associates
New York, New York

BONNET, PHILIP D., M.D.
Associate Professor
Hospital Administration
University Hospital
Boston, Massachusetts

BORGATTA, EDGAR F., PH.D.
Chairman
Social Behavior Research Center
Department of Sociology
University of Wisconsin
Madison, Wisconsin

BOULDING, KENNETH, M.A.
Professor of Economics
University of Michigan
Ann Arbor, Michigan

BRESLOW, LESTER, M.D.
Director
California Department
of Public Health
Berkeley, California

BROWN, RAY E.
Director
Graduate Program
in Hospital Administration
Duke University Medical Center
Durham, North Carolina

BUCK, CAROL W., M.D., PH.D.
Associate Professor
of Preventive Medicine
Department of Psychiatry
and Preventive Medicine
University of Western Ontario
London, Ontario, Canada

BURNS, EVELINE, PH.D.
Professor
School of Social Work
Columbia University
New York, New York

525

CAFFEE, FRANKLIN B.
Deputy Chief
Research Grants Branch
Division of Community Health
Services
Department of Health, Education
and Welfare
Washington, D.C.

CLARK, DUNCAN W., M.D.
Professor and Chairman
Department of Environmental
Medicine and Community Health
State University of New York
Downstate Medical Center
Brooklyn, New York

CONFREY, EUGENE A., PH.D.
Chief
Division of Research Grants
National Institutes of Health
Bethesda, Maryland

CONNERS, EDWARD J.
Associate Professor
and Superintendent
University of Wisconsin Hospitals
Madison. Wisconsin

CORNISH, J. B.
Ministry of Health
London, England

DENSEN, PAUL M., D.SC.
Deputy Health Services
Administrator
Health Services Administration
New York, New York

DIXON, JAMES P., M.D.
President
Antioch College
Yellow Springs, Ohio

DONABEDIAN, AVEDIS, M.D.
Professor of Public Health Economics
School of Public Health
University of Michigan
Ann Arbor, Michigan

DUNLOP, JOHN, PH.D.
David A. Wells Professor
of Politcal Economy
Harvard University
Boston, Massachusetts

DUNNER, EDWARD, M.D.
Special Assistant
to the Assistant Chief Medical
Director for Research
and Education in Medicine
Veterans Administration
Washington, D.C.

EDWARDS, CHARLES, M.D.
Director
Division, Socio-Economic Activities
American Medical Association
Chicago, Illinois

EDWARDS, SAMUEL A., PH.D.
Colonel
Medical Service Corps
United States Army
Department of Administration
Brooke Army Medical Center
Fort Sam Houston, Texas

ENTERLINE, PHILIP E., PH.D.
Professor of Medical Statistics
McGill University
Montreal, Canada

ERBE, WILLIAM, PH.D.
Associate Professor of Sociology
and Associate Director
Iowa Urban Community
Research Center
University of Iowa
Iowa City, Iowa

ESTEL, DOLLY W.
Grants Clerk
Division of Research Grants
National Institutes of Health
Bethesda, Maryland

EVANS, LESTER J., M.D.
Executive Director
New York State Committee
on Medical Education
New York, New York

FELDMAN, JACOB J., PH.D.
Senior Research Associate
in Biostatistics
Department of Biostatistics
Harvard University
Boston, Massachusetts

FELDSTEIN, PAUL J., PH.D.
Assistant Professor
Bureau of Hospital Administration
School of Business Administration
University of Michigan
Ann Arbor, Michigan

FIEDLER, GOTTHELF O.
Chief
Research and Demonstration Grants
Division of Hospital
and Medical Facilities
United States Public Health Service
Washington, D.C.

FLAGLE, CHARLES D., D. ENG.
Professor
of Public Health Administration
School of Hygiene and Public Health
The Johns Hopkins University
Baltimore, Maryland

FLOOK, EVELYN
Chief
Research Grants Branch
Division, Community Health Services
Department of Health, Education
and Welfare
Washington, D.C.

FREEMAN, HOWARD E., PH.D.
Professor of Social Research
and Director of the Research Center
Florence Heller Graduate School
Brandeis University
Waltham, Massachusetts

FREIDSON, ELIOT, PH.D.
Professor
Department of Sociology
and Anthropology
Graduate School of Arts and Sciences
New York University
New York, New York

FUCHS, VICTOR R., PH.D.
Associate Director of Research
National Bureau
of Economic Research
New York, New York

GRANING, HARALD M., M.D.
Assistant Surgeon General
Department of Health, Education
and Welfare
Washington, D.C.

HAGGERTY, ROBERT J., M.D.
Professor and Chairman
Department of Pediatrics
University of Rochester
Rochester, New York

HARTMAN, GERHARD, PH.D.
Professor and Director
Graduate Program in Hospital
and Health Administration
University Hospitals
Iowa City, Iowa

HIESTAND, DALE L., PH.D.
Research Associate
Conservation of Human Resources
Project
Columbia University
New York, New York

HOCHBAUM, GODFREY, PH.D.
Chief
Behavioral Science Section
Division of Community Health
Services
Washington, D.C.

HORVATH, WILLIAM J., PH.D.
Assistant Director
Mental Health Research Institute
University of Michigan
Ann Arbor, Michigan

JAMES, GEORGE, M.D.
Dean
Mount Sinai School of Medicine
and Vice President
Mount Sinai Medical Center
New York, New York

DE JANOSI, PETER E., PH.D.
Associate
Ford Foundation
New York, New York

JOSIE, GORDON H., SC.D., M.P.H.
M.SC.
Consultant
Planning and Evaluation
Health Services Branch
Department of National Health
and Welfare
Ottawa, Canada

JUDEK, STANISLAW, PH.D.
  Professor of Economics
  University of Ottawa
  Ottawa, Canada

KAUFMAN, HERBERT, PH.D.
  Chairman
  Department of Political Science
  Yale University
  New Haven, Connecticut

KISSICK, WILLIAM L., M.D.
  Office of the Surgeon General
  Department of Health, Education
  and Welfare
  Washington, D.C.

KLARMAN, HERBERT E., PH.D.
  Professor
  of Public Health Administration
  Department of Public Health
  Administration and Political
  Economy
  The Johns Hopkins University
  Baltimore, Maryland

DE LEIN, HORACE
  Agency for International
  Development
  Washington, D.C.

LEVINE, SOL, PH.D.
  Director
  Social Science Program
  Harvard School of Public Health
  Harvard University
  Boston, Massachusetts

LORD LLEWELYN-DAVIES
  Professor of Architecture
  Bartlett School of Architecture
  University College
  London, England

MAYES, W. FRED, M.D.
  Dean
  School of Public Health
  University of North Carolina
  Chapel Hill, North Carolina

MC CARTHY, THOMAS, PH.D.
  Executive Secretary
  Health Services Research
  Study Section
  Division of Research Grants
  National Institutes of Health
  Bethesda, Maryland

MC LACHLAN, GORDON
  Secretary
  The Nuffield Provincial
  Hospitals Trust
  London, England

MC NULTY, MATTHEW F., JR.
  General Director
  University Hospital
  and Hillman Clinics
  University of Alabama
  Medical Center
  Birmingham, Alabama

MELSTRADS, ILONA
  Public Health Analyst
  Research Grants Branch
  Community Health Services
  Department of Health, Education
  and Welfare
  Washington, D.C.

MENZEL, HERBERT, PH.D.
  Professor of Sociology
  Department of Sociology
  New York University
  New York, New York

MERRIAM, IDA C., PH.D.
  Assistant Commissioner
  for Research and Statistics
  Social Security Adminstration
  Washington, D.C.

MILLER, S. M., PH.D.
  Visiting Professor
  of Education and Sociology
  School of Education
  New York University
  New York, New York

MULLER, JONAS N., M.D.
  Professor and Chairman
  Department of Preventive Medicine
  New York Medical College
  New York, New York

MUSHKIN, SELMA, PH.D.
  Project Director
  Council of State Governments
  Washington, D.C.

NEWTON, QUIGG
  President
  The Commonwealth Fund
  New York, New York

528

PATTULLO, ANDREW
Director
Division of Hospitals
W. K. Kellogg Foundation
Battle Creek, Michigan

PETT, L. B., M.D., PH.D.
Principal Medical Officer
Research Development
Department of National Health
and Welfare
Ottawa, Ontario, Canada

REVANS, REGINALD W., PH.D.
Research Fellow
Association Europeenne des Centres
de Perfectionnement dans
la Direction des Entreprises
Bruxelles, Belgium

RIEDEL, DONALD C., PH.D.
Director of Research and Planning
Blue Cross Association
Chicago, Illinois

ROBERTSON, ALEXANDER, M.D.
Executive Director
Milbank Memorial Fund
New York, New York

ROSENBLUM, MARCUS
Deputy Special Assistant
to the Surgeon General
Department of Health, Education
and Welfare
Washington, D.C.

ROSENFELD, LEONARD S., M.D.
Director
Division of Medical Services
Hospital Review
and Planning Council
New York, New York

ROSENSTOCK, IRWIN M., PH.D.
Codirector of Research Programs
and Professor
of Public Health Administration
University of Michigan
Ann Arbor, Michigan

ROSENTHAL, GERALD, PH.D.
Assistant Professor
Department of Economics
Harvard University
Cambridge, Massachusetts

ROSSI, PETER, PH.D.
Director
National Opinion Research Center
Chicago, Illinois

SANAZARO, PAUL J., M.D.
Director
Division of Education
Association of American Medical
Colleges
Evanston, Illinois

SCHOTTLAND, CHARLES, A.B.
Dean
Florence Heller Graduate School
for Advanced Studies
in Social Welfare
Brandeis University
Waltham, Massachusetts

SCOTT, W. RICHARD, PH.D.
Associate Professor
Department of Sociology
Stanford University
Stanford, California

SHAPIRO, SAM
Director
Division of Research and Statistics
Health Insurance Plan
of Greater New York
New York, New York

SHEFFIELD, FREDERICK D., PH.D.
Professor
Department of Psychology
Yale University
New Haven, Connecticut

SHEPS, CECIL G., M.D.
General Director
Beth Israel Medical Center
New York, New York

STOREY, PATRICK B., M.D.
Director
Department of Postgraduate
Education
American Medical Association
Chicago, Illinois

THOMPSON, JAMES D., PH.D.
Professor of Business Administration
and Sociology
School of Business
University of Indiana
Bloomington, Indiana

WEINERMAN, E. RICHARD, M.D.
M.P.H.
Professor of Medicine
and Public Health
Department of Epidemiology
and Public Health
Yale University
New Haven, Connecticut

WESSEN, ALBERT F., PH.D.
Associate Chairman
Department of Sociology
and Anthropology
Washington University
St. Louis, Missouri

WHARTON, JAMES D., M.D.
Chief
Division of Community Health
Services
Public Health Service
Washington, D.C.

WHITE, KERR L., M.D.
Director
Division of Medical Care
and Hospitals
School of Hygiene
The Johns Hopkins University
Baltimore, Maryland

WILLIAMS, T. FRANKLIN, M.D.
Associate Professor
of Medicine and Preventive Medicine
Department of Medicine
University of North Carolina
Chapel Hill, North Carolina

WRIGHT, CHARLES R., PH.D.
Professor
Department of Sociology
University of California
Los Angeles, California

YOUNG, JOHN, DR.ENG.
Associate Professor
Public Health Administration
and Operations Research
Operations Research Division
The Johns Hopkins Hospital
Baltimore, Maryland

YOUNG, WESLEY O., D.M.D., M.P.H.
Chairman
Department of Community Dentistry
University of Kentucky
Lexington, Kentucky

ZOLA, IRVING KENNETH, PH.D.
Assistant Professor of Sociology
Brandeis University
Waltham, Massachusetts

Two members of the Scandinavian Study Group did not participate in the Conference:

HOFSTRA, RAYMOND
Associate Chief
for Preventive Services
Division of Chronic Diseases
Bureau of State Services
United States Public Health Service
Washington, D.C.

THORNER, ROBERT M.
Chief
Research Grants
Division of Chronic Disease
Bureau of State Services
United States Public Health Service
Washington, D.C.

530

Milbank Memorial Fund

October 1966

533

Fund Staff

Alexander Robertson, M.D.   *Executive Director*

Helen S. McGuire   *Secretary of the Fund*

OFFICE OF THE EXECUTIVE DIRECTOR

Suzanne Calhoun   *Private Secretary*
Juan A. Inclán   *Personal Assistant*
Catherine McKeever   *Private Secretary*

TECHNICAL STAFF

Robin F. Badgley, Ph.D.   *Senior Member*
Clyde V. Kiser, Ph.D.   *Senior Member*
Richard V. Kasius, M.P.H.   *Member*
Myrna E. Frank, M.A.   *Member*
Marjorie Schulte, B.A.   *Research Assistant*

PUBLICATIONS STAFF

Larry E. Blaser   *Editorial Associate*
Katherine C. Gensamer   *Publications Associate*
Barbara A. Brazaitis   *Publications Clerk*

ADMINISTRATIVE STAFF

Catherine I. L. Bartsch   *Receptionist*
Barbara J. Chudiak   *Private Secretary*
Andrea Gubbins   *Assistant Clerk*
Sally F. Klepper   *General Secretary*
Mary P. Mele   *Filing and Library Clerk*
Catherine F. O'Malley   *Private Secretary*
Mirtha T. Pascal   *General Secretary*
Eugene Rouff   *Messenger*
Betty A. Vorwald   *General Secretary*

534

Fin